A LEVEL
CHEMISTRY

Bob McDuell
Deputy Headmaster, Berry Hill High School
Stoke-on-Trent

D1223904

Letts
EDUCATIONAL

Every effort has been made to trace copyright holders and to obtain their permission for the use of copyright material. The author and publishers will gladly receive information enabling them to rectify any reference or credit in subsequent editions.

First published 1982
Revised 1984, 1986, 1988, 1991, 1993, 1995
Reprinted 1984, 1985, 1992, 1994, 1996, 1997, 1998

Letts Educational
Aldine House
Aldine Place
London W12 8AW
Tel: 0181-740 2266

British Library Cataloguing in Publication Data
A CIP record for this book is available from the British Library.

ISBN 1 85758 336 1

Printed and bound in Great Britain by
Ashford Colour Press, Gosport, Hants

Letts Educational is the trading name of BPP (Letts Educational) Ltd

PREFACE

This A-level Chemistry Study Guide has been written to provide a complete guide to students preparing for A-level, AS-level and Scottish Higher examinations. Previous editions of this book have been well accepted by students and teachers. Since the writing of the last edition in 1993, two changes have taken place and these have been incorporated in this new edition.

❶ All Chemistry A and AS syllabuses from 1996 have to include the Subject Core for Chemistry produced by the School Curriculum and Assessment Authority (previously SEAC). New syllabuses have been written by all of the Examination Groups and these are analysed in greater detail on pages 3–16.

❷ There has been an increase in the number of students taking the modular route to A-level Chemistry. This book has always been intended to be used alongside the student during the course rather than as a last-minute crammer. Remember that module tests must be marked to the same standard as the final examinations. This book has been written to help you through a course involving module tests and to help everybody with terminal examinations.

Some new content has been added in areas new to syllabuses, e.g. fullerenes, carbohydrates, etc. New questions have been added, and very few have been removed, so that there should be more questions for you to try. On this point, I would like to thank the Associated Examining Board, the University of Cambridge Local Examinations Syndicate, the University of London Examinations and Assessment Council, the Northern Examinations and Assessment Board, the Northern Ireland Council for the Curriculum Examinations and Assessment, the Oxford and Cambridge Schools Examination Board, the University of Oxford Delegacy of Local Examinations, the Scottish Examination Board and the Welsh Joint Education Committee for permission to reproduce both past examination questions and sample questions for the 1996 examinations. It should be noted that the answers given are mine and are not official mark schemes.

I would like to take this opportunity to thank all of the staff of Letts Educational, especially Wayne Davies (my editor), for all their highly professional work in turning my manuscript into a finished book so quickly.

Lastly, but certainly not least, I must thank my wife Judy and my sons, Robin and Timothy, for all their help and also their patience when I become engrossed in writing.

Bob McDuell 1995

CONTENTS

SECTION 1: STARTING POINTS

SECTION 2: A-LEVEL CHEMISTRY

SECTION 3: TEST RUN

INDEX   377

STARTING POINTS

HOW TO USE THIS BOOK

THE STRUCTURE OF THIS BOOK

The key aim of this book is to guide you in the way you tackle A-level Chemistry. It should serve as a study guide, work book and revision aid throughout any A-level/AS-level Chemistry course, no matter what syllabus you are following. It is not intended to be a complete guide to the subject and should be used as a companion to your textbooks, which it is designed to complement rather than duplicate.

We have divided the book into three sections. **Section One, Starting Points**, contains study tips and syllabus information – all the material you need to get started on your A-level study – plus advice on planning your revision and tips on how to tackle the exam itself. Use the **Syllabus Checklists** to find out exactly where you can find the study units which are relevant to your particular syllabus.

Section Two, the main body of the text, contains the core of A-level Chemistry. It has been devised to make study as easy – and enjoyable – as possible, and has been divided into chapters which cover the themes you will encounter on your syllabus. The chapters are split into units, each covering a topic of study.

The **Chapter Objectives** at the beginning of each chapter direct you towards the key points of what you are about to read. The **Chapter Roundup** at the end gives a summary of the text just covered and brings the topics of the chapter into focus. To reinforce your learning, there are **Worked Questions and Answers** at the end of each chapter. Recent examinations from all the examination boards (including Scottish Higher) provide the question practice. The tutorial notes give you practical guidance on how to answer A-level questions, and provide additional information relevant to that particular topic. There is also a **Question Bank**, with further examples of A-level exam questions for you to attempt and hints on how to tackle them.

In **Section Three, Test Run**, we turn our attention to the examination you will face at the end of your course. First, you can assess your progress using the **Test Your Knowledge Quiz** and analysis chart. Then, as a final test, you should attempt the **Mock Exam**, under timed conditions. This will give you invaluable examination practice and, together with the specimen answers specially written by the author, will help you to judge how close you are to achieving your A-level pass.

USING YOUR SYLLABUS CHECKLIST

Whether you are using this book to work step-by-step through the syllabus or to structure your revision campaign, you will find it useful to use our checklist to record what you have covered – and how far you still have to go. Keep the checklist at hand when you are doing your revision – it will remind you of the chapters you have revised, and those still to be done.

The checklist for each examination – A, AS or Higher Grade – is in two parts. First there is a list of topics covered by this book which are part of the syllabus. Although the checklists are detailed, it is not possible to print entire syllabuses. **You are therefore strongly recommended to obtain an official copy of the syllabus for your examination and consult it when the need arises**. The examination board addresses are given after the syllabus checklists (page 18).

When you have revised a topic make a tick in the column provided and, if there are questions elsewhere in the book, try to answer them.

The second part of the checklist gives you information about the examination, providing useful details about the time allocated for each paper and the weighting of the questions on each paper. The different types of questions which may be set are explained in detail later in this section under the heading **The Examination** (page 22).

SYLLABUS CHECKLISTS AND PAPER ANALYSIS

ASSOCIATED EXAMINING BOARD
Syllabus 0654   A level (modular or terminal examination)

The syllabus is assessed either by a terminal examination (in June) or by a modular route. The syllabus is divided into four modules – C1, C2, C3 and C4. Each module contains four themes:

Structure and Bonding
Physical Chemistry
Inorganic Chemistry
Organic Chemistry

Syllabus topic	Notes	Covered in Unit No	✔
C1.1 Structure and Bonding			
Atomic structure	not electronic structure	1.1–1.3	
Elementary mass spectrometry		1.5	
The mole and calculations using equations		3.3, 19.1	
Ionic bonding and covalent bonding	single and double covalent bonds	4.1, 4.2	
C1.2 Physical Chemistry			
Kinetic theory and changes of state	not osmosis	8.1, 8.9	
The gaseous state and $pV = nRT$	only ideal gases	8.2–8.4	
Relative molecular mass of gases and volatile liquids		8.7, 8.8	
Conservation of energy and Hess's law	calculation of molar enthalpy changes	13.1–13.8	
Bond energy and average bond enthalpies	predict enthalpy changes	13.9	
C1.3 Inorganic Chemistry			
Periodic Table		2.1–2.8	
Trends within Groups I, II, VII and VIII		22, 27	
C1.4 Organic Chemistry			
Introduction		7.1	
Empirical and molecular formulae		7.4–7.6, 7.8	
Types of reaction	only a brief introduction to this	38.1, 38.4, 38.5	
Alkenes and haloalkanes		29.3–29.5, 30.1, 30.3, 36.1	
C2.1 Structure and Bonding			
Electron arrangements	up to Z = 36	1.4	
Relate position in Periodic Table to electron arrangement		2	
Crystal structures		10.1–10.3	
Born–Haber cycle		13.1	
Metallic bonding		4.7	
Covalent structures	e.g. iodine, graphite and diamond	10.4	
Shapes of simple molecules		5	

Syllabus topic	Notes	Covered in Unit No	✓
C2.2 Physical Chemistry			
Distribution of energies		8.11	
Factors affecting rates of chemical reactions		14	
Activation energies and reaction profiles		15.5	
C2.3 Inorganic Chemistry			
s- and *p*-block elements		22	
Oxidation numbers and redox	includes ionic equations	6	
C2.4 Organic Chemistry			
Study of functional groups	–OH	31	
	–COOH and derivatives	33, 34	
	–NH$_2$	35	
	–CN	34.6	
S$_N$1 and S$_N$2 reactions	of bromoalkanes	38.4	
C3.1 Structure and Bonding			
Van der Waals forces, bond polarity, electronegativity		2.5, 4.6	
Hydrogen bonding		4.5	
Delocalisation of electrons	e.g. benzene, sulphate	29.8	
C3.2 Physical Chemistry			
Equilibrium		15, 16.1–16.5	
Buffer solutions and indicators		16.6, 17.2	
Distribution law and chromatography		7.2, 15.6	
C3.3 Inorganic Chemistry			
d-Block elements		28	
C3.4 Organic Chemistry			
Free radical reactions		38.1–38.3	
Aldehydes and ketones		32	
Arenes and aromatic compounds		29.8–29.10, 30.4, 30.5, 31.5, 31.6, 35	
Alkanes			
C4.1 Structure and Bonding			
Spectroscopy		1.5, 7.5	
Isomerism		7.5–7.7	
C4.2 Physical Chemistry			
Feasibility of reactions/Ellingham diagrams		40.1	
Electrochemical cells		18	
C4.3 Inorganic Chemistry			
Industrial processes involving manufacture of ammonia, sulphuric acid, zinc and aluminium		23.1, 40.2, 40.6	
C4.4 Organic Chemistry			
Polymers		36	
Natural products	proteins, carbohydrates	36.3, 36.5	

Terminal examination

Three papers and either a practical examination or centre-based assessment.

Paper 1 *2 hours*   30% of total mark – 15 marks for each section
Section A. 4 compulsory structured questions testing C1 and requiring short answers
Section B. 4 compulsory structured questions testing C2 and requiring short answers

Paper 2 *2 hours*   30% of total mark – 15 marks for each section
Section A. 4 compulsory structured questions testing C3 and requiring short answers
Section B. 4 compulsory structured questions testing C4 and requiring short answers

Paper 3 *1½ hours*   General paper
20% of total mark
Section A. Comprehension passage with a series of compulsory questions testing comprehension
7.5% of total mark
Section B. 2 questions requiring extended answers – 1 to be attempted
6.25% of total mark
Section C. 2 questions requiring extended answers – 1 to be attempted
These questions will test social, economic and environmental aspects of chemistry
6.25% of total mark

Practical examination or centre-based assessment (see pages 27–30)
20% of total mark

Modular route

Four module tests –

Test 6 *1 hour*   Testing C1   Available in January
15% of total mark

Test 7 *1 hour*   Testing C2   Available in June
15% of total mark

Test 8 *1 hour*   Testing C3   Available in January
15% of total mark

Test 9 *1 hour*   Testing C4   Available in June
15% of total mark

Each module test consists of four compulsory structured questions requiring short answers.

The student then takes the same Paper 3 as students taking the terminal route and either the practical examination or the centre-based assessment.

UNIVERSITY OF CAMBRIDGE LOCAL EXAMINATIONS SYNDICATE

Syllabus 9254	A level – Terminal examination
Syllabus 9535	A level – Modular route
Syllabus 8405	AS level – Terminal examination
Syllabus 8535	AS level – Modular route

Analysis of terminal route – 9254

Paper	Duration in hours	Weighting	Type of paper	Available
1	2	29%	8 free response questions†	June/Nov
2	1¼	19%	Compulsory structured questions on the core	June/Nov
3	1	16%	40 multiple choice questions based on core	June/Nov
4	1¼	16%	3 questions on each option topic. 4 questions to be attempted, not more than 2 on any topic	June/Nov
5 (June) 6 (Nov)	2½	20%	Practical exam or	June/Nov
9	–	20%	Centre-based assessment (alternative to practical exam)	June, but may be carried forward

† Section A – 3 physical chemistry questions
Section B – 2 inorganic chemistry questions
Section C – 3 organic chemistry questions

Analysis of modular route – 9535

For A level six modules have to be taken.

Compulsory (4)
4820 Chemistry foundation
4821 Chains and rings
4826 How far, how fast?
4852 Teacher assessment of practical
4858 Practical exam
(Only one of 4852 and 4858)

Optional (2):
(a) 4822 Trends and patterns
    4823 Materials
    4824 Environmental chemistry
    4825 Methods of analysis and detection
    4827 Biochemistry
Not more than one from list b:
(b) 4841 Instrumental electronics
    4842 Scientific communication
    4843 Food technology

Content of the A-level syllabuses (modules in brackets):

Syllabus topic	Covered in Unit No	✓	Syllabus topic	Covered in Unit No	✓
*1 Atoms, molecules and stoichiometry (4820)	1.5, 3, 7.4		*9.5 Transition elements (4822)	28	
*2 Atomic structure (4820)	1.1–1.4		*9.6 Nitrogen and sulphur (4824)	25, 26, 40.2, 40.6	
*3 Chemical bonding (4820)	4		10 Organic Chemistry		
*4 States of matter (4822)	8–10		*10.1 Introductory topics (4820, 4851)	5.2, 7.4–7.8, 38	
*5 Chemical energetics (4820, 4826)	13		*10.2 Hydrocarbons (4851)	29	
*6 Electrochemistry (4822, 4826)	6, 18		*10.3 Halogen derivatives (4851)	30	
*7 Equilibrium (4826)	15, 16, 17.1, 17.2		*10.4 Hydroxy compounds (4851)	31.1–31.4 (31.5, 31.6 not AS)	
*8 Reaction kinetics (4826)	14		*10.5 Carbonyl compounds (4851)	32	
9 Inorganic chemistry			10.6 Carboxylic acids and derivatives (4851)	33, 34.1–34.4	
*9.1 The Periodic Table and periodicity (4822, 4820)	2, 21		10.7 Nitrogen compounds (4851)	34.5, 34.6, 35	
*9.2 Group II (4822)	22		*10.8 Polymerisation (4823)	36	
9.3 Group IV (4822)	24		Options		
*9.4 Group VII (4822)	27				

Analysis of AS terminal route – 8405

Paper	Duration in hours	Type of paper	Available
1	$2\frac{1}{2}$	Three sections A (32%) Variable number of compulsory structured questions, based on the core B (48%) 6 free response questions: 1 inorganic, 2 physical, 2 organic + 1 other. Students required to answer inorganic question and 3 others C (20%) 3 questions on each option. Any 2 to be answered.	June
2 3	$1\frac{3}{4}$	Practical assessment or Centre-based practical assessment	 June

The content of the syllabus is shown as starred topics in the A-level Syllabus table on page 6.

Analysis of AS modular route – 8535
For AS level three modules have to be taken.
They are 4820, 4826 and 4846 (this is a module unique to AS level consisting of half modules of organic reactions and practical skills.)

UNIVERSITY OF LONDON EXAMINATIONS AND ASSESSMENT COUNCIL
Syllabus 9081   A level (modular or terminal examination)
Syllabus 8081   AS level (modular or terminal examination)

The A-level syllabus is examined by either:
❶ a modular scheme consisting of 4 modular tests containing structured questions, a terminal synoptic paper and either a centre-based practical assessment or a practical test
or
❷ a terminal assessment consisting of 4 structured papers (i.e. the same papers as the modular tests), a synoptic paper and either a centre-based practical assessment or a practical test.

For AS-level Chemistry the assessment involves 2 module tests CH1 and CH2 and the synoptic paper CH5. All AS-level candidates must complete the centre-based practical assessment. The practical test is not available for AS level.

The following table summarises the assessment of A- and AS-level Chemistry.

Exam component	Duration in hours	Weighting AS level	Weighting A level	Style of component	Availability
CH1	$1\frac{1}{3}$	30%	15%	Each module test	Jan/June
CH2	$1\frac{1}{3}$	30%	15%	CH1–CH4 consists	Jan/June
CH3	$1\frac{1}{3}$		15%	of compulsory	Jan/June
CH4	$1\frac{1}{3}$		15%	structured questions – 60 marks	Jan/June
CH5 synoptic	$1\frac{1}{3}$	20%		40 marks	June
CH6 synoptic	2		20%	80 marks	Jan/June
CH7 practical assessment		20%	20%	Based on 4 skills	Jan/June
CH8 practical test	3	not available	20%	1 qualitative and 1 quantitative	Jan/June

Module tests (CH1–CH4) will examine mainly knowledge and understanding. The synoptic papers (CH5 for AS level and CH6 for A level) will contain questions which test skills acquired during the whole course as well as some questions on cross-modular themes which integrate knowledge from two modules (for AS level) or two or more modules (for A level).

The content of the four modules is as follows:

Syllabus topic	Covered in Unit No	✓
CH1		
Atomic structure	1	
Quantitative chemistry	7, 19	
Structure and bonding	4, 5	
Oxidation and reduction and transition elements	6, 28	
Periodic Table	2	
CH2		
Energetics I	13	
Chemical equilibrium	15	
Acid–base equilibrium	16	
Chemical kinetics	14	
Nomenclature of organic compounds	7.8	
Isomerism	7.6	
Reaction mechanisms	38	
Characteristic tests for organic compounds	page 30	
Important applications	34.4, 36.1, 36.5 detergents and polymers	
Bonding in organic compounds	29.8, 38.1	

Syllabus topic	Covered in Unit No	✓
CH3		
Energetics II	13	
Redox equilibrium	18	
Gaseous and heterogeneous equilibrium	15	
Groups I, II, III, IV, VII	22–24, 27, 40.4 include chlor-alkali industry	
CH4		
Chemistry of organic compounds	29, 31–33, 34.2, 34.6, 35, 36.3 alkanes, alkenes, alcohols, amines, amino acids, carboxylic acids, arenes, acid chlorides, nitriles, carbonyls	
Organic synthesis	7.2, 37	
Organic analysis	1.5, 7.5 include spectra	
Phase equilibrium	9	

NORTHERN EXAMINATIONS AND ASSESSMENT BOARD

Syllabus 4171   **A level – Terminal examination**
Syllabus 4174   **A level – Modular route**
Syllabus 3171   **AS level – Terminal examination**
Syllabus 3174   **AS level – Modular route**

These syllabuses are based on 9 modules.
*Ch1 Atomic structure, bonding and periodicity
*Ch2 Equilibria and inorganic chemistry
*Ch3 Kinetics and organic chemistry
 Ch4 Further physical chemistry
 Ch5 Further inorganic chemistry
 Ch6 Further organic chemistry
 Ch7 Chemistry of modern materials: ceramics, metals and polymers
 Ch8 Chemistry of colour
 Ch9 Chemistry of living systems and food

The 3 starred modules contain the chemistry within the National Core. For AS level, students are required to study only the 3 starred modules. For A level, students are required to study the starred modules and any 3 of the other modules Ch4–Ch9.

A level 4171

2 written papers (I and II), each of 3 hours, plus a centre-based assessment of practical skills.

Paper I will test the content of Ch1–Ch3. It will be divided into 3 sections.
- Section A will consist entirely of objective questions in the form of multiple choice and either matching pairs or multiple completion items. ¾ of an hour should be spent on this section.
- Section B will consist of questions requiring short answers. 1¼ hours should be spent on this section.
- Section C will consist of longer questions. 1 hour should be spent on this section.

All questions in Sections A and B are compulsory and 2 questions out of 5 should be answered from Section C.

Paper II will consist of from 4 to 7 questions on each of the 6 modules Ch4–Ch9. The questions within each module will not necessarily carry equal marks. Students will be required to attempt all questions from 3 modules only.

AS level 3171

1 written paper of 3 hours plus a centre-based assessment of practical skills. The written paper will be identical to Paper I of Chemistry 4171.

A level 4174

6 module tests should be taken during the course. The tests, each of 1½ hours duration, are set in late February/early March and June each year. Students must take at least 3 module tests after 14th February in the year in which they intend to receive a grade in the subject as a whole. Each test will consist of a number of structured questions of varying lengths. They will allow for both short answers and those of a more extended nature, including an answer in continuous prose.

For A level each module will be allocated $16\frac{2}{3}\%$ of the total marks, with $13\frac{2}{3}\%$ allocated to the module test and 3% to practical skills.

AS level 3174

The same module tests (Ch1, Ch2, Ch3) as Chemistry 4174. For the AS syllabus each module will be allocated $33\frac{1}{3}\%$ of the total mark, with $27\frac{1}{3}\%$ for the module test and 6% for practical skills. At least 2 of the module tests must be taken after 14th February.

Centre-based assessment of practical skills

Four skills will be assessed:

A Designing	C Interpreting
B Implementing	D Communicating

Summary of the content of modules

Syllabus topic	Covered in Unit No	✔
*Ch1 Atomic structure, bonding and periodicity	1.1–1.4, 2.1–2.3, 2.5, 3.1–3.3, 4.1–4.3, 4.5, 5, 7.4, 8.1, 8.4, 8.8, 13.1–13.9, 19.1, 21.1, 21.3, 22.1, 22.2 (not Group II)	
*Ch2 Equilibria and inorganic chemistry	15.1–15.5 (reference to K_c not K_p), 16.1–16.4, 17.2, 27, 28, 40.2	
*Ch3 Kinetics and organic chemistry	1.5, 7.5, 7.6, 7.8, 8.11, 14, 29.1–29.5, 29.8, 29.9, 30.1–31.4, 32.1–32.6, 33.1–33.3	
Ch4 Further physical chemistry	13.10, 13.12, 13.13, 14.3, 15 (include K_p), 16.5, 16.6, 18	
Ch5 Further inorganic chemistry	23.1, 23.2, 28	
Ch6 Further organic chemistry	13.11, 34.2, 34.3, 35, 38.2, 38.4, 38.5, 39	
Ch7 Chemistry of modern materials: ceramics, metals and polymers	36.1–36.5, 40.1 ceramics not covered in this book	
Ch8 Chemistry of colour	not covered	
Ch9 Chemistry of living systems and food	not covered	

NORTHERN IRELAND COUNCIL FOR THE CURRICULUM EXAMINATIONS AND ASSESSMENT

A level

	Duration in hours	Weighting	Type of paper
Paper 1	$2\frac{1}{2}$	36%	8 compulsory structured questions, testing topics A–F only
Paper 2	$1\frac{1}{4}$	25%	40 compulsory objective questions – multiple choice, matching pair (classification) and multiple completion – testing topics A–F
Paper 3 Part A	$\frac{3}{4}$	10%	Single compulsory comprehension-type question
Part B	$1\frac{1}{4}$	14%	12 free response questions on topic G
Coursework		15%	Centre-based assessment of practical skills

Syllabus topic	Covered in Unit No	✓
A Atomic structure and bonding	1.1–1.4, 1.6, 2.1–2.3, 4–5, 7.6, 20.1–20.3	
B Substances: structure, physical properties and physical characteristics	8.1–8.10, 9, 10	
C Chemical reactions and reactivity	3, 6, 7.4, 8.11, 13.1–13.10, 14–19	
D Inorganic chemistry	2, 21, 22, 24, 27, 28, 40.2	
E Organic chemistry	7.1, 29, 30, 31.1–31.4, 32–35, 36.3, 36.5, 39	
F Analytical chemistry	pages 27–30; 7.2, 7.3, 19	
G Chemistry in the world 1 question should be answered on industrial chemistry and 1 on environmental chemistry	Industrial chemistry 36.1, 36.2, 36.4, 40.2, 40.4, 40.6 Environmental chemistry 36.3	

Centre–based practical assessment

Students will be assessed on at least 2 occasions in 8 skill areas.

1. Planning — 10%
2. Following instructions efficiently and safely — 10%
3. Manipulation of apparatus and materials — 15%
4. Observation of qualitative change — 15%
5. Measurement — 15%
6. Recording — 15%
7. Interpretation — 10%
8. Attitudes – enthusiasm, commitment, initiative, etc. — 10%

NUFFIELD (UNIVERSITY OF LONDON EXAMINATIONS AND ASSESSMENT COUNCIL)
Syllabus 9087   A level (modular or terminal examination)

The A-level syllabus is examined by either:

❶ a modular scheme consisting of 4 modular tests containing structured questions, a terminal synoptic paper and a centre-based practical assessment

or

❷ a terminal assessment consisting of 4 structured papers (i.e. the same papers as the modular tests), a synoptic paper and a centre-based practical assessment.

The following table summarises the assessment of A-level Nuffield Chemistry.

Exam component	Duration in hours	Weighting	Style of component	Availability
CN1	$1^1/_2$	15%	Each module test	Jan/June
CN2	$1^1/_2$	15%	CN1–CN4 consists	June
CN3	$1^1/_2$	15%	of compulsory	Jan/June
CN4	$1^1/_2$	15%	structured questions – 60 marks	June
CN5 synoptic	5A – $^3/_4$ 5B – $1^1/_2$	10% 10%	30 marks 30 marks	June
CN6 practical assessment		20%	Assessment of 4 skills – 40 marks	June

CN5 will consist of 2 sections with a short break between sections. Section A will contain 1 question on each of the prescribed *Special Studies*. Normally, each question will be partly structured and partly free response and will be concerned with all aspects of the study – background theory, experimental work and technological applications. All parts of each question will be compulsory. 1 question should be attempted. Section B will test the ability of drawing together and integrating the understanding of all 18 topics in the syllabus. Both questions should be attempted, but there will be choice within each question.

There are 11 themes which run throughout the syllabus. The following table summarises the themes, shows in which of the Nuffield topics these themes appear and gives their weightings.

Themes in the syllabus	Nuffield topics	Target weighting (%)
The mole	All	3
Metals and non-metals in the Periodic Table	1, 5, 15, 17	10
Organic reactions	2, 7, 12, 14, 16	15
Structure and bonding	3, 6, 9	5
Energy	4, 10, 13	5
Rates of reaction	8	3
Equilibria	11	3
Redox reactions and electrode potentials	5, 13	3
Applications/general	All, 18	3
Practical skills	All	20
Synoptic skills (special study, summary/comprehension, laboratory situation, data analysis, open-book questions)	All	30

The content of the 18 Nuffield topics is as follows:

Syllabus topic	Covered in Unit No	✓	Syllabus topic	Covered in Unit No	✓
Paper CN1 (Topics 1–4)			**Paper CN3 (Topics 9–12)**		
Topic 1 Iron compounds: an introduction to inorganic chemistry	1, 2.1, 3.1, 3.2, 3.5, 4.1–4.3, 6, 28		Topic 9 Intermolecular forces and solubility	4.1, 4.5, 4.6	
			Topic 10 Entropy	13.12, 13.13, 18.6, 18.7	
Topic 2 Alcohols: an introduction to organic chemistry	3.3, 3.4, 7.6, 7.8, 9.6, 31.1–31.7		Topic 11 How far? Reversible reactions	15.1–15.5, 16.1–16.6, 17.2	
Topic 3 Atoms, ions and acids	1.4, 1.6, 2.2-2.8, 4.1, 16, 19 see also page 28 – flame tests		Topic 12 Carbon compounds with acidic and basic properties	31.5, 31.6, 33, 34	
			Paper CN4 (Topics 13–15)		
Topic 4 Energy and reactions	4.1, 13.1–13.8, 13.10, 22.2		Topic 13 Redox equilibria and electrochemical cells	18	
Paper CN2 (Topics 5–8)			Topic 14 Natural products and polymers	7.2, 7.6, 36.1–36.5	
Topic 5 The halogens and redox reactions	6, 27		Topic 15 The transition elements	4.7, 10.2, 14.3, 18.2, 28	
Topic 6 Covalent bonding	4.2–4.4, 13.9, 13.11, 21.1, 21.3		**Paper CN5** (Synoptic paper) All parts of the syllabus, but including Topics 16–18		
Topic 7 Hydrocarbons and haloalkanes	7.8, 29.1–29.5, 29.8, 30.1, 36.1, 38.1–38.6 chemistry of alkanes, arenes, alkenes and haloalkanes		Topic 16 Organic synthesis	7.5, 37	
			Topic 17 Nitrogen compounds	25.1–25.4, 35.4, 40.2, 40.3	
Topic 8 How fast? Rates of reaction	8.11, 14, 15.5, 38.5		Topic 18 Instrumental methods	1.5, 7.5, 10.1, 16.4, 24.3 includes X-ray diffraction, pH, conductivity, IR, NMR, mass spectrometry	

Special studies – not included in this book:
• Biochemistry
• Chemical Engineering
• Food Science
• Materials Science
• Mineral Process Chemistry

NUFFIELD (UNIVERSITY OF LONDON EXAMINATIONS AND ASSESSMENT COUNCIL)
Syllabus 8087   AS level (modular or terminal examination)

The AS-level syllabus is examined by either:
❶ a modular scheme consisting of A-level module 1 (CN1), a synoptic paper (CN7), the special study paper (CN8) and a centre-based practical assessment
or
❷ a terminal assessment consisting of 1 structured paper (CN1), a synoptic paper, the special study paper and a centre-based practical assessment.

The following table summarises the assessment of AS-level Nuffield Chemistry.

Exam component	Duration in hours	Weighting	Style of component	Availability
CN1	$1\frac{1}{2}$	30%	Tests topics 1–4 60 marks	Jan/June
Synoptic	$1\frac{1}{2}$	30%	Tests all topics, but especially 5–15 60 marks	June
Special study	$\frac{3}{4}$	20%	30 marks	June
Practical assessment		20%	Assessment of 4 skills – 30 marks	June

The content of the AS-level syllabus is similar to the Nuffield A-level syllabus, but certain reductions have been made to compensate for the reduced time. The main differences in content are:

- **Topics 1–4**   Exactly the same treatment as the A-level syllabus.
- **Topic 5**   Omit reactions of halogens with alkalis, estimation of iodine with sodium thiosulphate, study of halogens in oxidation state +5.
- **Topic 6**   Omit dative covalency and delocalisation of electrons.
- **Topic 8**   Omit kinetics and reaction mechanisms including S_N1 and S_N2 mechanisms of haloalkanes.
- **Topic 9**   Omit the solubility of molecular compounds and ionic compounds.
- **Topic 10**   Omit acid–base titrations and all references to entropy.
- **Topics 12 and 14**   Restrict to a study of carboxylic acids and optical activity (chiral and achiral compounds).
- **Topic 13**   Omit completely.
- **Topic 15**   Omit crystal structures of metals, transition metals as catalysts, study of chlorides of iron.
- **Topics 16–18** Omit completely.

UNIVERSITY OF OXFORD DELEGACY OF LOCAL EXAMINATIONS
Syllabus 9855   **A level (modular or terminal examination)**
Syllabus 9855   **AS level (modular or terminal examination)**

AS level consists of the first 3 modules plus coursework.
This syllabus is available at A and AS levels by either:
❶ terminal examination route, taking all papers at the end of the course
or
❷ a modular route, taking modules in December, March and June.

Paper		Duration in hours	Weighting A level	Weighting AS level
9855/1	General & physical chemistry	$1\frac{1}{4}$	16%	32%
9855/2	General & organic chemistry	$1\frac{1}{4}$	16%	32%
9855/3	General & inorganic chemistry Two sections: A (both A and AS level) and B (A level only)	$1\frac{1}{4}$	16%	16% part A only (40 min)
9855/41	Further physical chemistry	$1\frac{1}{4}$	16%	
/42	Further organic chemistry	$1\frac{1}{4}$	candidates	
/43	Polymers and plastics	$1\frac{1}{4}$	choose	
/44	Biochemistry	$1\frac{1}{4}$	1 option	
9855/51	Further physical chemistry	$1\frac{1}{4}$	16%	
/52	Further inorganic chemistry	$1\frac{1}{4}$	candidates	
/53	Electrochemistry	$1\frac{1}{4}$	choose	
/54	Chemistry of the environment	$1\frac{1}{4}$	1 option	
9855/61	Coursework *		20%	20%
/62	Written/practical **	1 + 2		

* Centre-based coursework assessment is based on the following skills, each marked on a 1–5 scale.

- **Planning**
    - (a) Applying knowledge and understanding of scientific laws, theories and models to develop hypotheses and make predictions.
    - (b) Identifying key variables and deciding which variables to control; retrieving and evaluating relevant information from multiple sources.
    - (c) Selecting, with due regard to safety, appropriate techniques, apparatus, materials and order and scale of working; providing appropriate precision of measurement and recording.

- **Implementing**
    - (a) Setting up and manipulating apparatus and materials with sufficient skill and safety needed for the specific technique used.
    - (b) Making and recording accurate observations and measurements.
    - (c) Checking operation of apparatus; evaluating and modifying procedures in the light of observation and experience.

- **Concluding**
    - (a) Assessing the reliability and accuracy of experimental data; identifying and assessing errors.
    - (b) Interpreting information gathered from experimental investigations; recognising patterns and trends; drawing appropriate conclusions.
    - (c) Communicating scientific information and ideas in an appropriate way using tables, graphs, continuous prose, etc.

For A level the student should submit 2 investigations and submit 1 investigation for AS level.

** This is an alternative to the centre-based coursework assessment, and is set in two parts.

- Part 1 is an exercise to assess a student's ability to plan an investigation into any area of chemistry in modules 1–3.
- Part 2 assesses a student's ability to implement experimental procedures and draw conclusions from the experimental results.

A summary of the content of the syllabus is given below:

Syllabus topic	Covered in Unit No	✓
Module 1 General and physical	1.1–1.3, 3, 4, 8.11, 13–16, 17.2, 40.2, 40.6	
Module 2 General and organic	5.2, 7.1, 7.4, 7.6, 7.8, 29, 30, 31.1–31.4, 32–34, 38	
Module 3 General and inorganic	Topics in bold **not** required for AS level 1.4, 2.1, **2.2–2.7**, 5.1, 6, 14.3, **18.2**, 18.5, **18.6, 21.1, 21.3**, 22, 27, 28, 40.2, 40.3, 40.6	
Module 4	There are 4 alternatives:	
/41 Further physical chemistry	1.5, 7.2, 7.5, 8–10, 13, 14.2, 15	
/42 Further organic chemistry	29.8–29.10, 33–35, 36.3, 37–39	
/43 Polymers and plastics	24.5, 36	
/44 Biochemistry	36.5	
Module 5	There are 4 alternatives:	
/51 Further physical chemistry	1.5, 7.2, 7.5, 8–10, 13, 14.2, 15	
/52 Further inorganic chemistry	7.7, 24–26, 28, 40.6	
/53 Electrochemistry	3.5, 4.1, 6, 8, 16–18, 23.2, 40.4	
/54 Chemistry of the environment	19	

OXFORD AND CAMBRIDGE SCHOOLS EXAMINATION BOARD
Structured Science Scheme A Level 9684, AS level 8384

This syllabus can be modular, taking the module tests in January or June, or terminal, taking all the tests at the end of the course. If it is taken as modular, at least three modules for A level and two for AS level must be taken at the end of the course.

For AS level just modules C1, C2 and C3 are required. For A level, these three are required, plus three from C4–C9, S1 and S2. Each module will be tested by a written test (of 80 marks) and coursework (20 marks).

Content	Covered in Unit No	✔
C1 Fundamental concepts		
Formulae, equations and amounts of substance	3	
Atomic structure (not electron structures)	1.1–1.4	
Volumetric calculations	19.1	
Gases	8.2–8.4	
Bonding	4	
Enthalpy changes	13.9	
Equilibrium (qualitative)	15.1, 15.5	
Acid-base equilibria and pH	16.1–16.5	
Reaction kinetics	14	
C2 Periodicity, structure & bonding		
Electronic structure of atoms	1.5	
Bonding and structure (further)	4, 5	
Redox properties	6	
Periodicity and the Periodic Table	2	
Group IV	24	
Electrolysis of sodium chloride	41	
Contact process	26.9	
Transition elements	28	
C3 Essential organic chemistry		
Structural aspects and isomerism	7	

Content	Covered in Unit No	✔
Types of reaction	38	
Reactions of hydrocarbons	29	
Concept of functional groups	30–35	
C4 How far and how fast?		
Thermodynamics	13.1–13.8	
Quantitative treatment of equilibria	15.3–15.4	
Solubility product, buffer solutions	17.2, 16.6	
Further treatment of kinetics	14	
C5 Elements and compounds		
Electrode potentials and redox reactions	18	
s-block elements	22	
p-block elements	23–27	
Transition elements	28	
C6 Further organic chemistry		
Structural aspects and reactions	7, 38	
Polymers	36	
Reactions and properties of organic compounds	29–35	
C7 Environmental chemistry	19, 36.3	
C8 Analytical chemistry	1.6, 7.5, 19	
C7 Biochemistry	36	

Units S1 (Science and Technology in Society) and S2 (Energy) are outside the scope of this book.

SALTERS (OXFORD AND CAMBRIDGE SCHOOLS EXAMINATION BOARD)
Syllabus 9663   A level

	Duration in hours	Weighting	Type of paper
Paper 1	2½	35%	Questions requiring relatively short responses with main emphasis on knowledge and understanding
Paper 2	2½	35%	Questions requiring longer responses with main emphasis on application of knowledge and understanding
Paper 3		10%	Open-book exam *
Coursework		20%	Centre-based coursework investigation **

* **Paper 3**: 1 question based on a collection of scientific papers, extracts from books, etc. (up to 10 sides of A4). The response to the question should consist of 800–1000 words. Reports of over 1000 words are liable to be penalised. The report should show an understanding of chemical issues and be aimed at an audience with an understanding of A-level chemistry. It should have a clear and helpful structure and should show evidence of planning. Extensive copying will not gain credit. Graphs, tables, charts, diagrams, etc. can be used, but large tables filled with text will be included in the word count.

A period of 2 weeks is allowed to complete this report. These 2 weeks will be towards the end of the fifth term.

The marking criteria used to mark the report are:
❶ Understanding the basic chemical content of the paper   (6 marks);

❷ Evaluation of the chemical content in the context of the question   (8 marks);

❸ Quality of communication in the response   (6 marks).

** **Centre-based coursework investigation**: The student is required to carry out 1 extended practical-based investigation. This should require the student to obtain information from a wide range of different sources. The assessment will be made by the teacher and moderated externally under the following headings.

    A Research   B Planning   C Manipulation

    D Observation and Measurement   E Conclusions

Syllabus topic	Covered in Unit No	✓
Amount of substance	3.2, 3.3, 7.4, 7.5, 8.4, 19.1	
Atomic structure	1.1–1.4, 20.1, 20.2	
Structure and bonding	2.3, 2.4, 4, 5	
Thermochemistry	13	
Photochemistry	1.6, 38.3	
Spectroscopy and chromatography	1.5, 7.2, 7.5	
Equilibria	15.1–15.5, 16, 17.1, 17.2	
Solutions	3.5, 4.1, 15.6	
Reaction kinetics	14	
Redox	6, 18	
Periodicity	2, 21	
Group II	22	
Group IV	24	
Group V	25	
Group VI	26	

Syllabus topic	Covered in Unit No	✓
Group VII	27	
d-Block elements	28	
Stereochemistry and isomerism	7.6, 7.7	
Organic reaction mechanisms	38	
Homologous series	7.2, 29	
Alkanes	29	
Alkenes	29	
Arenes	29	
Halogenoalkanes	30	
Alcohols and phenols	31.1–31.7	
Carboxylic acids and their derivatives, carbonyl compounds	32–34	
Nitrogen compounds	34.5, 34.6, 35	
Proteins and DNA	36.3	
Polymers	36.1, 36.2, 36.5	
Organic synthesis	37	
Chemical industry	40	

SCOTTISH EXAMINATION BOARD
Higher Grade

Syllabus topic	Covered in Unit No	✓
Controlling reaction rates	14	
Feedstocks and fuels	7, 29, 31, 32, 36	
Molecules to moles	3, 6, 8, 19	
Biomolecules	34, 36	
From bonds to behaviour	4, 5, 21, 26, 27	
Thermochemistry	13	
Chemical equilibrium	15–17	
Radioisotopes	20	

Paper analysis

Two papers with some questions on Paper 2 testing Prescribed Practical Activites.

Paper 1   *1⅔ hours*   Fixed response paper
This will include at least 40 multiple choice questions and grid questions
    60 marks

Paper 2   *2½ hours*   Extended answer questions
    90 marks

There will be no choice of questions on either paper.

WELSH JOINT EDUCATION COMMITTEE
A level (modular or terminal examination)
AS level (modular or terminal examination)

Terminal	Duration in hours	Weighting	Type of paper
Paper A1	3	40%	6 compulsory structured questions. 1 compulsory comprehension question. 2 free response questions – 1 to be answered.
Paper A2	3	40%	3 compulsory structured questions – 1 inorganic, 1 organic, 1 physical. 3 sections of free response questions – each containing 2 questions. Students required to answer 1 question from each section.
Coursework		20%	Centre-based practical work

AS level is Paper A1 (80%) plus coursework. Additional content is required for A level compared to AS level. This is shown in the following table. Numbers in brackets refer to the module in which the content is included for modular courses.

Syllabus topic		Required for AS and A level	Required for A level only (A2)	✓
1	Atomic structure (C1)	1.1–1.4, 2.1–2.3, 20.1–20.3		
2	The mole and stoichiometry (C1)	7.3, 19	1.5	
3	Spectroscopy (C3)		1.6, 7.5	
4	Principles of energetics (C2)	13.1–13.8		
5	Forces within molecules (C1)	4.1, 4.2	2.5, 4.3	
6	Energy changes and bond strengths (C4)		13.8–13.10	
7	Forces between molecules (C1)	4.5, 4.6		
8	Shapes of molecules and ions (C1)	5		
9	Gases, liquids and solids (C1)	8–10		
10	Principles of chemical equilibria (C2, C4)	15.1–15.3, 40.2, 40.6		
11	Acid–base equilibria (C2)	16, 17.2	17.1	
12	Redox equilibria (C4)	6	18	
13	Rates of chemical reaction (C2)	14		
14	The Periodic Table (C1)	2, 21		
15	Inorganic chemistry of selected groups: Groups II, IV, VII, transition metals (C4)	22, 24, 27, 28		
16	Principles of organic chemistry (C2, C3))	7.2, 7.6, 7.8, 38		
17	Organic analysis, conversions (C2)		1.5, 7.4, 37	
18	Classes of organic compounds: hydrocarbons, haloalkanes, alcohols and phenols, aldehydes and ketones, carboxylic acids and derivatives, amines, amino acids (C2,C3)	11, 13, 29.1–29.3, 29.5, 29.8, 29.9, 31.1–31.6, 32–34, 36.1, 36.2	35, 36.3	
19	Industrial processes (C2)	36.2, 40	36.7	
20	Environmental chemistry (C2)	36.3		

The linear A level syllabus is available for first examination in 1996. A modular route, based on compulsory modules C1–C4, is also available at A level, for first award in 1997 (1996 for the modular AS level course). The content is the same for both the terminal and modular syllabuses.

Paper analysis A level (modular)

C1, C2, C3, C4	1⅔ hrs each	16% each	based on the content of each compulsory module
C5 – synoptic paper	1⅔ hrs	16%	synoptic paper covering content from the whole course
Coursework		20%	centre-based practical work

Paper analysis AS level (modular)
Candidates take C1 and C2 (40% each) which cover the Core, plus the centre-based practical work (20%).

EXAMINATION BOARD ADDRESSES

AEB   The Associated Examining Board
                 Stag Hill House, Guildford, Surrey GU2 5XJ
                 Tel: 01483 506506

Cambridge   University of Cambridge Local Examinations Syndicate
                 Syndicate Buildings, 1 Hills Road, Cambridge CB1 2EU
                 Tel: 01223 553311

NEAB   Northern Examinations and Assessment Board
                 12 Harter Street, Manchester M1 6HL
                 Tel: 0161 953 1180

NICCEA   Northern Ireland Council for the Curriculum Examinations and
                 Assessment
                 Beechill House, 42 Beechill Road, Belfast BT8 4RS
                 Tel: 01232 704666

Oxford   University of Oxford Delegacy of Local Examinations
                 Ewert House, Ewert Place, Summertown, Oxford OX2 7BZ
                 Tel: 01865 54291

Oxford and   Oxford and Cambridge Schools Examination Board
Cambridge   (a) Purbeck House, Purbeck Road, Cambridge CB2 1PU
                 Tel: 01223 411211
                 (b) Elsfield Way, Oxford OX2 8EP
                 Tel: 01865 54421

SEB   Scottish Examination Board
                 Ironmills Road, Dalkeith, Midlothian EH22 1LE
                 Tel: 0131 663 6601

ULEAC   University of London Examinations and Assessment Council
                 Stewart House, 32 Russell Square, London WC1 5DN
                 Tel: 0171 331 4000

WJEC   Welsh Joint Education Committee
                 245 Western Avenue, Cardiff CF5 2YX
                 Tel: 01222 265000

STUDYING AND REVISING CHEMISTRY

THE DIFFERENCE BETWEEN GCSE AND A/AS LEVEL

The majority of students who start an A-level course in Chemistry come from a background of GCSE Science or GCSE Chemistry. The most difficult part of A level is bridging the gap between GCSE and A/AS level.

Whether you are studying A or AS levels, the standard of work, and the quality and detail of your answers will be the same. The only difference is that the quantity of material will be greater for A level. AS level is not therefore an easy alternative for students not capable of A level, but is a chance for students of A-level standard to take extra subjects.

There are three basic problems in making the jump from GCSE to A/AS level. The first is making sure that there are no gaps in your knowledge and understanding from GCSE. For this reason, the first seven chapters in this book are based on topics you will have studied at GCSE and you should work through these in detail before attempting any others.

The second problem is the quantity of material you will have to cover and sorting out what is most important. It is useful to establish patterns which will help you to 'hang on' facts as you need them. For example, much of the inorganic chemistry you will need can be linked to patterns in the Periodic Table.

The third problem is getting sufficient detail into your answers. Very often students know the facts but do not know when and how to use them. This can be illustrated by looking at a GCSE question (1) and an A-level question (2) which look similar. Look at the sample answers and try to appreciate the amount of detail you will be expected to give.

Sample questions

1 Outline the manufacture of sulphuric acid from a rich sulphur-bearing ore such as iron(II) disulphide (iron pyrites). No description of the technical plant is required but the essential conditions for each stage of the process should be given. What is the action of sulphuric acid upon (a) powdered crystals of copper(II) sulphate-5-water, (b) magnesium? Specify the necessary conditions.

Sample answer
The manufacture of sulphuric acid is in four stages.
(i)   Burning of iron(II) disulphide in excess air to produce sulphur(IV) oxide (sulphur dioxide).

$$4FeS_2(s) + 11O_2(g) \rightarrow 2Fe_2O_3(s) + 8SO_2(g)$$
(The word equation here would be sufficient)

(ii) Purification of sulphur(IV) oxide to remove the impurities which would poison the catalyst in the next stage. The gases are dried.

(iii) Conversion of sulphur(IV) oxide to sulphur(VI) oxide (sulphur trioxide) by passing the sulphur(IV) oxide and air over a vanadium(V) oxide catalyst at about 450 °C and normal pressure.

$$2SO_2(g) + O_2(g) \rightleftharpoons 2SO_3(g)$$

(iv) Absorption of the sulphur(VI) oxide in concentrated sulphuric acid to produce oleum which, on dilution with the correct amount of water, produces concentrated sulphuric acid.

$$SO_3(g) + H_2SO_4(l) \rightarrow H_2S_2O_7(l)$$
$$H_2S_2O_7(l) + H_2O(l) \rightarrow 2H_2SO_4(l)$$

(a) Concentrated sulphuric acid acts as a dehydrating agent when added to blue crystals of copper(II) sulphate-5-water. The water is removed and white anhydrous copper(II) sulphate remains. No heat is required.

$$CuSO_4.5H_2O(s) \rightleftharpoons CuSO_4(s) + 5H_2O(l)$$

(b) Magnesium reacts with dilute sulphuric acid to produce magnesium sulphate and hydrogen. Again no heat is required.

$$Mg(s) + H_2SO_4(aq) \rightarrow MgSO_4(aq) + H_2(g)$$

2 (a) Describe the manufacture of sulphuric acid, explaining carefully the reasons for the chemical and physical conditions used in each stage of the process. Details of the industrial plant are not required. (12 marks)

(b) Give two uses of sulphuric acid. (2 marks)

(c) How and under what conditions does sulphuric acid react with (i) potassium bromide, (ii) oxalic acid (ethanedioic acid), (iii) hydrogen sulphide? (6 marks)

Sample answer

As for the previous question but in addition:

(a) (i) Alternative sources of sulphur(IV) oxide should be included, e.g. oxidation of hydrogen sulphide present in certain natural gases.

These reactions need to be carried out in a plentiful supply of air to provide the oxygen required for stage (iii). Air is used in preference to oxygen as it is cheaper.

(ii) Purification involves removing arsenic dust particles by passing the gases through electrostatic dust precipitators. Charged dust particles stick onto charged plates and provide a source of arsenic. The gases are then washed and dried with concentrated sulphuric acid.

(iii) This reaction is reversible and an equilibrium is established. The total yield of sulphuric acid produced will depend upon the conditions under which this step is carried out and the yield of sulphur(VI) oxide obtained.

The forward reaction is exothermic. To obtain the maximum yield of sulphur(VI) oxide the equilibrium must be moved as far to the right as is economically possible. Le Chatelier's principle can be used qualitatively to predict the position of the equilibrium.

Effect of temperature: According to Le Chatelier's principle, since the forward reaction is exothermic, reducing the temperature will increase the yield of sulphur(VI) oxide. However, this will also slow the rate of reaction. A compromise is therefore made and a vanadium(V) oxide catalyst is used to speed up the reaction.

Effect of pressure: Since there is a decrease in volume when sulphur(IV) oxide is produced, it can be predicted that an increased yield of sulphur(VI) oxide will be obtained by increasing the pressure. The reaction is carried out, however, at atmospheric pressure as the increased yield cannot offset the increased costs of building a plant to withstand high pressures.

(iv) These reactions are used as directly reacting sulphur(VI) oxide with water is an extremely exothermic process.

(b) Manufacture of ammonium sulphate which is used as a nitrogen fertiliser. Making synthetic detergents by sulphonation of hydrocarbons.

(c) (i) Potassium bromide reacts with concentrated sulphuric acid initially to produce hydrogen bromide but hot, concentrated sulphuric acid acts as an oxidising agent and oxidises bromide ions to bromine. Reddish-brown fumes of bromine are seen.

(ii) When concentrated sulphuric acid is added to ethanedioic acid, and the mixture is heated, the sulphuric acid acts as a dehydrating agent. A mixture of carbon monoxide and carbon dioxide is produced.

(iii) Hot concentrated sulphuric acid oxidises hydrogen sulphide to give sulphur, sulphur(lV) oxide and water.

MODULAR COURSES

Many Examination Groups now provide an alternative to the traditional A level Chemistry course and these are known as 'modular courses'. Traditionally, all of the credit for a course is allocated to examinations taken at the end of the course (terminal examinations).

However, modular courses are divided into small units (or modules), each of which is examined in an end-of-module test. The advantages of these tests is that they allow regular feedback on how well you are doing. There is also the possibility of retaking modules to improve your grade without having to repeat the whole examination. Furthermore, the results of the module tests can be 'banked' and then 'cashed-in' within four years to obtain a grade at A or AS level.

Advice on preparation for module tests is given on page 26.

STUDY STRATEGIES AND TECHNIQUES

It is important to remember that there is no short cut to examination success. Hard work and commitment over a long period of time are the essential ingredients. This is much more important at A level than at GCSE.

Organising your notes

It is important to organise your notes so that you can find whatever you need quickly. Do not write on odd scraps of paper. Either use notebooks or loose-leaf files. If you use a loose-leaf file divide your notes into sections with file dividers. Maintain a clear index of the contents of each book or file.

Start every topic on a fresh sheet of paper. Leave room for any additions you may wish to make later. Make sure that your notes are clearly written with striking headings. Identify important points by freehand underlining or using a highlighter pen. If there are a number of points to be remembered, it is easier if they are in a numbered list.

In writing your notes it is acceptable to use abbreviations. These may be recognised abbreviations, e.g. temp., or your own abbreviations, e.g. apd for acidified potassium dichromate(VI); you may also use chemical formulae such as Fe instead of iron in your notes. Never use abbreviations or formulae in writing your examination answers.

At A level detail of answer is of greatest importance. When making your notes ensure that all the detail is there, e.g. reagents, reaction conditions, likely observations and equations. Unless this is in your notes, it will not be in your examination answers.

Adding to your notes

Be prepared to add to your notes from information you gather outside your lessons. It is important that you read around the subject. Read the topic being covered in texts written by different authors.

Magazines such as *Scientific American, New Scientist* or *STEAM* (magazine for science teachers from ICI) are good sources of information and may be available at your school or local library. This type of reading will extend your knowledge of social, economic, environmental and industrial chemistry. Many A-level questions now have this emphasis. It will also improve your English, extend your scientific vocabulary and make you a more efficient communicator. You may also have the opportunity to attend lectures given by university lecturers. Radio and television programmes on scientific topics can be useful.

COURSEWORK

The only coursework you are likely to be assessed on is practical work done in school towards the Practical Assessment (see Syllabus checklists for details). This is an alternative to a practical examination that students often find more unnerving than written papers.

You will essentially be carrying out the same kind of exercises as in a practical examination (see pages 27–30), but you will not be under the same pressure to make everything work on one day. There will be time for you to demonstrate mastery of various skills during the course. Also, your teacher will be able to choose exercises which may use more equipment than is generally required in a practical examination or that are of particular interest to you, e.g. an environmental problem.

Discuss with your teacher how you are progressing and what you need to do to improve. Try to incorporate any suggestions your teacher makes.

REVISION TECHNIQUES

Serious revision should start at least twelve weeks before the examination. At this stage you should go through the appropriate examination syllabus and list topics according to whether you feel you understand them or not. This should give you a realistic assessment of where you stand. A discussion with your teacher at this stage is useful. Find out how he/she is going to complete the course.

Divide the topics that you do not understand into manageable sections of about 30–40 minutes work, e.g. alcohols, pH, electron arrangements. Then devise a plan to spend time on each section in turn. Such a *revision timetable* is essential. Allocate time for each of your subjects but be reasonable – you will need to leave periods of time unaccounted for to allow yourself the reward of a break, or to make up time lost due to illness, distractions, etc.

As you go through each section don't just read the information. This kind of passive revision is not effective. You must make rough notes. Try to learn important facts and definitions as you write them down. Write out an equation, turn the paper over and write it out from memory. Check there are no errors. Try to make your revision at this stage *active*. Finally, try to summarise the main points from each section on a single piece of paper or a postcard. Keep these summaries as they are very useful for last-minute revision. Look at them regularly over the following few days to ensure that the information has sunk in.

You should now be prepared to tackle past papers. This can highlight topics which are examined more frequently than others or in a certain way. However, be careful about trying to predict which topics will come up. There is no pattern in the topics covered from year to year. Looking at papers may also indicate certain topics that you should look at again.

In the final stage of revision try to go through the whole syllabus. Do not ignore certain sections and hope they will not come up. Check you know all the major definitions and facts.

FINAL PREPARATION

Do not spend too much time on last-minute revision. A three-hour written paper is very draining. Long hours spent revising at the last minute can make you overtired and lose you more marks than this revision would gain.

On the evening before the examination make sure you have all the equipment you need – pens, pencil, ruler, calculator, etc. The most important thing you can do is try to relax and get a good night's sleep.

THE EXAMINATION

QUESTION STYLES

Multiple choice

Each question consists of a *stem* together with four or five possible answers or responses labelled either A to D or A to E. One answer (called the *key*) is correct and the others (called the *distracters*) are incorrect. You are required to select your answer and record it on a printed answer sheet. These will be marked by machine. It is important to follow **exactly** the instructions for recording your answers on the sheet.

It is important to remember the following points:

- Read the questions **very** carefully and use **all** of the information given. Mistakes are often due to the candidate choosing an answer without reading them all.
- It **is** worth a guess if you cannot work out the correct answer. If you can eliminate any of the responses you will increase your chances of guessing correctly.
- There is **no** penalty for a wrong answer. **Never** leave any question without attempting it.
- The easier questions should be at the beginning of the test. The questions towards the end of the test are more difficult and will probably need more time. Do not spend too long on any one question. There are three different types of multiple choice questions.

1 Simple multiple choice

Which of the following elements is a *d*-block element?

A Aluminium   C Chromium
B Boron   D Sulphur

The correct answer is C.

2 Multiple completion questions

In this type of question you are given four answers labelled 1–4. On your answer sheet you have to answer A, B, C, D or E depending upon the combination of statements 1–4 which are correct. These are often summarised in a table:

Combination	1, 2 and 3	1 and 3	2 and 4	4 only	1 and 4
Response	A	B	C	D	E

No other combination of responses can be recorded. If for example you think that only 1 is correct, you have made a mistake!

3 Classification questions

These consist of a series of simple type multiple choice questions which have the same set of possible answers. You should not assume that each answer can only be used once.

Example:

These questions concern the following compounds:

A

B $CH_3 - CH_2 - CH_2 - CH_2 - CH - CH_3$ with CH_2Cl branch

C

D $CH_3 - CH_2 - CH_2 - CH - CH_2 - CH_2 - CH_3$ with Cl branch

E $CH_3 - CH_2 - CH_2 - CH_2 - CH_2 - CH_2 - CH_2 - Cl$

Select the compound which
1 rotates the plane of polarised light.
2 forms a precipitate fastest when shaken with alcoholic silver nitrate solution.
3 does NOT react with ammonia.

The answers to these questions are:
1 B   2 C   3 A

Structured questions

Each of these questions consists of a series of parts linked to a common theme. There is space on the paper for each answer and the amount of space given should be a guide to the length of the answer required. Generally the earlier parts of each question will be easier than the later parts. Sample question 2 at the start of this section is an example of a structured question.

Very often candidates do not do as well as they should because they misunderstand the question. There are a few key words which you should understand.

- **Define (the term)** requires only a formal statement.
- **State** implies a concise answer with little or no supporting argument.
- **State and explain** normally also implies a concise answer; **explain** may imply reasoning or some reference to theory, depending on the context.
- **Describe** is often used with reference to particular phenomena or experiments. In the former instance, it usually implies that the answer should include reference to (visual) observations associated with the phenomena.
- **Outline** implies brevity, i.e. giving the main points only.
- **Predict** implies that the candidate is not expected to produce the required answer by recall but by making a logical connection between other pieces of information. Such information may be wholly given in the question or may depend upon answers extracted from an earlier part of the question. It implies a concise answer with no supporting statement required.
- **Deduce** is used in a similar way to **predict** except that some supporting statement is required, e.g. reference to a law/principle or the necessary reasoning is to be included in the answer.
- **Suggest** is used in two main contexts, i.e. either to imply that there is no unique answer, or to imply that candidates are expected to apply their general knowledge to a 'novel' situation.
- **Find** is a general term that may variously be interpreted as **calculate, measure** or **determine**.
- **Calculate** is used when a numerical answer is required. Working should be shown.

These terms may also occur in essay questions.

Guided essays

It is important that you write a complete and well-constructed answer to an essay question. It is therefore essential that you take time before starting to write to construct an *essay plan*. Break down the essay into areas of knowledge (these may be provided by the way the question is structured, as in question 1 below), and underneath these headings briefly jot down important facts that must be included. An essay plan allows you to order your ideas sensibly and helps to ensure that nothing vital is left out.

The following are sample essay titles.

1 Write an account of the chemistry of halogenoalkanes.
   You should consider the reactions suitable for their preparation and their characteristic reactions. You should also refer to some industrial applications and to at least one of their reactions.   (*Nuffield*)

2 Describe the *chemistry* of THREE environmental problems that have arisen from the introduction of three products or processes by industry. Suitable examples include detergents, insecticides, aerosols, waste gases from factories and motor cars. *(Nuffield)*

Comprehension

AEB Syllabus 654 includes a compulsory comprehension question in Paper 3. Obviously, it is essential that you read all of the passage *thoroughly* and understand it before attempting the questions. Usually the chemistry in the passage will be unfamiliar to you.

Writing summaries

Nuffield papers require students to write a summary of a passage of technical writing. Read all the passage carefully before beginning to write. Select the most important points and make sure you include them. Don't copy word-for-word from the passage and try to write in good English using complete sentences. Make sure you don't go over the stated word count.

EXAMINATION TECHNIQUES

On the day of the examination try to avoid any upsets – family disagreements, delays in travel, etc. – and get to the examination centre in plenty of time. Try not to discuss what might come up with friends as this will just cause panic.

When entering the examination take a few deep breaths to get plenty of oxygen into your body. Try to relax and read the *whole* paper through carefully. If there is a choice of questions, look at parts of the questions and try to decide what you could score in each. Aim for your maximum overall mark. Once you have made your choice, do the questions in order, starting with your best question and finishing with your worse. Thus if you end up short of time the best is already done. Also research has shown that candidates who answer their first question well do better than candidates who start badly. Success in an examination is very much about confidence.

Do not spend too long on a question. Multiple choice questions should take about one minute each. If you cannot answer a multiple choice question have a guess – you will often be right. Do not leave any question unattempted.

On other papers work out beforehand how many minutes you should spend earning each mark, e.g. if the paper is worth 100 marks and is timed at 120 minutes, then you should spend 120/100, i.e. 1.2 minutes, per mark. So a question worth five marks should not take more than six minutes.

Many A-level questions are structured to help you answer them. They are split into parts which carry different numbers of marks. Use these 'weightings' to guide you to the length or complexity of the answer required. If a question is worth one mark, the examiner only expects a brief answer, perhaps giving a single point or numerical value. However, if a question is worth five marks, a more detailed answer is required.

Diagrams often help your answer by reducing the number of words you have to use or by showing relationships which are difficult to express in words. Do not waste time drawing overelaborate diagrams. Draw them clearly, freehand and large enough to be seen clearly. Label them thoroughly.

Try to ensure that your answer has detail and avoids basic mistakes. If you are asked about a particular reaction, you should:

❶ Name the reactants and products.

❷ Write the equation, balanced if possible and including structural formulae if organic species are involved.

❸ Describe the changes you would observe, e.g. solution turns dark blue and white precipitate disappears.

❹ Give the exact reaction conditions.

For example, consider the reaction of copper(II) oxide with sulphuric acid:

❶ Reactants - copper(II) oxide and dilute sulphuric acid.
Products - copper(II) sulphate and water.

❷ $CuO(s) + H_2SO_4(aq) \rightarrow CuSO_4(aq) + H_2O(l)$

❸ The black solid disappears and the solution becomes blue. (NB I have avoided saying dissolved because it has not dissolved but reacted. If it had dissolved it could be recovered by evaporation.)

❹ Add copper(II) oxide to warm acid until in excess and filter off the excess.

Failure to complete an answer in this way is the biggest difference between very good candidates and the rest. Points 3 and 4 are the most commonly neglected.

Giving incorrect formulae, e.g. $NaCl_2$, or writing that hydrogen is a common gas in the atmosphere are basic mistakes that are seen frequently on A-level scripts and, along with others of a similar type, look bad to an examiner. Answers in chemistry are precise!

TAKING MODULE TESTS

There are strict rules set by the School Curriculum and Assessment Authority (SCAA) for modular A level courses. These rules include:

❶ Tests must be taken on set dates and marked by examiners outside the school or college.

❷ The written papers taken in the final examination sitting (defined as after 14th February in the final year) must contribute at least 30% of the total assessment.

❸ All module tests must be marked to full A-level standard. No concession can be made to candidates on the grounds that tests may have been taken earlier in the course.

Application of these rules ensures that the modular route is not an easy option. In fact it could be a harder route, as the pressure of preparing for and taking examinations exists throughout the course. On the positive side, only part of a syllabus may have to be revised for a particular test and usually the tests can be repeated and the better mark achieved will be the one that counts. There is always a final or synoptic paper testing the whole syllabus, so it is unwise to forget earlier modules.

Preparing for a module test is similar to preparing for a terminal examination. Revision should be started in good time and not left until it is too late. Time for revision must be found even though there will be demands in other subjects. There is less content in a module, but revision must be done with the same rigour. The questions are still A-level questions.

Module tests are usually short, with 1–1¼ hours being typical. It is important to use the time during the test wisely and not spend too much time on any question. If you do fall behind there is little opportunity to catch up. Look at some previous module tests and get used to the typical wording used, especially the command words (page 24). Look at the space given for the answers and the way the marks are awarded. Any of the questions in this book can be used in preparation for module tests.

PRACTICAL EXAMINATION

❶ The practical examination will give you full instructions on what to do. You are being tested on your ability to follow these instructions accurately within the allotted time making all the correct observations and readings. Accuracy and attention to detail are essential, so carry out instructions to the letter. Many marks are lost through not reading the question sufficiently carefully.

❷ The examiner is not present when you take your practical examination. He or she can only mark what you write down on your answer paper. Do not assume anything. If you make observations or take readings, make sure they are all written down. Some candidates write down their readings in pencil and rub out the ones they later find to be incorrect. Examiners like to see all your results and you will not be penalised if you have made incorrect readings and then, at a second attempt, made correct readings.

❸ Plan the amount of time to be spent on each exercise and possibly the order of attempting the exercises at the start of the examination.

There are a great variety of exercises on A–level papers but they can be divided into two types: quantitative and qualitative exercises.

QUANTITATIVE EXERCISES

These can involve accurate weightings, titration readings, temperature measurements, etc.

If you are asked to weigh out a sample of a chemical accurately within a certain range, it is important to ensure that the mass obtained is within the range given. Never weigh directly on the balance pan. Record your weighings as in the example below.

$$Mass of weighing bottle + solid = 46.121 g$$
$$Mass of weighing bottle = 45.684 g$$
$$Mass of solid = 0.437 g$$

If you are preparing a standard solution it is important not to lose any of the compound during the dissolving and making up to the final volume. The standard solution should be thoroughly shaken before use.

When carrying out titrations, the first titration should be carried out quickly as a rough guide to the volume of solution required. Accurate titrations can then be made. Do not cheat by writing down results by guesswork. Your table of results should be as follows:

Titration of sodium hydroxide with hydrochloric acid using screened methyl orange. Using 25 cm³ samples of sodium hydroxide solution.

	Rough	1st	2nd	3rd	4th
Final burette reading	25.70 cm³	25.75 cm³	25.75 cm³	24.95 cm³	25.65 cm³
Initial burette reading	0.00 cm³	0.25 cm³	0.20 cm³	0.00 cm³	0.05 cm³
Volume of acid added	25.70 cm³	25.50 cm³	25.55 cm³	24.95 cm³	25.60 cm³

Average titration reading (average 1st, 2nd and 4th only) = 25.55 cm³

The following points should be noted:

❶ Record your burette readings to two decimal places. In the second place you should write a 0 if the bottom of the meniscus is exactly on a division. If the bottom of the meniscus is between two divisions, you should write a 5.

❷ It is not necessary to start each titration with the reading exactly zero. It should be close to zero and you should read the burette accurately.

❸ When averaging your results only average readings which are close to being correct. Don't use the rough reading where the end point has obviously been passed. In the example, titration 3 is suspect, and using it in the average would lead to inaccuracy.

❹ You should aim to get at least three titrations within 0.10 cm^3. You may need to carry out further titrations before you can make a reliable average.

QUALITATIVE EXERCISES

These exercises involve carrying out simple tests using inorganic or organic chemicals. The tests are given in full and you are required to make all the possible observations and draw all the correct conclusions from the tests. You may not be expected to identify the compounds being used. It is important to record exactly what you observe. For example, a precipitate is better described as a pale yellow precipitate or a lemon yellow precipitate rather than a yellow precipitate. If a gas is evolved you should attempt to identify it with chemical tests. The tests, your observations and your inferences should be given in the form of a table. The following information may be useful when attempting qualitative exercises.

INORGANIC

Appearance

The colour of an inorganic compound may suggest the presence of certain ions.
Coloured: probably contains a transition metal ion.
Blue: Cu^{2+}, Ni^{2+} Green: Cu^{2+}, Ni^{2+}, Fe^{2+}, Cr^{3+}
Yellow: Fe^{3+}, CrO_4^{2-} Orange: $Cr_2O_7^{2-}$ Purple: MnO_4^-

Flame test

Orange-yellow: Na^+ Lilac: K^+ Red: Ca^{2+}, Sr^{2+}, Li^+
Apple green: Ba^{2+} Blue-green: Cu^{2+} Blue: Pb^{2+}

Action of heat

Sublimation: NH_4^+ salts. Oxygen evolved (relights a glowing splint): certain oxides or nitrates. Carbon dioxide evolved (turns limewater milky): hydrogencarbonates or certain carbonates (not Na_2CO_3, K_2CO_3). Ammonia gas evolved (turns red litmus blue): decomposition of certain ammonium compounds. Water evolved (colourless liquid formed at the cooler part of test tube): hydrates, certain hydroxides or hydrogencarbonates. Brown gas evolved: NO_2 from certain nitrates (not $NaNO_3$ or KNO_3) or Br_2 from certain bromides.

Solubilities of inorganic compounds in water at room temperature

- All common salts of Na^+, K^+ and NH_4^+ are soluble.
- All nitrates and ethanoates are soluble.
- All sulphates are soluble except Ba^{2+}, Sr^{2+} and Pb^{2+} ($CaSO_4$ is only sparingly soluble).
- All chlorides, bromides and iodides are soluble except Ag^+, Cu^+, Pb^{2+}, Hg_2^{2+} (lead(II) halides are more soluble in hot water).
- All carbonates and phosphates are insoluble except those of Na^+, K^+ or NH_4^+.
- All hydroxides are insoluble except those of Na^+, K^+, NH_4^+, Sr^{2+} and Ba^{2+}.

Precipitation of metal hydroxides with aqueous sodium hydroxide

Cation	Addition of sodium hydroxide solution	
	A couple of drops	Excess
Potassium K^+	no precipitate	no precipitate
Sodium Na^+	no precipitate	no precipitate
Calcium Ca^{2+}	white precipitate	precipitate insoluble
Magnesium Mg^{2+}	white precipitate	precipitate insoluble
Aluminium Al^{3+}	white precipitate	precipitate soluble – colourless solution
Zinc Zn^{2+}	white precipitate	precipitate soluble – colourless solution
Iron(II) Fe^{2+}	green precipitate	precipitate insoluble
Iron(III) Fe^{3+}	red–brown precipitate	precipitate insoluble
Lead Pb^{2+}	white precipitate	precipitate soluble – colourless solution
Copper(II) Cu^{2+}	blue precipitate	precipitate insoluble
Silver Ag^+	grey–brown precipitate	precipitate insoluble
Manganese Mn^{2+}	buff precipitate (turns brown in air)	precipitate insoluble

Precipitation of metal hydroxides with ammonia solution

Cation	Addition of ammonia solution	
	A couple of drops	Excess
Potassium K^+	no precipitate	no precipitate
Sodium Na^+	no precipitate	no precipitate
Calcium Ca^{2+}	no precipitate	no precipitate
Magnesium Mg^{2+}	white precipitate	precipitate insoluble
Aluminium Al^{3+}	white precipitate	precipitate insoluble
Zinc Zn^{2+}	white precipitate	precipitate soluble – colourless solution
Iron(II) Fe^{2+}	green precipitate	precipitate insoluble
Iron(III) Fe^{3+}	red-brown precipitate	precipitate insoluble
Lead Pb^{2+}	white precipitate	precipitate insoluble
Copper(II) Cu^{2+}	blue precipitate	precipitate soluble – blue solution
Silver Ag^+	brown precipitate	precipitate soluble
Manganese Mn^{2+}	buff precipitate (turns brown in air)	precipitate insoluble

Tests for
- CO_3^{2-}. Carbon dioxide evolved when dilute hydrochloric acid added.
- SO_3^{2-}. Sulphur dioxide evolved when dilute hydrochloric acid added and mixture heated.
- NO_2^-. Brown NO_2 gas evolved when dilute hydrochloric acid added. Solution turns green.
- NO_3^-. Brown ring or ammonia formed when sodium hydroxide solution and aluminium powder (or De Varda's alloy) heated with solution.
- SO_4^{2-}. Add dilute hydrochloric acid and barium chloride solution to a solution. White ppt. of barium sulphate confirms SO_4^{2-}.
- Cl^-, Br^-, I^-. Add dilute nitric acid and silver nitrate solution to solution. White precipitate of silver chloride turning purplish in sunlight and dissolving completely in ammonia solution confirms Cl^-. Cream precipitate of silver bromide turning green in sunlight and partially soluble in ammonia solution confirms Br^-. Yellow precipitate of silver iodide unaffected by sunlight and insoluble in ammonia solution confirms I^-.
- PO_4^{3-}. Add ammonium molybdate solution and a few drops of concentrated nitric acid to a solution. A yellow precipitate confirms PO_4^{3-}.
- CrO_4^{2-}. Turns orange when dilute acid added to solution. Then add 1 drop of hydrogen peroxide and solution turns blue, then green and evolves oxygen.

ORGANIC

Appearance

The following are liquids at room temperature: alcohols, aliphatic carboxylic acids, esters, ethers, aldehydes, ketones, organohalogen compounds.

The following are solid at room temperature: aromatic carboxylic acids, phenols, amides, amino acids, carboxylic acid salts, amino salts, dicarboxylic acids.

Smell

Sharp, sour: carboxylic acids. Spirity: alcohols. Fruity: esters. Fishy: amines. Antiseptic: phenols.

Solubility in water

The following are soluble. Solids: carbohydrates, amino acids, urea, **phenols, carboxylic acids**, some amides. Also salts of carboxylic acids and *amines*. Liquids: some alcohols, aldehydes, ketones, **carboxylic acids, acid chlorides** and **amines**.

NB Substances in **bold type** form acidic solutions; substances in *italics* form alkaline solutions.

Reaction with sodium hydroxide solution

Ammonia gas evolved when ammonium salts and amides are heated with sodium hydroxide solution.

Reaction with neutral iron(III) chloride solution

Red colour: $HCOO^-$ or CH_3COO^- Violet colour: phenols
Green colour: ethanedioate ion   Buff precipitate: salt or aromatic acid

Tests for unsaturation

1. Bromine water or solution of bromine in hexane – decolourised.
2. Alkaline solution of potassium manganate(VII) – decolourised.

Tests for reducing agents

- Acidified potassium manganate(VII) turns colourless if warmed with methanoates, ethanedioates, aldehydes, primary alcohols and secondary alcohols.
- Acidified potassium dichromate(VI) turns from orange to green on warming with methanoates, ethanoates, aldehydes, primary alcohols and secondary alcohols.
- Fehling's solution (or Benedict's) forms an orange-red precipitate when warmed with aldehydes.
- Tollen's reagent forms a silver mirror on warming with aldehydes.

Tests with 2,4-dinitrophenylhydrazine or similar

Yellow or orange precipitate formed with aldehydes and ketones.

A-LEVEL CHEMISTRY

In this section:

Each chapter features:

■ *Units in this chapter*: a list of the main topic heads to follow.

■ *Chapter objectives*: a brief comment on how the topics relate to what has gone before, and to the syllabus. Key ideas which are covered in the chapter are introduced.

■ *The main text:* this is divided into numbered topic units for ease of reference.

■ *Chapter roundup*: a brief summary of the chapter.

■ *Worked questions*: typical exam questions, with tutorial notes and our suggested answers.

■ *Question bank*: further questions, with comments on the pitfalls to avoid and points to include in framing your own answers.

CHAPTER 1

ATOMIC STRUCTURE

Units in this chapter

Chapter objectives

An elementary treatment of atomic structure will be found in GCSE Science or Chemistry courses. However, at A level it is necessary to study this in much greater depth.

At GCSE level you might be expected to write the electronic structure of lithium, for example, as 2, 1. The three electrons in a lithium atom are in two shells: two in the first one and one in the second. At A level the arrangement is written as $1s^2 2s^1$. This gives the **orbitals** in which electrons are found. You must always give electronic structures in this form.

The ability to work out the electronic structure of an atom, in conjunction with the Periodic Table, is required throughout the course. This chapter should therefore be a starting point. There are links with other chapters, especially Chapters 2, 3, 4, 5, 6 and 21.

1.1 PARTICLES IN AN ATOM

Atoms are composed of **protons, neutrons and electrons**. Table 1.1 compares the properties of these three particles.

Table 1.1 Particles in an atom

Name of particle	Mass	Charge
proton p	1 amu*	+1
neutron n	1 amu	0
electron e	negligible	−1

*amu – atomic mass unit

An atom is neutral and contains equal numbers of protons and electrons.

Atomic number (Z) – the number of protons in an atom.

Mass number (A) – the total number of protons plus neutrons in an atom.

For example, $^{39}_{19}K$ represents a potassium atom with mass number 39 and atomic number 19.

The numbers of protons, neutrons and electrons in this potassium atom are 19, 20 (i.e. 39–19) and 19 respectively. It is possible to get other potassium atoms, namely

$^{40}_{19}$K and $^{41}_{19}$K, containing the same number of protons and electrons but different numbers of neutrons (21 and 22 respectively). These different atoms of the same element are called **isotopes**. A sample of potassium contains 93.1% potassium-39, 0.012% potassium-40 and 6.9% potassium-41.

The **relative atomic mass** (represented by A_r) is the mass of an atom based on a scale such that the $^{12}_{6}$C isotope has a mass of 12.00 units.

$$\text{relative atomic mass} = \frac{\text{mass of 1 atom of element} \times 12}{\text{mass of 1 atom of carbon-12}}$$

Relative atomic masses (formerly called atomic masses or atomic weights) will be given on your examination papers for you to use, e.g. (A_r(O) = 16 or O = 16).

1.2 EVIDENCE FOR PROTONS, NEUTRONS AND ELECTRONS

Electrons

J. J. Thomson discovered that a beam of rays was emitted from the cathode when an electric discharge was passed through a gas at a very low pressure. These rays were deflected by a magnetic field and behaved in the same way whichever gas was used. These rays consist of streams of **electrons**.

Protons

The passage of an electric discharge at very low pressures also produces a stream of particles from the anode. These particles are oppositely charged to electrons and were different for each gas used. The lightest particles were obtained when hydrogen was the gas used and these particles were assumed to be **protons**.

Neutrons

The neutron was more difficult to characterise than the electron or proton. Chadwick (1932) bombarded the element beryllium with α (alpha) particles and noticed that fast moving, highly penetrating particles were produced. These particles, now known to be **neutrons,** were not deflected by electric or magnetic fields. The following equation summarises the change taking place.

$$^{9}_{4}\text{Be} + ^{4}_{2}\text{He} \rightarrow ^{12}_{6}\text{C} + ^{1}_{0}\text{n}$$

($^{4}_{2}$He represents an alpha particle.)

1.3 THE NUCLEUS

The protons and neutrons in each atom are tightly packed in a positively charged **nucleus** and the electrons move around the nucleus. In chemical reactions the nucleus remains unchanged.

Radioactivity (Chapter 20) is the breaking down of the nucleus with the emission of α, β or γ rays. Radioactivity results in the formation of a new element.

Geiger and Marsden bombarded a thin gold foil with a beam of α particles. Most of the particles passed through the foil without deflection and were detected by a flash of light when the α particle struck a zinc sulphide screen. A few were deflected and some of these were deflected at angles greater than 90°, suggesting they had been repelled by large positive charges within the foil – nuclei of atoms of gold.

1.4 ARRANGEMENT OF ELECTRONS AROUND THE NUCLEUS

From GCSE work you should be familiar with a simple model of the arrangement of electrons around the nucleus. The electrons are in certain **energy levels** and each energy level can only hold up to a certain maximum number of electrons. This is summarised in Table 1.2.

Table 1.2 Energy levels

Energy level or shell	Maximum number of electrons
1st or K shell	2
2nd or L shell	8
3rd or M shell	18
4th or N shell	32
5th or O shell, etc.	50

A sodium atom containing 11 electrons has an electron arrangement of 2,8,1 – the 1st and 2nd shells being full. This is sometimes represented in a simple Bohr diagram (Fig. 1.1).

These ideas of electron arrangement, although useful, are very simplified and it is necessary for you to have a more refined model at A level. It has been found, by spectroscopic means, that all the electrons in the 2nd energy level are not exactly identical in energy. It is possible to break down this energy level into sub shells.

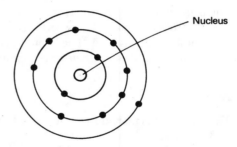

Nucleus

Fig. 1.1 Simple representation of a sodium atom

Electrons, partly because of their very small size, are impossible to locate exactly at any particular time. It is, however, possible to indicate a region or volume where the electron is most likely to be. This region is called an **orbital**. Each orbital is capable of holding a maximum of two electrons. Orbitals can be divided into *s*, *p*, *d* and *f* types. Each type has its own characteristic shape. The shapes of *s* and *p* orbitals are shown in Fig. 1.2 but it should be remembered that these orbitals are not flat, they are three-dimensional.

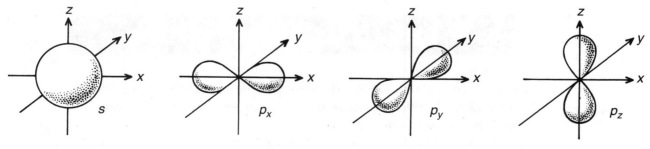

Fig. 1.2 The s and p orbitals

The first energy level holds a maximum of two electrons in one *s* type orbital (called 1*s*). There are no *p*, *d* or *f* orbitals available at this energy level.

The second energy level consists of one s type orbital and three types of p orbitals: $2s$, $2p_x$, $2p_y$, $2p_z$.

Note: There are three p orbitals of identical energy – one along the x axis, one along the y axis and one along the z axis.

These four orbitals can hold a total of eight electrons (i.e. two electrons each). There are no $2d$ or $2f$ orbitals.

The third energy level consists of one s type orbital, three p type orbitals and five d type orbitals. These nine orbitals can hold a maximum of 18 electrons altogether (two electrons each). You are not expected to know the shapes of d or f orbitals.

When filling the available orbitals with electrons two important principles should be remembered:

❶ Electrons fill the lowest energy orbitals first and other orbitals in order of ascending energy. As will be seen with d-block elements (Chapter 28), it is incorrect to assume that an energy level is always completely filled before electrons enter the next energy level. The order of filling orbitals is shown in Fig. 1.3. The order of filling orbitals is $1s$, $2s$, $2p$, $3s$, $3p$, $4s$, $3d$, $4p$, $5s$, $4d$, $5p$, $6s$, $4f$, $5d$, $6p$, etc.

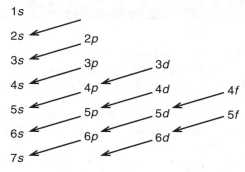

Fig. 1.3 The order of filling orbitals

❷ Where there are several orbitals of exactly the same energy (e.g. three $2p$ orbitals), electrons will occupy different orbitals whenever possible (e.g. nitrogen is $1s^2 2s^2 2p_x^1 2p_y^1 2p_z^1$ and not $1s^2 2s^2 2p_x^2 2p_y^1$). This principle is called **Hund's rule**. When an orbital only contains one electron then this electron is said to be **unpaired**.

Table 1.3 Electron arrangements of the first 20 elements

Element	GCSE level	A level
Hydrogen	1	$1s^1$
Helium	2	$1s^2$
Lithium	2, 1	$1s^2 2s^1$
Beryllium	2, 2	$1s^2 2s^2$
Boron	2, 3	$1s^2 2s^2 2p_x^1$
Carbon	2, 4	$1s^2 2s^2 2p_x^1 2p_y^1$
Nitrogen	2, 5	$1s^2 2s^2 2p_x^1 2p_y^1 2p_z^1$
Oxygen	2, 6	$1s^2 2s^2 2p_x^2 2p_y^1 2p_z^1$
Fluorine	2, 7	$1s^2 2s^2 2p_x^2 2p_y^2 2p_z^1$
Neon	2, 8	$1s^2 2s^2 2p_x^2 2p_y^2 2p_z^2$
Sodium	2, 8, 1	$1s^2 2s^2 2p_x^2 2p_y^2 2p_z^2 3s^1$
Magnesium	2, 8, 2	$1s^2 2s^2 2p_x^2 2p_y^2 2p_z^2 3s^2$
Aluminium	2, 8, 3	$1s^2 2s^2 2p_x^2 2p_y^2 2p_z^2 3s^2 3p_x^1$
Silicon	2, 8, 4	$1s^2 2s^2 2p_x^2 2p_y^2 2p_z^2 3s^2 3p_x^1 3p_y^1$
Phosphorus	2, 8, 5	$1s^2 2s^2 2p_x^2 2p_y^2 2p_z^2 3s^2 3p_x^1 3p_y^1 3p_z^1$
Sulphur	2, 8, 6	$1s^2 2s^2 2p_x^2 2p_y^2 2p_z^2 3s^2 3p_x^2 3p_y^1 3p_z^1$
Chlorine	2, 8, 7	$1s^2 2s^2 2p_x^2 2p_y^2 2p_z^2 3s^2 3p_x^2 3p_y^2 3p_z^1$
Argon	2, 8, 8	$1s^2 2s^2 2p_x^2 2p_y^2 2p_z^2 3s^2 3p_x^2 3p_y^2 3p_z^2$
Potassium	2, 8, 8, 1	$1s^2 2s^2 2p_x^2 2p_y^2 2p_z^2 3s^2 3p_x^2 3p_y^2 3p_z^2 4s^1$
Calcium	2, 8, 8, 2	$1s^2 2s^2 2p_x^2 2p_y^2 2p_z^2 3s^2 3p_x^2 3p_y^2 3p_z^2 4s^2$

Note: sometimes electronic structures are shown in a slightly condensed form, e.g. calcium $1s^2 2s^2 2p^6 3s^2 3p^6 4s^2$.

Table 1.3 summarises the electron arrangements of the first 20 elements. For comparison the simple GCSE level electron arrangements are given.

Notes on Table 1.3:

❶ The small number above the orbital refers to the number of electrons in the orbital, e.g. $1s^2$ means two electrons in a $1s$ orbital.

❷ The noble gases (helium, neon, argon, krypton, radon and xenon) contain filled s and, in all cases except helium, completely filled p orbitals. This s^2p^6 electron arrangement is very difficult to break down.

❸ The electron arrangements are sometimes abbreviated. For example, the electron arrangement of calcium may be written as $1s^22s^22p^63s^23p^64s^2$. It is important to remember, however, that the six electrons in $2p$ and $3p$ orbitals are in three separate orbitals, each holding two electrons.

1.5 MASS SPECTROMETER

The mass spectrometer (Fig. 1.4) is an instrument used for accurately measuring atomic mass and for finding the number of isotopes an element contains. The sample being tested is introduced into the instrument and is then ionised by heating, electrical discharge or electron bombardment. The ions produced are accelerated and passed through a slit to give a fine beam of ions all moving with the same velocity. The individual ions in the beam will differ slightly in mass and charge. The beam of ions is then subjected to a magnetic field which bends the beam into a circular path. Depending upon the mass and charge, the radius of the circular path for each ion is slightly different. The lighter the ion or the greater the charge on the ion the greater will be the deflection. The ions are detected by means of a photographic plate.

The results with neon as the sample are shown in Fig. 1.5. There are two sets of three lines. One set corresponds to the formation of Ne^+ ions in the spectrometer by the loss of one electron from each atom. The other set corresponds to the formation of Ne^{2+} ions by the loss of two electrons. There are three lines in each group because neon consists of three isotopes – neon-20, neon-21 and neon-22. From the intensities it is possible to work out the relative abundance of the three isotopes. The spectrometer can be calibrated by the use of carbon-12.

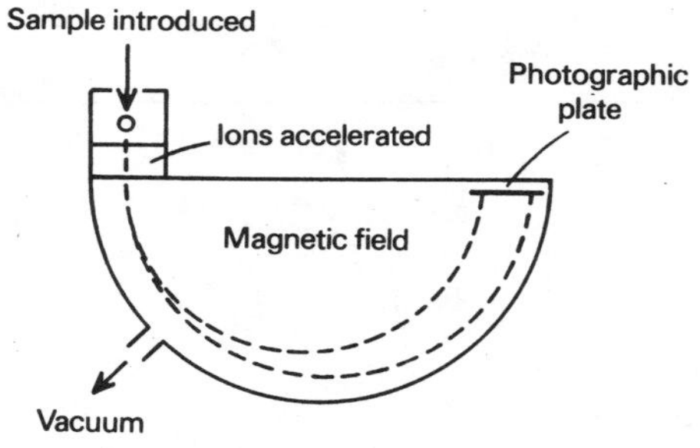

Sample introduced

Photographic plate

Ions accelerated

Magnetic field

Vacuum

Fig. 1.4 Mass spectrometer

Fig. 1.5 The mass spectrum of neon

1.6 ATOMIC SPECTRUM OF HYDROGEN

When an electrical discharge is passed through a sample of hydrogen gas at low pressure, a pinkish glow is observed. This glow can be examined using a simple spectroscope – a number of separate lines can be observed and there are also lines in the ultraviolet and infrared regions (Fig. 1.6).

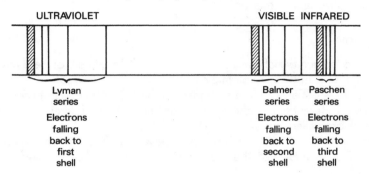

Fig. 1.6 The emission spectrum of the hydrogen atom

Lines in the spectrum correspond to electronic changes within the atoms. The fact that only certain lines are observed indicates that only certain energy changes are possible and this is evidence for the existence of distinct energy levels within the hydrogen atom.

When the electrical discharge is passed through hydrogen gas, energy is absorbed and the electron in the first energy level is promoted to a higher energy level. This electron may then drop back into a lower energy level, giving out energy in the form of electromagnetic radiation of a definite frequency. This energy change is related to the frequency of the radiation by the formula

$\Delta E = hv$

where ΔE is the energy change

h is a constant (Planck's constant)

v is the frequency of the radiation (light, etc.)

It is important to realise that each line in the spectrum corresponds to a transition between the separate energy levels.

When the electron drops back into the first energy level this results in one of the lines in the **Lyman series**. The **Balmer series** corresponds to electrons falling back into the second shell from a higher shell, while the **Paschen series** corresponds to electrons falling back to the third shell.

Chapter roundup

Atoms are composed of protons, neutrons and electrons. The protons and neutrons are tightly packed into a positively charged nucleus and the electrons move around the nucleus.

The electrons are assigned to certain clearly defined energy levels. These levels are subdivided into orbitals. Each orbital can hold a maximum of two electrons. Orbitals are filled up in order of energy – the lowest energy level first.

Atoms containing the same number of protons and electrons but different numbers of neutrons are called isotopes. Most elements exist in several or many isotopic forms. As a result the relative atomic mass of the element, which is a weighted average of the atomic masses of the different isotopes, is usually not a whole number. Evidence for different isotopic forms can be seen from a mass spectrometer.

Worked questions and answers

1 The element Q has the electronic arrangement $1s^2 2s^2 2p^6 3s^2 3p^6 4s^2 3d^{10} 4p^1$.
   (a) Write down the atomic number of Q.
   (b) Q occurs naturally as a mixture of ^{69}Q and ^{71}Q. Explain the significance of the numbers 69 and 71, and say what these two components in the natural element are called.
   (c) If ^{69}Q and ^{71}Q occur in the proportions 60% and 40% respectively, calculate the relative atomic mass of Q.

Tutorial note

(a) Count up the number of electrons. There are 31. To be neutral there must also be 31 protons and so the atomic number is 31.

(b) The numbers 69 and 71 are the mass numbers, i.e. numbers of protons plus neutrons. Different atoms of the same element containing different numbers of neutrons are called isotopes.

(c) The relative atomic mass is an average of the two mass numbers but with regard for the relative amounts of the two isotopes. This is called a weighted average.

$$\text{Relative atomic mass of } Q = \left(69 \times \frac{60}{100} \right) + \left(71 \times \frac{40}{100} \right)$$
$$= 41.4 + 28.4$$
$$= 69.8$$

This is a relatively straightforward question with numerical work kept to a minimum. Question 1 in the Question bank is similar but there a calculator is essential.

Look at the final answer. If the two isotopes had been present in equal amounts, i.e. 50% of each, the relative atomic mass would be exactly half way between 69 and 71, i.e. 70. However, since there is more ^{69}Q present the relative atomic mass should be between 69 and 71 but closer to 69 than to 71. Checking that your answer is reasonable can save many marks in examinations by showing up mathematical errors.

This question could also link with the Periodic Table (Chapter 2).

2 The diagram (Fig. 1.7) shows the mass spectrum of chlorine. If peak A represents the ion $^{35}Cl^+$, suggest possible ions which would give the peaks B and D.

(SEB)

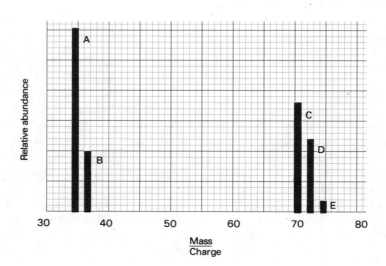

Fig. 1.7 The mass spectrum of chlorine

Tutorial note

Peaks B and D correspond to $^{37}Cl^+$ and $(^{35}Cl — ^{37}Cl)^+$.

This mass spectrum is complicated because chlorine exists in two isotopes. If there had been a single isotope of ^{35}Cl there would just be two peaks – one at 35 and one at 70. Imagine how complicated a mass spectrum of xenon would be. Xenon can exist in nine isotopic forms.

The mass spectrum tells us about the different isotopes present and also about the relative amounts of each isotope. Chlorine is composed of 75% ^{35}Cl and 25% ^{37}Cl. The chlorine-35 peak is three times higher than that of chlorine-37.

Question bank

1 The element gallium consists of 60.4% of an isotope of atomic mass 68.93 and 39.6% of an isotope of atomic mass 70.92. Calculate the relative atomic mass of gallium.

Points

This question is similar to Illustrative Question 1 but requires more mathematics. The chemistry, however, is the same. Looking at the answer you would expect, it should be closer to 68.93 than to 70.92. Take care with the way you express your answer. Your calculator will give an answer to several decimal places. Since relative atomic masses are quoted in the question to two decimal places, it is reasonable to quote your answer to two decimal places. Mistakes in giving answers to the wrong approximation are common in A-level Chemistry.

You should get a numerical answer of 69.72. There are no units as it is a relative mass (i.e. one mass compared to another) and not an actual mass.

CHAPTER 2

PERIODICITY AND THE PERIODIC TABLE

Units in this chapter

Chapter objectives

Most GCSE courses include a brief treatment of the Periodic Table. If you are at this stage, you probably have not done enough to realise the usefulness of the Periodic Table. At A level the Periodic Table becomes very important. You will probably be given a Periodic Table to use during the examination.

In this chapter we will revise what you may already know about the Periodic Table. In addition we will look at various properties of elements including electronegativity, ionisation energy and electron affinity. The way in which these properties change through the Periodic Table will be examined. This leads to the concept of periodicity.

This chapter is closely linked with Chapter 1. Chapters 21–28 use the Periodic Table extensively and you should not attempt these chapters until you have studied Chapters 1 and 2.

2.1 THE PERIODIC TABLE

The Periodic Table is an arrangement of all the chemical elements in order of increasing atomic number – elements with similar properties (i.e. the same chemical family) are placed in the same vertical column.

The Periodic Table was devised in 1869 by Mendeléef. At this time a number of elements that we now know had not been discovered, but Mendeléef left gaps in his table and even predicted the properties of some of these undiscovered elements. Fig. 2.1 shows the modern Periodic Table.

The main difference between Mendeléef's table and the modern table, apart from the extra elements, is that the latter arranges the elements in order of increasing atomic number rather than atomic mass.

The vertical columns are called **Groups**. A Group contains elements with similar properties and similar outer electron arrangements. The Groups are given Roman numbers, e.g. Group IV. The elements in the alkali metal family (Group I) all have a single electron in the highest energy level (see Chapter 22).

	I	II											III	IV	V	VI	VII	0
1							1 **H** Hydrogen 1											4 **He** Helium 2
2	7 **Li** Lithium 3	9 **Be** Beryllium 4					*d*-block						11 **B** Boron 5	12 **C** Carbon 6	14 **N** Nitrogen 7	16 **O** Oxygen 8	19 **F** Fluorine 9	20 **Ne** Neon 10
3	23 **Na** Sodium 11	24 **Mg** Magnesium 12					**Transition elements**						27 **Al** Aluminium 13	28 **Si** Silicon 14	31 **P** Phosphorus 15	32 **S** Sulphur 16	35.5 **Cl** Chlorine 17	40 **Ar** Argon 18
4	39 **K** Potassium 19	40 **Ca** Calcium 20	45 **Sc** Scandium 21	48 **Ti** Titanium 22	51 **V** Vanadium 23	52 **Cr** Chromium 24	55 **Mn** Manganese 25	56 **Fe** Iron 26	59 **Co** Cobalt 27	59 **Ni** Nickel 28	64 **Cu** Copper 29	65 **Zn** Zinc 30	70 **Ga** Gallium 31	73 **Ge** Germanium 32	75 **As** Arsenic 33	79 **Se** Selenium 34	80 **Br** Bromine 35	84 **Kr** Krypton 36
5	85.5 **Rb** Rubidium 37	88 **Sr** Strontium 38	89 **Y** Yttrium 39	91 **Zr** Zirconium 40	93 **Nb** Niobium 41	96 **Mo** Molybdenum 42	99 **Tc** Technetium 43	101 **Ru** Ruthenium 44	103 **Rh** Rhodium 45	106 **Pd** Palladium 46	108 **Ag** Silver 47	112 **Cd** Cadmium 48	115 **In** Indium 49	119 **Sn** Tin 50	122 **Sb** Antimony 51	128 **Te** Tellurium 52	127 **I** Iodine 53	131 **Xe** Xenon 54
6	133 **Cs** Caesium 55	137 **Ba** Barium 56	139 **La** Lanthanum 57	178.5 **Hf** Hafnium 72	181 **Ta** Tantalum 73	184 **W** Tungsten 74	186 **Re** Rhenium 75	190 **Os** Osmium 76	192 **Ir** Iridium 77	195 **Pt** Platinum 78	197 **Au** Gold 79	201 **Hg** Mercury 80	204 **Tl** Thallium 81	207 **Pb** Lead 82	209 **Bi** Bismuth 83	210 **Po** Polonium 84	210 **At** Astatine 85	222 **Rn** Radon 86
7	223 **Fr** Francium 87	226 **Ra** Radium 88	227 **Ac** Actinium 89	* **Db** Dubnium 104	* **Jl** Joliotium 105	* **Rf** Rutherfordium 106	* **Bh** Bohrium 107	* **Hn** Hahnium 108	* **Mt** Meitnerium 109									

f-block

139 **La** Lanthanum 57	140 **Ce** Cerium 58	141 **Pr** Praseodymium 59	144 **Nd** Neodymium 60	147 **Pm** Promethium 61	150 **Sm** Samarium 62	152 **Eu** Europium 63	157 **Gd** Gadolinium 64	159 **Tb** Terbium 65	162.5 **Dy** Dysprosium 66	165 **Ho** Holmium 67	167 **Er** Erbium 68	169 **Tm** Thulium 69	173 **Yb** Ytterbium 70	175 **Lu** Lutetium 71
227 **Ac** Actinium 89	232 **Th** Thorium 90	231 **Pa** Protactinium 91	238 **U** Uranium 92	237 **Np** Neptunium 93	242 **Pu** Plutonium 94	243 **Am** Americium 95	247 **Cm** Curium 96	247 **Bk** Berkelium 97	251 **Cf** Californium 98	254 **Es** Einsteinium 99	253 **Fm** Fermium 100	256 **Md** Mendelevium 101	254 **No** Nobelium 102	257 **Lr** Lawrencium 103

KEY:

Atomic Mass **Symbol** Name Atomic Number

Fig. 2.1 The Periodic Table of the elements

The outer electron arrangements of elements in the different Groups are shown in Table 2.1

Table 2.1 *Arrangements of outer electrons*

Group	Outer electron arrangement
I	s^1
II	s^2
III	s^2p^1
IV	s^2p^2
V	s^2p^3
VI	s^2p^4
VII	s^2p^5
0	s^2p^{6*}

*Helium (the first element in Group 0) has an electron arrangement of $1s^2$.

The horizontal rows in the Periodic Table are called **Periods.**

The elements shaded in Fig. 2.1 are called the *s*- and *p*-block elements. Most of the chemistry at A level involves the study of these main block elements. The elements between the two shaded portions are called the *d*-**block** or **transition elements.** A study of the first row of *d*-block elements Sc–Zn will be found in Chapter 28. The two rows of elements at the bottom of the table are called the *f*-**block** elements.

The bold line in Fig. 2.1 is an attempt to divide elements into metals and nonmetals. Elements on the right-hand side of this line are nonmetals and on the left-hand side are metals; elements close to the line often show both metallic and nonmetallic properties, particularly if they exist in allotropic (polymorphic) forms.

2.2 TRENDS WITHIN THE PERIODIC TABLE

Physical properties such as **ionisation energy, electron affinity, melting** and **boiling points** are related to electron arrangements. If one of these properties is plotted on a graph for each element, e.g. a graph of the property against atomic number, the graph has a characteristic shape. The shape consists of a series of peaks and troughs. An example is shown in Fig. 2.2.

You will notice that the element at the top of each peak is a noble gas (Group 0, except mercury) and the element at the bottom is an alkali metal (Group I). Elements in the same Group are found to occur at similar positions on the different peaks.

In the following some of these physical properties will be discussed in greater detail.

2.3 IONISATION ENERGY (IONISATION POTENTIAL)

Ionisation energy is the energy absorbed when a mole of electrons is removed from a mole of atoms of an element in the gaseous state to form a mole of positively charged ions, i.e.

$$M(g) \rightarrow M^+(g) + e^-$$

This is the **first ionisation energy.** The energy is usually quoted in units of kilojoules per mole (kJ mol^{-1}). Energy is required to remove an electron from any atom because

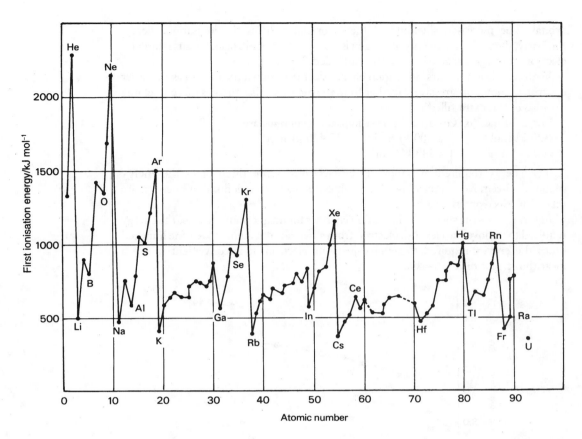

Fig. 2.2 The first ionisation energies of the elements

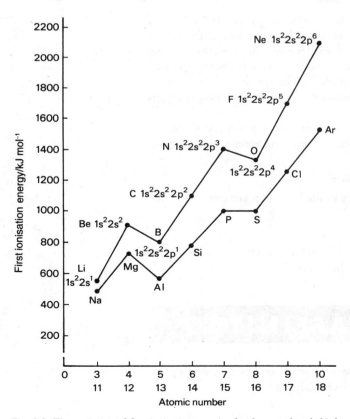

Fig. 2.3 The variation of first ionisation energies for the second and third Periods

there is an attractive force between the nucleus and the electron being removed which has to be overcome. The value of the first ionisation energy depends upon:

❶ the effective nuclear charge,

❷ the distance between the electron and the nucleus, and

❸ the 'shielding' produced by lower energy orbitals.

Shielding involves the repulsion between electrons in inner, filled orbitals and the electron being removed from the outer orbital.

Fig. 2.3 shows the variation of first ionisation energy within the second and third Periods. Across each Period there is an increase in ionisation energy.

Beryllium (Group II) has an extra electron and proton compared with lithium. The extra electron goes into the same $2s$ orbital. The increase in ionisation energy here can be attributed to the increased nuclear charge. The two breaks in the graphs (Be → B and N → O in the second Period) can be explained by the increased repulsion produced when two electrons are in the same orbital. The ionisation energy of boron is less than that of beryllium because, in boron, there is a complete $2s^2$

43

orbital. The increased shielding of the $2s$ orbital reduces the ionisation energy. Similarly, the ionisation energy of oxygen is less than that of nitrogen because the extra electron in oxygen is shielded by the half-filled $2p$ orbitals.

Within a Group the first ionisation energy decreases down the Group as the outer electron becomes progressively further from the nucleus. Also, there is more shielding because of the extra filled orbitals.

For example, for Group I the first ionisation energies are

Li 520 kJ mol^{-1} Na 500 kJ mol^{-1} K 420 kJ mol^{-1}
Rb 400 kJ mol^{-1} Cs 380 kJ mol^{-1}

The energy required to remove three electrons is not three times the energy required to remove one electron. The values for successive ionisation energies are related to electron structures.

Fig. 2.4 shows the successive ionisation energies for magnesium. Because the energy required to remove the eleventh electron from a magnesium atom is over one hundred times the energy required to remove just one electron, it is convenient to use a logarithmic plot on the y-axis.

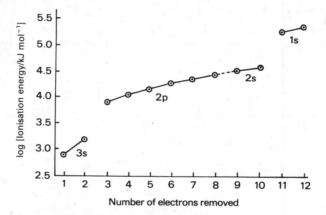

Fig. 2.4 Successive ionisation energies of magnesium

The electron structure of magnesium is $1s^2 2s^2 2p^6 3s^2$. The energy required to remove the first two electrons is relatively low. This corresponds to the loss of the two $3s$ electrons. To remove a third electron needs much greater energy because this electron is closer to the nucleus in a $2p$ orbital. There is a steady increase in energy required as electrons are removed from $2p$ and then $2s$ orbitals. The removal of the eleventh and twelfth electrons requires much greater amounts of energy, because these electrons are closer to the nucleus in the $1s$ orbital.

The distinction between **ionisation energy** and **electrode potential** should be clearly understood. **Ionisation energy** is the energy required to remove an electron in the gas phase.

$$M(g) \rightarrow M^+(g) + e^-$$

The **electrode potential** (Chapter 18) applies to the loss of an electron not in the gas phase.

$$M(s) \rightarrow M^+(aq) + e^-$$

The **electrochemical series** is a list of metals in order of electrode potential. The order of ionisation energies is not necessarily the same.

2.4 ELECTRON AFFINITY

Electron affinity is the energy change when one mole of isolated gaseous atoms gains one mole of electrons to form a mole of negatively charged ions.

$$X(g) + e^- \rightarrow X^-(g)$$

The atoms of elements on the right-hand side of a Period readily accept electrons to form negative ions. In these atoms there are greater nuclear charges to attract electrons. The electron affinities of chlorine, bromine and iodine are -364, -342 and -295 kJ mol^{-1} respectively. In each case the value is negative because energy is released.

2.5 ELECTRONEGATIVITY

The tendency of an atom to attract an electron to itself is called its **electronegativity**. The electronegativity of an element can be regarded as being related to ionisation energy and electron affinity, and can be evaluated in various ways. In a covalent bond, such as between two chlorine atoms, the two atoms attract the pair of electrons in the bond equally. However, in hydrogen fluoride, because fluorine is more electronegative than hydrogen, the pair of electrons is attracted more by the fluorine than the hydrogen. This results in a slight separation of charge.

$$\overset{\delta^+}{H} - \overset{\delta^-}{F}$$

Fig. 2.5 shows the variation of electronegativity (according to values obtained by Pauling) with atomic number for the first 60 elements.

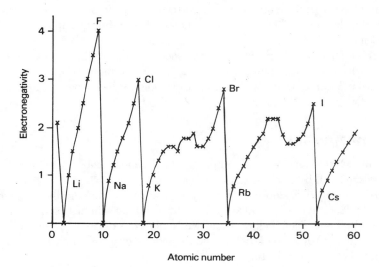

Fig. 2.5 Variation of electronegativity with atomic number

In any Group of the Periodic Table there is a decrease in electronegativity down the Group. Across a Period there is an increase in electronegativity from left to right. Elements in the top right-hand corner of the Periodic Table are therefore the most electronegative.

In bond formation, the difference in electronegativity between two atoms will determine whether the bonding is predominantly ionic or covalent (Chapter 4).

2.6 ATOMIC AND IONIC RADII

The atomic radius can be determined by X-ray or electron diffraction. In any Period there is a **decrease** in atomic radius from left to right. This surprises many students, because from sodium to chlorine there is an addition of six protons, six electrons and a number of neutrons and in spite of this the atomic radii fall from 0.157 nm to 0.099 nm. The explanation is that the extra electrons are being added to the same $3s$ and $3p$ orbitals (therefore there is no increase in size) but the extra nuclear charge attracts these electrons, drawing them closer to the nucleus.

For the elements in a Group of the Periodic Table, the atomic radii increase down the Group. Down the Group, extra electrons are added to additional orbitals. Despite the extra nuclear charge, and because of increased screening, there is a net increase in atomic radius down the Group.

Fig. 2.6 shows a graph of atomic radius against atomic number. The trends in ionic radii down a Group are similar to those for atomic radii.

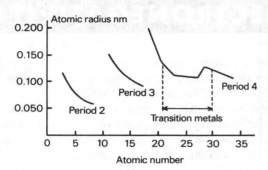

Fig. 2.6 Graph of atomic radius against atomic number

Cations (i.e. positive ions) have a smaller radius than the corresponding atoms, e.g. Na 0.157 nm, Na^+ 0.098 nm. The removal of one electron from a sodium atom empties the $3s$ orbital. The outer electron is therefore in a $2p$ orbital.

Anions have a larger radius than the corresponding atoms because of repulsion between the electrons. There is no extra nuclear charge. For example, F 0.064 nm, F^- 0.133 nm.

The three ions Na^+, Mg^{2+} and Al^{3+} are isoelectronic, i.e. they contain the same number of electrons in an arrangement $1s^2 2s^2 2p^6$. The ionic radii of these ions are 0.098, 0.065 and 0.045 nm respectively. The decreasing radius is due to the additional nuclear charge – Na^+ contains 11 protons, Mg^{2+} 12 and Al^{3+} 13.

Other properties

Oxidation states vary regularly through the Periodic Table. The variation in oxidation state will be discussed in Chapter 6.

Atomic volume is another property which varies periodically through the Periodic Table. Historically, Lothar Meyer plotted atomic volume to show periodicity within the Periodic Table before Mendeléef's table was devised. Atomic volume is the volume (in cm^3) of one mole of the solid element. A graph of atomic volume against atomic number is shown in Fig. 2.7.

Similar curves are obtained if other properties, such as melting point, boiling point and enthalpy of fusion, are plotted against atomic number.

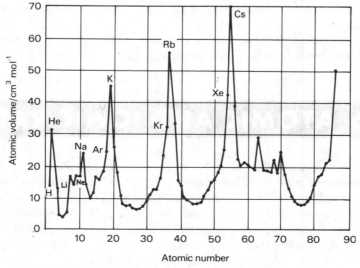

Fig. 2.7 Graph of atomic volume against atomic number

2.7 DIAGONAL RELATIONSHIPS

We will see obvious relationships between elements in the same Group of the Periodic Table. There are also trends within any Period.

In addition to these, there are similarities between elements diagonally related in the Periodic Table. The best example of this is probably the relationship between lithium and magnesium. The diagonal relationship is, however, limited to elements in the top left-hand corner of the Periodic Table.

Lithium and magnesium have similar electronegativities and the atomic and ionic radii are similar. As a result of these similarities, there are considerable similarities in the chemistries of these two elements. For example:

1 Lithium and magnesium form nitrides when burnt in nitrogen. These solid nitrides react with water to form ammonia.

$$6Li(s) + N_2(g) \rightarrow 2Li_3N(s)$$
$$3Mg(s) + N_2(g) \rightarrow Mg_3N_2(s)$$
$$Li_3N(s) + 3H_2O(l) \rightarrow 3LiOH(aq) + NH_3(g)$$
$$Mg_3N_2(s) + 6H_2O(l) \rightarrow 3Mg(OH)_2(s) + 2NH_3(g)$$

2 Many of the salts of lithium and magnesium are insoluble in water. In this lithium differs from other alkali metals. Lithium chloride and magnesium chloride are soluble in organic solvents, showing a tendency to covalent bonding.

Other common examples of diagonal relationships are given by beryllium and aluminium and boron and silicon.

2.8 GROUP 0 ELEMENTS

The noble gas elements were discovered after the Periodic Table had been devised. Their lack of reactivity was the reason for the delay in their discovery. The gases are helium He, neon Ne, argon Ar, krypton Kr, xenon Xe and radon Rn, and all are present in air.

The gases are all monatomic and sparingly soluble in water. The melting and boiling points increase regularly with increasing atomic number.

Compounds of noble gases are difficult to produce. The best known compound is xenon tetrafluoride, which is prepared by heating xenon and fluorine together at 400 °C under a pressure of 13 atmospheres.

$$Xe(g) + 2F_2(g) \rightarrow XeF_4(s)$$

Xenon tetrafluoride is a colourless, crystalline solid. It is hydrolysed by water to produce xenon(VI) oxide.

$$6XeF_4(s) + 12H_2O(l) \rightarrow 4Xe(g) + 3O_2(g) + 24HF(g) + 2XeO_3(s)$$

The structure of xenon tetrafluoride is shown in Fig. 2.8.

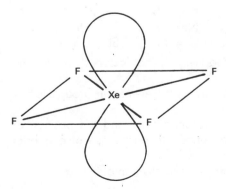

Fig. 2.8 Structure of xenon tetrafluoride

Chapter roundup

The Periodic Table is an arrangement of the elements in order of increasing atomic number. Elements with similar properties are arranged in the same vertical column, or Group.

Physical properties such as ionisation energy, electron affinity, melting and boiling points are related to electron arrangements. The graphs obtained show a series of peaks and troughs. Elements in the same Group appear in similar positions in a periodic graph.

Worked questions and answers

1 The table below shows the first eight ionisation energies of four different elements labelled A–D. (These are not the chemical symbols.) For each element, state the Group of the Periodic Table to which it belongs. Give a brief explanation of your answer.

	Ionisation energy/kJ mol^{-1}							
	1st	2nd	3rd	4th	5th	6th	7th	8th
A	418	3070	4600	5860	7990	9620	11 400	14 900
B	786	1580	3230	4360	16 000	20 000	23 600	29 100
C	1680	3400	6000	8400	11 000	15 200	17 900	92 000
D	2080	3950	6150	9290	12 100	15 200	20 000	23 000

Tutorial note

Many candidates actually try to identify each element. This is not what you are expected to do. You are not given enough information to be sure.

A This element is in Group I. The first electron can be removed easily but it is comparatively difficult to remove the second and subsequent electrons.

B This element is in Group IV. Four electrons can be removed (s^2p^2) before a sharp rise in ionisation energy occurs.

C This element is in Group VII. Seven electrons can be removed before there is a sharp rise. The atom has an electron arrangement of s^2p^5.

D This element is in Group 0. There is only a gradual change in ionisation energy with no sharp break.

2 This question concerns the following elements whose electronegativities are listed.

Al = 1.5   C = 2.5   H = 2.1   N = 3.0   P = 2.1
B = 2.0   Cl = 3.0   Li = 1.0   Na = 0.9   S = 2.5
Be = 1.5   F = 4.0   Mg = 1.2   O = 3.5   Si = 1.8

(a) What is meant by the term electronegativity? What factors determine the electronegativity of an element?

(b) What would you expect the electronegativity of an element in Group 0 to be? Explain your answer.

(c) What is the relationship between electronegativity and the position of elements in (i) a Group and (ii) a Period? In each case give a brief explanation.

(d) In what major respect do electronegativity and electron affinity differ?

(e) Arrange the following substances in order of increasing ionic character (i.e. putting the least ionic first).

CO_2 LiCl MgF_2 NaCl NH_3 S_2Cl_2

Tutorial note

(a) The electronegativity of an element is the ability of an atom of the element to attract electrons to itself. The factors which affect the electronegativity of the element are: (i) atomic radius; (ii) nuclear charge; and (iii) screening by inner orbitals. (NB These are the same factors we used in Chapter 1.)

(b) The electronegativity of a Group 0 element will be zero. Group 0 elements have no tendency to attract electrons. In compounds of noble gases, such as XeF_4, electrons are lost rather than gained.

(c) (i) Down a Group there is a decrease in electronegativity. This can be explained by increasing atomic radius and increased screening. This overcomes increasing nuclear charge.

(ii) Across a Period there is an increase in electronegativity. This can be explained by increasing nuclear charge and decreasing atomic radius. The screening of inner orbitals is the same.

(d) Both electronegativity and electron affinity concern electron attraction and they are often confused by students.

Electronegativity is only a tendency to attract electrons and is measured in arbitrary units. Electron affinity is the energy change when an electron is added.

$$X(g) + e^- \rightarrow X^-(g)$$

It has units of kJ mol^{-1}.

(e) You will need to have studied Chapter 4 before you look at this question. You need to know something about ionic bonding.

The type of bonding depends upon the difference in electronegativity between the two atoms. The bigger the difference in electronegativity the more ionic the bonding between the two atoms.

CO_2 1.0; LiCl 2.0; MgF_2 2.8; NaCl 2.1; NH_3 0.9; S_2Cl_2 0.5

The order is therefore:

S_2Cl_2 NH_3 CO_2 LiCl   NaCl MgF_2

Question bank

1 (a) (i) What is meant by periodicity in the Periodic Table? Illustrate your answer with two examples.

(ii) Discuss the use of the Periodic Table in the classification of elements as metals and nonmetals.

(iii) Discuss how the valencies of the nontransition elements are related to their position in the Periodic Table.

(iv) Explain why the position of hydrogen in the Periodic Table is a special case.

(b) Illustrate the transition from nonmetallic to metallic properties exhibited by the Group IV elements, C, Si, Sn and Pb, by considering the properties of their oxides and chlorides.

(Oxford 1989)

Points

Hydrogen (electron arrangements $1s^1$) is able to gain one electron and lose one electron. This makes it a special case. Part (b) – see Chapter 24.

CHAPTER 3

SYMBOLS, FORMULAE AND EQUATIONS

Units in this chapter

Chapter objectives

At GCSE level you may have used chemical symbols and formulae, written symbolic equations and used these equations to carry out calculations. However, at A level they are very important and frequent mistakes are seen. Writing $NaCO_3$, instead of Na_2CO_3, may seem a little mistake, but it shows very clearly to an examiner that the candidate has not mastered elementary work. Also these calculations form the theoretical basis of many calculations seen on practical papers.

3.1 SYMBOLS AND FORMULAE

Each **element** is represented by a symbol – either a capital letter alone or a capital letter and a small letter. The complete list of symbols can be obtained by reference to the Periodic Table (Fig. 2.1).

Each **compound** is represented by a formula which gives the proportions of the different elements it contains. For example, 24 g of magnesium combines with 16 g of oxygen in every 40 g sample of magnesium oxide. The formula is MgO, showing that 1 mole of magnesium atoms (24 g) combines with 1 mole of oxygen atoms (16 g).

The formulae of many compounds can be found by use of the list of ions in Table 3.1.

In forming the compound, the number of ions used is such that the number of positive charges equals the number of negative charges. For example, sodium chloride is made up from Na^+ and Cl^- ions. Since a sodium ion has a single positive charge and a chloride ion has a single negative charge, the formula of sodium chloride is $NaCl$. Sodium sulphate is made up from Na^+ and SO_4^{2-} ions. Twice as many sodium ions as sulphate ions are necessary in order to have equal numbers of positive and negative charges. The formula is Na_2SO_4. Chromium(III) sulphate is made up from Cr^{3+} and SO_4^{2-} ions and its formula is $Cr_2(SO_4)_3$. Table 3.2 contains further examples.

Table 3.1 *Common ions*

Positive ions	Negative ions
lithium Li^+	fluoride F^-
sodium Na^+	chloride Cl^-
potassium K^+	bromide Br^-
silver Ag^+	iodide I^-
copper(II) Cu^{2+}	hydroxide OH^-
lead(II) Pb^{2+}	*nitrate NO_3^- (nitrate(V))
magnesium Mg^{2+}	*nitrite NO_2^- (nitrate(III))
calcium Ca^{2+}	carbonate CO_3^{2-}
strontium Sr^{2+}	hydrogencarbonate HCO_3^-
barium Ba^{2+}	*sulphate SO_4^{2-} (sulphate(VI))
zinc Zn^{2+}	hydrogensulphate HSO_4^-
aluminium Al^{3+}	*sulphite SO_3^{2-} (sulphate(IV))
iron(II) Fe^{2+}	oxide O^{2-}
iron(III) Fe^{3+}	sulphide S^{2-}
chromium(III) Cr^{3+}	*phosphate PO_4^{3-} (phosphate(V))
manganese(II) Mn^{2+}	manganate(VII) MnO_4^-
cobalt(II) Co^{2+}	ethanedioate $C_2O_4^{2-}$
nickel(II) Ni^{2+}	chlorate(V) ClO_3^-
ammonium NH_4^+	chlorate(I) OCl^-
** hydrogen H^+	chromate(VI) CrO_4^{2-}
	dichromate(VI) $Cr_2O_7^{2-}$

NB　*Ions marked can be named in alternative ways. The systematic name is given in brackets, but the first name given is still preferred by IUPAC, national authorities and most Examination Boards. There are alternative names also for the parent acids, e.g. sulphuric acid (sulphuric(VI) acid), sulphurous acid (sulphuric(IV) acid), nitric acid (nitric(V) acid), nitrous acid (nitric(III) acid). **The hydrogen ion may be written as H^+ or in the hydrated form as H_3O^+ (oxonium ion) or H^+(aq).

Table 3.2 *Finding the formula*

Compound	Ions present		Formula
copper(II) oxide	Cu^{2+}	O^{2-}	CuO
ammonium sulphate	NH_4^+	SO_4^{2-}	$(NH_4)_2SO_4$
potassium manganate(VII)	K^+	MnO_4^-	$KMnO_4$
calcium ethanedioate	Ca^{2+}	$C_2O_4^{2-}$	CaC_2O_4
chromium(III) oxide	Cr^{3+}	O^{2-}	Cr_2O_3
hydrochloric acid	H^+	Cl^-	HCl
nitric acid	H^+	NO_3^-	HNO_3
sulphuric acid	H^+	SO_4^{2-}	H_2SO_4

NB (i) All acids contain hydrogen ions (but see Chapter 16).
(ii) A small number after a bracket multiplies everything inside the bracket, e.g. $(NH_4)_2SO_4$ is composed of three ions – two NH_4^+ ions and one SO_4^{2-} ion. Overall there are two nitrogen atoms, eight hydrogen atoms, one sulphur atom and four oxygen atoms.

All of the compounds above are composed of ions. Many compounds are not ionised. The formulae of some of these compounds are shown in Table 3.3.

Table 3.3 *Some compounds not composed of ions*

Compound	Formula	Compound	Formula
water	H_2O	sulphur dioxide	SO_2
carbon dioxide	CO_2	sulphur(VI) oxide	SO_3
carbon monoxide	CO	ammonia	NH_3
nitrogen monoxide	NO	hydrogen chloride	HCl
nitrogen dioxide	NO_2	methane	CH_4

3.2 CHEMICAL EQUATIONS

Chemical equations are widely used in textbooks and examination papers. An equation is a useful summary of a chemical reaction, and it is always theoretically possible to obtain the equation from the results of an experiment. It is advisable to be able to write equations in your answers to A-level questions. You should write any relevant equation even if you are not directly asked to do so.

The steps in writing a chemical equation are as follows:

❶ Write down the equation as a word equation using either the information given or your memory. Include all reacting substances (reactants) and all products (do not forget small molecules such as water), e.g.

$$\text{calcium hydroxide + hydrochloric acid} \rightarrow \text{calcium chloride + water}$$

❷ Fill in the correct formulae for all the reacting substances and products.

$$Ca(OH)_2 + HCl \rightarrow CaCl_2 + H_2O$$

❸ Now balance the equation. During a chemical reaction, atoms cannot be created or destroyed (Law of conservation of mass). There must be the same total numbers of the different atoms before and after the reaction. When balancing an equation only the *proportions* of the reacting substances and products can be altered – not the formulae.

$$Ca(OH)_2 + 2HCl \rightarrow CaCl_2 + 2H_2O$$

In organic chemistry the equations can be more complex. Frequently, in the interest of clarity, the formulae are drawn out as structural formulae to show clearly the changes that have taken place. Also, less emphasis may be given to balancing the equation. You should, however, balance the equation if possible.

For example, the reaction between bromoethane and a solution of potassium hydroxide in ethanol can be written.

It is better to write

$$CH_3CH_2Br \xrightarrow{-HBr} C_2H_4$$

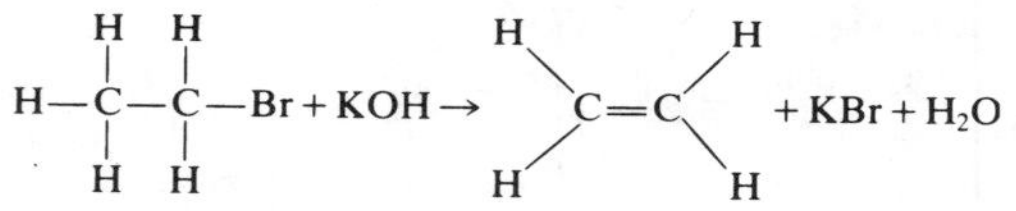

bromoethane   ethene

This equation is balanced and shows clearly the change taking place, i.e. elimination of HBr.

❹ Finally, the states of reacting substances and products can be included in small brackets after the formulae:

(s) for solid (sometimes (c) is seen for crystalline solid)
(l) for liquid
(g) for gas
(aq) for a solution with water as solvent

These state symbols may not be required and may not give you extra credit from the examiner but they do help your thinking considerably and give a good impression.

$$Ca(OH)_2(aq) + 2HCl(aq) \rightarrow CaCl_2(aq) + 2H_2O(l)$$

Sometimes, state symbols are specifically requested. Then, of course, they must be given. In the interests of simplicity in this text, state symbols are not included throughout the book, unless considered important.

3.3 INFORMATION PROVIDED BY AN EQUATION

$$CaCO_3(s) + 2HCl(aq) \rightarrow CaCl_2(aq) + CO_2(g) + H_2O(l)$$

This equation gives the following information: 1 mole of calcium carbonate reacts with 2 moles of hydrochloric acid to produce 1 mole of calcium chloride, 1 mole of carbon dioxide and 1 mole of water. The equation also gives the states of all reactants and products.

In general, a chemical equation gives:

❶ the chemicals reacting together and the chemicals produced,

❷ the physical states of reactants and products, and

❸ the quantities of chemicals reacting together and produced.

The equation does not, however, give information about energy changes, the feasibility of reaction, the rate of reaction or the conditions necessary for reaction to take place.

At GCSE level you will have attempted calculations of quantities of chemicals reacting. For example, using the above equation and the relative atomic masses ($A_r(H) = 1$, $A_r(C) = 12$, $A_r(O) = 16$, $A_r(Cl) = 35.5$, $A_r(Ca) = 40$), calculate the mass of solid calcium chloride which could be produced from 20 g of calcium carbonate.

From the equation, 1 mole of calcium carbonate ($CaCO_3$) produces 1 mole of calcium chloride ($CaCl_2$).

$$40 + 12 + (3 \times 16) \text{ g } CaCO_3 \text{ produces } 40 + (35.5 \times 2) \text{ g } CaCl_2$$

$$100 \text{ g } CaCO_3 \text{ produces } 111 \text{ g } CaCl_2$$

$$20 \text{ g } CaCO_3 \text{ produces } \frac{111}{100} \times 20 \text{ g } CaCl_2$$

$$= 22.2 \text{ g of } CaCl_2$$

You will attempt similar questions at A level. In some cases, for example when considering carbon dioxide as a product, it is more useful to measure the volume of gas produced. This can then be converted into numbers of moles of carbon dioxide by using the information (given on the examination paper) that 1 mole of any gas occupies 22 400 cm^3 at standard temperature and pressure, stp (see also Chapter 8). If the volume is measured at conditions other than stp, and it usually is, it is necessary to convert the volume measured to the volume the gas would occupy at stp (273 °K and 101.3 kPa) using the equation:

$$\frac{P_1 V_1}{T_1} = \frac{P_2 V_2}{T_2} \qquad \text{(Chapter 8)}$$

For example, what mass of calcium carbonate would react with dilute hydrochloric acid to produce 133.5 cm^3 of carbon dioxide at 27 °C and 100 kPa? Volume of carbon dioxide at stp = V_1 cm^3

$$\frac{V_1 \times 101.3}{273} = \frac{133.5 \times 100}{(273 + 27)}$$

$$V_1 = \frac{133.5 \times 100 \times 273}{101.3 \times 300}$$

$$= 120 \text{ cm}^3$$

From the equation,

100 g of calcium carbonate (1 mole) produces 22 400 cm^3 CO_2 at stp

$$\frac{100 \times 120}{22\,400} \text{ g of calcium carbonate produces } 120 \text{ cm}^3 \ CO_2 \text{ at stp}$$

Mass of calcium carbonate = 0.54 g

You will also use equations in calculations in Chapter 19.

USING CONCENTRATIONS OF SOLUTIONS

The concentrations of solutions can be recorded as:

$$g\ dm^{-3}\ or\ mol\ dm^{-3}$$

(A solution of 1 mol dm^{-3} is sometimes called a molar solution and written as 1 M.) The advantage of using concentrations in mol dm^{-3} is that all solutions of 1 mol dm^{-3} will contain the same number of particles. This enables direct comparisons to be made about how particles react together.

The concentration of a solution, in mol dm^{-3}, can be calculated using the formula:

$$\text{Concentration in mol } dm^{-3} = \frac{\text{mass of substance in 1 } dm^3}{\text{relative molecular mass}}$$

Calculate the concentration of sodium hydroxide, NaOH, in mol dm^{-3}, for a solution prepared by dissolving 1.0 g of sodium hydroxide in 250 cm^3 of water.

$$\begin{aligned}
\text{Mass of sodium hydroxide dissolving in 1 } dm^3 &= 4 \times 1.0 \\
&= 4.0\ g \\
\text{Relative molecular mass of sodium hydroxide} &= 23 + 16 + 1 \\
&= 40 \\
\text{Concentration of sodium hydroxide} &= 4.0/40 \\
&= 0.1\ mol\ dm^{-3}
\end{aligned}$$

Now let us use this solution in a titration calculation.

Sodium hydroxide reacts with sulphuric acid according to the following symbolic equation.

$$2NaOH(aq) + H_2SO_4(aq) \rightarrow Na_2SO_4(aq) + 2H_2O(l)$$

Calculate the volume of sulphuric acid (concentration 0.1 mol dm^{-3}) which would react with 25.0 cm^3 of sodium hydroxide (concentration 0.1 mol dm^{-3}).

From the equation, 2 mol of NaOH reacts with 1 mol of H_2SO_4. Therefore half the volume of H_2SO_4 is needed, i.e. 12.5 cm^3.

3.4 CALCULATION OF PERCENTAGE YIELD

In organic chemistry, a 100% conversion of reactants into products is rarely achieved. From an equation it is possible to calculate a theoretical yield, i.e. the mass that would be produced if a 100% conversion were achieved. If you are given the actual mass produced, it is possible to calculate the percentage yield by:

$$\text{Percentage yield} = \frac{\text{mass obtained}}{\text{theoretical yield}} \times 100$$

Example: Propan-2-ol reacts with iodine and sodium hydroxide on warming to produce triiodomethane. In an experiment a student obtained 39 g of triiodomethane from 10 g of propan-2-ol. What was the percentage yield? ($A_r(H) = 1$, $A_r(C) = 12$, $A_r(O) = 16$, $A_r(Na) = 23$, $A_r(I) = 127$.)

$$CH_3CH(OH)CH_3 + 4I_2 + 6NaOH \rightarrow CHI_3 + CH_3COONa + 5NaI + 5H_2O$$

Mass of 1 mole of propan-2-ol = $(12 \times 3) + 8 + 16$ g = 60 g

Mass of 1 mole of triiodomethane = $12 + 1 + (3 \times 127)$ = 394 g

From 60 g of propan-2-ol, 394 g of triiodomethane would be produced if 100% conversion was achieved.

Theoretical mass of triiodomethane from 10 g propan-2-ol $= \dfrac{394}{6}$ g $= 65.66$ g

$$\text{Percentage yield} = \dfrac{39}{65.66} \times 100$$
$$= 59.4\%$$

3.5 IONIC EQUATIONS

You may well have written ionic equations at GCSE level but they become much more significant at A level. Ionic equations are useful because they emphasise the important changes taking place in a chemical reaction.

Taking the reaction between acidified potassium manganate(VII) and iron(II) sulphate as an example. The full equation is:

$$2KMnO_4 + 8H_2SO_4 + 10FeSO_4 \rightarrow 2MnSO_4 + 8H_2O + 5Fe_2(SO_4)_3 + K_2SO_4$$

In this equation there are a number of ions which take no part in the chemistry; they are present before and after the reaction. These tend to confuse the change taking place and can often be ignored.

Expanding the equation to show the ions present.

$$2(K^+MnO_4^-) + 8(2H^+SO_4^{2-}) + 10(Fe^{2+}SO_4^{2-}) \rightarrow 2(Mn^{2+}SO_4^{2-}) + 8H_2O$$
$$+ 5(2Fe^{3+}3SO_4^{2-}) + 2K^+SO_4^{2-}$$

Cross out ions appearing on both sides of the equation:

$$2MnO_4^- + 16H^+ + 10Fe^{2+} \rightarrow 2Mn^{2+} + 8H_2O + 10Fe^{3+}$$

The equation can be divided through by 2 to give the simplest equation.

$$MnO_4^- + 8H^+ + 5Fe^{2+} \rightarrow Mn^{2+} + 4H_2O + 5Fe^{3+}$$

This represents the simplest ionic equation for this reaction. The equation must be balanced in the usual way with equal numbers of each type of atom on the left- and right-hand sides. In addition, the algebraic sum of the charges on the left-hand side equals that of the right-hand side.

In the example,

$$LHS \quad (-) + 8(+) + 5(2+) = 17(+)$$
$$RHS \quad (2+) + 4(0) + 5(3+) = 17(+)$$

The ionic equation can be broken down into 2 half equations which added together produce the overall equation.

❶ $$MnO_4^- + 8H^+ + 5e^- \rightarrow Mn^{2+} + 4H_2O$$
❷ $$5Fe^{2+} \rightarrow 5Fe^{3+} + 5e^-$$

$$MnO_4^- + 8H^+ + 5Fe^{2+} \rightarrow Mn^{2+} + 4H_2O + 5Fe^{3+}$$

Equation 1 represents the reduction of manganese(VII) to manganese(II). Equation 2 represents the oxidation of iron(II) to iron(III). A list of common half equations and their use in building up ionic equations is given in Chapter 6.

Chapter roundup

Symbols and formulae can be used to represent elements and compounds. These can be used to construct symbolic equations. Symbolic equations also provide quantitative information about reactants and products.

Before moving on to the questions here is a little test to check that you are writing formulae correctly.

(a) potassium carbonate; (b) lead(II) nitrate;
(c) potassium hydrogencarbonate; (d) silver nitrate;
(e) ammonium chloride; (f) calcium hydroxide; (g) iron(III) hydroxide;
(h) cobalt(II) chloride; (i) potassium dichromate(VI);
(j) sodium chlorate(I).

You will find the answers at the foot of the page.

Worked questions and answers

1 Balance the following equations:

(a) $Zn(s) + Fe^{3+} (aq) \rightarrow Zn^{2+} (aq) + Fe^{2+} (aq)$

(b) $Sn(s) + HNO_3 (l) \rightarrow SnO_2 (s) + NO_2 (g) + H_2O (l)$

(c) $Cu^{2+} (aq) + I^- (aq) \rightarrow Cu_2I_2 (s) + I_2 (aq)$

(d) $SO_2 (aq) + Br_2 (aq) + H_2O (l) \rightarrow H^+ (aq) + SO_4^{2-} (aq) + Br^- (aq)$

Points

Despite the practice that students should have during an A-level course, many make mistakes in balancing equations. Remember in (a), (c) and (d), where equations are ionic equations, the charges on the left-hand side and the right-hand side must be algebraically the same.

(a) $Zn(s) + 2Fe^{3+} (aq) \rightarrow Zn^{2+} (aq) + 2Fe^{2+} (aq)$

(b) $Sn(s) + 4HNO_3 (l) \rightarrow SnO_2 (s) + 4NO_2 (g) + 2H_2O (l)$

(c) $2Cu^{2+} (aq) + 4I^- (aq) \rightarrow Cu_2I_2 (s) + I_2 (aq)$

(d) $SO_2 (aq) + Br_2 (aq) + 2H_2O (l) \rightarrow 4H^+ (aq) + SO_4^{2-} (aq) + 2Br^- (aq)$

2 A compound PBr_x contains 88.6% by mass of bromine. Deduce the formula of PBr_x. $(A_r(P) = 31, A_r(Br) = 80)$

(Oxford and Cambridge)

Tutorial note

This is similar to questions which might appear at higher levels in GCSE.
In a 100 g sample of the bromide of phosphorous,
88.6 g of bromine combine with (100 – 88.6) g of phosphorus
88.6 g of bromine combine with 11.4 g of phosphorus

$$31 \text{ g of phosphorus combine with } \frac{88.6}{11.4} \times 31 \text{ g of bromine}$$
$$= 240.9 \text{ g of bromine}$$

Dividing 240.9 by the relative atomic mass of bromine to find the number of moles of bromine atoms = 3 (to the nearest whole number).(It has to be a whole number. Some candidates write $PBr_{3.01}$.) The phosphorus bromide has the formula PBr_3.

Answers:

(a) K_2CO_3; (b) $Pb(NO_3)_2$; (c) $KHCO_3$; (d) $AgNO_3$; (e) NH_4Cl; (f) $Ca(OH)_2$; (g) $Fe(OH)_3$; (h) $CoCl_2$; (i) $K_2Cr_2O_7$; (j) $NaOCl$.

CHEMICAL BONDING

Units in this chapter

Chapter objectives

In GCSE courses you should have met two methods of bonding or joining atoms together – ionic and covalent bonding. Usually these are very confused by GCSE candidates. In this chapter ionic and covalent bonding will be considered in more detail and we will look at coordinate (or dative) bonding, hydrogen bonding, dipole–dipole forces and metallic bonding. The nature of the forces of attraction between particles will have a considerable bearing on the properties of the substance, e.g. melting or boiling point. This is very important at A level.

We have already established a link between this chapter and Chapter 2. It also links with Chapters 1, 3 and 14.

In any atom the electrons in the highest energy levels are involved in the process of bonding. These electrons are sometimes called valency electrons. In Chapter 1 electron arrangements of elements were explained. You will remember that the electron arrangements of the noble gases are as follows:

Helium	$1s^2$
Neon	$1s^2 2s^2 2p^6$
Argon	$1s^2 2s^2 2p^6 3s^2 3p^6$
Krypton	$1s^2 2s^2 2p^6 3s^2 3p^6 4s^2 3d^{10} 4p^6$
Xenon	$1s^2 2s^2 2p^6 3s^2 3p^6 4s^2 3d^{10} 4p^6 5s^2 4d^{10} 5p^6$, etc.

These electron arrangements are regarded as particularly stable and are not easily broken down. The electron theory of bonding states that, on bonding, atoms attempt to achieve noble gas electron arrangements.

4.1 IONIC (OR ELECTROVALENT) BONDING

Atoms can achieve noble gas electron configurations by loss or gain of electrons to form ions. Metals (with low electronegativities) lose electrons to form positive ions and nonmetals gain electrons.

The most frequently quoted example of ionic bonding is sodium chloride. A complete transfer of one electron from a sodium atom to a chlorine atom leads to the formation of a positive sodium ion and a negative chloride ion. These ions are held together by strong electrostatic forces. Both sodium and chloride ions have electron configurations identical to noble gas atoms. The changes are summarised in Table 4.1.

Table 4.1

$$\underset{1s^22s^22p^63s^1}{Na} \xrightarrow{-e^-} \underset{1s^22s^22p^6}{Na^+} \qquad \underset{1s^22s^22p^63s^23p^5}{Cl} \xrightarrow{+e^-} \underset{1s^22s^22p^63s^23p^6}{Cl^-}$$

Another example of ionic bonding is magnesium oxide. In this case each magnesium atom loses two electrons to form an ion with a 2+ charge. Each oxygen gains two electrons to form an ion with a 2– charge. This is summarised in Table 4.2.

Table 4.2

$$\underset{1s^22s^22p^63s^2}{Mg} \xrightarrow{-2e^-} \underset{1s^22s^22p^6}{Mg^{2+}} \qquad \underset{1s^22s^22p^4}{O} \xrightarrow{+2e^-} \underset{1s^22s^22p^6}{O^{2-}}$$

A detailed account of the energy changes involved in the formation of an ionic compound will be found in Chapter 13.

Properties of compounds with ionic bonds

It is incorrect to speak of, for example, a molecule of sodium chloride (NaCl) as this suggests that one particular sodium ion is associated with one particular chloride ion. Sodium chloride consists of a regular, three-dimensional arrangement of sodium and chloride ions called a **lattice** (Fig. 10.5). Within the sodium chloride lattice, each sodium ion is surrounded by six chloride ions and each chloride ion by six sodium ions.

The electrostatic forces holding the ions together in the lattice are very strong, and a large amount of energy (called the **lattice energy**) is required to break up the lattice. As a consequence of the high lattice energies of ionic compounds, these compounds have high melting and boiling points. The lattice energies of sodium chloride and magnesium oxide are 771 and 3889 kJ mol^{-1} respectively. The much higher value for magnesium oxide can be explained because the ions have 2+ and 2– charges and therefore the forces of attraction are greater. The melting points of these two compounds are approximately 800 °C and 1400 °C.

Although different crystal lattices are possible, magnesium oxide and sodium chloride have similar lattice structures. Caesium chloride (CsCl) has a different crystal structure in which each caesium ion is surrounded by eight chloride ions (Fig. 10.6). A caesium ion is considerably larger than a sodium ion and it is geometrically possible to pack eight chloride ions around a caesium ion but not a sodium ion.

The particular lattice structure for an ionic compound is determined by the **relative radii** of the two ions (Chapter 10).

Water and other polar liquids are very good solvents for compounds containing ionic bonds. This process is explained using water as the solvent in simplified diagrams like Fig. 4.1. Such diagrams are only two-dimensional representations and they cannot show the movements of the particles.

The energy released when ions are surrounded by polar solvent molecules is called **solvation energy**. If the solvent is water this energy may be called the **hydration energy**.

The solvation energy released when the ions are surrounded by solvent molecules provides the energy required to break up the lattice (lattice energy). In a compound with a very high lattice energy (e.g. calcium fluoride) the solvation energy may not be sufficient to break down the lattice and, in this case, the compound will be insoluble.

Compounds containing ionic bonding are electrolytes: when molten or in solution they conduct electricity and undergo electrolysis. The electricity is carried by ions released and able to move when the compound melts or dissolves.

Ionic compounds do not dissolve in nonpolar liquids such as methylbenzene and hexane. Polar liquids contain slight positive and negative charges called **dipoles** (see 4.3) but these charges are not present to any degree in nonpolar liquids. They cannot, therefore, break down ionic lattices in the same way.

Fig. 4.1 Dissolving an ionic crystal   *Fig. 4.2 Silicon(IV) oxide structure*

4.2 COVALENT BONDING

The simplest case of covalent bonding is within a hydrogen molecule (H_2). Each hydrogen atom has a single electron in a $1s$ orbital. It is highly unlikely that one hydrogen atom will lose an electron and the other atom gain an electron to produce ions. Instead, each atom donates its electron to form a **shared pair** of electrons in a **molecular orbital** between the two hydrogen atoms. This is called a **covalent bond** and each hydrogen atom has a share of two electrons. (Remember a helium atom has an electron configuration $1s^2$.) The bonding can be represented by the simplified diagrams:

$$H \overset{x}{\underset{x}{}} H \qquad H—H$$

The small crosses represent valency electrons and the single stroke represents a covalent bond. Other simple examples of covalent bonding are shown in Table 4.3.

Table 4.3

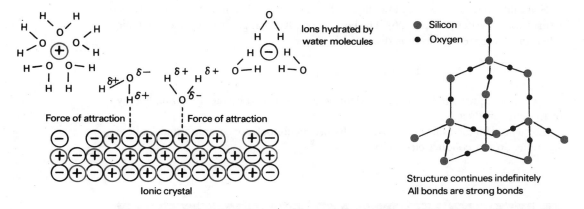

methane   water   carbon dioxide   chlorine

ethane   ethene   ethyne

In all the above examples covalent bonding leads to the formation of small molecules. It is also, however, possible for covalent bonding to produce an extremely large arrangement of atoms called a **giant structure**. Silicon(IV) oxide (silicon dioxide) is an example of this and can be represented in a simplified form (Fig. 4.2).

Properties of covalent compounds

Substances containing covalent bonding, unless they are giant structures, are relatively small molecules and the forces between the molecules (see 4.6) are weak. As a result these substances have low melting and boiling points. At room temperature and pressure they are likely to be gases, volatile liquids or low melting point solids.

Solubility in water is usually low, although some covalently bonded compounds are hydrolysed by water (Chapter 26). The bonding in HCl changes from covalent to ionic when dry hydrogen chloride is dissolved in water.

$$H—Cl(g) \rightarrow H^+(aq) + Cl^-(aq)$$

The energy required to break the covalent bond is provided by the hydration energy of the ions produced.

Covalently bonded substances usually dissolve in nonpolar or organic liquids. These solutions do not conduct electricity.

4.3 ELECTRONEGATIVITY AND ITS RELATIONSHIP TO BOND TYPE

In Chapter 2 the variation of electronegativity in the main block of the Periodic Table was discussed. There is a correlation between the electronegativities of the combining elements and the type of bonding. Bonding is rarely entirely ionic or covalent but usually some mixture of the two. Ionic and covalent bonding are extremes of bonding. In the same way black and white paints are extremes and it is possible to obtain all shades of grey by mixing these extremes.

Fajans (1923) produced rules which enabled predictions to be made about which ionic compounds would have appreciably covalent tendencies, i.e. show **polarisation**. The factors which produce polarisation are:

❶ if either the positive or negative ion is highly charged,

❷ if the positive ion is small, or

❸ if the negative ion is large.

Consider three chlorides of the alkali metals – lithium chloride LiCl, sodium chloride NaCl and potassium chloride KCl. The greatest covalent character will occur in lithium chloride because the Li^+ ion is smaller than Na^+ or K^+.

In a covalent bond where the two atoms combined have equal or very similar electronegativities it would be reasonable to assume that the shared pair of electrons in the bond is evenly distributed between the two atoms. Where the two atoms differ greatly in electronegativity it is reasonable to assume that the pair of electrons in the covalent bond is more closely associated with the more electronegative atom. This slight shift of electrons within the covalent bond produces slight positive and negative charges (represented by $\delta+$ and $\delta-$). Examples of this include

$$\underset{\delta+}{H} \diagdown \overset{O^{\delta-}}{} \diagup \underset{\delta+}{H} \qquad \text{and} \quad \underset{\delta+}{H} — \underset{\delta-}{F}$$

The slight charges in these molecules can lead to the formation of **hydrogen bonds** (see 4.5).

4.4 COORDINATE BONDING (OR DATIVE COVALENCY)

Coordinate bonding is a type of covalent bonding. In this case, a pair of electrons is shared between two atoms to form a bond but one atom supplies both electrons and the other atom supplies none.

An example of coordinate bonding is the compound formed between boron trifluoride BF_3 and ammonia NH_3. Both electrons in the N and B bond are donated by the nitrogen atom. The molecule produced is

$$
\begin{array}{cc}
H & F \\
| & | \\
H-N \rightarrow B-F \\
| & | \\
H & F
\end{array}
$$

As a result of the coordinate bond formation there is a slight positive charge on the nitrogen atom and a slight negative charge on the boron atom.

Other examples of coordinate bonding are:

❶ Ammonium ion

$$
\left[\begin{array}{c}
H \\
| \\
H-N \rightarrow H \\
| \\
H
\end{array}\right]^{+}
$$

Lone pair of electrons on nitrogen donated to form the coordinate bond.

❷ Oxonium ion

$$
\left[\begin{array}{c}
H \\
\diagdown \\
O \rightarrow H \\
\diagup \\
H
\end{array}\right]^{+}
$$

Lone pair of electrons on oxygen donated to form the coordinate bond.

❸ Aluminium chloride (see Chapter 23).

There are many examples of coordinate bonding with transition metal ions (Chapter 28).

4.5 HYDROGEN BONDING

Hydrogen bonding is more commonly encountered *between* molecules (**intermolecular**) rather than *within* molecules (**intramolecular**). It occurs in compounds whose molecules consist of a hydrogen atom covalently bonded to an electronegative atom – usually fluorine, oxygen or nitrogen. There are slight charges within the molecules caused by a slight shift of electrons in the covalent bond (see 4.3). As a result of these charges, weak electrostatic attractions exist between molecules and these are called **hydrogen bonds**.

$$
\begin{array}{ccccccc}
H & & H & & & H \\
\diagdown & & \diagdown & & & \diagdown \\
O \cdots & & O \cdots & & & O \\
\diagup & \cdots & \diagup & \cdots & \diagup \\
H & & H & & H
\end{array}
$$

This association of molecules has no effect on chemical properties but alters physical properties. For example, the boiling point is increased as extra energy is required to break these bonds before the molecules can escape from the liquid and boiling takes place. These extra bonds also increase the viscosity of the liquid.

Organic acids such as ethanoic acid and benzenecarboxylic acid exist as dimers when in nonpolar solvents such as methylbenzene.

4.6 DIPOLE–DIPOLE ATTRACTIONS

There are permanent forces of attraction in polar molecules which contain permanent dipoles. For example, in propanone

$$
\begin{array}{ccc}
CH_3 & & CH_3 \\
\diagdown \!\!\!\!\!\!\overset{\delta+}{C} = \overset{\delta-}{O} \cdots\cdots\cdots & \overset{\delta+}{C} = \overset{\delta-}{O} \cdots \\
\diagup & & \diagup \\
CH_3 & & CH_3 \\
\end{array}
$$

The weakest forms of attraction between molecules are found in alkanes, noble gases, etc. There are no permanent charges in these molecules. However, when two atoms or molecules approach one another, slight charges are momentarily induced owing to a slight movement of electrons. There are forces of attraction between these particles. These induced forces are called van der Waals forces. They become greater as the number of electrons involved increases.

4.7 METALLIC BONDING

The atoms in a metal are closely packed together in a metallic lattice and the bonding within the lattice is very strong. The bonding between the atoms in a metal is rather complicated and cannot be explained by any of the types of bonding already discussed.

The metallic lattice can be considered as a regular arrangement of metal ions. The outer valency electrons have been lost and form a 'sea', occupying the spaces between the ions and binding them together. The electrons are in orbitals delocalised throughout the lattice. This bonding accounts for the good conductivity of heat and electricity in metals. A study of possible metal structures will be found in Chapter 10.

Chapter roundup

Ionic bonding usually involves the joining together of an atom of an electropositive element (e.g. sodium) and an atom of an electronegative element (e.g. chlorine). It involves a complete transfer of one or more electrons from the metal to the nonmetal. This causes the formation of positive and negative ions which are held together by strong, nondirectional electrostatic forces in a lattice. As a result, most compounds containing ionic bonding have high melting points. The lattice can be broken down by melting or dissolving in water. In both cases free ions are formed, enabling the melt and the aqueous solution to conduct electricity.

In covalent bonding the two atoms being joined are similar in electronegativity and no complete transfer of electrons occurs. Instead, in a single covalent bond, both atoms supply one electron to form a pair of electrons which is distributed between the two atoms, holding them together. Covalent bonds have definite direction and give molecules definite shape (Chapter 5). Compounds containing covalent bonding are usually soluble in organic solvents but not in water.

Coordinate bonding is similar to covalent bonding but one of the pair of atoms being bonded supplies both electrons in the pair while the other supplies none – a kind of 'unfair' sharing.

If both atoms have the same electronegativity (e.g. in a chlorine molecule, Cl_2), the electrons are fairly distributed between the two atoms. If, however, the atoms have different electronegativities, the electrons will not be fairly distributed and this leads to small charges being set up within the molecule. This leads to hydrogen bonding (e.g. in water) and dipole–dipole bonding.

In a metal the ions are closely packed and held together by delocalised electrons. These free moving electrons are able to flow through the metal and enable it to conduct electricity.

Worked questions and answers

1 (a) Describe (by drawing suitable dot-and-cross diagrams) the type of bonding in
(i) solid sodium chloride
(ii) gaseous hydrogen chloride
(iii) the addition compound formed between boron trichloride, BCl_3, and ammonia.
(b) Write equations to show the processes that occur when
(i) sodium chloride and (ii) hydrogen chloride are dissolved in water.

(AEB 1991)

Tutorial note

(a) (i) Dot-and-cross diagrams are not recommended by some people as they can give an oversimplistic view of electron structure. Remember, when drawing these diagrams we are not saying that the electrons, shown by dots or crosses, are permanently placed in the positions shown. By using two symbols for the electrons we are trying to show where the electrons come from and go to. In solid sodium chloride it shows that one electron is completely transferred from the sodium atom to the chlorine atom. By convention we only show the outer valency electrons in these diagrams. Don't forget to show the charges on these ions.

$$\left[\begin{smallmatrix} & \times\times & \\ \times & Na & \times \\ & \times\times & \end{smallmatrix} \right]^{+} \left[\begin{smallmatrix} & \bullet\bullet & \\ \bullet & Cl & \bullet \\ \times & \bullet\bullet & \end{smallmatrix} \right]^{-}$$

(ii)

$$H \overset{\bullet\bullet}{\underset{\bullet\bullet}{\times Cl}} \bullet$$

(iii) To obtain the two marks here you have to show two different things.

① The pair of electrons in the N—B coordinate bond.
This was the lone pair on the nitrogen atom.

② The pair of electrons in the N—H and B—Cl bonds where one electron comes from each atom.

$$\begin{array}{ccc}
 & \overset{\times\times}{H \; \overset{\times}{Cl} \times} & \\
 & \overset{\bullet\times}{} \quad \overset{\bullet\times}{} \quad \overset{\times\times}{} & \\
H \overset{\bullet}{\underset{\times\bullet}{\times}} N \overset{\times}{\underset{\times\bullet}{\times}} B \overset{\bullet}{\underset{\times\times}{\times}} Cl \times & \\
 & \overset{\times}{H \; \overset{\times}{Cl} \times} & \\
 & \underset{\times\times}{} &
\end{array}$$

(b) (i) Sodium chloride: Na^+Cl^- (s) + aq $\rightarrow$ Na^+(aq) + Cl^- (aq)
This equation shows the process of dissolving, where the ionic lattice is broken down and the ions are hydrated. It is essential to give the state symbols to show this.

(ii) Hydrogen chloride: HCl (g) + aq → H$^+$ (aq) + Cl$^-$ (aq)
or HCl (g) + H$_2$O(l) → H$_3$O$^+$ (aq) + Cl$^-$ (aq)

2 The table below shows the melting and boiling points of four organic compounds. They all have approximately the same relative molecular masses.

Compound	Structural formula	Boiling point/°C
pentane		36
2,2-dimethylpropane		9
butan-1-ol		117
butanal		80

Explain why
(a) pentane has a higher boiling point than 2,2-dimethylpropane.
(b) butan-1-ol and butanal have higher boiling points than pentane.

Tutorial note

(a) Compounds with the same relative molecular mass should have similar boiling points as the van der Waals forces should be approximately the same. We are looking for reasons why the forces are not the same.

Pentane is a long molecule but 2,2-dimethylpropane, because of branching, is approximately spherical. 2,2-Dimethylpropane molecules have a much smaller surface area to come into contact with other molecules. The van der Waals forces are stronger between pentane molecules than between 2,2-dimethylpropane molecules. Pentane therefore has the higher boiling point.

(b) Both butan-1-ol and butanal contain an electronegative oxygen atom which causes small charges within the molecules. Butan-1-ol shows hydrogen bonding and butanal dipole–dipole bonding.

From these results it is reasonable to conclude that hydrogen bonding is stronger than dipole–dipole bonding. Both are much stronger than van der Waals forces.

Question bank

1 Explain briefly the following.
For the compounds H$_2$O, C$_2$H$_5$OH and C$_2$H$_5$OC$_2$H$_5$ the boiling points are, respectively, 100 °C, 78 °C and 35 °C, despite the increase in relative molecular mass along the series (18, 46 and 74, respectively).

(WJEC 1991)

SHAPES OF MOLECULES

Units in this chapter

Chapter objectives

We saw in Chapter 4 that molecules containing covalent bonding will have a definite shape. At A level there is emphasis on spatial arrangements. It has considerable bearing on organic reaction mechanisms (Chapter 38), for example. It is difficult to show three-dimensional molecules on a flat piece of paper. Some people have difficulty in imagining three-dimensional structures. Models often help. You don't have to buy expensive materials. Plasticine and cocktail sticks can be used to make simple molecules. Try making some of the molecules mentioned in this chapter.

The shapes of these molecules can be explained using the electron pair repulsion theory. This theory relies on the fact that electrons in different electron pairs will repel each other and move as far from each other as possible. It is essential to include lone, nonbonding pairs as well as pairs in covalent bonds.

5.1 ELECTRON PAIR REPULSION THEORY

This theory assumes that the electron pairs in the valency shells of the atoms will repel one another and try to get as far apart as possible.

In methane

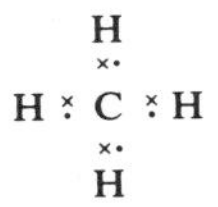

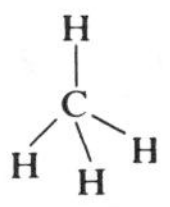

$$H : C : H$$

with H above and below, arranged tetrahedrally

tetrahedral

there are four electron pairs in bonds between carbon and hydrogen atoms. These four electron pairs distribute themselves as far apart as possible and this produces a tetrahedral configuration. The angle between the bonds is 109° 28′.

Ammonia contains three nitrogen–hydrogen bonds, each containing a pair of electrons, and a pair of electrons in a nonbonding orbital.

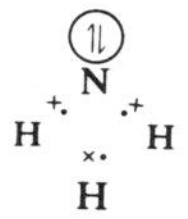

pyramidal

Again there are four electron pairs and the spatial arrangement is approximately tetrahedral. The nonbonding orbital occupies more space than the bonding orbitals. As a result the HNH angle is reduced to approximately 107°.

Table 5.1

Shape		Examples
Linear	 180°	$Cl—Be—Cl$ $O=C=O$ $H—C\equiv N$ $H—C\equiv C—H$
Bent		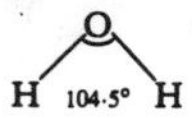 $\underset{104.5°}{H\overset{O}{\diagup\diagdown}H}$ $H_2S\ (92°)$ $NO_2^-\ (115°)$ $ClO_2^-\ (110.5°)$
Trigonal planar	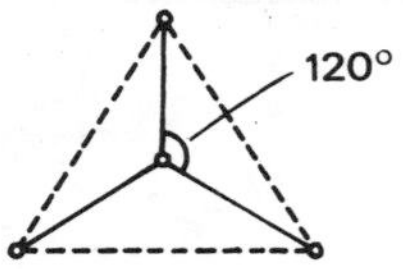 120°	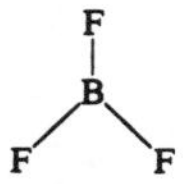 $\underset{F\quad F}{\overset{F}{B}}$ NO_3^- CO_3^{2-} SO_3 C_2H_4
Pyramidal	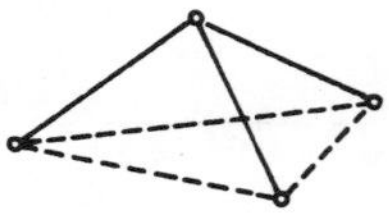	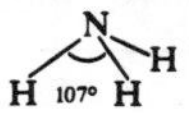 $\underset{107°}{H\overset{N}{\diagup\diagdown}H}H$ $PH_3(93°)$ ClO_3^- SO_3^{2-} PCl_3
T-shape	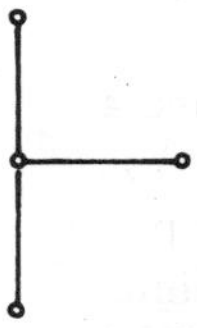	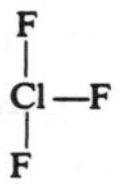 $\overset{F}{\underset{F}{Cl}}—F$
Tetrahedral	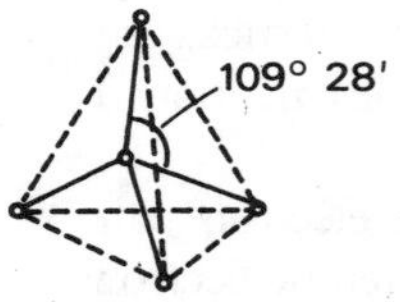 109° 28'	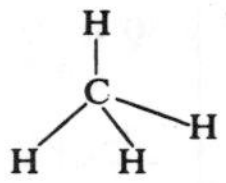 $\underset{H\quad H}{\overset{H}{H—C}}$ NH_4^+ ClO_4^- SO_4^{2-} PO_4^{3-}
Square planar	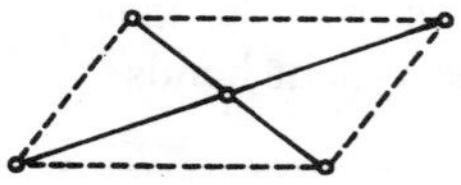	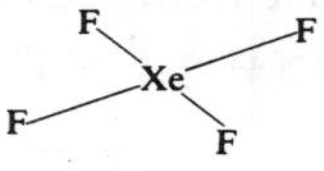 $\underset{F\quad F}{\overset{F\quad F}{Xe}}$ ICl_4^-
Trigonal bipyramidal	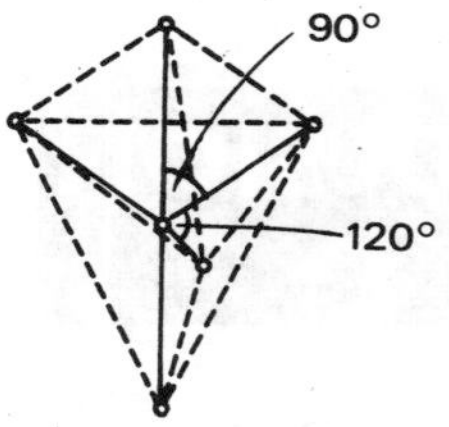 90° 120°	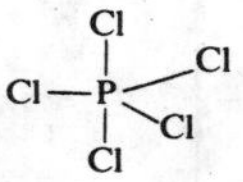 $\underset{Cl}{\overset{Cl}{Cl—P}}\overset{Cl}{\underset{Cl}{}}$
Octahedral	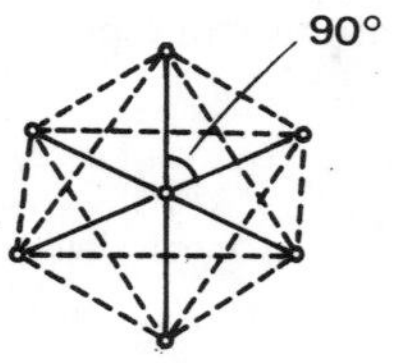 90°	 $\underset{F\quad F}{\overset{F\quad F}{S}}$
Pentagonal bipyramidal	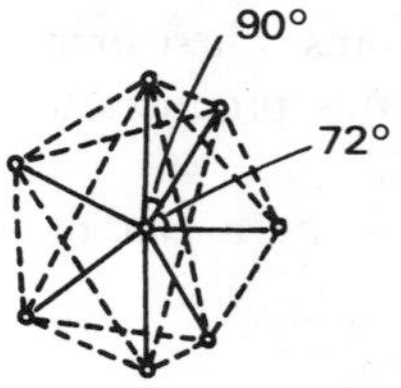 90° 72°	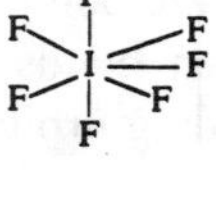 $\underset{F\ F}{\overset{F\ F}{I}}\overset{F}{\underset{F}{}}$

Water contains two oxygen–hydrogen bonds, each containing a pair of electrons, and two pairs of electrons in nonbonding orbitals.

bent

There are still four pairs of electrons and the spatial arrangement is again approximately tetrahedral. Because of the extra space occupied by the nonbonding orbitals, the HOH angle is reduced to approximately 104.5°.

Table 5.1 gives the shapes of some simple molecules and ions. In Chapter 28 shapes of *d*–block complexes are given.

5.2 SHAPES OF ALKANE, ALKENE AND ALKYNE MOLECULES

The carbon atoms in alkanes are sp^3 **hybridised,** i.e. the four orbitals ($2s$, $2p_x$, $2p_y$, $2p_z$) are combined to produce four new orbitals which are tetrahedrally arranged around the carbon atom.

In an alkene such as ethene, the carbon atoms are sp^2 hybridised ($2s$, $2p_x$, $2p_y$) to produce three new hybrid orbitals all in the same plane with the angles between these orbitals being 120°. The p_z orbitals on two adjacent atoms overlap to produce a weak additional bond. The ethene molecule is planar.

In an alkyne such as ethyne, the carbon atoms are sp hybridised ($2s$, $2p_x$) to produce two new hybrid orbitals. The p_y and p_z orbitals on two adjacent carbon atoms can overlap to produce two additional bonds. The molecule is linear.

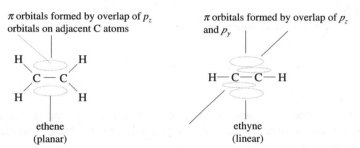

π orbitals formed by overlap of p_z orbitals on adjacent C atoms

ethene
(planar)

π orbitals formed by overlap of p_z and p_y

ethyne
(linear)

Chapter roundup

There are certain common shapes of molecules – linear, tetrahedral, square planar, octahedral, etc. The shapes are geometrical and regular. Probably the most important example is water. Too often students assume it is linear

H—O—H

rather than bent with an angle of 104.5°. This is due to four pairs of electrons being arranged around the oxygen atom – two pairs in O—H bonds and two pairs in nonbonding orbitals. These arrange themselves around the oxygen atom tetrahedrally. The nonbonding orbitals are not seen so the molecules appear bent.

Worked questions and answers

1 (a) For each of the following give the formula of a *molecule* which has the stated shape: linear, trigonal planar, tetrahedral, octahedral.

(b) The element aluminium forms an anionic complex with hydrogen of formula AlH_4^-. Use electron pair repulsion theory to predict the shape of the AlH_4^- ion. Briefly explain your answer. What is the approximate H—Al—H bond angle?

(AEB 1991)

Tutorial note

(a) Before answering the question two points should be made.
    ❶ The example given must be a *molecule* and not an *ion*.
    ❷ The linear molecule must have more than two atoms. H—Cl would not be acceptable.
    There are obviously many example which could be chosen,
    e.g. CO_2, BCl_3, CH_4, SF_6, respectively.
(b) The shape is tetrahedral. This is because there are four bonding pairs and no nonbonding pairs. For minimum repulsion between electron pairs the shape is tetrahedral. The bond angle is $109.5°$ (although you would be given the mark if you were one or two degrees out).

2 (a) *Use* the electron-pair repulsion theory to *predict and explain* the shapes of the following covalent species. (Note that both species in each of the pairs contain the same number of valence pairs of electrons.)
    (i) CH_4 and H_2O.   (ii) PCl_5 and XeF_2.   (iii) PCl_6^- and ICl_4^-
  (b) (i)   What is the hydrogen bond?
     (ii)   Use this concept to explain:
         (1) the boiling temperature of NH_3;
         (2) the solubility of NH_3 in water.
  (c) Explain how and why N_2F_2 shows geometric isomerism.

(Oxford 1994)

Tutorial note

(a) See 5.1.   (b) See 4.5.
(c) The two geometric isomers are:

They exist because rotation about a double bond is impossible and both molecules are planar but not linear because of the pair of nonbonding electrons on each N atom.

Question bank

1 Explain briefly the following:
The bond angles in the molecules of the compounds CH_4, NH_3 and H_2O are respectively $109.5°$, $107.3°$ and $104.5°$.

(WJEC 1991)

2 (a) State or draw the shape of the ammonia molecule.
  (b) State or draw the shape of the boron trifluoride molecule and give its bond angle.
  (c) Boron trifluoride reacts with ammonia to form an addition compound.
    (i) State which features of the electronic structures of the two molecules make such addition possible. State the type of bond formed.
    (ii) What is the effect, if any, on the F—B—F bond angle when the addition compound is formed? Give a reason for your answer.
    (iii) What is the effect, if any, on the H—N—H bond angle when the addition compound is formed? Give a reason for your answer.

(NEAB 1990)

OXIDATION AND REDUCTION

Units in this chapter

Chapter objectives

You will probably have used the terms oxidation and reduction in your GCSE course but the terms were probably not clearly defined. These terms become much more significant at A level. There are links with other chapters, including Chapter 3. In Chapter 18 the subject will be covered quantitatively with the introduction of electrode potentials which can be used to predict the likelihood of a reaction.

In a GCSE course, oxidation might have been defined as a chemical reaction where oxygen is gained or hydrogen is lost. Reduction is the opposite process to oxidation. It is, therefore, a reaction where oxygen is lost or hydrogen is gained.

For example, when hydrogen is passed over heated copper(II) oxide, the following reaction takes place.

$$CuO(s) + H_2(g) \rightarrow Cu(s) + H_2O(g)$$

The copper(II) oxide loses oxygen and is reduced while the hydrogen gains electrons and is oxidised. The hydrogen, which is required to reduce the copper(II) oxide, is called the reducing agent (remember the reducing agent is oxidised). The copper(II) oxide is an oxidising agent and is itself reduced.

This elementary treatment of oxidation and reduction is easy to understand but it does not include all oxidation and reduction reactions. Oxidation and reduction occur together and the term **redox reaction** means a reaction where oxidation and reduction take place.

In this chapter we will try to extend your understanding of oxidation and reduction in terms of loss or gain of electrons.

6.1 OXIDATION AND REDUCTION IN TERMS OF ELECTRON TRANSFER

Defining oxidation and reduction in terms of electron loss and gain is more useful, as not all reactions involve oxygen and hydrogen.

Oxidation is a process where electrons are lost and reduction where electrons are gained. (Remember: **leo** – **l**oss of **e**lectrons **o**xidation.) A reducing agent is an electron donor and an oxidising agent is an electron acceptor.

For example, the elementary definition given at the beginning of this chapter is too simplistic to cope with the reaction of chlorine with iron(II) chloride solution which is not obviously a redox reaction. The equation is

$$2FeCl_2(aq) + Cl_2(g) \rightarrow 2FeCl_3(aq)$$

Writing this equation as an ionic equation gives

$$2Fe^{2+}(aq) + Cl_2(g) \rightarrow 2Fe^{3+}(aq) + 2Cl^-(aq)$$

There are two processes taking place here:

❶ Iron(II) ions are losing electrons to form iron(III) ions

$$Fe^{2+}(aq) \rightarrow Fe^{3+}(aq) + e^-$$

❷ Chlorine atoms are gaining electrons to form chloride ions

$$Cl_2(g) + 2e^- \rightarrow 2Cl^-(aq)$$

During the reaction, iron(II) ions lose electrons and are therefore oxidised and chlorine which gains electrons is reduced. Chlorine is the electron acceptor and is therefore the oxidising agent and the iron(II) ion the reducing agent (electron donor).

From this example it should be noted that ionic equations and the simple ionic equations (like 1 and 2 above) called **half equations** are useful when considering oxidation and reduction.

6.2 COMMON OXIDISING AGENTS

In this section the common oxidising agents are listed. It is a good idea to learn the half equation which accompanies each oxidising agent. In all of these equations electrons are shown on the left-hand side since all oxidising agents are electron acceptors. (NB For the sake of simplicity the ion H_3O^+ is represented in these equations by $H^+(aq)$.)

oxygen $\qquad O_2(g) + 4e^- \rightarrow 2O^{2-}(s)$
chlorine $\qquad Cl_2(g) + 2e^- \rightarrow 2Cl^-(s)$
bromine $\qquad Br_2(g) + 2e^- \rightarrow 2Br^-(s)$
iodine $\qquad I_2(aq) + 2e^- \rightarrow 2I^-(aq)$
manganate(VII) in acid solution
$\qquad MnO_4^-(aq) + 8H^+(aq) + 5e^- \rightarrow Mn^{2+}(aq) + 4H_2O(l)$
manganate(VII) in alkaline solution
$\qquad MnO_4^-(aq) + 2H_2O(l) + 3e^- \rightarrow MnO_2(s) + 4OH^-(aq)$
dichromate(VI) in acid solution
$\qquad Cr_2O_7^{2-}(aq) + 14H^+(aq) + 6e^- \rightarrow 2Cr^{3+}(aq) + 7H_2O(l)$
iron(III) salts
$\qquad Fe^{3+}(aq) + e^- \rightarrow Fe^{2+}(aq)$

hydrogen ions
$$2H^+(aq) + 2e^- \rightarrow H_2(g)$$
hydrogen peroxide (in the absence of another oxidising agent)
$$H_2O_2(aq) + 2H^+(aq) + 2e^- \rightarrow 2H_2O(l)$$
manganese(IV) oxide (in the presence of acid)
$$MnO_2(s) + 4H^+(aq) + 2e^- \rightarrow Mn^{2+}(aq) + 2H_2O(l)$$
concentrated sulphuric acid
$$2H_2SO_4(l) + 2e^- \rightarrow SO_4^{2-}(aq) + 2H_2O(l) + SO_2(g)$$
You will find other examples elsewhere in the book.

6.3 COMMON REDUCING AGENTS

In a similar way, a list of reducing agents can be drawn up. In all of these half equations, electrons appear on the right-hand side of the equation as reducing agents are electron donors.

metals
$$M(s) \rightarrow M^{n+}(aq) + ne^-$$
$$\text{e.g. } Zn(s) \rightarrow Zn^{2+}(aq) + 2e^-$$
iron(II) salts
$$Fe^{2+}(aq) \rightarrow Fe^{3+}(aq) + e^-$$
acidified potassium iodide
$$2I^-(aq) \rightarrow I_2(aq) + 2e^-$$
thiosulphate
$$2S_2O_3^{2-}(aq) \rightarrow S_4O_6^{2-}(aq) + 2e^-$$
ethanedioic acid and ethanedioates (oxalic acid and oxalates)
$$C_2O_4^{2-}(aq) \rightarrow 2CO_2(g) + 2e^-$$
hydrogen sulphide and sulphides
$$S^{2-}(aq) \rightarrow S(s) + 2e^-$$
sulphurous acid (sulphuric(IV) acid)
$$SO_3^{2-}(aq) + H_2O(l) \rightarrow SO_4^{2-}(aq) + 2H^+(aq) + 2e^-$$
hydrogen peroxide (in the presence of a strong oxidising agent)
$$H_2O_2(aq) \rightarrow O_2(g) + 2H^+(aq) + 2e^-$$
tin(II) ions in hydrochloric acid
$$Sn^{2+}(aq) \rightarrow Sn^{4+}(aq) + 2e^-$$
hydrogen $\quad H_2(g) + O^{2-}(s) \rightarrow H_2O(l) + 2e^-$
carbon $\quad C(s) + O^{2-}(s) \rightarrow CO(g) + 2e^-$
carbon monoxide
$$CO(g) + O^{2-}(s) \rightarrow CO_2(g) + 2e^-$$

6.4 USING IONIC HALF EQUATIONS TO WRITE FULL IONIC EQUATIONS

Combination of two ionic half equations, one representing an oxidising action and one representing a reducing action, will produce a full ionic equation. This could be used, if required, to produce a molecular equation. Remember, however, that it is possible to write equations for reactions which do not in fact take place. Whether a reaction takes place depends upon the standard electrode potentials (Chapter 18).

For example, the reaction of acidified potassium manganate(VII) with iron(II) sulphate solution. Write out the relevant half equations.

OA $MnO_4^-(aq) + 8H^+(aq) + 5e^- \rightarrow Mn^{2+}(aq) + 4H_2O(l)$

RA $Fe^{2+}(aq) \rightarrow Fe^{3+}(aq) + e^-$

On combining these equations the electrons must cancel out. Multiply the RA equation by 5 and add.

$MnO_4^-(aq) + 8H^+(aq) + 5Fe^{2+}(aq) \rightarrow Mn^{2+}(aq) + 4H_2O(l) + 5Fe^{3+}(aq)$

In this equation, manganate(VII) acts as the oxidising agent and the iron(II) ion as the reducing agent.

The reaction of acidified potassium manganate(VII) with acidified potassium iodide. Write the relevant half equations.

OA $MnO_4^-(aq) + 8H^+(aq) + 5e^- \rightarrow Mn^{2+}(aq) + 4H_2O(l)$

RA $2I^-(aq) \rightarrow I_2(aq) + 2e^-$

In order to remove the electrons, multiply the OA equation by 2 and RA by 5 and add.

$2MnO_4^-(aq) + 16H^+(aq) + 10I^-(aq) \rightarrow 2Mn^{2+}(aq) + 8H_2(l) + 5I_2(aq)$

6.5 RECOGNISING OXIDATION AND REDUCTION FROM AN IONIC EQUATION

If you are given a full ionic equation it is possible to split it up into its constituent half equations, e.g.

$Zn(s) + 2H^+(aq) \rightarrow Zn^{2+}(aq) + H_2(g)$

The half equations are:

OA $2H^+(aq) + 2e^- \rightarrow H_2(g)$

RA $Z(s) \rightarrow Zn^{2+}(aq) + 2e^-$

In this reaction $H^+(aq)$ ions are reduced and zinc atoms are oxidised.

6.6 HYDROGEN PEROXIDE AS OXIDISING AND REDUCING AGENT

Hydrogen peroxide can act as an oxidising agent or a reducing agent according to the conditions.

In the absence of a stronger oxidising agent, hydrogen peroxide acts as an oxidising agent. For example, hydrogen peroxide and acidified potassium iodide

OA $H_2O_2(aq) + 2H^+(aq) + 2e^- \rightarrow 2H_2O(l)$

RA $2I^-(aq) \rightarrow I_2(aq) + 2e^-$

Add $H_2O_2(aq) + 2H^+(aq) + 2I^-(aq) \rightarrow 2H_2O(l) + I_2(aq)$

When a stronger oxidising agent is present, hydrogen peroxide then acts as a reducing agent.

OA $MnO_4^-(aq) + 8H^+(aq) + 5e^- \rightarrow Mn^{2+}(aq) + 4H_2O(l)$

RA $H_2O_2(aq) \rightarrow O_2(g) + 2H^+(aq) + 2e^-$

Multiply the OA equation by 2 and the RA equation by 5 and add:

$$2MnO_4^-(aq) + 16H^+(aq) + 5H_2O_2(aq) \rightarrow 2Mn^{2+}(aq) + 8H_2O(l) + 5O_2(g) + 10H^+(aq)$$

This equation can be slightly simplified. There are $16H^+(aq)$ on the left-hand side and $10H^+(aq)$ on the right-hand side. An equation should show change and $10H^+(aq)$ can be subtracted from both sides.

$$2MnO_4^-(aq) + 6H^+(aq) + 5H_2O_2(aq) \rightarrow 2Mn^{2+}(aq) + 8H_2O(l) + 5O_2(g)$$

If the two equations for hydrogen peroxide are written down and added together we get

OA	$H_2O_2(aq) + 2H^+(aq) + 2e^- \rightarrow 2H_2O(l)$
RA	$H_2O_2(aq) \rightarrow O_2(g) + 2H^+(aq) + 2e^-$
Add	$2H_2O_2(aq) \rightarrow 2H_2O(l) + O_2(g)$

This equation represents the decomposition of hydrogen peroxide into water and oxygen. The reaction can be regarded as the disproportionation of hydrogen peroxide with hydrogen peroxide acting simultaneously as oxidising and reducing agent.

6.7 OXIDATION STATE (OR OXIDATION NUMBER)

The system of **oxidation states** (or **oxidation numbers**) has been devised to give a guide to the extent of oxidation or reduction in a species. The system is without direct chemical foundation, but is extremely useful, being appropriate to both ionic and covalently bonded species.

The oxidation state can be defined simply as the number of electrons which must be added to a positive ion to get a neutral atom or removed from a negative ion to get a neutral atom, e.g. $Fe^{2+}(aq)$ – two electrons have to be added and the oxidation state is $+2$; $Cl^-(aq)$ – one electron has to be removed and the oxidation state is -1.

It is relatively easy to understand for simple ions because the electrons are definitely associated with certain ions.

For covalent species it is assumed that the electrons in the covalent bond actually go to the atom which is most electronegative. For example in ammonia, NH_3, nitrogen is the more electronegative element and it is assumed that the three electrons (one from each hydrogen atom) are associated with the nitrogen atom. Nitrogen therefore (like nitrogen in N^{3-}) has an oxidation state of -3 and hydrogen $+1$.

The system will be clear with practice but the following rules are worth remembering.

❶ The oxidation state of all elements uncombined is zero. Therefore the oxidation state of oxygen in oxygen gas is zero.

❷ The algebraic sum of the oxidation states of the elements in a compound is always zero.

For example, in NH_3

N	OS	-3
H	OS	$+1$
H	OS	$+1$
H	OS	$+1$
		0

❸ The algebraic sum of the oxidation states of the elements in an ion is equal to the charge on the ion.

For example, in CO_3^{2-}

C	OS	+4
O	OS	–2
O	OS	–2
O	OS	–2
		——
		–2

❹ The oxidation state of oxygen is –2 (except in oxygen gas and peroxides).

❺ The oxidation state of hydrogen is +1 (except when combined with Group I or II metals as hydrides).

In chemical names the oxidation state of a particular species may be shown in Roman numerals in brackets if there is the chance of any uncertainty. In these cases the sign is not given.

For example, iron(III) chloride – iron is in oxidation state +3;

tetracarbonylnickel(0) – nickel is in oxidation state zero.

If during a chemical reaction a species changes its oxidation state, then oxidation and reduction are taking place. An increase in oxidation state corresponds to oxidation and a decrease to reduction.

For example, the reaction of chlorine with hydrogen sulphide

$$Cl_2(g) + H_2S(g) \rightarrow 2HCl(g) + S(s)$$

This could be written in two ionic half equations

OA	$Cl_2(g) + 2e^- \rightarrow 2Cl^-(g)$
RA	$S^{2-}(g) \rightarrow S(s) + 2e^-$
Add	$Cl_2(g) + S^{2-}(g) \rightarrow 2Cl^-(g) + S(s)$

The oxidation state of chlorine in Cl_2 is zero (because it is an element) and in HCl is –1. (Remember H is usually in OS +1 and the sum must be zero.)

The chlorine therefore is reduced because the oxidation state is reduced from 0 to –1. Similarly, the oxidation state of sulphur increases from –2 in H_2S to zero in S. The sulphur is oxidised as there is an increase in oxidation state.

With *d*-block elements (Chapter 28), a variety of oxidation states is possible for each element.

Chapter roundup

Oxidation and reduction in terms of electron loss or gain is key issue at A level. The half equations in 6.2 and 6.3 are very important and you should try to learn them. Then practice writing ionic equations by using one oxidising agent and one reducing agent.

The concept of oxidation state is also very important, especially when studying Chapter 28.

Worked questions and answers

1 In the following molecular equations, work out the oxidation states of the element in bold type in each case. Then decide whether this element is oxidised, reduced or neither oxidised nor reduced in that particular reaction.

(a) $2\mathbf{Cu}SO_4(aq) + 4KCN(aq) \rightarrow 2\mathbf{Cu}CN(s) + C_2N_2(g) + 2K_2SO_4(aq)$

(b) $10\mathbf{Fe}SO_4(aq) + 2KMnO_4(aq) + 8H_2SO_4(aq) \rightarrow$

$$5\mathbf{Fe}_2(SO_4)_3(aq) + K_2SO_4(aq) + 2MnSO_4(aq) + 8H_2O(l)$$

(c) $K\mathbf{I}(aq) + AgNO_3(aq) \rightarrow Ag\mathbf{I}(s) + KNO_3(aq)$

(d) $CuSO_4(aq) + \mathbf{Zn}(s) \rightarrow Cu(s) + \mathbf{Zn}SO_4(aq)$

(e) $\mathbf{Sn}Cl_2(aq) + HgCl_2(aq) \rightarrow Hg(l) + \mathbf{Sn}Cl_4(aq)$

Tutorial note

(a) Oxidation state of Cu in $CuSO_4$ = +2

　　　　　　　　　　　in CuCN = +1

　　Copper is reduced during the reaction (+2→ +1).

(b) Oxidation state of Fe in $FeSO_4$ = +2

　　　　　　　　　　in $Fe_2(SO_4)_3$ = +3

　　Iron is oxidised during the reaction (+2 → +3).

(c) Iodine is oxidation state –1 in KI and AgI – neither oxidation nor reduction.

(d) Oxidation state of zinc changes from 0 to +2 – it is therefore oxidised.

(e) Oxidation state of tin changes from +2 to +4. Tin is oxidised.

Question bank

1 (a) Write down the oxidation state of iodine in the IO_3^- anion.

(b) Write down the two ion/electron half equations for the reaction of the IO_3^- anion with the iodide ion (I^-) in acidic solution.

Hence write down the stoichiometric equation for the overall reaction.

(c) An unknown mass of KIO_3 was treated in aqueous solution with excess iodide ion and acidified. The resulting solution, on titration against 0.2000 mol dm^{-3} sodium thiosulphate solution, required 53.70 cm^3 thereof for complete reaction. Find the mass of KIO_3 used.

(WJEC 1991)

Points

The question in (c) links with Chapter 19.

CHAPTER 7

INTRODUCTION TO ORGANIC CHEMISTRY

Units in this chapter

Chapter objectives

Organic chemistry is the study of the compounds of carbon, but excluding simple compounds such as carbon monoxide, carbon dioxide, carbonates, hydrogencarbonates and carbides. The elements present in organic compounds are usually restricted to carbon, hydrogen, oxygen, nitrogen, sulphur, fluorine, chlorine, bromine, iodine and metals.

Most GCSE courses contain a little organic chemistry – perhaps something about hydrocarbons, alcohols and polymers. In this book Chapters 29–39 contain the necessary organic chemistry.

In this chapter we will consider techniques used for purification of organic compounds. Some of these, e.g. distillation, chromatography, will be familiar to you from GCSE.

In particular, organic chemistry is very systematic and there are certain clearly defined pathways from one compound to another. Chapter 37 will help you to appreciate the relationships between organic compounds. You should spend some time on this when you feel you have mastered organic chemistry.

7.1 ALIPHATIC AND AROMATIC

There are a very large number of organic compounds because carbon forms four very stable covalent bonds. As a result long chains of carbon atoms, branched chains and rings can be formed.

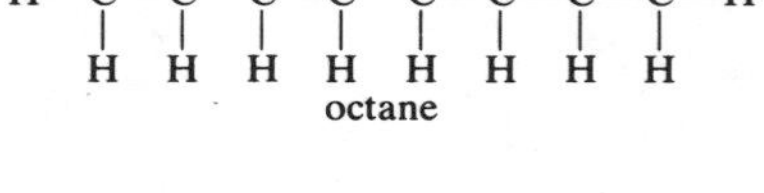

octane

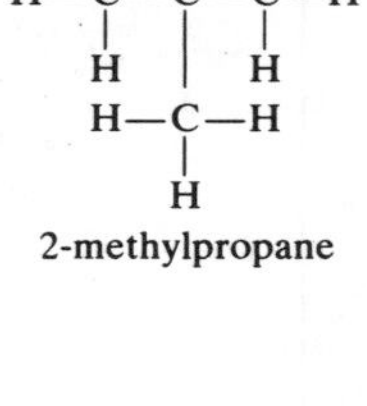

2-methylpropane

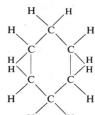

cyclohexane
(sometimes abbreviated to ⬡)

Unlike the other similar elements in Group IV (Chapter 24) of the Periodic Table, carbon can also form double and triple bonds.

H—C≡C—H
ethyne

benzene
(sometimes abbreviated to ⬡ or ⌬)

Compounds containing a benzene ring or similar are called **aromatic** compounds. Other organic compounds are called **aliphatic** compounds.

7.2 PURIFICATION OF ORGANIC COMPOUNDS

Provided it is not chemically changed by the heating process, a pure compound has a melting point at a definite temperature. If impurities are present the melting point is reduced and the compound will melt over a range of temperature.

There are various methods of purifying organic compounds including solvent extraction (or partition), using drying agents, simple distillation, fractional distillation, steam distillation, crystallisation, reduced-pressure filtration and chromatography.

Solvent extraction

Most organic compounds are more soluble in nonpolar solvents than in aqueous solutions. (Water is a polar solvent and dissolves most ionic compounds well but only a few organic compounds.) When ethoxyethane (diethyl ether) is shaken with water in a tap funnel, two layers are produced. If an organic compound is initially in the water, most of it will have transferred to the ethoxyethane after shaking.

Drying solutions with drying agents

There are various chemicals that can be used to remove the last traces of water from a pure liquid. These are summarised in Table 7.1

Table 7.1 Drying agents

Drying agent	Use
Anhydrous calcium chloride	Not suitable for alcohols, phenols, amines and acidic compounds
Anhydrous sodium sulphate	For most substances but it is very slow
Potassium hydroxide	For amines – not suitable for acids, phenols and esters
Anhydrous magnesium sulphate	For most substances – faster than sodium sulphate
Sodium wire	For ethers or hydrocarbons

Distillation

The apparatus in Fig. 7.1 can be used for simple distillation where a volatile solvent is to be removed from a nonvolatile solid. An example is the removal of ethoxyethane from a solution of a nonvolatile organic compound in ethoxyethane.

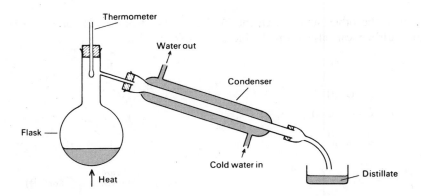

Fig. 7.1 Distillation

If the boiling point of the liquid distilling off is above about 140 °C, an air condenser is used. An air condenser is simply a glass tube. The air around the tube cools the contents of the tube.

If the liquid being distilled off decomposes at a temperature close to its boiling point, it is possible to distil it under reduced pressure or by **steam distillation**. Mixtures of volatile liquids can be separated by **fractional distillation** (Chapter 11) using the apparatus in Fig. 7.2.

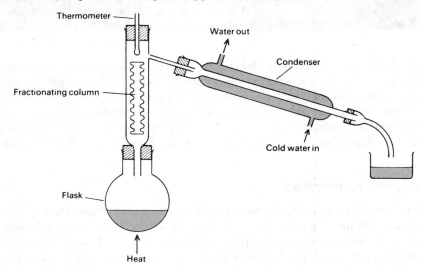

Fig. 7.2 Fractional distillation

Crystallisation

The impure solid is added to a small volume of hot solvent in which it dissolves. On cooling, the pure solid crystallises out and the impurities, which are present in small amounts, remain dissolved in the solvent. It is necessary to choose the solvent carefully. The pure solid should be readily soluble in the hot solvent and much less soluble in the cold solvent. The pure crystals can be removed by filtration under reduced pressure using a Buchner funnel and flask (Fig. 7.3). Finally the crystals can be washed with cold solvent and dried by pressing between filter papers.

Benzenecarboxylic acid (benzoic acid) can be recrystallised using water as the solvent.

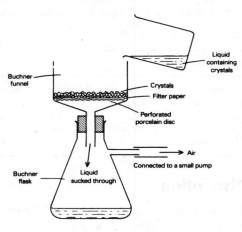

Fig. 7.3 Filtration under reduced pressure

Chromatography

Paper chromatography can be used to show whether a substance is pure or contains

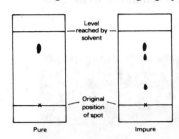

Fig. 7.4
Chromatography of
pure and impure
substances

other substances. If a small spot of the substance in solution is put on a strip of filter paper and the end of the filter paper dipped into a suitable solvent a separation will occur if the substance is impure. In Fig. 7.4 the chromatograms of pure and impure substances are compared.

This technique requires only a very small amount of material, and is not used to purify compounds except on the minutest scale.

Compounds are often identified by calculating R_f values which can be compared with values in a data book. The R_f value is calculated using the formula

$$R_f \text{ value} = \frac{\text{distance moved by the spot}}{\text{distance moved by the solvent}}$$

The value is a ratio and therefore has no units. It will always be less than 1. The R_f value depends upon the solvent used.

Fig. 7.5 shows the chromatogram for a mixture of two amino acids. In the data book you will find the following R_f values.

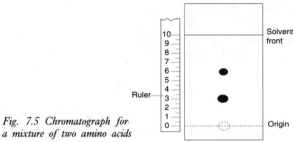

Fig. 7.5 Chromatograph for
a mixture of two amino acids

Amino acid	R_f value
Histidine	0.20
Glycine	0.26
Glutamic acid	0.30
Tryptophan	0.50
Valine	0.60

Calculate the R_f values of the two spots and so identify the two amino acids. You will find the answer in the chapter roundup.

Two-way paper chromatography is a useful technique for separating complex mixtures of similar compounds. In Fig. 7.6 two amino acids were separated by using (i) a mixture of butan-1-ol and ethanoic acid and (ii) phenol as solvents in turn. After (i) the chromatography paper was turned through 90°. The R_f values for amino acid A are 0.27 and 0.34, respectively. What are the R_f values for amino acid B?

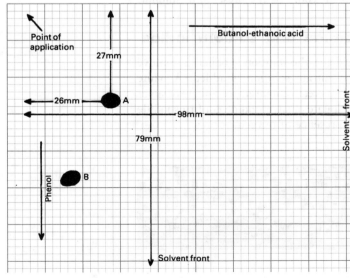

Fig. 7.6 Two-way paper
chromatogram

Answer: 0.14 and 0.65

NB Amino acids are colourless and the chromatogram has to be developed by spraying with a solution of ninhydrin and heating. A red-to-blue spot is obtained. Ninhydrin is a test for —NH_2 groups.

Gas–liquid chromatography (GLC) is a most useful technique for analysis of complex mixtures. A minute quantity of the mixture to be analysed is injected into the apparatus and vaporised. The vapour is swept along by a 'carrier' gas through a long heated column packed with a suitable packing material. The different components pass through the column at different rates and the exit of each component is detected and registered graphically. GLC is used to detect and measure ethanol in breath in new breath-testing machinery.

7.3 FINDING THE ELEMENTS PRESENT IN AN ORGANIC COMPOUND

When a mixture of an organic compound and dry copper(II) oxide is heated, carbon dioxide and water are produced. The carbon dioxide is produced when carbon in the organic compound is oxidised. It can be detected by testing with limewater, which turns milky. Water vapour is produced by oxidation of hydrogen in the original compound and can be detected with cobalt(II) chloride paper which turns from blue to pink.

The elements nitrogen, sulphur, chlorine, bromine and iodine are detected by means of the **Lassaigne's test.** The organic compound is fused with molten sodium which breaks up the compound. Any nitrogen, sulphur, chlorine, bromine and iodine in the compound are converted into sodium cyanide, sodium sulphide, sodium chloride, sodium bromide and sodium iodide respectively. The residue is added to water and the solution filtered. The following tests for the sodium compounds are then carried out.

Sodium cyanide

Fresh iron(II) sulphate solution and sodium hydroxide solution are added to the extract and the solution is heated. The solution is then acidified and iron(III) chloride solution added. A finely divided dark-blue precipitate confirms the presence of nitrogen (Chapter 28).

Sodium sulphide

A freshly prepared solution of sodium pentacyanonitrosylferrate(II) $Na_4Fe(CN)_5NO_2$ (sodium nitroprusside) is added. A purple colour confirms the presence of sulphur.

Sodium chloride, sodium bromide and sodium iodide

The extract is acidified with dilute nitric acid and the solution is boiled to remove any sulphide that might be present. Silver nitrate solution is added. A white precipitate of silver chloride confirms chloride, a cream coloured precipitate of silver bromide confirms bromide and a yellow precipitate of silver iodide confirms iodide (Chapter 27). It is not usual to test for the presence of oxygen.

7.4 FINDING THE MOLECULAR FORMULA OF AN ORGANIC COMPOUND

Having found the elements that are present by qualitative analysis, it is usual to carry out experiments to find the percentage of each element (apart from oxygen) by quantitative analysis. You are not required to study details of these methods, but the following calculation will illustrate how the percentage of carbon and hydrogen can be found.

Sample calculation

0.152 g of an organic compound produced 0.223 g of carbon dioxide and 0.091 g of water on complete combustion. Calculate the percentage of carbon and hydrogen in the compound. ($A_r(H) = 1$, $A_r(C) = 12$, $A_r(O) = 16$)

Carbon dioxide CO_2

Mass of 1 mole of carbon dioxide molecules = $12 + (2 \times 16)$ = 44 g
1 mole of carbon dioxide molecules contain 12 g of carbon.

0.223 g of carbon dioxide contains $0.223 \times \dfrac{12}{44}$ g of carbon = 0.061 g
This carbon must all have come from the organic compound.

Percentage of carbon in organic compound = $\dfrac{0.061}{0.152} \times 100\%$ = 40.1%

Water H_2O

Mass of 1 mole of water molecules = $(2 \times 1) + 16$ = 18 g
1 mole of water molecules contains 2 g of hydrogen.

0.091 g of water contains $0.091 \times \dfrac{2}{18}$ g of hydrogen = 0.010 g

∴ Percentage of hydrogen in organic compound = $\dfrac{0.010}{0.152} \times 100\%$ = 6.6%

Assuming no other elements have been found to be present by qualitative analysis, the percentage of oxygen can be found:

Percentage of oxygen = $100 - (40.1 + 6.6)\%$ = 53.3%

Having found the percentage of each element present it is possible to calculate the **empirical formula,** or simplest formula.

Elements present	C	H	O
Percentage	40.1%	6.6%	53.3%
Relative atomic mass	12	1	16
Percentage ÷ relative atomic mass	3.34	6.6	3.33
Divide by the smallest, i.e. 3.33	1	2	1
Empirical formula $C_1H_2O_1$ or CH_2O			

The empirical formula contains the elements in the correct proportions, but the actual or molecular formula may be the same as the empirical formula or a multiple of it, e.g. in this case $C_2H_4O_2$, $C_3H_6O_3$, $C_4H_8O_4$, etc.

In order to find the molecular formula the relative molecular mass is found by experiment (Chapters 8 and 12). In this example if the relative molecular mass was found to be approximately 60, the molecular formula would be $C_2H_4O_2$.

7.5 STRUCTURAL FORMULAE

The **molecular formula** gives the number of atoms of each element in a molecule of the compound. It does not give any information about how the atoms are joined together. This information is given by the **structural formula**.

In order to obtain the structural formula it is necessary to identify which **functional groups** are present. A functional group is a group of atoms within a compound which gives characteristic properties. The common functional groups are given later in Table 7.3.

The functional groups can be identified by specific chemical tests in Chapters 29–35 or by physical means including infrared (ir) spectroscopy.

Infrared radiation is light with a wavelength of between 2500 nm and 25 000 nm (longer wavelength than visible light). When ir radiation is passed through a compound, certain wavelengths are absorbed. The absorbed energy is used to make certain bonds within the molecule vibrate more vigorously. These vibrations involve stretching or bending. The wavelengths absorbed and the extent of absorption can be recorded on instruments (see Fig. 7.7).

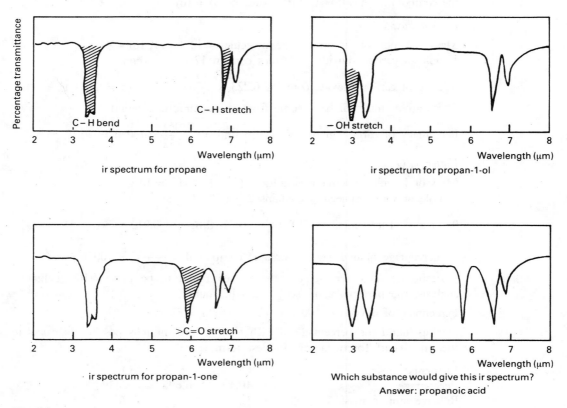

Fig. 7.7

7.6 ISOMERISM

It is sometimes possible to obtain two or more structural formulae from the same molecular formula. Examples include:

Molecular formula   *Structural formulae*

C_4H_{10}

C_3H_6O

Aldehyde   Ketone

Molecular formula	Structural formulae

C_2H_6O

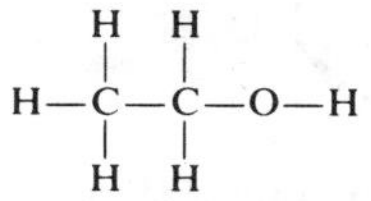

Alcohol 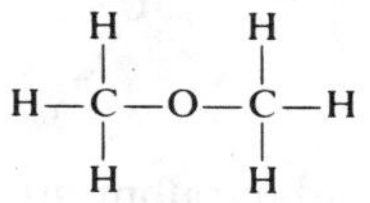   Ether

$C_2H_4O_2$

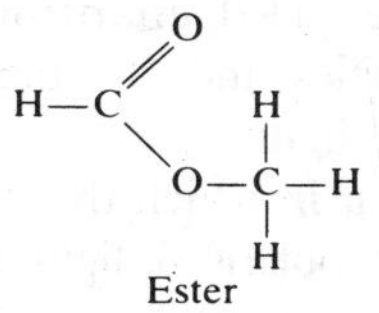

Ester 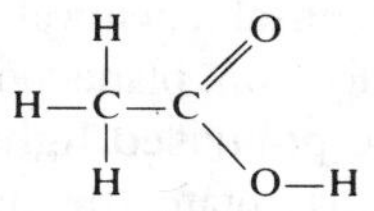   Acid

The existence of two or more forms of the same compound with the same structural formula but with different spatial arrangements is called **stereoisomerism**. There are two types – **geometric isomerism** and **optical isomerism**.

Geometric isomerism

There is normally free rotation about a carbon–carbon single bond but there is no free rotation about a carbon–carbon double or triple bond.

The butenedioic acids give a common example of geometric isomerism. There are two possible isomers.

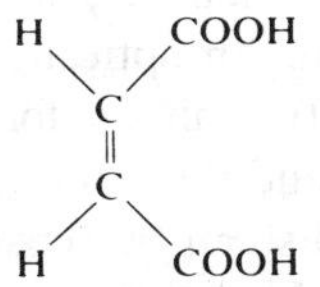

cis-butenedioic acid
(maleic acid)

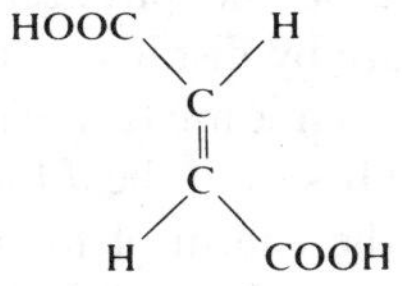

trans-butenedioic acid
(fumaric acid)

Lack of rotation in the carbon–carbon double bond explains the existence of the two isomers. The isomer with the two functional groups on the same side of the molecule is called the *cis* form; when the functional groups are on opposite sides of the molecule it is called the *trans* form.

The two isomers have different physical and chemical properties. The *cis* form melts at a lower temperature and loses a molecule of water to form the anhydride, because the two carboxyl groups are in close proximity. The *trans* form loses a molecule of water only at a much higher temperature and the anhydride formed is identical to the anhydride formed from the *cis* form. At this higher temperature rotation has presumably taken place.

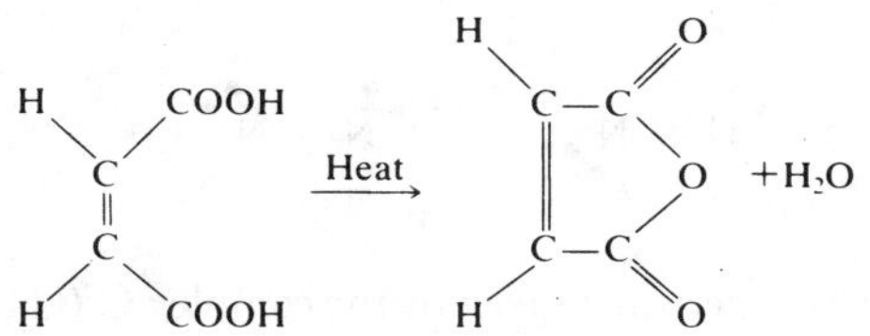

cis-butenedioic anhydride
(maleic anhydride)

Optical isomerism (or chirality)

Optical isomerism in organic compounds exists because the four covalent bonds formed by a carbon atom are tetrahedrally arranged. When four different groups are attached to one carbon atom it is possible to produce two optical isomers that are mirror images and are not superimposable.

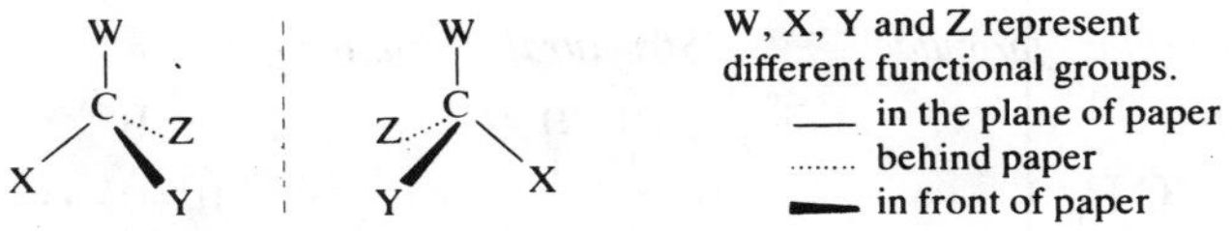

W, X, Y and Z represent different functional groups.
——— in the plane of paper
.... behind paper
▬▬ in front of paper

The carbon atom attached to four different groups is called an **asymmetric carbon atom** (or chiral centre).

The two optical isomers are called **enantiomers** or **enantiomorphs**. They have identical chemical properties and identical physical properties except for their effect on plane polarised light.

Plane polarised light is light in which the vibrations are all in one plane. The two forms rotate the plane of polarised light by equal angles but in opposite directions. The form which rotates polarised light to the right is said to be **dextrorotatory** (and this form is called the d or + form). The form which rotates to the left is said to be **laevorotatory** (and is called the l or − form).

A mixture of equal amounts of the d and l forms has no effect on the plane of polarised light and is called a **racemic** (or ± or dl) **mixture**.

A common example of optical isomerism is given by 2-hydroxypropanoic acid.

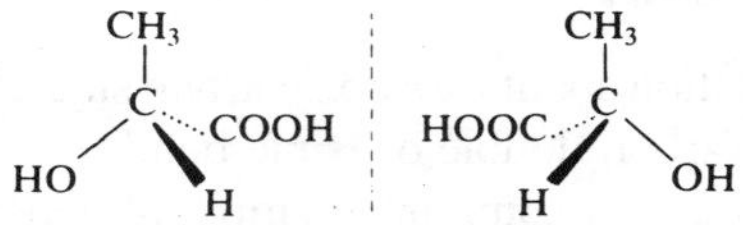

The separation of a racemic mixture into the separate d and l forms is called **resolution**. Because the physical properties are identical, it is not possible to resolve the mixture by distillation or crystallisation. An optically active base can be used to resolve a racemic mixture of an acid because two salts are formed – one between the d form of the base and the d form of the acid and the other between the d form of the base and the l form of the acid. These salts can be separated by fractional crystallisation as they have different properties. The acid can be regenerated by hydrolysis.

7.7 ISOMERISM IN INORGANIC COMPOUNDS

There is sometimes among students the mistaken idea that organic chemistry is completely separate from other branches of chemistry. Although isomerism is usually regarded as organic chemistry, here are a couple of examples from inorganic chemistry.

An example of geometric isomerism is given by N_2F_2. The diagram shows that two distinct forms exist and they cannot be easily interchanged because there is no free rotation around the N=N bond.

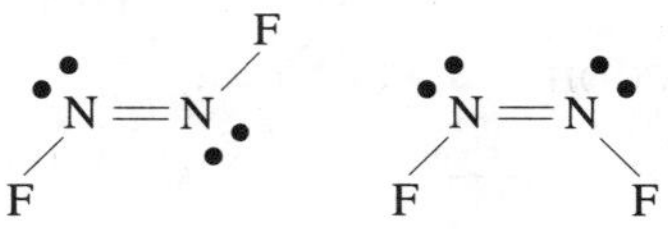

An example of optical isomerism is given by the complex $Cr(C_2O_4)_3^{3-}$. This can exist in two forms which have opposite effects on the plane of polarised light.

represents $C_2O_4^{2-}$

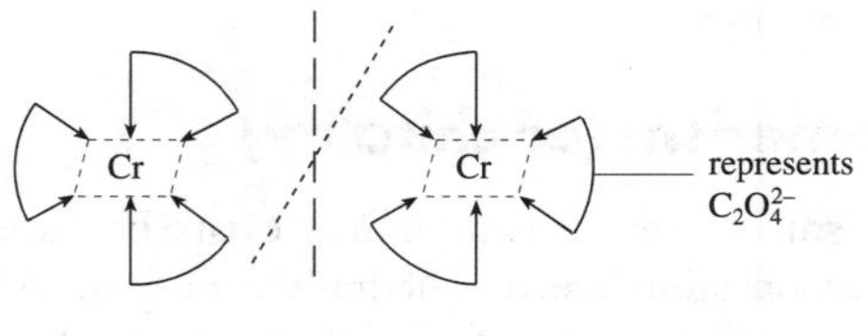

Two mirror image forms

7.8 NAMING ORGANIC COMPOUNDS

Many common organic compounds still retain a common name which is not related to the chemical composition, e.g. propanone is still frequently called acetone.

Since 1948, attempts have been made to systematise the names of all organic compounds.

Aliphatic compounds

The basis of systematic naming of aliphatic compounds is that every name consists of a **root**, one **suffix** and as many **prefixes** as necessary. The root is determined by the number of carbon atoms in the longest continuous chain. In the examples below the longest carbon chain in **A** is 3 and in **B** is 4.

A   **B**

Table 7.2 lists the alkanes from which the roots are derived.

Table 7.2 Alkane roots for aliphatic nomenclature

Number of carbon atoms in chain	Root
1	methane
2	ethane
3	propane
4	butane
5	pentane
6	hexane
7	heptane
8	octane
9	nonane
10	decane

Any organic compound containing a continuous chain of five carbon atoms has a name based upon the alkane pentane. In **B** above, the name is based upon butane because the longest carbon chain contains four carbon atoms.

Having identified the longest carbon chain, it is necessary to identify the various functional groups and name them. Table 7.3 lists some of the common functional groups.

Table 7.3 Common functional groups

Functional group	Structure	Chapter	Name as prefix	Name as suffix
Double bond	$\diagdown$C=C$\diagup$	29	–	ene
Triple bond	—C≡C—	29	–	yne
Halogen (X = Cl, Br, I)	—C—X	30	chloro bromo iodo	chloride bromide iodide
Amine	—C—NH$_2$	35	amino	amine
Hydroxyl	—C—OH	31	hydroxy	ol
Carbonyl	$\diagdown$C=O	32	oxo	al (in aldehydes) one (in ketones)
Carboxyl	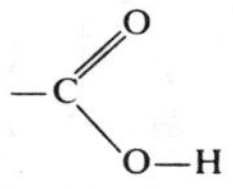 —C(=O)—O—H	33	carboxy	oic acid
Acid chloride	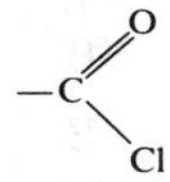 —C(=O)—Cl	34	–	oyl chloride
Amide	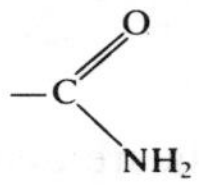 —C(=O)—NH$_2$	34	amido	amide
Acid anhydride	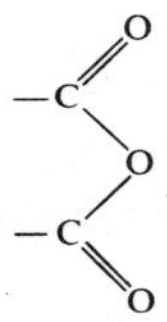 —C(=O)—O—C(=O)—	34	–	oic anhydride
Ester	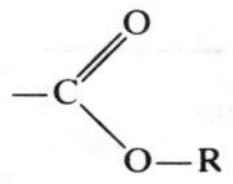 —C(=O)—O—R	34	–	oate
Nitrile	—C≡N	34	cyano	nitrile

The carbon atoms in the longest chain are numbered. Each functional group is then named and added to the root. The following examples illustrate the system.

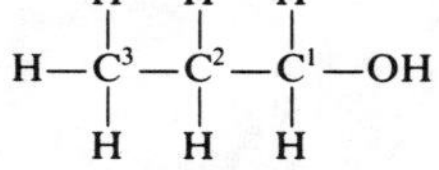

propan-1-ol

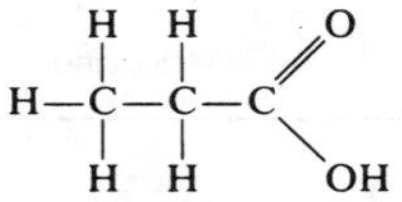

propanoic acid

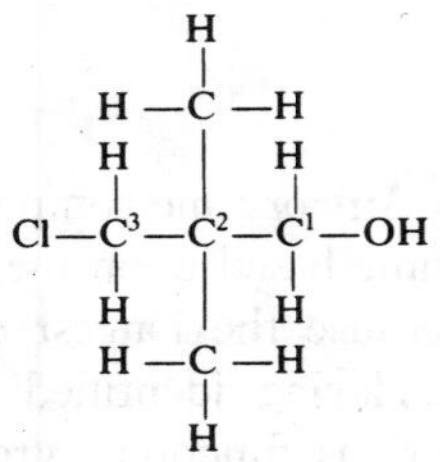

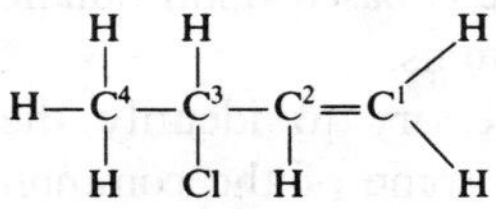

3-chlorobut-1-ene

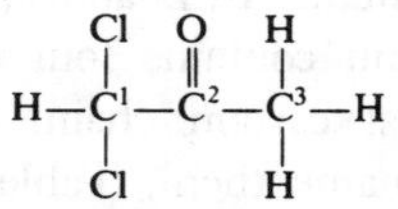

1,1-dichloropropanone

3-chloro-2,2-dimethylpropan-1-ol

NB ❶ The chain is numbered to ensure that the *lowest* possible numbers appear in the name. Propan-1-ol could be named propan-3-ol if the numbering had been from the left-hand end, i.e.

$$H-\overset{\overset{\displaystyle H}{|}}{\underset{\underset{\displaystyle H}{|}}{C^1}}-\overset{\overset{\displaystyle H}{|}}{\underset{\underset{\displaystyle H}{|}}{C^2}}-\overset{\overset{\displaystyle H}{|}}{\underset{\underset{\displaystyle H}{|}}{C^3}}-OH$$

❷ Where a name contains a number of prefixes the prefixes are arranged in alphabetical order. In 3-chloro-2,2-dimethylpropan-1-ol, the chloro prefix is placed before the methyl prefix (ignore di- and tri-).

❸ With practice you should encounter no problems in using the system. Practice will be obtained as you work through Chapters 29–39.

Aromatic compounds

The names of aromatic compounds are derived from benzene or similar aromatic hydrocarbons. The carbon atoms in the benzene ring are numbered from the carbon atom to which the principal group is attached.

benzene-1,3-dicarboxylic acid

1-hydroxy-2-methylbenzene

You may still encounter a system for naming disubstituted benzene rings in which the prefixes *ortho-*, *meta-* and *para-* are used.

ortho (abbreviated *o*-)   *meta-*(*m*-)   *para-*(*p*-)

substituents attached to adjacent carbon atoms

A fuller guide to the naming of organic (and inorganic) compounds will be found in the booklet: *Chemical nomenclature, symbols and terminology* (1979), The Association for Science Education, College Lane, Hatfield, Herts.

Chapter roundup

Organic chemistry forms an important area of study at A level. Why are there so many carbon compounds possible? It is because carbon is good at **catenation**, i.e. carbon forms strong carbon–carbon bonds and therefore forms long chains or rings of carbon atoms. Even silicon, the closest element to carbon in properties, can only form small chains and so the number of compounds possible is limited.

The two amino acids in the chromatography experiment in 7.2 were glutamic acid and valine.

Worked questions and answers

1 Use the following compounds in a discussion of the various types of isomerism which occur in organic chemistry.

(a) C_3H_8O (b) $C_2H_2Cl_2$ (c) $C_3H_6O_3$ (only acids)

Tutorial note

Different types of isomerism are discussed in 7.6–7.7. It is reasonable to expect that the examiner is going to include all types of isomerism in the examples given.

(a) C_3H_8O
Three possible structural isomers

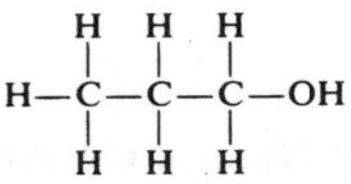

propan-1-ol   (Alcohols)   propan-2-ol 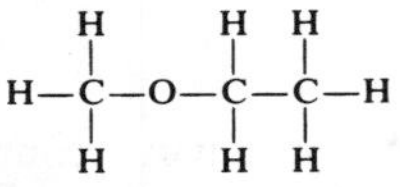   methoxyethane (Ether)

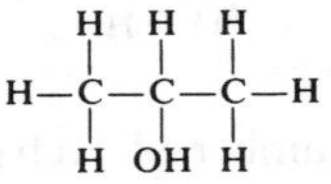

(b) $C_2H_2Cl_2$
Two structural isomers

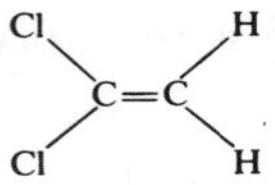

1,1-dichloroethane 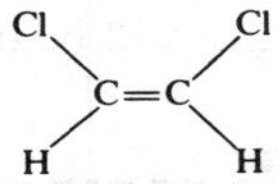   1,2–dichloroethane

1,2-dichloroethene can exist in *cis* and *trans* forms because of restricted rotation.

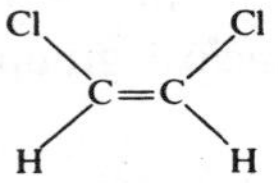

cis 1,2-dichloroethene 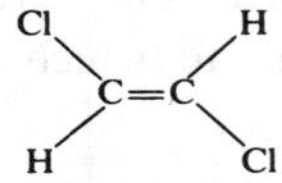   *trans* 1,2-dichloroethene

(c) Since the question restricts possibilities to acids, the compounds will contain a —COOH group

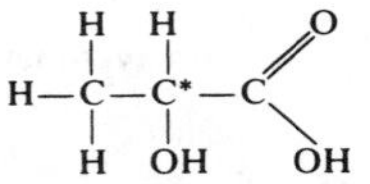

2-hydroxypropanoic acid 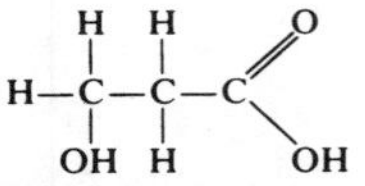   3-hydroxypropanoic acid

2-Hydroxypropanoic acid and 3-hydroxypropanoic acid are structural isomers but 2-hydroxypropanoic acid contains an asymmetric carbon atom (marked *) and therefore exists in two optically active forms.

Many questions rely upon appreciating that an optically active compound contains an asymmetric carbon atom, i.e. a carbon atom attached to four different groups.

For example, an alcohol X with a molecular formula $C_4H_{10}O$ is optically active. Identify X.

The only alcohol with the formula $C_4H_{10}O$ that is optically active is

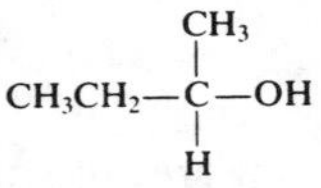

butan-2-ol

2 (a) Write a systematic name for each of the following compounds.

A $CH_3CH(OH)CH_2CH_3$ B $(CH_3)_3CBr$ C $CH_3CH_2CH_2CHO$
D $CH_3CH_2CH{=}CH_2$ E $HO_2CCH_2CH_2CO_2H$

(b) Use the letter A to E to refer to the compounds (if any) which (i) exhibit optical isomerism, (ii) react with concentrated sulphuric acid to form an alkene, (iii) polymerise under appropriate conditions.

(c) Which two compounds, A to E, react to form (i) an ester, (ii) an acetal?

(d) Give the mechanism for the reaction of (i) D with bromine, (ii) B with aqueous alkali.

(ULEAC)

Tutorial note

(a) A butan-2-ol, B 2-bromo-2-methylpropane, C butanal, D but-1-ene
E butanedioic acid.
(b) (i) A (see 7.6). (ii) A (see 31.4, 29.4). (iii) D (see 36.1).
(c) (i) A and E (see 34.4). (ii) Aldehydes react with alcohols in two stages in
the presence of dry hydrogen chloride to form an acetal, e.g.

$$CH_3C=O+2\ H-\underset{\underset{H}{|}}{\overset{\overset{H}{|}}{C}}-\underset{\underset{H}{|}}{\overset{\overset{H}{|}}{C}}-OH \rightleftharpoons CH_3-\underset{\underset{OC_2H_5}{|}}{\overset{\overset{H}{|}}{C}}-OC_2H_5 + H_2O$$

ethanal   ethanol   1,1-diethoxyethane (an acetal)

Compounds reacting to form an acetal are A and C.
(d) (i) See 38.4.
   (ii) See 38.5.

3 The peak of highest mass/charge (m/e) ratio in the mass spectrum of a
hydrocarbon has m/e of value 54.
(a) Write down the molecular formula and the empirical formula of the
hydrocarbon.
(b) Draw two possible, isomeric structural formulae A and B for the hydrocarbon.
(Oxford 1988)

Tutorial note

(a) The molecular formula is C_4H_6 and the empirical formula is C_2H_3. The results from
the mass spectrum are another way of getting the relative molecular mass of the
compound.
(b) There are three possibilities which fit the facts. You can give any two from
$CH_3-C\equiv C-CH_3$, $CH_3CH_2-C\equiv C-H$ and $CH_2=CH-CH=CH_2$.

Question bank

1 For each of the following draw structures of isomers and state the types of
isomerism exhibited.
(a) Dinitrobenzenes of formula $C_6H_4(NO_2)_2$.
(b) Hydroxy acids of formula $C_3H_6O_3$.
(c) Alkenes of formula C_4H_8.

(AEB 1991)

Points

In this question you must draw out the structures in full. In (a) you should show
structural isomerism (look at 7.6 for help), in (b) optical isomerism and in (c) both
structural and geometric isomerism. Again, simple models made with Plasticine
and cocktail sticks may help you with spatial arrangements.

GASES

Units in this chapter

Chapter objectives

From GCSE you will know that matter can exist in three states – solid, liquid and gas. The particles are arranged in different ways and these are summarised along with changes of state in Fig. 8.1.

For A level you will need to make a more detailed study of solids, liquids and gases. This study will be in Chapters 8–10.

Some of the content of this chapter, i.e. the gas laws, may have been covered at the highest levels of GCSE and also in A-level Physics courses.

It is important to remember that gas laws apply to ideal gases rather than real gases. Gases are never strictly ideal and it is necessary to understand why and how these laws can be applied to the nonideal situation.

Work on the gas laws requires measurements of volume, temperature and pressure. Temperature is usually measured on the Kelvin scale.

$$\text{Temperature/K} = \text{Temperature/°C} + 273$$

Pressure is force divided by the area it acts on. It can be measured in different ways.

❶ If the force is measured in newtons (N) and the area in square metres (m^2), then pressure is measured in newtons per square metre ($N\,m^{-2}$). This is the same as $kg\,m^{-1}\,s^{-1}$, and is also sometimes called the pascal (Pa). Normal atmospheric pressure is about 100 kPa and this is called 1 bar.

❷ Millimetres of mercury (mm Hg). This is the height of a column of mercury supported by that pressure. Standard pressure corresponds to 760 mm Hg.

❸ Atmosphere (atm). This is useful for measuring high pressures. Standard pressure is 1 atmosphere.

The important thing to remember in all calculations is to be consistent. If information is given in kPa, work in kPa, if in atm work in atm. The units will not let you down providing you are consistent. Make sure, however, that you always quote the units in your answer.

8.1 GAS LAWS

Changes in temperature and pressure have little effect on the volume of a liquid or a solid, but a considerable effect on the volume of a gas. Various gas laws have been devised following experiments and they are considered individually in 8.2 and 8.3.

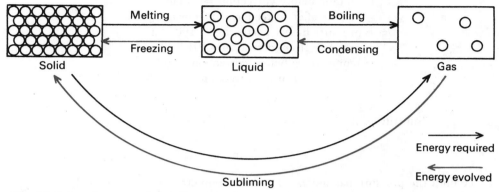

Fig. 8.1 States of matter and their interconversion

8.2 BOYLE'S LAW

The volume of a fixed mass of gas is inversely proportional to the pressure providing the temperature is kept constant.

That is, as the pressure (P) increases, the volume (V) decreases. This is expressed mathematically as

$$P = \text{constant} \times \frac{1}{V}$$

A graph of P against $1/V$ is a straight line passing through the origin.

8.3 CHARLES' LAW

The volume of a fixed mass of gas, at constant pressure, is directly proportional to the absolute temperature.

That is, as the temperature (T) increases and the particles move faster, they move farther apart and the volume (V) increases.

Mathematically, $V = \text{constant} \times T$, where T is temperature in K (The temperature in kelvin (K) is found by adding 273 to the temperature in Celsius, e.g. 20 °C = 20 + 273 = 293 K.)

This law is based upon work done by Gay Lussac. He found that a gas expands or contracts by approximately 1/273 of its volume at 0 °C for every °C that the temperature rises or falls.

273 cm³ of a gas at 0 °C will have a volume of 272 cm³ at −1°C, 263 cm³ at −10 °C, and 293 cm³ at 20 °C. If the gas were cooled to −273 °C (0 K) its volume would theoretically be zero. −273 °C (0 K) is called the **absolute zero** and is the starting point of the Kelvin scale.

Boyle's law and Charles' law can be combined in a general gas equation.

$$\frac{P_1 V_1}{T_1} = \frac{P_2 V_2}{T_2}$$

This equation is useful for correcting the volume of a fixed mass of gas under one set of conditions of temperature and pressure to the volume of gas under a different set of conditions.

If a gas is at 0 °C (273 K) and 101.3 kPa, these conditions are called **standard temperature and pressure** (stp).

Example: A fixed mass of gas has a volume of 76 cm^3 at 27 °C and 100 kPa pressure. Find the volume that the gas would have at stp.

V_1 = volume before correction = 76 cm^3
V_2 = volume after correction – unknown
P_1 = pressure before correction = 100 kPa
P_2 = pressure after correction = 101.3 kPa
T_1 = temperature before correction = 300 K
T_2 = temperature after correction = 273 K

Substitute in $\dfrac{P_1 V_1}{T_1} = \dfrac{P_2 V_2}{T_2}$. $\dfrac{100 \times 76}{300} = \dfrac{101.3 \times V_2}{273}$

$$V_2 = 68.3\,\text{cm}^3$$

Since both the pressure has increased and the temperature has decreased, it is expected that the answer should be less than 76 cm^3.

8.4 IDEAL GAS EQUATION

This equation applies only for ideal gases. The equation is

$$PV = nRT$$

where P = pressure, V = volume, n = number of moles of gas, R = molar gas constant and T = absolute temperature.

The **molar gas constant** R is the same for all gases. It can be calculated using the information that 1 mole of a gas at 0 °C and 101 325 Pa pressure occupies 0.0224 m^3.

Substituting in the equation $PV = nRT$

$$R = \frac{101300 \times 0.0224}{1 \times 273} = 8.31 \text{ J mol}^{-1}\text{K}^{-1}$$

The value for R is given on the examination paper and it is important that the units you use are in agreement with the units for R.

8.5 DALTON'S LAW OF PARTIAL PRESSURES

In a mixture of gases, the total pressure is equal to the sum of the partial pressures of the individual gases.

Mathematically, for three gases A, B and C in a mixture,

$$P = P_A + P_B + P_C$$

where P is the total pressure of the mixture, P_A is the partial pressure of A, P_B is the partial pressure of B and P_C is the partial pressure of C.

The **partial pressure** of a gas is the pressure that the gas would exert if it alone occupied the whole volume of the mixture at the same temperature.

For A the partial pressure

$$P_A = \frac{\text{number of moles of A} \times \text{total pressure}}{\text{total number of moles in mixture}}$$

Example: Calculate the partial pressures of carbon dioxide and oxygen in a mixture of the two gases with total pressure 100 kPa. The mixture consists of 4.4 g of carbon dioxide and 6.4 g of oxygen (Relative atomic masses C = 12, O = 16).

$$\text{Number of moles of carbon dioxide} = \frac{\text{mass of carbon dioxide}}{\text{molar mass of carbon dioxide}}$$

$$= \frac{4.4}{12 + (2 \times 16)} = 0.1 \text{ moles}$$

$$\text{Number of moles of oxygen molecules} = \frac{\text{mass of oxygen}}{\text{relative molecular mass of oxygen}}$$

$$= \frac{6.4}{32} = 0.2 \text{ moles}$$

Total number of moles of carbon dioxide and oxygen = 0.1 + 0.2 = 0.3 mole

$$\text{Partial pressure of carbon dioxide} = \frac{\text{no. of moles } CO_2 \times \text{total pressure}}{\text{total number of moles}}$$

$$= \frac{0.1}{0.3} \times 100 \text{ kPa} = 33.3 \text{ kPa}$$

$$\text{Partial pressure of oxygen} = \frac{\text{no. of moles oxygen} \times \text{total pressure}}{\text{total number of moles}}$$

$$= \frac{0.2}{0.3} \times 100 \text{ kPa} = 66.6 \text{ kPa}$$

(Check that the two answers add up to the total pressure.)

8.6 AVOGADRO'S HYPOTHESIS AND GAY LUSSAC'S LAW

Avogadro's hypothesis states that equal volumes of different gases under the same conditions of temperature and pressure contain the same number of molecules.

Gay Lussac's law states that the volumes of gases reacting and the volumes of products if gaseous bear a simple numerical relation to one another, providing all measurements are made at the same temperature and pressure.

For example, by experiment, it can be found that 10 cm³ of nitrogen gas (1 volume) combines with 30 cm³ of hydrogen gas (3 volumes) to produce 20 cm³ of ammonia gas (2 volumes).

Find the volume of oxygen required and the volume of gaseous product formed when 10 cm³ of methane CH_4 is burnt in sufficient oxygen for complete combustion.

All measurements were made at room temperature and pressure.
First write the equation.

$$CH_4(g) + 2O_2(g) \rightarrow CO_2(g) + 2H_2O(l)$$

methane	+	oxygen	→	carbon	+	water
1 vol		2 vol		dioxide		0
				1 vol		

When 10 cm^3 of methane gas (CH$_4$) burn, 20 cm^3 of oxygen are required. Volume of carbon dioxide produced = 10 cm^3.

NB   When gases are cooled to room temperature, the steam condenses and the volume of water produced is negligible.

8.7 VAPOUR DENSITY

The vapour density of a gas or vapour is given by

$$\text{vapour density} = \frac{\text{mass of a volume of the gas}}{\text{mass of an equal volume of hydrogen}}$$

at the same temperature and pressure.

Since equal volumes of all gases under the same conditions of temperature and pressure contain the same number of molecules (Avogadro's hypothesis)

$$\text{vapour density} = \frac{\text{mass of } n \text{ molecules of gas}}{\text{mass of } n \text{ molecules of hydrogen}}$$

$$= \frac{\text{mass of 1 molecule of gas}}{\text{mass of 1 molecule of hydrogen}}$$

But relative molecular mass $= \dfrac{\text{mass of 1 molecule of gas}}{\text{mass of 1 atom of hydrogen}}$

Since a molecule of hydrogen is composed of 2 atoms,
  relative molecular mass = 2 × vapour density

The relative molecular mass of a gas or volatile liquid can be found by finding the vapour density of the vapour produced.

8.8 RELATIVE MASSES OF MOLECULES

One mole of molecules of any gas can be assumed to occupy 22.4 dm^3 at stp. M$_r$ of a gas can be found if the volume of a known mass of the gas can be found at known temperature and pressure (see question at the end of this chapter).

The experiment can be modified to find M$_r$ of a low boiling point (or volatile) liquid. A gas syringe is sealed with a self-sealing rubber cap placed tightly over the nozzle. The syringe is heated in a syringe oven to a steady temperature above the boiling point of the volatile liquid to be used. The volume of any expanded air in the syringe is taken. A hypodermic syringe containing the liquid is weighed and some of the liquid is injected through the cap into the syringe. The mass of the hypodermic syringe is recorded after injection to enable the mass of liquid used to be found. The liquid is vaporised and the volume of gas in the syringe is recorded. Finally the temperature of the oven and atmospheric pressure should be recorded.

Sample calculation for propanone
Mass of hypodermic syringe containing propanone before injection = 25.246 g
Mass of hypodermic syringe after injection = 25.100 g
Mass of propanone injected = 0.146 g
Reading on gas syringe in oven before injection = 3 cm^3
after injection = 75 cm^3

0.146 g of propanone on vaporisation occupies 72 cm^3 at 87 °C and 101.3 kPa.

Volume at stp $\doteq$ 72 $\times$ $\dfrac{273}{360}$ cm^3 = 54.6 cm^3

0.146 g of propanone would occupy 54.6 cm^3 at stp.

Mass which would occupy 22 400 cm^3 at stp = $\dfrac{0.146 \times 22400}{54.6}$ = 59.90 g

M_r (propanone) = 59.90

8.9 THE KINETIC THEORY OF GASES

In a gas, the particles of the gas are in continual, rapid, random motion. The particles are very widely spaced. The pressure of a gas is the result of continuous collisions between the particles and the walls of the container.

The following assumptions are made for ideal gases.

❶ The particles are in a state of continuous random motion.

❷ The volume of the particles is negligible compared to the total volume of the gas.

❸ The attractive forces between the particles are negligible.

❹ The collisions between particles of the gas are perfectly elastic – no energy is exchanged when the particles collide.

Gases deviate from ideal behaviour as temperature decreases, pressure increases and as they approach their point of liquefaction.

8.10 REAL AND NONIDEAL GASES

The ideal gas does not exist in practice; two of the major assumptions of an ideal gas are that its particles are negligible in volume and that the forces of attraction between the molecules are negligible.

A gas behaves more ideally at low pressure (when the molecules are widely spaced) and high temperatures (when molecules are moving rapidly and the intermolecular forces are not significant); in other words, when the gas is under conditions most like a gas and least like a liquid.

The gas laws and the ideal gas equation relate only to ideal gases. The ideal gas equation is modified in van der Waals equation.

$$(P + \frac{a}{V^2})\,(V - b) = nRT \quad \text{where } a \text{ and } b \text{ are constants for a particular gas.}$$

The term $(P + \dfrac{a}{V^2})$ takes account of the intermolecular forces in the gas and the term $(V - b)$ compensates for the volume of the particles in the gas.

The forces which exist between the molecules in a gas are mostly due to van der Waals forces, dipole–dipole attraction or hydrogen bonding.

8.11 VELOCITIES OF THE MOLECULES IN A GAS

At a particular temperature, the molecules in a gas are moving with a wide range of velocities (and a wide range of kinetic energies). Only a relatively few molecules possess low or high velocities.

Fig. 8.2 shows the distribution of the velocities of molecules in a gas. An increase in temperature causes a shift towards higher velocities and a flattening of the peak indicates that a wider range of velocities exists.

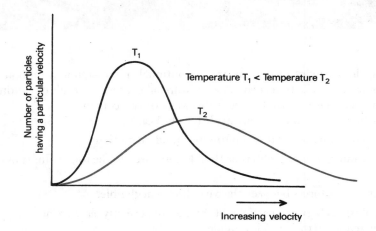

Fig. 8.2 Distribution of the velocities of molecules in a gas

Chapter roundup

Unlike liquids and solids, whose volumes remain largely unchanged by increasing pressure and only slightly changed by increasing temperature, gases change considerably with changes in temperature and pressure. The general gas equation

$$PV = nRT$$

where P = pressure, V = volume, T = temperature in K, R = general gas constant, n = number of moles of gas, is a useful equation for calculations involving gases.

Also at stp (standard temperature and pressure, i.e. 273 K and 1 atm pressure) 1 mol of any gas occupies 22 400 cm³.

Worked questions and answers

1 Define the term partial pressure. 200 cm³ of hydrogen at 100 kPa (1 atm) and 20 °C, and 150 cm³ of helium at 200 kPa (2 atm) and 20 °C were mixed in a total volume of 500 cm³. Calculate the partial pressure at 20 °C of each gas in the mixture.

(AEB)

Tutorial note

Partial pressures: see 8.5.

150 cm³ of helium at 200 kPa and 20 °C. If the pressure of this mass of gas was

reduced to 100 kPa and the temperature maintained at 20 °C, the volume would be 300 cm³ (using Boyle's law).

Mixing 300 cm³ of helium with 200 cm³ of hydrogen and using a vessel of 500 cm³ means that there is no change in pressure. Total pressure = 100 kPa. Now, the number of moles of gas present is proportional to the volume.

$$\text{partial pressure of hydrogen} = \frac{200}{500} \times 100 = 40 \text{ kPa}$$

$$\text{partial pressure of helium} = \frac{300}{500} \times 100 = 60 \text{ kPa}$$

(Check that the sum of partial pressures equals the total pressure.)

2 Use the following information to find the relative molecular mass of a volatile liquid X.

0.20 g of X on vaporisation gave 40 cm³ of vapour measured at 373 K and a pressure of 1 atm (i.e. 10^2 kPa).

The molar gas constant R is 0.0821 litre atm K^{-1} mol^{-1} or 8.31 J K^{-1} mol^{-1}.

Tutorial note

Using $PV = nRT$ where $P = 1$ atm (10^5 Pa), $V = 0.04$ litres (0.0004 m³), $T = 373$ K, $R = 0.0821$ litre atm K^{-1} mol^{-1} (8.31 J K^{-1} mol^{-1}), $n = 0.0013$ moles.

Now, 0.2 g of X ≡ 0.0013 moles

$$\text{Relative molecular mass of X} = \frac{0.2}{0.0013} = 153.8$$

3 (a) Draw a diagram to show the distribution of the velocities of molecules in a gas at a certain temperature.
(b) In what two ways would the graph differ at a higher temperature?
(c) How is the variation in the rate of a gaseous reaction with temperature related to the change in the velocity distribution?

Tutorial note

(a) See Fig. 8.2.
(b) See 8.11.
(c) This is a frequent link between Chapter 8 and Chapter 14. The rate of a gaseous reaction depends upon the number of 'fruitful' collisions between reacting molecules. For a collision to be 'fruitful', the energy possessed by the colliding molecules must be greater than the activation energy. Increasing the temperature causes the molecules to possess greater kinetic energy and more collisions leading to reaction take place.

Question bank

1 (a) The values below show the effect of increasing pressure, P, on the product of pressure and volume, PV, for 1 mole of ammonia gas at 25 °C.

P/atm	1.0	2.0	5.0	9.8	10.0	20.0
PV/atm dm³	24.4	24.2	23.8	23.1	0.2	0.4

(i) Plot these data as a curve of PV against P, labelling and numbering the axes.
(ii) Also plot on the grid PV against P for 1 mole of an ideal gas at 25 °C, given that it occupies a volume of 22.4 dm³ at 1 atm (1.01 × 10^5 Pa) pressure and a temperature of 0 °C (273 K).

(b) Use your knowledge of kinetic-molecular theory and intermolecular forces present in ammonia to account for the shape of the ammonia graph, and to explain what happens when the pressure on ammonia gas is increased at 25 °C.

(WJEC 1990)

Points

This questions revolves around the work of the famous chemist, Andrews. For an ideal gas PV is a constant ($= RT$ for 1 mol of gas). This means that for an ideal gas the graph of PV against P will be a horizontal line.

1 mole of gas at 1 atm pressure and 273 K occupies 22.4 dm^3
and at 298 K occupies $22.4 \times 298/273$ dm^3
(fraction this way up because gases expand when heated)
$= 24.45$ dm^3

Therefore, $PV = 24.45 \times 1 = 24.45$ atm dm^3

Notice that this is also close to the value of PV for ammonia at low pressure.

LIQUIDS

Units in this chapter

Chapter objectives

In Chapter 8 we saw that gases became less ideal as pressure increased and temperature decreased. Increasing pressure moves the particles closer together and decreasing temperature slows the movement of the particles. Then intermolecular forces become significant and the gas starts to liquefy.

In this chapter the important concept is vapour pressure, which concerns the escape of particles from a liquid.

9.1 LIQUEFYING GASES

A gas may be liquefied by cooling the gas or increasing the pressure (within limits discussed below). Andrews (1861) carried out experiments to investigate the effect of changes of temperature and pressure on the volume of carbon dioxide. The results are summarised in Fig. 9.1.

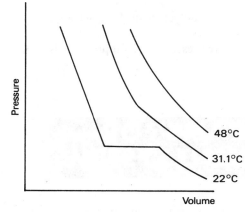

Fig. 9.1 Andrews' isothermals

Each curve represents the variation of the volume of a fixed mass of carbon dioxide with changes of pressure at constant temperature. These curves are called **isothermals.** The isothermal at 48 °C represents the usual behaviour of a gas. The isothermal at 22 °C shows a horizontal portion where the volume changes rapidly for only a small change in pressure. This horizontal portion corresponds to liquefaction of carbon dioxide.

There is only a slight kink in the isothermal at 31.1 °C. At this temperature liquefaction barely occurs and at temperatures higher than this liquefaction cannot be achieved by simply increasing pressure. This temperature is called the **critical temperature** of carbon dioxide. The critical temperature is that temperature above which a gas cannot be liquefied by applying pressure. The minimum pressure required to liquefy a gas at its critical temperature is called the **critical pressure**.

9.2 THE LIQUID STATE

The particles in a liquid are much closer together than the particles in a gas. They are constantly moving and colliding. This is illustrated by **Brownian motion**. Particles of pollen on the surface of water are in a state of constant random motion. This movement of pollen grains can be seen with a microscope and can be explained by the constant bombardment of the pollen grains by water molecules.

The particles are moving with different kinetic energies. Some of the particles possess greater than average kinetic energy and, close to the surface of the liquid, may escape from the liquid into the space above. This process is called **evaporation** and, because the particles have above average kinetic energies, the temperature of the liquid falls during evaporation.

9.3 VAPOUR PRESSURE

Consider a liquid in a closed container with a vacuum in the space above the liquid. The system is kept at constant temperature. Molecules of the liquid escape from the liquid into the space above the liquid. Eventually, an equilibrium (Chapter 15) is produced. Molecules are still leaving the liquid, but molecules are also hitting the surface of the liquid and are re-entering the liquid. In this equilibrium the pressure in the space above the liquid is unchanged and is called the **saturated vapour pressure** of the liquid at that temperature.

At a higher temperature, the molecules in the liquid possess greater kinetic energies and more escape. The gaseous molecules are moving faster and more collide with the surface and re-enter.

An equilibrium is again set up but there are more molecules in the space and, therefore, the vapour pressure is greater.

A liquid exposed to the air boils when the vapour pressure of the liquid equals atmospheric pressure.

9.4 PHASE DIAGRAMS FOR ONE-COMPONENT SYSTEMS

A **phase** is defined as a part of the whole system which is physically distinct from the rest of the system but its composition is the same throughout (i.e. it is homogeneous). A mixture of gases or a solution are examples of a single phase.

Fig. 9.2 shows a phase diagram for water. It is a diagram showing how the physical state of water changes with changes in temperature and pressure.

Referring to Fig. 9.2, TC represents the change of vapour pressure of liquid water with temperature. The line pq represents atmospheric pressure. TC meets pq at X. X is the boiling point of water.

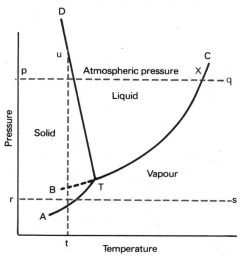

Fig. 9.2 Phase diagram for water

TD represents the equilibrium between solid and liquid, i.e. the change of melting point of ice with change in pressure. As the pressure increases, the melting point of ice decreases but big changes in pressure are required to make a significant change in melting point. For all substances apart from water, antimony and bismuth, the line DT slopes slightly forward (rather than slightly backward) and an increase in pressure produces a slight increase in the melting point.

AT represents the equilibrium between solid and vapour and TB represents the **supercooling** of liquid water.

Point T is called the **triple point** and under this set of conditions ice, water and water vapour can be in equilibrium together. For water, this unique situation exists at 0.0075 °C and 530 Pa pressure.

Point C is called the **critical point**. Above this pressure (22.12×10^3 kPa) and this temperature (647.4 K) a gas cannot be liquefied by decreasing only the temperature or increasing only the pressure.

If a sample of ice is heated at atmospheric pressure, it changes from solid to liquid to vapour (follow dotted line pq). If a sample of ice is heated at a low pressure, the solid ice can turn directly to a vapour. Also under these conditions a vapour can turn directly to a solid (follow dotted line rs). This process is called **sublimation**.

A sample of water vapour maintained at constant temperature undergoes changes of state with increasing pressure. As the pressure increases, the water vapour turns directly to a solid and then, at a higher pressure, the solid melts (follow dotted line tu).

A simple phase diagram has to be modified for substances which can exist in different forms in the same physical state. Sulphur, for example, shows enantiotropy and the phase diagram is shown in Fig. 9.3.

Up to 96 °C, α–sulphur is the stable allotrope of solid sulphur. At the triple point T_1, α–sulphur, β–sulphur and sulphur vapour can exist in equilibrium. T_2 and T_3 are other triple points and T_4 is an unstable triple point for α-sulphur, liquid sulphur and sulphur vapour.

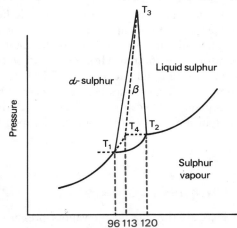

Fig. 9.3 Phase diagram for sulphur

9.5 LOOKING AT BOILING POINTS OF LIQUIDS

For most liquids there is a simple relationship between boiling point and standard molar energy change for evaporation ($\Delta H^{\ominus}_{evaporation}$). For most liquids, when the standard molar energy change for evaporation is plotted against boiling point, the points fall on a straight line (Fig. 9.4).

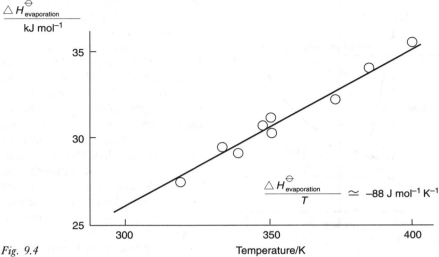

Fig. 9.4

This is expressed in **Trouton's rule**, which states that **the molar enthalpy change of vaporisation of a liquid, at its normal boiling point, divided by its boiling point, in Kelvin, is constant.**

9.6 STEAM DISTILLATION

Steam distillation is a method used to separate an organic compound with a high molar mass from a mixture. It works when the two liquids – organic liquid and water – are immiscible.

If the vapour pressure of the organic liquid is p_o and water p_w at the same temperature, total vapour pressure of the mixture, $p = p_o + p_w$.

This mixture will boil when the total vapour pressure equals atmospheric pressure (say 760 mm Hg). The mixture therefore boils at a lower temperature than either ingredient, i.e. below 100 °C. This method is useful if the organic compound decomposes before its normal boiling point. You should remember, of course, that because p_w is much larger than p_o, the product distilling over will contain more water than organic compound.

Chapter roundup

Here are the data for the vapour pressure of water at different temperatures.

Temperature °C	0	10	20	30	40	50	60	70	80	90	100
Vapour pressure/kPa	0.6	1.2	2.3	4.2	7.4	12.3	20	31	47	70	101

Without plotting these on a graph, which you can do if you wish, you can see that there is a gradual increase in vapour pressure at low temperature but a very rapid increase in vapour pressure close to the boiling point of the liquid. Remember that the vapour pressure becomes equal to the external pressure at the boiling point of the liquid. At high altitudes, where pressure is 80 kPa, the boiling point of water will be about 93 °C.

Worked questions and answers

1 Draw carefully a single diagram showing:
  (a) how the vapour pressure of liquid water varies with temperature,
  (b) how the vapour pressure of ice varies with temperature,
  (c) the effect of pressure on the melting point of ice, and
  (d) the effect of an involatile solute on the vapour pressure of liquid water.
    On your diagram, label the appropriate areas solid, liquid and vapour and indicate the positions of the critical point and the triple point.
    Give two differences between the phase diagram you have drawn for water and the phase diagram for carbon dioxide.

(Oxford and Cambridge)

Tutorial note

The diagram required is Fig. 9.2.
(a) This is the curve CT.
(b) This is the curve AT.
(c) This is DT.
(d) This is not shown on Fig. 9.2 but is shown on Fig. 12.2.
Two differences between the phase diagrams of water and carbon dioxide.

❶ For carbon dioxide the line DT slopes forward rather than backward.

❷ For carbon dioxide the triple point T lies above atmospheric pressure (in fact 5.01 atm, although you would not be expected to remember the value). At 1 atm pressure the solid changes directly from solid to vapour on heating.

Question bank

1 The table below shows the standard molar enthalpy of vaporisation of six liquids which obey Trouton's rule.

Liquid	Boiling point/K	Standard molar enthalpy of vaporisation/kJ mol^{-1}
Oxygen	90	7.9
Chloromethane	250	22.0
Hexane	341	30.0
Benzene	353	31.06
Methylbenzene	384	33.79
Hexadecane	560	49.28

(a) Plot these results on a suitable graph and draw the line.
(b) If the standard molar enthalpy of X is 40 kJ mol^{-1}, what would you expect the boiling point to be?
(c) Methanol has a boiling point of 337 K and a standard molar enthalpy of vaporisation of 34 kJ mol^{-1}. Plot this point and comment on its position.
(d) Suggest, with a reason, two other liquids which might show similar results to methanol.

Points

The graph obtained is similar to Fig. 9.4. You can work out the boiling point of X because it obeys Trouton's rule and it will be on the line. Methanol does not obey Trouton's rule. Other liquids could be water and ethanol. All liquids have hydrogen bonding additional to normal intermolecular forces. The particles find it more difficult to escape from a hydrogen bonded liquid and the boiling point is raised.

SOLIDS

Units in this chapter

Chapter objectives

Solids are crystalline if the particles which make them up, whether they be atoms, ions or molecules, are regularly arranged. The arrangement of particles in a crystal is based on certain geometric shapes and, like Chapter 5 on shapes of molecules, requires a good appreciation of spatial arrangement in three dimensions. Again models can help, either with Plasticine and cocktail sticks, or, perhaps better in this case, with drinking straws and pipecleaners. Important distinctions in this chapter are made between close-packed structures in metals (whether hexagonal close packing or cubic close packing) and body centred cubic, and between the crystal structures in sodium chloride and caesium chloride. Finally, distinctions are made between covalent crystals that are built up of atoms (e.g. diamond) and those that are built up of molecules (ice).

10.1 X-RAY DIFFRACTION

X-ray diffraction is used to determine the arrangements of particles in a solid. The wavelength of X-rays is approximately the same as the distance between the particles in the lattice (10^{-10}m).

X-rays are produced when cathode rays fall upon metals. A beam of X-rays (of one wavelength) strikes a crystal and the X-rays are diffracted by the crystal and are detected by a photographic plate.

If a beam of X-rays strikes a crystal (Fig. 10.1) with the waves of the X-rays in phase, the reflected rays will only remain in phase if the difference in distance travelled is a whole number of wavelengths.

If the X-rays are to remain in phase, then

extra distance travelled = CB + BD and CB + BD = $n\lambda$

where n is an integer and λ is the wavelength of the X-rays.

If the angle between the crystal face and the incident X-ray is θ, then angles CAB and BAD equal θ. By trigonometry, CB = AB sin θ and BD = AB sin θ.

The distance AB is the distance between the first and second layers of particles in the crystal = d

$$\therefore 2d \sin \theta = n\lambda$$

This equation is called the **Bragg equation**.

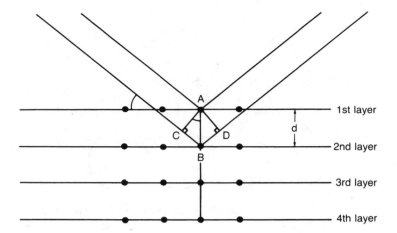

Fig. 10.1 Beam of X-rays striking a crystal

In a particular experiment, using one face of a crystal, the wavelength (λ) and the distance between the layers (d) are fixed. For a given angle θ, a series of spots will appear on the photographic plate corresponding to $n = 1, 2, 3$, etc. From these results d can be calculated.

X-ray diffraction is used for single crystals or for a fine powder. Electron diffraction can also be used to determine the structure of a solid. Electrons, however, have a poorer penetrating power than X-rays.

10.2 METAL CRYSTAL STRUCTURES

A metal consists of a close-packed, regular arrangement of positive ions, which are surrounded by a 'sea' of delocalised electrons that bind the ions together. The ions in a close-packed layer are arranged in a regular hexagon.

The close-packed layers of ions can be stacked in two ways – both being equally likely. Some metals have one type of stacking, some metals have the other type and some metals can exist in either depending upon the conditions. The two ways of stacking these layers are:

❶ ABAB **or hexagonal close packing** (Fig. 10.2(a)). The ions in the third layer are immediately above ions in the first layer. The stacking of the layers will continue ABAB... Magnesium and zinc are examples of metals with this structure.

❷ ABC or **cubic close packing** (sometimes called face centred cubic) (Fig. 10.2(b)). The ions in the third layer are not immediately above ions in the first layer. The stacking of the layers will continue ABCABC... Aluminium and copper are examples of metals with this structure.

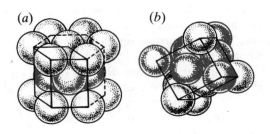

Fig. 10.2 Hexagonal close packing (a) and cubic close packing (b)

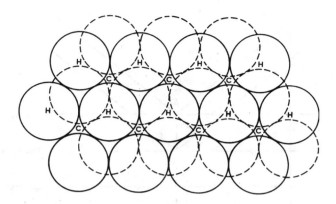

Fig. 10.3 Difference between hexagonal close packing and cubic close packing

The difference between these two structures may be seen clearly in Fig. 10.3. The ions in the first layer are shown in continuous lines. The ions in the second layer are shown in dotted lines. There are two sets of hollows in the second layer in which ions in the third layer can rest. These are labelled H or C. Ions cannot rest in both H and C. If they rest in hollows H, hexagonal close packing is produced but if they rest in hollows C, cubic close packing results.

In both hexagonal close packing and cubic close packing any ion in the structure has twelve other ions touching it – six in the same layer, three in the layer above and three in the layer below. The number of ions in contact with any ion in the structure is called the **coordination number**. The coordination number in both close-packed structures is twelve. In both structures about 75% of the available space is filled by the ions.

Alkali metals (Chapter 22) and some other metals have a **body centred cubic** structure (Fig. 10.4). In this structure the ions are not as closely packed (about 32% of the available space is unfilled). This explains the low density of alkali metals. The coordination number in this structure is eight.

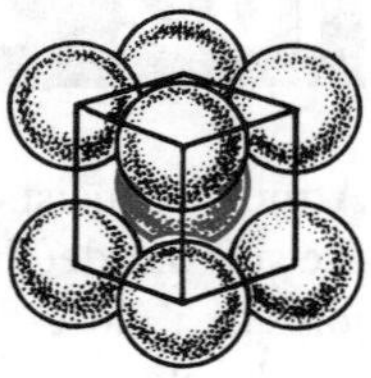

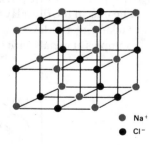

Fig. 10.4 Body centred cubic structure

10.3 IONIC CRYSTALS

An ionic crystal is a regular arrangement of positive and negative ions. The ions are held together by strong electrostatic forces. The sodium chloride lattice is shown in Fig. 10.5. The sodium chloride lattice consists of a face centred cube of sodium ions and an interpenetrating face centred cube of chloride ions.

In simple terms, each sodium ion in the lattice is surrounded by six chloride ions and each chloride ion by six sodium ions. The coordination is called 6:6.

Although sodium chloride NaCl and caesium chloride CsCl have similar formulae they have different crystal structures. In the caesium chloride structure (Fig. 10.6), the coordination is 8:8. Eight chloride ions surround each caesium and eight caesium ions surround each chloride ion.

The caesium ion is much larger than the sodium ion (ionic radii Cs^+ 0.167 nm and Na^+ 0.098 nm). In sodium chloride, six chloride ions (ionic radius 0.181

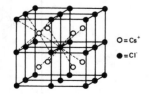

● Na^+
● Cl^-

Fig. 10.5 Structure of sodium chloride

O = Cs^+
● = Cl^-

Fig. 10.6 Structure of caesium chloride

nm) surround the sodium ion but, in caesium chloride, it is possible to pack eight chloride ions around each caesium ion.

Other substances with stoichiometry XY (e.g. MgO) can have a similar structure to sodium chloride if the ratio of the ionic radii is similar to the ratio in sodium chloride.

10.4 COVALENT CRYSTALS

Crystals containing covalent bonding can be subdivided into:

❶ Giant covalent structures
In a giant covalent structure the atoms are bonded together to give a three-dimensional (or two-dimensional) structure with a high melting point.

Diamond and graphite are two of the allotropic forms of carbon (see 24.3). In diamond, all of the carbon atoms are sp^3 hybridised (see 5.2) and joined by four covalent bonds to four other atoms pointing towards the corners of a regular tetrahedron. All of the C–C bond lengths are the same. The bonds are very strong.

Graphite is a layer structure. The carbon atoms in each layer are sp^2 hybridised and the bonds between carbon atoms in the layer are strong. The forces between the layers are weak van der Waals forces and the layers are able to slide over one another.

❷ Molecular crystals
In a molecular crystal there are discrete molecules containing *strong* covalent bonds held together by *weak* van der Waals forces or hydrogen bonding. A substance which exists as molecular crystals melts at a low temperature because the weak forces are easily overcome. Examples are iodine and ice.

10.5 ISOTROPY AND ANISOTROPY

An isotropic substance is one whose properties are the same in whichever direction they are measured. For example, the refractive index (a measure of the speed of light through a crystal) of a sodium chloride crystal is the same whichever direction light passes through the crystal. Isotropy occurs when spherical ions such as Na^+ and Cl^- are arranged in a spherically symmetrical arrangement (Fig. 10.5). All substances that crystallise in a cubic system are isotropic. Other properties that could be considered include thermal conductivity and electrical conductivity.

An anisotropic substance is one whose properties depend upon the direction in which they are measured. For example, the refractive index of calcite (a natural form of calcium carbonate) can vary between 1.49 and 1.66 depending upon the direction that light passes through the crystal. Anisotropic substances contain nonspherical ions, e.g. CO_3^{2-}, or a nonspherically symmetric arrangement.

Whether a crystal is isotropic or anisotropic can be found easily by illuminating a crystal and viewing it through crossed polaroids. Isotropic substances appear dark or faintly illuminated whatever their orientation. Anisotropic substances appear dark or faintly illuminated in some orientations and brightly illuminated in others.

Chapter roundup

The particular arrangement of particles in an ionic crystal is determined by the numbers of each ion and the ratio of the ionic radii. The coordination number of an ion in an ionic crystal is the number of oppositely charged ions at equal distance from the ion.

Generally, the crystal structure in an ionic crystal is related to the radius ratio:

$\dfrac{\text{Small ion radius}}{\text{Large ion radius}}$	<0.41	>0.41 and <0.73	>0.73
Coordination number	4	6	8

In a metal structure, since all of the ions have an equal radius, the radius ratio is 1.0, and the coordination number is 8 (in a body centred cubic structure) or 12 (in a close-packed structure).

Worked questions and answers

1 Representations of the structures of sodium metal, diamond, caesium chloride and carbon dioxide are included in the diagrams A–E.

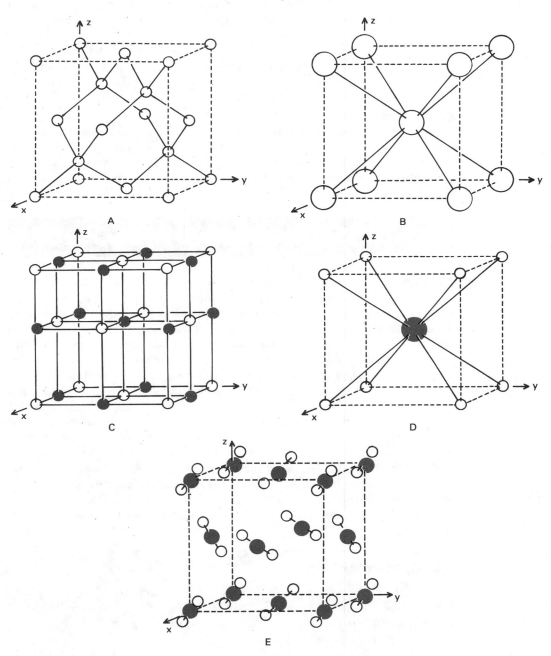

(a) (i) Identify the caesium chloride structure by giving the appropriate letter.
   (ii) Give the coordination numbers of Cs^+ and Cl^-.
(b) (i) Name the hardest substance.
   (ii) Identify the appropriate structure.
   (iii) Give reasons for its hardness.
(c) (i) Name the most volatile substance.
   (ii) Identify its structure.
   (iii) Explain its volatility.
(d) One of the substances having a structure in which the coordination is 6:6 shatters when tapped with a hammer.
   (i) Identify the structure.
   (ii) Explain why the substance shatters.
(e) Only one substance has a high electrical conductance.
   (i) Name it and identify its structure.
   (ii) Explain this property.

(WJEC)

Tutorial note

Three of these five substances are compounds and contain two different types of atom.

   C, D and E must be caesium chloride, carbon dioxide and sodium chloride. A and B are elements – diamond and sodium metal.

(a) (i) D (ii) $Cs^+ = 8$, $Cl^- = 8$.
(b) (i) The hardest substance is diamond. In the diamond structure the four covalent bonds from each carbon atom are tetrahedral.
   (ii) A
   (iii) All bonds in diamond are equally strong C—C bonds. The structure cannot be broken up without breaking these bonds.
(c) (i) The most volatile (or easily vaporised) substance is carbon dioxide.
   (ii) E
   (iii) The bonds within each carbon dioxide molecule are strong covalent bonds but the forces between the molecules are very weak. At room temperature solid carbon dioxide turns directly to a gas.
(d) (i) C
   (ii) There are four planes within the crystal along which the crystal can be cleaved.
(e) (i) Sodium – B
   (ii) See 10.2.

Question bank

1 Describe and explain how X-rays have been used to determine the arrangement of atoms and ions in a crystal.
   What do you understand by the terms hexagonal close packing, cubic close packing (face centred cubic close packing) and body centred cubic packing as they apply to the structures of metals? Illustrate your answers with diagrams and give examples where possible.

(ULEAC)

Points

See Units 10.1 and 10.2.

SOLUTIONS

Units in this chapter

11.1 *Solutions of gases in liquids*
11.2 *Solutions of liquids in liquids*
11.3 *Deviations from Raoult's law*

Chapter objectives

Having studied the situation where only one substance exists as solid, liquid or gas (Chapters 8–10), we are now going to consider mixtures of two substances which mix together to form a solution. A solution is a single phase but there are two or more components.

At GCSE level you will have studied solutions of a solid solute in a solvent, e.g. sodium chloride dissolved in water. Now we are going to study where a gas or gases dissolve in water and the more complicated situation where two liquids mix together to form a single phase. Here, rather like with gases, the result depends on whether the components interact with one another.

11.1 SOLUTIONS OF GASES IN LIQUIDS

Most gases dissolve in a solvent with the evolution of heat, i.e. the process is **exothermic**. In accordance with Le Chatelier's principle (see 15.5), the solubility is decreased by increasing temperature.

The most important factor affecting the solubility of a gas in a solvent is expressed by **Henry's law**: the mass of gas dissolved by a given volume of solvent, to give a saturated solution, is directly proportional to the pressure of the gas, providing the temperature remains constant and there is no reaction between the gas and the solvent.

Gases such as ammonia, hydrogen chloride and carbon dioxide react when they are dissolved in water. The law does not apply to these gases but applies satisfactorily for gases such as oxygen, hydrogen, helium, etc.

The solubility of a gas in a liquid is usually expressed as an **absorption coefficient**. This is defined as the number of cm^3 of gas at stp which saturate 1 cm^3 of the liquid at a given temperature and 1 atm (101.3 kPa).

If a mixture of gases is in equilibrium with a solvent (e.g. air with water), each gas dissolves according to its own partial pressure (see 8.5).

11.2 SOLUTIONS OF LIQUIDS IN LIQUIDS

In this section it is useful to consider the mixing of two completely miscible ideal liquids and then to consider the effects of deviations from ideality. Ideal liquids show no heat or volume change when they are mixed and obey Raoult's law over the whole composition range.

Raoult's law states that the vapour pressure of a constituent of an ideal solution is equal to the vapour pressure exerted by the pure constituent at that temperature multiplied by the mole fraction of that constituent.

Mole fraction is a convenient way of expressing the composition of each component in a mixture. The mole fraction of A in a mixture of A and B is

$$x_A = \frac{n_A}{n_A + n_B}$$

The mole fraction of B is

$$x_B = \frac{n_B}{n_A + n_B}$$

The sum of the mole fractions of the components in the mixture equals one.

$$x_A + x_B = 1$$

Raoult's law can be expressed as

$$P_A = x_A P_A^\circ$$

where P_A is the vapour pressure of A over the liquid

x_A is the mole fraction of A

P_A° is the vapour pressure of A over pure A at that temperature.

Similarly

$$P_B = x_B P_B^\circ$$

Total pressure of vapour over the liquid $P = P_A + P_B$. This is expressed in the graph in Fig. 11.1.

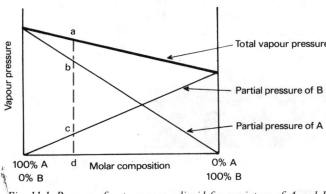

Fig. 11.1 Pressure of vapour over a liquid for a mixture of A and B

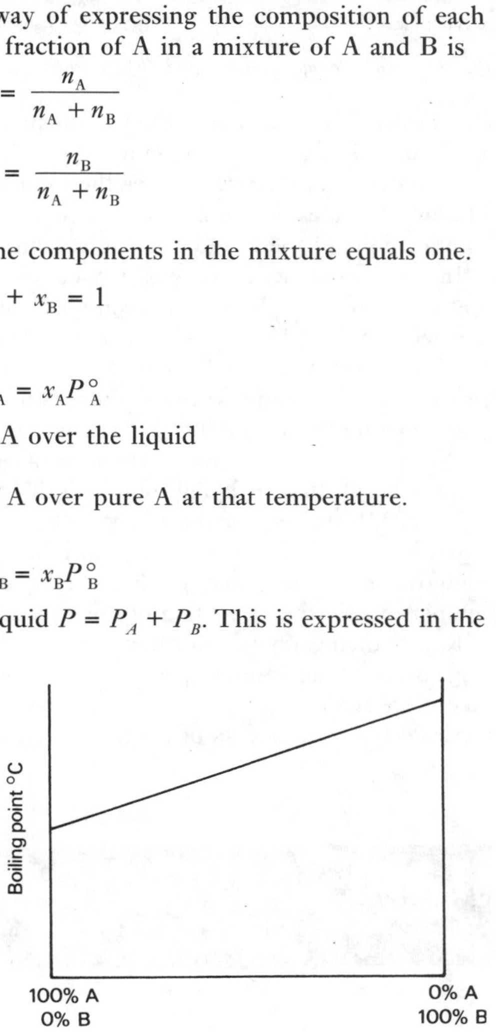

Fig. 11.2 Boiling point/composition graph for a mixture of A and B

The vertical dotted line in Fig. 11.1 represents a solution of composition 20% B and 80% A. The total vapour pressure of this solution, ad, is equal to the sum of the partial pressures due to A (db) and to B (cd).

Fig. 11.2 shows the boiling point/composition graph for the same mixture of A and B. A liquid which has a high vapour pressure will have a low boiling point and vice versa.

Some pairs of liquids obey Raoult's law closely, e.g. benzene and methylbenzene or hexane and heptane. The two components in each mixture are very similar

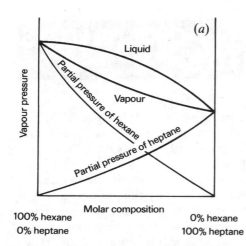
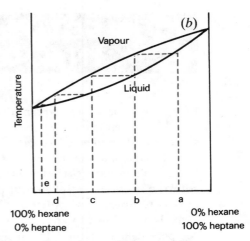

Fig. 11.3 (a) Vapour pressure and (b) boiling point diagrams for a mixture of hexane and heptane

chemically. Fig. 11.3 shows the vapour pressure and boiling point diagrams for a mixture of hexane and heptane.

The biggest difference between the vapour pressure/composition curve in Fig. 11.3 and the ideal curve in Fig. 11.1 is the existence of separate curves for the compositions of the liquid and the vapour.

In the temperature/composition curves (Fig. 11.3(*b*)), the variation of the boiling point of the liquid with composition of the liquid is shown by the curve labelled 'liquid'. The 'vapour' curve shows the composition of the vapour in equilibrium with a liquid mixture at its boiling point. The composition of the vapour in equilibrium with a liquid of any composition is always richer in the more volatile (lower boiling point) component.

When a mixture of hexane and heptane of composition a (in Fig. 11.3(*b*)) is heated, the vapour which is in equilibrium with this mixture has the composition b (richer in hexane). If this vapour is condensed the liquid still has the composition b. If this liquid is reheated the liquid of composition b is in equilibrium with the vapour of composition c. Each step produces a liquid richer in the lower boiling point component. Further repetition of this process will eventually give pure hexane.

Rather than carry this out in a series of steps, it is usual to carry it out in one stage using a **fractionating column**. A series of condensations and evaporations take place as the vapour moves up the column. Fractional distillation is used to separate the components of a pair of miscible liquids that are near ideal.

11.3 DEVIATIONS FROM RAOULT'S LAW

Deviations from the ideal behaviour can be of two types – positive and negative.

Negative deviations

If trichloromethane and ethoxyethane are mixed together the temperature rises. This is because extra intermolecular forces exist in the mixture which do not exist in the pure liquids.

These extra, weak hydrogen bonds **reduce** the vapour pressure of the mixture of liquids and **increase** the boiling point. On the vapour pressure/composition graph there is a minimum, and on the temperature/composition graph a maximum (Fig.11.4).

A mixture of ethoxyethane and trichloromethane of composition X distils over without change of composition and with boiling point T. A mixture of this type is called an **azeotropic** or **constant boiling point** mixture.

If a mixture of any other composition is heated, one of the pure components ethoxyethane or trichloromethane distils off until the composition of the mixture becomes the same as the azeotropic mixture. Then the pure azeotropic mixture distils off. Whether ethoxyethane or trichloromethane distils off first depends upon which one is in excess. Other examples of pairs of liquids behaving in this way include: hydrochloric acid and water, and sulphuric acid and water.

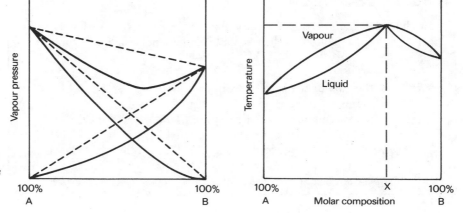

Fig. 11.4 Vapour pressure/ composition and temperature/ composition graphs (minimum vapour pressure)

Positive deviations

When trichloromethane and ethanol are mixed together the temperature falls. There are strong forces of hydrogen bonding which exist in pure ethanol (Fig. 11.5(*a*)).

(a) *(b)*

Fig. 11.5

Hydrogen bonds form between the molecules on mixing the two liquids (Fig. 11.5(*b*)) but these are weaker than those in pure ethanol. (The important factor is how the bonding between the molecules (intermolecular bonding) in the mixture compares with the intermolecular bonding in the original, separate components.) The tendency for molecules to escape therefore increases. This **increases** the vapour pressure and **reduces** the boiling point – there is a minimum on the temperature/composition graph (Fig. 11.6).

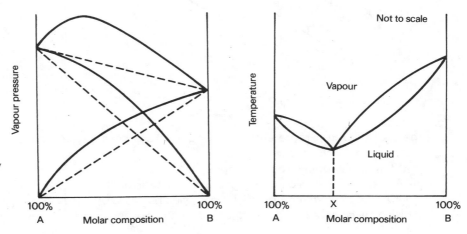

Fig. 11.6 Vapour pressure/ composition and temperature/ composition graphs (maximum vapour pressure)

The mixture of composition X distils over without change of composition. Fractional distillation of a mixture will produce the azeotropic mixture X and this will distil over until one of the components is used up. The remaining component distils over pure.

A mixture of ethanol and water behaves in this way. When a mixture of 10% ethanol and 90% water is heated, the azeotropic mixture containing 95.6% ethanol and 4.4% water distils over until all the ethanol has been used up. Then pure water distils over. It is impossible to obtain pure ethanol by distilling solutions of ethanol in water.

Chapter roundup

If two liquids are similar, e.g. benzene and methylbenzene, they are likely to mix together to form a solution and behave ideally. Then they will obey Raoult's law

$$P_A = x_A P_A^\circ$$

where P_A = the vapour pressure of A in the mixture
$\quad x_A$ = the mole fraction of A in the mixture
$\quad P_A^\circ$ = the vapour pressure of the pure liquid A.

If the two liquids interact so that heat is generated, it can be assumed that extra bonds have been formed between the molecules. These will reduce the vapour pressure of the solution and cause it to be nonideal. Similarly, if two liquids mix and the temperature falls the opposite is true, and bonds have been broken.

Worked questions and answers

---

1 (a) Heptane and octane form an ideal solution.

(i) Give a mathematical expression for Raoult's vapour pressure law for a solution of two liquids, A and B, explaining the terms used.

(ii) Under what circumstances will a mixture of two liquids behave as an ideal solution?

(iii) Calculate the vapour pressure of a solution containing 50 g heptane (C_7H_{16}) and 38 g octane (C_8H_{18}) at 20 °C. ($A_r(H) = 1$, $A_r(C) = 12$. The vapour pressure of heptane at 20 °C = 473.2 Pa. The vapour pressure of octane at 20 °C = 139.8 Pa.)

(b)

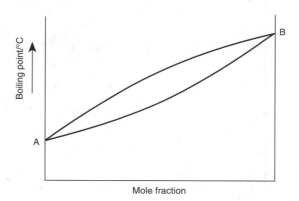

The above diagram represents the boiling point composition diagram for a solution of heptane and octane.

(i) What do the points A and B represent?

(ii) An equimolar solution of heptane and octane is distilled. Mark on the diagram the temperature T at which the solution begins to boil and the point C giving the composition of the vapour given off when the solution begins to boil.

(iii) Explain briefly how the solution can be separated into pure heptane and pure octane.

(AEB)

Tutorial note

(a) (i) Raoult's law can be expressed as follows:

$P_A = x_A P_A^\circ$ where P_A represents the vapour pressure of A over the solution, P_A° represents the vapour pressure of A over pure A at the same temperature and x_A represents the mole fraction of A in the solution.

$$x_A = \frac{n_A}{n_A + n_B}$$
n_A – number of moles of A
n_B – number of moles of B

Similarly $P_B = x_B P_B^\circ$ and total pressure $P = P_A + P_B$

(ii) A mixture of two liquids is ideal if the forces between the molecules in the separate liquids are similar in strength and nature to the forces which exist in the mixture of liquids.

(iii) Relative molecular mass of heptane = $(7 \times 12) + (16 \times 1) = 100$

$$\text{Number of moles of heptane} = \frac{50}{100} = 0.5$$

Relative molecular mass of octane = $(8 \times 12) + (18 \times 1) = 114$

$$\text{Number of moles of octane} = \frac{38}{114} = 0.33$$

Total number of moles = $n_A + n_B = 0.83$

$$\text{Mole fraction of A, } x_A = \frac{0.5}{0.83} = 0.602$$

$$\text{Mole fraction of B, } x_B = \frac{0.33}{0.83} = 0.398$$

(Check $x_A + x_B = 1$)

Vapour pressure of A above solution = $x_A P_A^\circ = 0.602 \times 473.2 = 284.9$ Pa
Vapour pressure of B above solution = $x_B P_B^\circ = 0.398 \times 139.8 = 55.6$ Pa
Total pressure above the solution = $284.6 + 55.6 = 340.5$ Pa.

(b) (i) A represents the boiling point of A, and B the boiling point of B.

(ii)

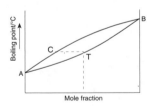

(iii) A series of evaporations and condensations will produce pure A. This can be achieved in a fractional distillation column.

Question bank

1 Ethanol (boiling point 78.5 °C) and water form a constant boiling point mixture having a boiling point of 78.2 °C and a composition of 95.6% ethanol.
  (a) Define the term constant boiling point mixture.
  (b) Sketch, and label fully, the boiling point/composition diagram for ethanol and water.

(c) An ethanol/water mixture shows positive deviations from Raoult's law. Explain and account for this and state the law.

(d) What intermolecular change takes place when ethanol is added to water.

(e) State qualitatively the result of distilling (i) a mixture containing 75% ethanol and (ii) a mixture containing 97.5% ethanol.

(f) State, with reasons, which one of the following pairs of substances most closely obeys Raoult's law.

(i) $C_2H_5NH_2$ and $C_6H_5NH_2$

(ii) CH_3COCH_3 and $CH_3COC_2H_5$

(iii) C_6H_6 and $C_6H_5CH_3$

Points

(a) A constant boiling point mixture is a mixture of liquids which boils at a constant temperature and without change in composition.

(b) See Fig. 11.6.

(c) See 11.3.

(d) See 11.3.

(e) (i) The azeotropic mixture distils over until all the ethanol has gone. Then water distils over. (ii) The azeotropic mixture distils over unchanged.

(f) (iii) The forces between molecules in C_6H_6 and between molecules in $C_6H_5CH_3$ are similar and also similar to forces between molecules of C_6H_6 and $C_6H_5CH_3$ in the mixture.

12

COLLIGATIVE PROPERTIES

Units in this chapter

Chapter objectives

There are many methods used for determining relative molecular masses. These include the mass spectrometer, using vapour densities for volatile liquids, etc. In this chapter we are going to look at methods which are suitable for nonionised solutes, i.e. solutes which dissolve in a solvent and do not dissociate. As we will see, there are four closely related methods using colligative properties. This chapter is closely linked with work on ionisation (Chapter 15).

12.1 COLLIGATIVE PROPERTIES

When a nonvolatile solute is added to a solvent, there are changes in certain colligative properties. A **colligative property** is a property which depends upon the number of particles in a given volume of solvent and not on the nature of the particles. Colligative property measurements are used to determine the relative molecular masses of dissolved solutes.

The four colligative properties are:

1. lowering of vapour pressure;

2. elevation of boiling point;

3. depression of freezing point; and

4. osmotic pressure.

Each of these four properties will be considered separately. It is important to remember that the determination of relative molecular masses can be carried out only if **nonelectrolytes** are used in **dilute** solution.

12.2 LOWERING OF VAPOUR PRESSURE

If a nonvolatile solute, e.g. urea, is added to water, there is a lowering of vapour pressure of the solution.

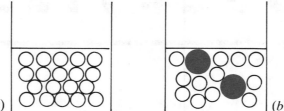

Fig. 12.1 Vapour pressure of solutions   (a)   (b)

In Fig. 12.1(*a*), all of the pure solvent molecules at the surface can escape into the vapour if they possess sufficient energy. In the dilute solution (*b*) the solid circles represent solute molecules which are involatile; hence, there is a reduced number of molecules at that temperature which can escape into the vapour and, therefore, a lowering of the vapour pressure.

There is a relationship between the lowering of the vapour pressure and the concentration of the solution. It is given by Raoult's law (see 11.2).

Raoult's law states that the relative lowering of vapour pressure is equal to the mole fraction of the solute.

$$\frac{P^{\circ}-P}{P^{\circ}} = \frac{n}{N+n}$$

where P° represents the vapour pressure of the pure solvent, P represents the vapour pressure of the solution, n is the number of moles of solute and N is the number of moles of solvent.

If the masses of solvent and solute are W and w respectively and the molar masses of solvent and solute are M and m, the equation becomes:

$$\frac{P^{\circ}-P}{P^{\circ}} = \frac{\dfrac{w}{m}}{\dfrac{w}{m}+\dfrac{W}{M}}$$

For very dilute solutions, the number of moles of solute is small and the above expression approximates to:

$$\frac{P^{\circ}-P}{P^{\circ}} = \frac{n}{N}$$

One problem that a candidate has is to decide whether to use the approximation or work out the answer in full. The best advice is to work out the answer without using the approximation. With a calculator it does not take much longer. Use the approximate expression if you have insufficient time or if the question asks for an approximate answer.

Raoult's law applies only to dilute solutions.

Example: 10 g of a nonvolatile solute X were dissolved in 90 g of water. The vapour pressure of this solution was lowered to 742 mm Hg. The vapour pressure of water at this temperature was 750 mm Hg. Calculate the relative molecular mass of solute X.

Substitute in the above equation, knowing that the relative molecular mass of water is 18.

$$\frac{750-742}{750} = \frac{10/M}{10/M + 90/18} \quad \therefore M = 185.5$$

(If you had used the approximation, you would have obtained a value of 187.5.)

12.3 ELEVATION OF BOILING POINT

Fig. 12.2 shows part of Fig. 9.2. The blue curve represents the vapour pressure of the dilute solution and the solid black line the vapour pressure of the pure solvent. The vapour pressure of the solution is less than the vapour pressure of the pure solvent at all temperatures. In consequence, the vapour pressure of the dilute solution does not reach atmospheric pressure until a higher temperature.

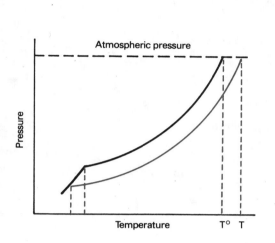

Fig. 12.2 Elevation of boiling point

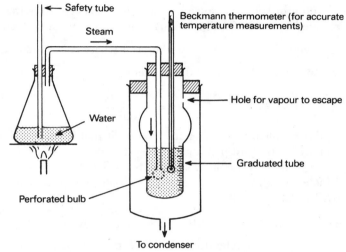

Fig. 12.3 Apparatus to determine elevation of boiling point

For dilute solutions, the elevation of boiling point ($T - T°$) is proportional to the lowering of the vapour pressure.

$$\Delta T \propto P° - P$$
$$\Delta T = k(P° - P) \qquad (1)$$

Raoult's law for very dilute solutions is:

$$\frac{P° - P}{P°} = \frac{n}{N} (P° - P) = \cdot \frac{P° n}{N}$$

Substituting in equation (1)

$$\Delta T = kP° \frac{n}{N}$$

The vapour pressure of a solvent is constant at a particular temperature. Therefore $kP°$ is a constant.

$$\text{Now, } n = \frac{w}{m} \text{ and } N = \frac{W}{M}$$

$$\Delta T = k' \frac{wM}{mW}$$

If a fixed mass of 1000 g of solvent is taken, the ratio $\frac{M}{W}$ is a constant.

$$\Delta T = \frac{Kw}{m}$$

where K is called the boiling point (or ebullioscopic) constant
w is the mass of solute
m is the **relative molecular mass** of the solute.

119

The boiling point constant is the elevation of the boiling point which would occur if one mole of a nonionising and nonvolatile solute was dissolved in 1000 g of solvent.

The experimental determination of the relative molecular mass of urea in solution in water can be carried out by elevation of boiling point measurements. Using the apparatus in Fig. 12.3, steam is passed through the water in the graduated tube until the water starts to boil. The temperature of the boiling water is recorded.

A weighed amount of solute is dissolved in the water in the graduated tube and steam is again passed until the solution boils. The temperature of the solution and the final volume of the solution are recorded. Heating the solution with steam prevents superheating.

Example: Calculate the relative molecular mass of a nonvolatile solute from the following results.

1.00 g of solute dissolved in 40 g of benzene causes the boiling point to be elevated by 0.20 °C. The boiling point constant for benzene is 2.7 °C kg^{-1}.

The equation $\Delta T = K\dfrac{w}{m}$ can be used where $\Delta T = 0.20$ °C, $K = 2.7$ °C kg^{-1}, w = mass of solute in 1000 g benzene = 25 g

$$m = \frac{2.7 \times 25}{0.2} = 337.5$$

The problem with using an equation is that if you get the equation incorrect you are unlikely to pick up any marks.

An alternative method, starting from first principles, is:
1 mole (i.e. m g) of solute dissolved in 1000 g of solvent elevates the boiling point by 2.7 °C.

1 g of solute dissolved in 1000 g of solvent elevates the boiling point by $\dfrac{2.7\,°C}{m}$

(elevation of boiling point $\propto$ concentration)

1 g of solute dissolved in 40 g of solvent elevates the boiling point by $\dfrac{2.7}{m} \times \dfrac{1000}{40}$

(This solution is more concentrated and therefore elevation of the boiling point is greater.)

$$\frac{2.7}{m} \times \frac{1000}{40} = 0.2$$

$$m = 337.5$$

12.4 DEPRESSION OF FREEZING POINT

A dilute solution freezes at a slightly lower temperature than the pure solvent. This small difference in temperature is called the **depression of freezing point**.

For dilute solutions, the depression of freezing point is proportional to the lowering of vapour pressure. The equation

$$\Delta T = K\frac{w}{m}$$

applies but in this case K is called the **freezing point** (or cryoscopic) **constant**. It is the depression of freezing point which would occur if one mole of any nonionising and nonvolatile solute was dissolved in 1000 g of solvent. The depression of freezing point can be found using the apparatus in Fig 12.4.

A known mass of the solvent is put into the centre tube and is stirred thoroughly to minimise supercooling. The temperature is recorded every half minute and a

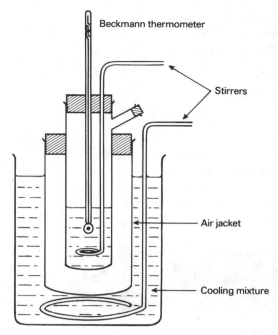

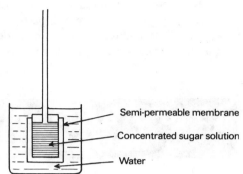

cooling curve is plotted. The solvent is then warmed until it melts and a known mass of solute is added. The process is repeated and the freezing point is determined.

The calculations are similar to the elevation of boiling point calculations.

Fig. 12.4 Apparatus to determine depression of freezing point

Fig. 12.5 Apparatus to demonstrate osmosis

12.5 OSMOSIS AND OSMOTIC PRESSURE

If two solutions of different concentrations are separated by a semipermeable membrane, solvent molecules pass through the membrane and equalise the concentrations of the two solutions. This process is called **osmosis**. Solvent molecules pass through the membrane in both directions but the rate at which the solvent passes from the dilute to the concentrated solution is greater than the reverse rate.

A semipermeable membrane is a membrane which will allow solvent molecules but not solute molecules to pass through it. The simplest semipermeable membrane is a piece of pig's bladder, but this is not very strong in practice. A good semipermeable membrane is produced when copper(II) hexacyanoferrate(II) is precipitated in a porous pot.

The apparatus in Fig. 12.5 is used to demonstrate osmosis.

Over a period of time the water level in the tube rises as the water molecules pass through the semipermeable membrane into the sugar solution.

When the level in the tube no longer rises, the pressure of this column of solution is equal to the **osmotic pressure**. The osmotic pressure of a solution is the pressure which has to be applied to the solution side of a semipermeable membrane in order *just* to prevent passage of solvent molecules from pure solvent to solution. Solutions which have the same osmotic pressure are said to be **isotonic**.

The two laws of osmosis are:

❶ At a given temperature, the osmotic pressure Π (pi) of a dilute solution is proportional to the concentration c.

$$\Pi \propto c \text{ (but } c \propto \frac{1}{V} \therefore \Pi \propto \frac{1}{V})$$

❷ The osmotic pressure of a given solution is directly proportional to the absolute temperature $\Pi \propto T$.

These two laws are similar to Boyle's and Charles' laws for gases (see 8.2, 8.3). They can be combined to form an equation.

$\Pi V = nRT$, where the value of R is equal to the gas constant. The number of moles of solute $n = w/m$ where w = mass of solute in solution and m is the relative molecular mass of the solute.

$$m = \frac{wRT}{\Pi V}$$

Osmotic pressure measurements can be used to find the relative molecular mass of a nonionised solute. It is particularly useful for polymers which produce such small elevations of boiling point or depressions of freezing point that relative molecular masses cannot be determined accurately by these methods.

12.6 ABNORMAL RELATIVE MOLECULAR MASSES

Accurate relative molecular masses can be obtained for undissociated solutes in dilute solution. For partially or completely dissociated solutes the relative molecular masses obtained will be less than the true value due to the extra particles present.

For a partially dissociated electrolyte AB, the following equilibrium exists:

$$AB \rightleftharpoons A^+ + B^-$$

If one mole of AB is used and α moles of AB have dissociated, after dissociation

$$
\begin{array}{ccc}
(1-\alpha) & \alpha & \alpha \\
\text{moles} & \text{moles} & \text{moles} \\
\text{AB} & \text{A}^+ & \text{B}^-
\end{array}
$$

The ratio of the number of particles after dissociation and before dissociation is $\dfrac{1+\alpha}{1}$. This is equal to the van't Hoff factor i, where

$$i = \frac{\text{observed effect on colligative property}}{\text{calculated effect on colligative property}}$$

By equating, the value of α can be calculated. It is important to realise that an electrolyte such as $CaCl_2$ does not dissociate as before.

$$
\begin{array}{ccc}
CaCl_2 \rightleftharpoons & Ca^{2+} & + \ 2Cl^- \\
1-\alpha & \alpha & 2\alpha
\end{array}
$$

$$\frac{\text{Number of moles after dissociation}}{\text{Number of moles before}} = \frac{1+2\alpha}{1}$$

Chapter roundup

Remember that colligative properties rely on numbers of particles. Temperature is not a colligative property because it remains the same whether small or large numbers of particles are present. There are four important colligative properties:

❶ lowering of vapour pressure;

❷ elevation of boiling point;

3 depression of freezing point;

4 osmotic pressure.

Remember that these properties can be used to calculate the relative molecular masses of nonelectrolytes, e.g. glucose and urea, which remain as molecules when dissolved in water. However, the answers obtained by applying these principles to electrolytes, e.g. sodium chloride, can be used to calculate the degree of ionisation.

Worked questions and answers

1

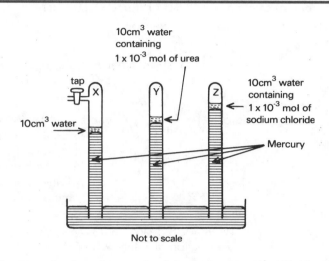

10cm³ water containing 1 x 10⁻³ mol of urea

10cm³ water containing 1 x 10⁻³ mol of sodium chloride

tap

X   Y   Z

10cm³ water

Mercury

Not to scale

(a) (i) What is to be found in each of the spaces marked X, Y and Z?
(ii) Explain the differences in mercury levels in the three tubes in terms of the properties of dilute solutions.
(iii) What changes, if any, would occur to the mercury levels if the apparatus was placed in a thermostatic bath maintained at a higher temperature? Explain your answer.
(iv) If the pressure in X was reduced by means of a vacuum pump, explain what would happen.

(b) Calculate the boiling point of an aqueous solution of urea, $CO(NH_2)_2$, of concentration 12.0 g dm⁻³ at a pressure of 101.3 kPa.
Assume that the volume of the solute is negligible compared to that of the solution, and that the boiling point elevation constant for water is 0.52 mol⁻¹ kg.

(c) Write an expression for the mole fraction of a solute in solution.
Calculate the mole fraction of sodium chloride in an aqueous solution containing 10 g of sodium chloride per 100 g of water ($A_r(C)$ = 12.0, $A_r(H)$ = 1.0, $A_r(O)$ = 16.0, $A_r(Na)$ = 23.0, $A_r(Cl)$ = 35.5).

Tutorial note

(a) (i) The only substance present in X, Y and Z will be water vapour. Remember urea and sodium chloride are nonvolatile.
(ii) The different mercury levels are due to the different vapour pressures of the liquids in X, Y and Z. The vapour pressure of pure water is higher than any aqueous solution. The changes in vapour pressure are dependent upon particle numbers (colligative properties). The more particles in solution the greater the lowering of vapour pressure.

No lowering of vapour pressure for water.

Twice as many particles in sodium chloride as in urea. Sodium chloride is dissociated into ions.

$$NaCl \rightarrow Na^+ + Cl^-$$

Vapour pressure lowered more for sodium chloride than for urea.

(iii) Level in each tube would fall as vapour pressure increases with temperature.

(iv) Water would evaporate or boil. Mercury level rises. The equilibrium will be disturbed to replace water molecules removed by evaporation.

(b) Relative molecular mass of urea = 60.

60 g of urea in 1 kg of water elevates boiling point by 0.52 K

12 g of urea in 1 kg water elevates boiling point by $0.52 \times \dfrac{12}{60} = 0.104$ K

Boiling point of solution is 373.104 K (or 100.104 °C)

(c) The mole fraction of a solute in a solution

$$= \frac{n}{n+N} \text{ where } n = \text{number of moles of solute}$$
$$N = \text{number of moles of solvent.}$$

This can be expressed as $\dfrac{w/m}{w/m + W/M}$ where w is the mass of solute

m is the relative molecular mass of the solute

W is the mass of solvent

M is the relative molecular mass of the solvent.

Substitute in this equation

$w = 10$, $m = 58.5$, $W = 100$, $M = 18$

Mole fraction of solute = 0.0298

Question bank

1 (a) A solution of glucose in water of concentration 0.005 mol dm^{-3} freezes at a temperature of −0.01 °C. A solution in water of KCl at the same concentration freezes at −0.02 °C. What can be deduced from these observations?

(b) (i) Describe concisely the essential features of osmosis.

(ii) Define osmotic pressure.

(iii) At 293 K a solution containing 30.0 g of a polymer in 1.00 dm^3 of water was found to have an osmotic pressure of 2400 Pa (N m^{-2}). Calculate to three significant figures the relative molecular mass of the polymer.

(Oxford 1990)

Points

In (a) you will show that there are twice as many particles present in the KCl solution as in the glucose solution because of the dissociation

$$KCl \, (s) \rightarrow K^+ \, (aq) + Cl^- \, (aq)$$

ENERGETICS

Units in this chapter

Chapter objectives

Chemistry can be summarised by the following triangle:

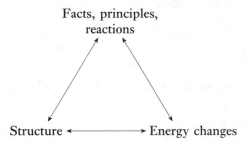

At GCSE level the emphasis is probably more on facts, principles and reactions. At A level, although the number of facts, principles and reactions you need to know will go up many times, structure and energy changes will become more important. Energy changes which accompany chemical reactions often give information about structural changes and are evidence for structural changes.

A simple example is the melting of ice to form water. At A level you should appreciate that ice has an open crystal structure. Because there are considerable spaces within the crystal, ice has a lower density than water and floats on water. The process of melting, i.e.

$$\text{ice} \rightarrow \text{water}$$

requires energy. This energy is required to break the bonds between the water molecules and break up the ice structure. The water molecules are then free to move.

A process which requires energy such as this is said to be **endothermic** and a process which evolves energy is said to be **exothermic**. In this chapter we will use the word **enthalpy** instead of energy. It merely means total energy in all forms and the term **enthalpy change** will be common.

13.1 FIRST LAW OF THERMODYNAMICS

This law is the equivalent of the law of conservation of energy. It states that **energy cannot be created or destroyed but may be converted from one form into another**

$$q = \Delta U + w$$

where ΔU is the change in the internal energy
q is the actual heat change, and
w is the work done by the system.

The term w involves the gas produced expanding and pushing back the atmosphere. This can be estimated by using a syringe with a piston. The work done $w = P\Delta V$ where P is external pressure and ΔV is the change in volume.

$P\Delta V$ (and hence w) only becomes significant when either P and/or ΔV is large. In reactions involving only solids and liquids as reactants and products, $P\Delta V$ is negligible. For gases ΔV is frequently large and w can be significant.

Reactions carried out at constant volume. In these cases $\Delta V = 0$ (i.e. no change in volume) and $P\Delta V = w = 0$

$$q_v = \Delta U$$

q_v represents heat change at constant volume. Any heat change recorded corresponds to a change in the internal energy of the system.

Reactions carried out at constant pressure. Most reactions carried out in the laboratory are carried out at constant pressure, e.g. in an open beaker. Work is done by any gas expanding against the pressure of the atmosphere.

$q_p = \Delta U + P\Delta V$ where q_p represents the heat change at constant pressure

$$q_p = (U_{final} - U_{initial}) + P(V_{final} - V_{initial})$$

$$= (U_{final} + PV_{final}) - (U_{initial} + PV_{initial})$$

The term $U + PV$ represents the energy possessed by the system and is called the **enthalpy** or **heat content** H:

$$q_p = H_{final} - H_{initial} = \Delta H$$

Substituting,

$$\Delta H = \Delta U + P\Delta V$$

13.2 ENTHALPY CHANGE OF REACTION

The equation for the reaction between carbon and excess oxygen is

$$C(graphite) + O_2(g) \rightarrow CO_2(g) \quad \Delta H = -393.5 \text{ kJ mol}^{-1}$$

(Note mol^{-1} means per quantity shown in the equation *not* per mole of product.)

The combustion of 12 g of graphite in excess oxygen liberates 393.5 kJ. (The negative sign for ΔH shows, by convention, that energy is **liberated** or the reaction is **exothermic.**)

The quantity of energy liberated or absorbed is given by the equation. ΔH is called the **enthalpy change of reaction.** Often standard enthalpy changes are quoted. These are the enthalpy changes at standard atmospheric pressure and at constant temperature, usually 25 °C (or 298 K). The reactants and products are in their usual or standard states at 25 °C. Carbon is in the form of graphite and oxygen and carbon dioxide are gases. The standard enthalpy change of reaction is represented by $\Delta H^\ominus$. If solutions are used they must have a concentration of 1 mol dm^{-3}.

It is impossible to estimate absolute enthalpies – only enthalpy changes can be calculated. Elements in their standard states are regarded as having zero enthalpy.

There are a number of standard enthalpy changes which are important and should be clearly defined.

13.3 STANDARD ENTHALPY CHANGE OF FORMATION

The standard enthalpy change of formation of a compound is the enthalpy change when one mole of the compound is formed from its constituent elements in their standard states at 25 °C. Energy may be given out or taken in during the reaction (see 13.2).

For example, $\Delta H_f^\ominus = -393.5$ kJ mol^{-1} for the formation of carbon dioxide.

13.4 STANDARD ENTHALPY CHANGE OF COMBUSTION

The standard enthalpy change of combustion of a substance $\Delta H_c^\ominus$ is the enthalpy change when one mole of the substance in its standard state undergoes complete combustion.

If the compound contains carbon, hydrogen and oxygen, the complete combustion will produce carbon dioxide and water, e.g.

$$C_2H_6(g) + 3\tfrac{1}{2}O_2(g) \rightarrow 2CO_2(g) + 3H_2O(l) \quad \Delta H_c^\ominus = -1560 \text{ kJ mol}^{-1}$$

13.5 STANDARD ENTHALPY CHANGE OF NEUTRALISATION

The standard enthalpy change of neutralisation is the enthalpy change when 1 mole of H_3O^+ ions is just neutralised by an alkali in dilute solution. The acid and base are in their standard states at 25 °C and in solutions containing 1 mol dm^{-3}.

$$HCl(aq) + NaOH(aq) \rightarrow NaCl(aq) + H_2O(l) \quad \Delta H_n^\ominus = -57.1 \text{ kJ mol}^{-1}$$

The values obtained for standard enthalpy changes of neutralisation of strong acids and strong bases are constant.

13.6 ENTHALPY CHANGE OF SOLUTION AND ENTHALPY CHANGE OF DILUTION

The enthalpy change of solution is the enthalpy change when 1 mole of a substance is dissolved in a specified volume of solvent. The enthalpy change will depend upon the volume of solvent used.

The enthalpy change of dilution is the enthalpy change when 1 mole of a substance is dissolved in a large volume of solvent such that further dilution produces no further enthalpy change.

13.7 MEASURING ENTHALPY CHANGES

Enthalpy changes are determined by simple calorimetry experiments. For example, to determine the enthalpy change of neutralisation of sodium hydroxide and hydrochloric acid, a known volume of sodium hydroxide solution of known concentration is placed in a vacuum flask and the temperature is accurately measured. The volume of hydrochloric acid, of known concentration, required to neutralise the sodium hydroxide solution is rapidly added, the mixture stirred and the final temperature recorded.

If the initial temperature of both the acid and alkali is t_1 °C and the final temperature is t_2 °C, the temperature change is $t_2 - t_1$ °C. If the mass of the mixture is m g, the specific heat capacity of the solutions is 4.2 J deg^{-1} (dilute solutions can be assumed to have the same specific heat capacity as water), and the heat capacity of the vacuum flask is W, then

$$\text{heat evolved} = m \times 4.2 \times (t_2 - t_1) + W(t_2 - t_1) \text{ J}$$

From these results the enthalpy change of neutralisation can be calculated.

13.8 HESS'S LAW

Hess's law can be used for calculating enthalpy changes which cannot be determined by experiment. The law states that the total enthalpy change for a reaction is independent of the route taken.

For example, if X is converted to Y and Y to Z, the total enthalpy change will be the same as when X is converted directly to Z.

Example: Calculate the standard enthalpy change of formation of carbon monoxide from the following information.

Enthalpy changes of combustion of carbon (graphite) and carbon monoxide are −393.5 kJ mol^{-1} and −283 kJ mol^{-1}.

The following equations can be written

Required: Enthalpy change of formation of carbon monoxide

$$C(\text{graphite}) + \tfrac{1}{2}O_2(g) \rightarrow CO(g)$$

Given: Enthalpy changes of combustion of graphite and carbon monoxide.

❶ $C(graphite) + O_2(g) \rightarrow CO_2(g)$ $\Delta H^\ominus = -393.5$ kJ

❷ $CO(g) + \frac{1}{2}O_2(g) \rightarrow CO_2(g)$ $\Delta H^\ominus = -283$ kJ

A diagram can be drawn to summarise the situation

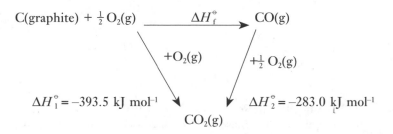

$$\Delta H_f^\ominus = \Delta H_1^\ominus - \Delta H_2^\ominus$$
$$= -393.5 + 283.0$$
$$= -110.5 \text{ kJ mol}^{-1}$$

Alternatively, from equations 1 and 2 above, equation 2 can be reversed when the enthalpy change is the same numerically but the sign is changed.

$$C(graphite) + O_2(g) \rightarrow CO_2(g) \qquad \Delta H^\ominus = -393.5\,\text{kJ}$$
$$CO_2(g) \rightarrow CO(g) + \frac{1}{2}O_2(g) \qquad \Delta H^\ominus = +283.0\,\text{kJ}$$

Adding these two equations together

$$C(graphite) + \frac{1}{2}O_2(g) \rightarrow CO(g) \qquad \Delta H_f^\ominus = -393.5 + 283.0$$
$$= -110.5\,\text{kJ mol}^{-1}$$

The **negative** sign shows, by convention, that the process is **exothermic**. A **positive** sign shows that the process is **endothermic**. Candidates lose many marks in this type of work by either getting a sign wrong or by missing out units. It is advisable when an enthalpy change is positive to put in a positive sign. This shows the examiner that you have thought about it and decided that the process is endothermic.

13.9 BOND ENTHALPIES

During a chemical reaction a number of bonds will be formed or broken. **Forming bonds liberates energy and breaking bonds requires energy.** It would be useful to be able to attribute specific enthalpy changes to various bond changes. The sum of these enthalpy changes would equal the total enthalpy change.

Consider the breaking of the four C—H bonds in methane:

$$\begin{array}{c} H \\ | \\ H\!-\!C\!-\!H \ (g) \rightarrow C(g) + 4H(g) \qquad \Delta H^\ominus = +1662\,\text{kJ mol}^{-1} \\ | \\ H \end{array}$$

It is reasonable to assume that the energy required to break each C—H bond is the same and the same as is required to break a C—H bond in any other compound, and for all practical purposes this can be taken as true at this level.

For a diatomic molecule XY, the bond enthalpy is defined as the enthalpy change for the process:

$$X\!-\!Y\ (g) \rightarrow X(g) + Y(g)$$

Table 13.1 lists some of the average bond enthalpies at 25 °C.

Table 13.1 *Some average bond enthalpies at 25 °C*

Bond	$\Delta H/\text{kJ mol}^{-1}$
H—H	+436
C—C	+348
C≡C	+612
C—F	+484
C—Cl	+338
C—Br	+275
C—I	+238

(Don't try to remember these figures. They will be given if required.)

It must be remembered that these bond enthalpies can only be used as a guide. The actual value of a bond enthalpy will depend upon the nature of the other atoms or groups joined to it.

The enthalpy change is positive when a bond is broken and negative when a bond is made. Bond enthalpies can be used to explain a number of facts from inorganic and organic chemistry; for example, the increased reactivity of phosphorus compared with nitrogen (Chapter 25) or the increased rate of substitution reactions for iodoalkanes compared with other haloalkanes.

The enthalpy change for atomisation can be estimated using bond enthalpies. For example, the atomisation of ethane C_2H_6 involves the breaking of one C—C bond and six C—H bonds. The enthalpy of atomisation therefore is:

$$= 1(C—C) + 6(C—H)$$
$$= 348 + (6 \times 412)$$
$$= +2820\,\text{kJ mol}^{-1}$$

Bond enthalpies can also be used to estimate likely enthalpy changes in chemical reactions, e.g. the hydrogenation of ethene (29.5).

$$
\begin{array}{c}
H \qquad\qquad H \\
\diagdown \quad\quad \diagup \\
C{=}C \quad + H{-}H \rightarrow H{-}\overset{\displaystyle H}{\underset{\displaystyle H}{C}}{-}\overset{\displaystyle H}{\underset{\displaystyle H}{C}}{-}H \\
\diagup \quad\quad \diagdown \\
H \qquad\qquad H
\end{array}
$$

Using the information in Table 13.1

Bonds broken 1(C=C) + 1(H—H) enthalpy change $= +612 + 436 = +1048$ kJ

Bonds formed 1(C—C) + 2(C—H) enthalpy change $= -348 + 2(-412)$
$$= -1172\ \text{kJ}$$

Net enthalpy change $= 1048 - 1172 = -124\,\text{kJ}$.

13.10 BORN–HABER CYCLE

Lattice enthalpies cannot be determined directly but may be found indirectly by using an **energy diagram**. These diagrams are called **Born–Haber cycles**. The most common one seen on examination papers is the one for sodium chloride.

The standard enthalpy change when one mole of sodium chloride crystal is produced from sodium metal and chlorine gas can be determined experimentally and is, in fact, the standard enthalpy change of formation of sodium chloride.

$$\Delta H_f^\ominus = -411\ \text{kJ mol}^{-1}$$

We can consider the various steps which are required to bring about this change:

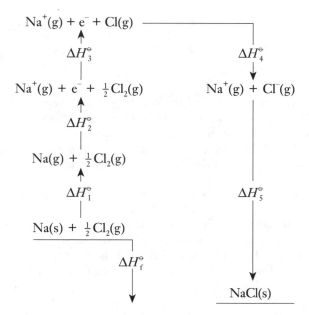

$\Delta H_1^{\ominus}$ corresponds to the **standard enthalpy change of atomisation** of sodium. It is the enthalpy change when one mole of solid sodium is converted to free sodium atoms. $\Delta H_1^{\ominus} = +108.4 \text{ kJ mol}^{-1}$.

$\Delta H_2^{\ominus}$ corresponds to the **first ionisation energy** of sodium (see 2.3), i.e. the enthalpy change when one mole of electrons in their ground state is totally removed from 1 mole of sodium atoms in the gas phase. $\Delta H_2^{\ominus} = +500 \text{ kJ mol}^{-1}$.

$\Delta H_3^{\ominus}$ corresponds to the **standard enthalpy change of atomisation** of chlorine. It is the enthalpy change when one mole of gaseous chlorine atoms is produced from chlorine molecules. $\Delta H_3^{\ominus} = +121 \text{ kJ mol}^{-1}$.

$\Delta H_4^{\ominus}$ corresponds to the **first electron affinity** of chlorine. This is the enthalpy change when one mole of chlorine atoms each accept one electron to form one mole of chloride ions. $\Delta H_4^{\ominus} = -364 \text{ kJ mol}^{-1}$.

$\Delta H_5^{\ominus}$ corresponds to the **lattice enthalpy** (sometimes called **lattice energy**) of sodium chloride.

By Hess's law $\Delta H_f^{\ominus} = \Delta H_1^{\ominus} + \Delta H_2^{\ominus} + \Delta H_3^{\ominus} + \Delta H_4^{\ominus} + \Delta H_5^{\ominus}$
$\Delta H_5^{\ominus} = -776.4 \text{ kJ mol}^{-1}$

An understanding of lattice enthalpy is extremely useful in various ways at A level for the following reasons.

❶ Substances with high lattice enthalpies will have high melting points.

❷ The solubility of an ionic compound will depend upon the relative values of the lattice and hydration enthalpies or energies.

❸ Comparison of the calculated and experimental values for lattice enthalpy gives an indication of the degree of covalent bonding in a compound (see worked question 1).

❹ Lattice enthalpies can be used to explain the nonexistence of some compounds.

13.11 THE STABILITY OF BENZENE

The enthalpy change of hydrogenation is the enthalpy change when one mole of hydrogen molecules is added to one mole of alkene. The enthalpy change of hydrogenation of cyclohexene is -120kJ mol^{-1}.

$$\bigcirc + H_2 \rightarrow \hexagon$$

If it is assumed that benzene contains three double bonds, i.e. it is a triene, the enthalpy change of hydrogenation should be $3 \times (-120)$ kJ mol^{-1}, i.e. -360 kJ mol^{-1}.

$$\bigcirc + 3H_2 \rightarrow \bigcirc$$

The experimental value for the enthalpy change of hydrogenation of benzene is -208 kJ mol^{-1}. The difference between these two values (152 kJ mol^{-1}) is a measure of the extra stability of benzene compared with similar nonaromatic systems.

The standard enthalpy change of formation of benzene can be obtained by using the bond enthalpies in Table 13.1 and assuming benzene is a cyclic triene.

$$\Delta H_f^\ominus = -(3 \times C{=}C + 3 \times C{-}C + 6 \times C{-}H) = -5352 \text{ kJ mol}^{-1}$$

The experimental value found by a Hess's law calculation is -5549 kJ mol^{-1}. The difference between these two values (197 kJ mol^{-1}) again is a measure of the stability of benzene. The difference between this value and the one obtained previously from hydrogenation calculations is probably due to the use of average values for bond enthalpies.

13.12 SECOND LAW OF THERMODYNAMICS– ENTROPY

The majority of reactions are exothermic and it was once believed that only exothermic reactions could take place. However, there is another factor which governs the feasibility of a reaction.

The second factor is **entropy**, which is related to the degree of randomness or disorder in the system. If two gases in separate bulbs are allowed to come into contact, the gases mix and there is an increase in the disorder.

Given an opportunity, the disorder of a system, and hence its entropy, will spontaneously increase. The dissolving of an ionic crystal in water produces an increase in entropy. In the lattice the ions are regularly arranged. The dissolving of ammonium nitrate is an endothermic process and would not take place purely on energy considerations. There is, however, an increase in entropy which makes the process possible.

One statement of the second law of thermodynamics is that in any system a change that takes place spontaneously (i.e. of its own accord) will always involve an increase in entropy.

Entropy change ΔS is defined as the heat involved in a particular process divided by the temperature at which the process occurs, i.e. $\Delta S = \dfrac{q}{T}$

Systems having perfect order, i.e. the perfect ionic crystal lattice at 0 K, possess zero entropy. The entropy of a given mass of matter increases in the order:

$$\text{solid} \rightarrow \text{liquid} \rightarrow \text{gas}$$

The entropy of substances not possessing perfect order and of all substances at temperatures above 0 K will be greater than zero, e.g. the standard entropy S (at 298 K and 1 atmosphere pressure) of water = 70 J K^{-1} mol^{-1}.

The entropy change in a reaction can be found.

Example: Find $\Delta S^\ominus$ for the reaction $H_2(g) + I_2(g) \rightarrow 2HI(g)$, given that the standard entropies of hydrogen, gaseous iodine and hydrogen iodine are +131, +261 and +207 J K^{-1} mol^{-1} respectively.

$$\Delta S^\ominus = 2 \times S^\ominus_{HI} - S^\ominus_{H_2} - S^\ominus_{I_2} = 414 - 131 - 261 = +22 \text{ J K}^{-1}\text{mol}^{-1}$$

There is an increase in entropy and a spontaneous reaction is feasible, although no indication is given of the possible rate of reaction.

For spontaneous processes (i.e. ones that take place of their own accord)

$$\Delta S_{TOTAL} > 0$$

$$\Delta S_{TOTAL} = \Delta S_{SYSTEM} + \Delta S_{SURROUNDINGS}$$

$$\Delta S_{SYSTEM} = \Sigma \Delta S^\ominus_{PRODUCTS} - \Sigma \Delta S^\ominus_{REACTANTS}$$

$$\Delta S_{SURROUNDINGS} = -\Delta H/T$$

$$\therefore \Delta S_{TOTAL} = \Delta S_{SYSTEM} - \Delta H/T$$

$$\therefore -T\Delta S_{TOTAL} = \Delta H - T\Delta S_{SYSTEM}$$

$$\text{But } -T\Delta S_{TOTAL} = \Delta G$$

$$\therefore \Delta G = \Delta H - T\Delta S$$

13.13 FREE ENERGY G

This is a measure of the useful work which can be obtained from a system (apart from volume changes).

A reaction can only proceed spontaneously if ΔG is negative. ΔG depends upon ΔH and ΔS and they are related by the equation $\Delta G = \Delta H - T\Delta S$.

Since for a reaction to proceed ΔG must be negative, for an endothermic reaction (ΔH positive), a reaction will take place only if $T\Delta S > \Delta H$. If ΔG is positive, no useful work can be obtained and the reaction is not feasible. If $\Delta G = 0$ the system will be in dynamic equilibrium.

Chapter roundup

This chapter concerns enthalpy changes which occur during chemical reactions. Most reactions are exothermic and are accompanied by an enthalpy loss, i.e. by convention a negative value for ΔH. In fact at one time all reactions were believed to be exothermic and it was thought that endothermic ones did not take place. As you should realise, endothermic reactions are less common because for a reaction to take place ΔG must be negative and

$$\Delta G = \Delta H - T\Delta S$$

If ΔH is positive the reaction will only take place if

$$T\Delta S > \Delta H$$

Enthalpy changes clearly depend upon the quantities of materials used.

Worked questions and answers

1

$$Cd^{2+}(g) + 2I(g) \xrightarrow{\text{(v)}} Cd^{2+}(g) + 2I^-(g)$$

$$\uparrow \text{(iv)}$$

$$Cd^{2+}(g) + I_2(g)$$

$$\uparrow \text{(iii)}$$

$$Cd(g) + I_2(g)$$

$$\uparrow \text{(ii)}$$

$$Cd(g) + I_2(s)$$

$$\uparrow \text{(i)}$$

$$Cd(s) + I_2(s) \xrightarrow{\text{(vi)}} CdI_2(s)$$

(a) Use the above diagram and the following data to determine the experimental value of the standard molar lattice energy of cadmium(II) iodide,
$$CdI_2(s) \rightarrow Cd^{2+}(g) + 2I^- (g).$$

(i) $Cd(s) \rightarrow Cd(g)$	$\Delta H^\ominus = +113$ kJ mol^{-1}
(ii) $I_2(s) \rightarrow I_2(g)$	$\Delta H^\ominus = +19.4$ kJ mol^{-1}
(iii) $Cd(g) \rightarrow Cd^{2+}(g)$	$\Delta H^\ominus = +2490$ kJ mol^{-1}
(iv) $I_2(g) \rightarrow 2I(g)$	$\Delta H^\ominus = +151$ kJ mol^{-1}
(v) $2I(g) \rightarrow 2I^-(g)$	$\Delta H^\ominus = -628$ kJ mol^{-1}
(vi) $Cd(s) + I_2(s) \rightarrow CdI_2(s)$	$\Delta H^\ominus = -201$ kJ mol^{-1}

(b) By assuming that cadmium and iodide ions are charged spheres, a theoretical value for the molar lattice energy is calculated to be -2050 kJ mol^{-1}. Give an explanation for the difference between this value and the value determined in (a).

(AEB)

Tutorial note

(a) If the standard molar lattice energy is $\Delta H^\ominus$,

$\Delta H^\ominus = +113 + 19.4 + 2490 + 151 - 628 + 201 = +2346.4$ kJ mol^{-1}

(b) The difference between these two values is due to the fact that the bonding in cadmium(II) iodide is not purely ionic but there is an appreciable covalent character. To consider the lattice as an arrangement of charged spheres is incorrect.

2

$$CH_3OH(l) \rightleftharpoons CH_3OH(g)$$

The equation represents the equilibrium between liquid methanol and methanol vapour at 338 K. Given that $\Delta H = +35.3$ kJ mol^{-1}, calculate the entropy change when methanol is vapourised.

Tutorial note

The entropy change should be positive as there is an increase in disorder.

$$\Delta G = \Delta H - T\Delta S$$

The system is in equilibrium, therefore $\Delta G = 0$ and $\Delta H = T\Delta S$

$$\Delta S = \frac{35300}{338} = +104.4 \text{ J K}^{-1} \text{ mol}^{-1}$$

Question bank

1 (a) The combustion of some fuels produces large amounts of carbon dioxide, which may modify the Earth's climate (the 'greenhouse effect').

Substance	$CH_4(g)$	$CO_2(g)$	$H_2O(l)$	$C(s)$	$O_2(g)$
Standard enthalpy of formation, $\Delta H^{\ominus}_{f, 298}$/kJ mol^{-1}	–75.0	–394.0	–296.0	0.0	0.0

(i) Use the data given to calculate the standard enthalpy changes of combustion for coal (essentially carbon) and for natural gas (essentially methane).

(ii) Using these results, calculate which fuel produces more energy on combustion.

❶ Per gram of fuel.

❷ Per mole of carbon dioxide formed.

(iii) State which of these two fuels is likely to have the smaller effect on the climate per kilojoule of energy produced, and give a reason.

(WJEC 1981)

Points

This question emphasises a trend towards environmental questions within the syllabus.

REACTION KINETICS

Units in this chapter

Chapter objectives

At GCSE level you will have investigated some of the factors which alter the rate of a chemical reaction. The factors which you might have studied include:

1. physical state of reactants;

2. concentration (and for gases, pressure);

3. temperature;

4. catalysts; and

5. light.

For example, you might have studied the effects of physical state of reactants (or particle size). This could be done by comparing the volumes of carbon dioxide produced at intervals when equal masses of powdered calcium carbonate and lumps of calcium carbonate react with dilute hydrochloric acid. The powder has a much larger surface area in contact with the acid and so reacts faster.

Rates of reaction (or reaction kinetics) are linked closely with structure (Chapters 5, 8, 9 and 10) and mechanisms of reactions (Chapter 38).

14.1 EFFECT OF CONCENTRATION

This is probably the most important factor to understand at A level. During a reaction the reactants are used up and so the rate of reaction decreases.

The exact relationship between the rate of reaction and the concentration of the reactants in a particular reaction can only be determined experimentally. Most reactions take place in a series of steps and the rate of the overall reaction depends upon the rate of the slowest step, called the **rate-determining step.**

It is vital for you to distinguish clearly the meaning of the terms **order of reaction** and **molecularity.** Few candidates understand the distinction and many questions test this. The order of reaction is determined experimentally. In the reaction

$$A + B \rightarrow C + D$$

experiment may show that the rate of reaction is proportional to the concentration of A to the power of x,

$$\text{i.e. rate} \propto [A]^x$$

and the rate of reaction may also be proportional to the concentration of B to the power y,

$$\text{i.e. rate} \propto [B]^y$$

The overall equation is therefore

$$\text{rate} = k[\text{A}]^x[\text{B}]^y$$

k is the **rate constant** and the overall equation is called the **rate equation**. The rate equation normally indicates what species are involved in the rate-determining step and how many of each species are involved. In this example, the order of the reaction with respect to A is x and the order with respect to B is y and the total order of the reaction is $x + y$.

In the reaction between peroxodisulphate and iodide ions, the equation is

$$S_2O_8^{2-}(aq) + 2I^-(aq) \rightarrow 2SO_4^{2-}(aq) + I_2(aq)$$

The rate equation determined experimentally is

$$\text{rate} = k[S_2O_8^{2-}][I^-]$$

and the total order is 2. The order is not related to the equation. The order may be integral, i.e. 1, 2 or 3, etc., but it can also be fractional, e.g.

$$H_2 + I_2 \rightarrow 2HI$$
$$\text{rate of reaction} = k[H_2][I_2]$$
Order with respect to hydrogen = 1
Order with respect to iodine = 1

Total order of reaction = 1 + 1 = 2

$$H_2 + Br_2 \rightarrow 2HBr$$
$$\text{rate of reaction} = k[H_2][Br_2]^{\frac{1}{2}}$$
Order with respect to hydrogen = 1
Order with respect to bromine = $\frac{1}{2}$

Total order of reaction = $1 + \frac{1}{2} = 1\frac{1}{2}$

Molecularity is the number of particles colliding in the rate-determining step. It is always integral. It may or may not be the same as the order.

14.2 EFFECT OF TEMPERATURE

Fig. 8.2 shows the distribution of the velocities of molecules in a gas. The number of molecules, n, possessing the activation energy, E_a, necessary for reaction is given by

$$n = n_0 \exp(-E_a/RT)$$

where n_0 is the total number of molecules, R is the gas constant and T is the absolute temperature.

From the simple collision theory, the rate of reaction is proportional to the number of molecules possessing energy greater than or equal to E_a.

$$k = A \exp(-E_a/RT)$$

where k is the rate constant and A is the Arrhenius constant. The equation is called the Arrhenius equation.

The activation energy can be found by plotting a graph of $\ln k$ against $1/T$. The activation energy can be found from the gradient of the straight line graph. The gradient is $\dfrac{-E_a}{R}$. (Be careful with the units of R.)

14.3 EFFECT OF CATALYSTS

A **catalyst** is a substance which alters the rate of a chemical reaction without being used up. The catalyst may be changed physically but the mass of catalyst is unchanged at the end of the reaction.

An example of a catalyst is manganese(IV) oxide in the decomposition of hydrogen peroxide.

$$2H_2O_2(aq) \rightarrow 2H_2O(l) + O_2(g)$$

This is an example of a catalyst which speeds up a chemical reaction. A substance which slows down the rate of a reaction is called an inhibitor.

A catalyst does not alter the position of an equilibrium or increase the yield of products. It merely alters the rate at which the equilibrium is achieved or the products are obtained. A catalyst provides an alternative route with a lower activation energy barrier for the reaction. More molecules possess the lower activation energy and so the reaction is speeded up.

For example, $2HI \rightarrow H_2 + I_2$

Activation energy without catalyst	183 kJ mol^{-1}
with gold catalyst	105 kJ mol^{-1}
with platinum catalyst	58 kJ mol^{-1}

There are two types of catalyst – **homogeneous catalysts** and **heterogeneous catalysts**. A homogeneous catalyst is in the same phase as the reactants, e.g. the reaction between an organic acid and an alcohol is catalysed by the presence of hydrogen ions. A heterogeneous catalyst is not in the same phase, e.g. manganese(IV) oxide is solid and hydrogen peroxide is a liquid. There are two theories of catalysis.

(i) Intermediate compound theory

The catalyst reacts with one of the reactants to produce an intermediate compound which eventually produces the required product and regenerates the catalyst, e.g. manganese(IV) oxide and hydrogen peroxide.

The intermediate compound theory explains most examples of homogeneous catalysis.

(ii) Adsorption or surface action theory

A gas is adsorbed when its particles collide with and adhere to the catalyst surface. When gas molecules are adsorbed they are brought close together, and in a state which enables them to react together. On desorption the catalyst surface is available for further reaction. An example is the reaction of an alkene with hydrogen using a nickel catalyst.

The *d*-block elements (Chapter 28) and their compounds are good catalysts. The elements can exist in a variety of oxidation states and the metal surfaces are ideal for adsorption purposes.

In some reactions one of the products of the reaction acts as a catalyst for the reaction. For example, in the reaction of an ethanedioate (oxalate) with acidified potassium manganate(VII), the reaction has to be heated to about 60 °C to get the reaction to start but the manganese(II) ions produced catalyse the reaction and the reaction continues even if the solution is cooled to room temperature. This is an example of what is called **autocatalysis**.

14.4 EFFECT OF LIGHT

Some reactions are greatly affected by light. For example, the reaction of hydrogen and chlorine is explosive in sunlight. The ultraviolet light in sunlight splits some of the chlorine molecules into free chlorine atoms or chlorine **free radicals**.

$$Cl_2 \rightarrow 2Cl\cdot$$

Then a free radical chain reaction takes place, producing hydrogen chloride.

$$Cl\cdot + H_2 \rightarrow HCl + H\cdot$$
$$H\cdot + Cl_2 \rightarrow HCl + Cl\cdot$$

The reaction between chlorine and methane (see 29.2) is another example of a reaction affected by light.

Fig. 14.1 summarises the changes which take place when chemicals are excited.

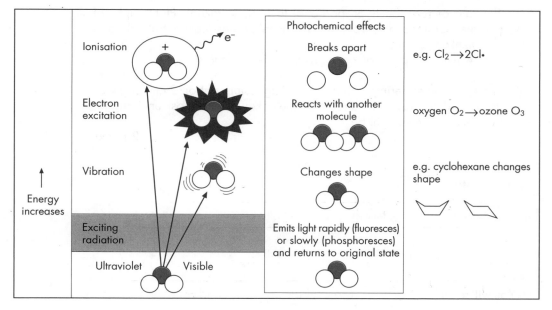

Fig. 14.1

14.5 FOLLOWING THE PROGRESS OF REACTIONS

There are a number of methods which can be used to follow the progress of a reaction, including the following.

➊ Measuring the volume of gas evolved at intervals using a gas syringe, e.g. in the reaction between calcium carbonate and hydrochloric acid.

➋ Measuring the electrical resistance of the solution.

➌ Measuring the change of colour in the solution with a colorimeter.

➍ Removing samples from the reaction mixture and titrating, e.g. the hydrolysis of ethyl ethanoate with alkali. Portions of the reaction mixture are removed at intervals and titrated with dilute hydrochloric acid using phenolphthalein as indicator.

Chapter roundup

The subject of reaction kinetics provides a good source of experimental work at all levels. It is important to control carefully the conditions so that only one variable is changed at a time.

The key issues of order of reaction and molecularity should be mastered before moving on.

Worked questions and answers

1 (a) The rate of reaction of magnesium with solutions of hydrochloric acid can be investigated by finding out how long it takes for a piece of magnesium ribbon 1 cm long to dissolve in 50 cm³ of solutions of varying concentrations. In a typical experiment the results were:

| Concentration HCl (mol dm⁻³) | 1 | 0.7 | 0.4 |
| Time (s) | 17 | 36 | 107 |

The rate of reaction is proportional to (1/time taken). Plot graphs of (1/time) against concentration and (1/time) against (concentration)², and comment on your results.
(You will need a piece of 2 mm graph paper to do this)

9 marks

(b) In a separate experiment, a piece of magnesium ribbon 2 cm long was used, and it was found that the time taken was almost unchanged. Suggest·why this might be.

2 marks
(AEB)

Tutorial notes

(a)

Conc (M)	Time (s)	1/time (s⁻¹)	Conc² (M²)
1	17	5.9×10^{-2}	1
0.7	36	2.8×10^{-2}	0.49
0.4	107	0.9×10^{-2}	0.16

You will receive 3 marks for correctly calculating $1/t$ and conc².

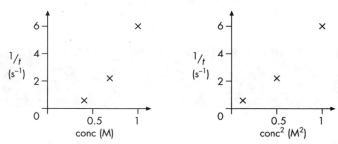

You will receive 2 marks for correctly labelling the axes, including units, and 2 marks for plotting the points.
In the second graph the points are in a straight line (1 mark), making the reaction 2nd order (1 mark).

(b) If a longer piece of magnesium ribbon is used, the surface area is doubled (1 mark). The time to use up twice as much magnesium is the same because the rate doubles (1 mark).

Question bank

1 In colour photography, the film consists of three layers of 'emulsion', each of which is a suspension containing silver halides in gelatin. Each layer is sensitive to one of the three primary colours in light – red, green and blue.

(a) The first stage in processing the film is development. Control of development is critical for the correct colours. Any variation in temperature must be allowed for by altering the time allowed for development. The instructions for one make of colour developer include a temperature/time table:

Temperature/°C	Development time
38	3 min
37	3 min 15 sec
36	3 min 40 sec
35	4 min 10 sec
34	4 min 35 sec
33	5 min 15 sec
32	5 min 45 sec

(i) Suggest a reason why control of the development is likely to be more accurate at a lower temperature.

(ii) At a given temperature:

rate of development $\propto$ 1/time required for normal development

Hence 1/(development time in seconds) may be used as a measure of the reaction rate at that temperature.

In the table below, most of the data in the temperature/time table above has been converted into values of 1/(temperature/K) and ln[1/(development time)]. Complete the table by calculating the missing values and writing them into the appropriate spaces.

Temperature/°C	$\dfrac{1}{\text{temperature}}$/$K^{-1}$	ln[1/(development time)]
38	3.215×10^{-3}	−5.19
37	3.226×10^{-3}	−5.27
36	3.236×10^{-3}	−5.39
35	3.247×10^{-3}	−5.52
34	3.257×10^{-3}	−5.62
33	3.215×10^{-3}	−5.75
32	– – – – – –	– – –

(iii) Plot a graph of ln[1/(development time)] on the y axis against 1/temperature.

(iv) The relationship between reaction rate and temperature is given by the equation:

$$\text{rate} \propto A\,e^{-E/RT}$$
$$\textit{or } \ln(\text{rate}) = \text{constant} - E/RT$$

where T is the temperature in kelvin, E is the activation energy, and R is the gas constant.

Use your graph from (iii) to calculate the activation energy, E, for the development process. ($R = 8.31\ J\ K^{-1}\ mol^{-1}$.)

(b) The second stage of processing the film is called *bleaching*. This involves the conversion of the silver deposit back to a silver halide. An oxidising agent is used, such as potassium hexacyanoferrate(III), $K_3Fe(CN)_6$, which contains the complex ion $Fe(CN)_6^{3-}$.

(i) The hexacyanoferrate(III) ion is reduced to the ion $Fe(CN)_6^{4-}$. Write down the name of this ion.

(ii) Explain what is meant by the term *complex ion*.

(iii) Draw a diagram to show the shape and arrangement of atoms in the hexacyanoferrate(III) complex ion.

(ULEAC Nuffield 1991)

Points

This question involves using graphical data. Remember that for a straight line graph

$$y = mx + c$$

where m is the gradient of the graph and c is the intercept on the y axis.

EQUILIBRIUM

Units in this chapter

15.1 *What is meant by chemical equilibrium?*
15.2 *Quantitative approach to equilibrium*
15.3 *K_p*
15.4 *Equilibrium in a heterogeneous system*
15.5 *Qualitative approach to equilibrium – Le Chatelier's principle*
15.6 *Distribution of a solute between two immiscible solvents*

Chapter objectives

The topic of equilibrium used to be part of most GCE O-level courses. Now, with GCSE, very few students will start A level with any knowledge and understanding of this topic. The concept of equilibrium is a most important one and one you should fully master before looking at Chapters 16 and 17. Also, equilibrium has considerable importance in industrial chemistry, e.g. sulphuric acid and ammonia production (Chapter 40), where controlling the equilibrium will enable the factory to run efficiently.

15.1 WHAT IS MEANT BY CHEMICAL EQUILIBRIUM?

The reaction between iron and steam is a reversible reaction

$$3Fe(s) + 4H_2O(g) \rightleftharpoons Fe_3O_4(s) + 4H_2(g)$$

If steam is passed over heated iron in an open vessel, the forward reaction takes place and the iron oxide and hydrogen are produced. The steam displaces the hydrogen from the system, thereby limiting the reverse reaction.

When hydrogen is passed over the heated iron oxide, iron and steam are produced.

An equilibrium is established, however, if iron and steam are heated in a *closed* container so the products cannot escape. In equilibrium, the concentrations of the two products and the two reactants remain constant provided that the external conditions are unchanged. The reactions have not stopped, however. The rate of the forward reaction is equal to the rate of the reverse reaction and so the concentrations are unchanged. Using the term **dynamic equilibrium** is probably better because it emphasises that the two reactions are continuing.

15.2 QUANTITATIVE APPROACH TO EQUILIBRIUM

The **law of equilibrium** states that, at constant temperature, the rate of a reaction is proportional to the active mass of the reacting substances. For A-level purposes, active mass is the same as concentration in mol dm^{-3}. The law of mass action applies to an equilibrium in a homogeneous system. The sign $\rightleftharpoons$ shows the system can reach equilibrium.

In the equilibrium

$$a\text{A} + b\text{B} \rightleftharpoons c\text{C} + d\text{D}$$

the equilibrium constant $K_c = \dfrac{[\text{C}]^c[\text{D}]^d}{[\text{A}]^a[\text{B}]^b}$ at constant temperature.

By convention, the concentrations of products are divided by the concentrations of reactants.

Equilibrium constants can be calculated using concentrations in mol dm^{-3}, and the equilibrium constant is represented by K_c. Partial pressures can also be used to calculate equilibrium constants and the equilibrium constant is then represented by K_p.

Example:

$$CH_3COOH(l) + C_2H_5OH(l) \rightleftharpoons CH_3COOC_2H_5(l) + H_2O(l)$$

Calculate K_c in terms of a, b and x if a moles of ethanoic acid and b moles of ethanol are mixed and left to reach equilibrium and x moles of ethanoic acid are used up.

	CH$_3$COOH	+ C$_2$H$_5$OH	$\rightleftharpoons$ CH$_3$COOC$_5$H$_5$	+ H$_2$O
Initially	a moles	b moles	0	0
At equilibrium	$(a-x)$ moles	$(b-x)$ moles	x moles	x moles

If the total volume of the mixture is V dm^{-3}

$$[CH_3COOH] = \frac{a-x}{V} \quad [C_2H_5OH] = \frac{b-x}{V} \quad [CH_3COOC_2H_5] = \frac{x}{V} \quad [H_2O] = \frac{x}{V}$$

(All units are mol dm^{-3}.)

$$K_c = \frac{[CH_3COOC_2H_5][H_2O]}{[CH_3COOH][C_2H_5OH]}$$

Substituting

$$K_c = \frac{\dfrac{x}{V} \times \dfrac{x}{V}}{\dfrac{(a-x)}{V} \times \dfrac{(b-x)}{V}} = \frac{x^2}{(a-x)(b-x)}$$

In this case, the volume of the mixture has no effect on the equilibrium constant. If 1 mole of ethanoic acid and 1 mole of ethanol come to equilibrium, two thirds of a mole of acid is used up. Calculate K_c.

Substitute $a = 1$ mole, $b = 1$ mole, $x = \dfrac{2}{3}$ mole

$$K_c = \frac{\frac{2}{3} \times \frac{2}{3}}{\frac{1}{3} \times \frac{1}{3}} = 4$$

(NB K_c has no units)

15.3 K_p

In reactions involving gases, measuring the concentrations of the gases is difficult to do. It is more convenient to use partial pressures.

For the reaction

$$N_2(g) + 3H_2(g) \rightleftharpoons 2NH_3(g)$$

$$K_p = \frac{p_{NH_3}^2}{p_{N_2} \times p_{H_2}^3}$$

The numerical values for K_c and K_p for a particular reaction at the same temperature are clearly different, although mathematically related. Just be consistent.

15.4 EQUILIBRIUM IN A HETEROGENEOUS SYSTEM

The law of equilibrium can be modified to include heterogeneous systems. The common example is the heating of calcium carbonate in a closed system to prevent the escape of carbon dioxide

$$CaCO_3(s) \rightleftharpoons CaO(s) + CO_2(g)$$

The vapour above the solid is a homogeneous system and

$$\frac{p_{CaO}}{p_{CaCO_3}} \times p_{CO_2} = \text{constant}$$

where p represents partial pressure. Thus at constant temperature the partial pressures of calcium carbonate and calcium oxide are constant. This is because the vapour pressures of solids are constant at constant temperature

$$K_p = p_{CO_2}$$

From this it follows that at any particular temperature, the partial pressure of carbon dioxide is constant.

15.5 QUALITATIVE APPROACH TO EQUILIBRIUM – LE CHATELIER'S PRINCIPLE

The way in which the position of an equilibrium will change if one of the conditions is changed is predicted qualitatively using **Le Chatelier's principle.**

Le Chatelier's principle states that if one of the conditions is changed, the position of equilibrium will alter in such a way as to tend to restore the original conditions.

Consider the equilibrium

$$A + B \rightleftharpoons C + D$$

At equilibrium A, B, C and D are present, and the concentrations of these substances remains constant providing conditions are unchanged. If the forward reaction is encouraged, a new equilibrium will be set up. In this equilibrium [C] and [D] will have increased and [A] and [B] will have decreased. The equilibrium is said to have 'moved to the right'.

A system 'moves to the left' if the new equilibrium established contains higher concentrations of A and B and lower concentrations of C and D.

The conditions which are commonly changed are:

❶ concentrations of reactants or products;

❷ temperature; and

❸ pressure (this is only important in reactions involving gases).

These conditions are considered separately.

Concentration

If the product C is removed by liquefaction, escapes into the atmosphere, etc., the reverse reaction cannot occur. The position of the equilibrium moves to the right. If the concentration of A or B is increased, again the forward reaction is encouraged and again the equilibrium moves to the right. K_c and K_p remain constant.

Temperature

The change that takes place in an equilibrium when temperature is altered depends upon whether the forward reaction is exothermic or endothermic (Fig. 15.1).

If the forward reaction is exothermic, the reverse reaction will be endothermic. The equilibrium can be written

$$A + B \rightleftharpoons C + D \qquad \Delta H \text{ is negative}$$

If the temperature of the system is raised, the equilibrium moves to the left as the endothermic process will tend to reduce the temperature, i.e. restore the original conditions. Conversely, if the temperature is decreased, the equilibrium moves to the right. K_c and K_p change.

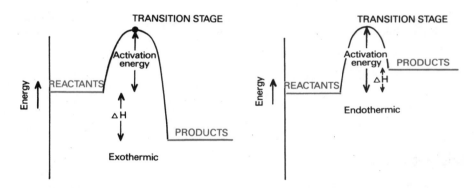

Fig. 15.1 Energy changes in exothermic and endothermic reactions

Pressure

For a reaction involving gases, altering the pressure may cause a change in the position of the equilibrium.

For the reaction

$$H_2(g) + I_2(g) \rightleftharpoons 2HI(g)$$

at 700 °C, the numbers of moles of reactants and products are the same. Pressure has no effect on the position of the equilibrium.

For a reaction where there is an increase in the number of moles from reactants to products, increasing the pressure moves the equilibrium to the left. Where there is a decrease in the number of moles from reactants to products, increasing the pressure moves the equilibrium to the right. K_c and K_p remain constant.

15.6 DISTRIBUTION OF A SOLUTE BETWEEN TWO IMMISCIBLE SOLVENTS

Ethoxyethane (diethyl ether) and water only dissolve very slightly in each other and can be considered to be **immiscible**. When mixed they form two separate layers.

If a solute is added to the mixture of ethoxyethane and water, and the mixture is shaken until an equilibrium exists, the following relationship usually applies.

$$\frac{\text{Concentration of solute in ethoxyethane}}{\text{Concentration of solute in water}} = \text{constant}$$

This constant is called the **distribution ratio** or **partition coefficient** and the relationship is called the **distribution law** or **partition law**.
This simple relationship applies providing:

❶ the temperature is constant;

❷ the solubility of the solute in either solvent is not exceeded; and

❸ the solute is in the same molecular state in both solvents.

It is possible that either **association** or **dissociation** of the solute may occur in one or more of the solvents.

Association

If benzenecarboxylic acid (benzoic acid) is added to a mixture of water and benzene (two immiscible solvents), association of benzenecarboxylic acid occurs in the benzene layer.

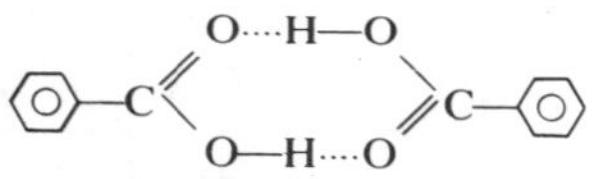

Dissociation

In the aqueous layer, benzenecarboxylic acid is partially dissociated into ions.

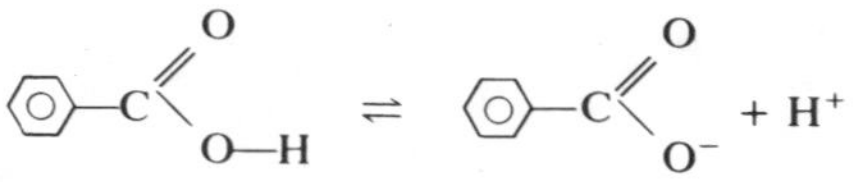

The distribution law is modified where the solute is associated or dissociated in one or more of the immiscible solvents.

If solute S is distributed between two immiscible solvents X and Y and exists in the form of single molecules in X but as S_n in Y, then at constant temperature,

$$\frac{\text{Concentration of S in X}}{\sqrt[n]{\text{Concentration of S in Y}}} = \text{constant}$$

Solvent extraction (see 7.2) is the principal application of the distribution law.

Chapter roundup

Equilibrium can exist in a reaction when the reaction is reversible and the reactants and products cannot escape. When a system is at equilibrium the rate of the forward reaction equals the rate of the reverse reaction. However, this is a very unstable situation and a slight change in external conditions can alter the position of the equilibrium.

It takes time to establish an equilibrium but when it is established the concentrations of reactants and products remain constant. Students often then state that the reaction is complete. The reaction still continues but the rate of the forward reaction balances the rate of the reverse reaction. A catalyst does not alter the position of an equilibrium. It does, however, speed up the establishment of equilibrium.

Your consideration of equilibrium can be on two levels:

❶ a qualitative treatment using Le Chatelier's principle; or

❷ a quantitative treatment using the equilibrium law.

Look carefully at the questions to see which approach you should take.

Worked questions and answers

1   The following equilibrium is exothermic for the left to right reaction.

$$2SO_2(g) + O_2(g) \rightleftharpoons 2SO_3(g)$$

(a) Write down the equilibrium expression for K_c.

(b) In which units will K_c be expressed?

(c) Write down the equilibrium expression for K_p, explaining the symbols you use.

(d) State the effect, if any, of each of the following on the equilibrium concentrations of SO_3 in particular
(i) decrease of pressure,
(ii) decrease of temperature,
(iii) addition of an inert gas to the system at equilibrium, while maintaining the pressure constant.

(WJEC)

Tutorial note

(a)
$$K_c = \frac{\left[SO_3\right]^2}{\left[SO_2\right]^2\left[O_2\right]}$$

(b) Concentrations are expressed in units of mol dm^{-3}

$$K_c = \frac{\left(\text{mol dm}^{-3}\right)^2}{\left(\text{mol dm}^{-3}\right)^2\left(\text{mol dm}^{-3}\right)}$$

$$= \text{mol}^{-1}\,\text{dm}^3$$

NB The units for an equilibrium constant will depend upon the expression for K_c. For the reaction between ethanol and ethanoic acid, K_c has no units.

(c)
$$K_p = \frac{p_{SO_3}^2}{p_{SO_2}^2 \times p_{O_2}}$$

The units of K_p are atm^{-1} or kPa^{-1}.

(d) (i) Decreasing the pressure would move the equilibrium to the left, decreasing the concentration of SO_3. There are more molecules and, on decreasing the pressure, the equilibrium moves to increase the number of molecules. This is in accordance with Le Chatelier's principle.

(ii) The forward reaction is exothermic. A decrease in temperature moves the equilibrium to the right to produce more sulphur trioxide. This is in accordance with Le Chatelier's principle. The equilibrium moves to the right to produce more heat.

(iii) K_p is constant but reduction of the partial pressure of the gases moves the equilibrium to the left. The inert gas, as such, has no effect and the situation is effectively the same as in (d) (i).

2 The following equation represents the decomposition of hydrogen iodide into hydrogen and iodine.

$$2HI \rightleftharpoons H_2 + I_2$$

0.256 g of hydrogen iodide was heated at 764 K in a bulb of volume 100 cm³. When an equilibrium was established, the bulb was cooled to room temperature and the iodine present determined by titration. It was found that 0.00028 moles of iodine were present.

(a) Why is there almost no change in the concentration of iodine when the bulb is cooled quickly to room temperature?

(b) Calculate:
  (i) the number of moles of HI in 0.256 g;
  (ii) the number of moles of hydrogen formed;
  (iii) the number of moles of hydrogen iodide unreacted.

(c) Calculate K_c for the reaction at 764 K.
$$(A_r(H) = 1, A_r(I) = 127)$$

Tutorial note

(a) The equilibrium mixture can be cooled quickly to room temperature or quenched without significantly changing the position of the equilibrium because the rate of reaction is decreased dramatically by lowering the temperature.

(b) (i) Number of moles of HI = $\frac{0.256}{128}$ = 0.002

(ii) From the equation the number of moles of iodine present equals the number of moles of hydrogen present. Number of moles of hydrogen = 0.00028

(iii) Number of moles of hydrogen iodide remaining = 0.002 − 0.00056 = 0.00144

NB Twice as many HI molecules are used up as I_2 molecules produced.

(c)
$$K_c = \frac{[H_2][I_2]}{[HI]^2}$$

The volume is 100 cm³.

$[H_2] = 0.0028$ mol dm⁻³, $[I_2] = 0.0028$ mol dm⁻³, $[HI] = 0.0144$ mol dm⁻³.

Substitute and calculate. $K_c = 0.00378$.

Question bank

1 (a) State Le Chatelier's principle.

(b) Many commercially important processes involve equilibrium reactions. Give *two* examples of such processes, naming each process and giving the appropriate equation(s).

(c) In the Mond process for the purification of nickel, carbon monoxide is passed over impure nickel at 50 °C to form, at this temperature, gaseous nickel tetracarbonyl, $Ni(CO)_4$. This vapour is then passed over pure nickel pellets at 230 °C, when the nickel tetracarbonyl decomposes, depositing pure nickel.

(i) Write one equation which summarises both processes.

(ii) Give the expression for K_c for the reaction in (c) (i).

(iii) If the concentration of $CO(g)$ in an equilibrium mixture is doubled, calculate the change in nickel tetracarbonyl concentration.

(iv) Hence, suggest a reason why a new Canadian plant operates at an elevated pressure of 20 atm in the first stage, compared to atmospheric pressure in older plants.

(ULEAC 1991)

ACIDS AND BASES

Units in this chapter

Chapter objectives

You probably have some idea about what acids and bases are from your GCSE course. You should know that

$$\text{acid} + \text{base} \rightarrow \text{salt} + \text{water}$$

You will also perhaps have some experience of using pH indicators and measuring pH. In this chapter we need to extend your understanding of the terms acid and base in terms of proton donors and acceptors or electron pair acceptors and donators. Extending the definition includes substances which you did not previously appreciate as acids.

Also you need to be very clear about terms such as strong and weak acids or bases. A popular misconception is that an acid is strong if it is corrosive and weak if it is not corrosive. Strong or weak refers to the degree of ionisation of the acid or base. A strong acid or base is completely ionised in solution.

Finally, the section on indicators should explain to you which indicator could be used in a particular acid–alkali titration.

16.1 DEFINITIONS OF ACIDS AND BASES

Brønsted and Lowry defined an **acid** as a **proton donor** and a **base** as a **proton acceptor.** A proton is the same as a positively charged hydrogen ion (H^+). In practice, H^+ ions do not exist in solution and are more likely to exist as H_3O^+.

The equation for the ionisation of hydrochloric acid is:

$$HCl(aq) + H_2O(l) \rightleftharpoons H_3O^+(aq) + Cl^-(aq)$$

Hydrochloric acid is an acid because it loses an H^+ ion to form a Cl^- ion. Water is a base because it accepts H^+ ions to form H_3O^+ ions.

Looking at the reverse reaction, H_3O^+ ions lose H^+ ions in forming H_2O and, therefore H_3O^+ is acting as an acid. Chloride ions accept H^+ ions to form HCl and, therefore, act as a base. The H_3O^+ is called the **conjugate acid** and Cl^- the **conjugate base** (i.e. the acid and base for the reverse process).

In the case of a general acid HA

$$HA(aq) + H_2O(l) \rightleftharpoons H_3O^+(aq) + A^-(aq)$$

The position of this equilibrium depends upon the strength of the acid. For a strong acid such as HCl the equilibrium lies well to the right, i.e. the acid may be considered as completely ionised. In such a case the base Cl^- is a very weak base. With a weak acid the equilibrium lies well to the left and A^- is a fairly strong base.

Water can also act as an acid:

$$NH_3 \quad + \quad H_2O \quad \rightleftharpoons \quad NH_4^+ \quad + \quad OH^-$$

$$\textit{base} \qquad\quad \textit{acid} \qquad\qquad \textit{conjugate} \quad\; \textit{conjugate}$$
$$\textit{acid} \qquad\quad\; \textit{base}$$

Lewis widened the definitions of acid and base by defining an acid as an **electron pair acceptor**. This definition includes examples of acids and bases which would not be recognised using the other definitions. For example, the reaction between trimethylamine and boron trifluoride forms a solid salt.

$$CH_3-N \xrightarrow{\quad} B-F$$

Trimethylamine has an electron pair which can be donated to the boron trifluoride. Boron in BF_3 is electron deficient because it only has six electrons in the outer shell.

Trimethylamine acts as a Lewis base and boron trifluoride is a Lewis acid. Aluminium chloride also acts as a Lewis acid (see 23.1).

16.2 OSTWALD'S DILUTION LAW

Since the ionisations of weak acids and bases are equilibrium processes, the law of mass action (see 15.2) can be applied to them at constant temperature.

For example, consider the dissociation of 1 mole of a weak acid HA. If the volume of the solution containing one mole of acid is V dm^3 and α is the degree of dissociation, then

$$HA \quad \rightleftharpoons \quad H^+ \quad + \quad A^-$$

Before ionisation   1 mole   0   0

After ionisation $1 - \alpha$ mole α mole α mole

$$[HA] = \frac{1-\alpha}{V} \text{ mol dm}^{-3} \qquad \frac{\alpha}{V} \text{ mol dm}^{-3} \qquad \frac{\alpha}{V} \text{ mol dm}^{-3}$$

Applying the law of mass action

$$K = \frac{[H^+][A^-]}{[HA]}$$

$$K = \frac{\alpha^2}{(1-\alpha)V} \text{ mol dm}^{-3}$$

This expression is called **Ostwald's dilution law**. The equilibrium constant in this case is the **dissociation constant**. For very weak electrolytes, where little dissociation takes place, $(1 - \alpha)$ is approximately equal to 1 and the expression simplifies to

$$K = \frac{\alpha^2}{V} \text{ or } K = \alpha^2 c$$

where V is the volume containing one mole and c is the concentration in mol dm^{-3}.

Although the degree of dissociation of the acid changes with dilution, the value of K is unchanged at constant temperature.

Example: The degree of dissociation of 0.02 M benzenecarboxylic acid, C_6H_5COOH, is 0.056 at 25 °C. Calculate the dissociation constant of the acid at this temperature.

$$C_6H_5COOH \rightleftharpoons C_6H_5COO^- + H^+$$

Using Ostwald's dilution law

$$K = \frac{\alpha^2}{(1-\alpha)V} \qquad V = 50 \text{ dm}^{-3}$$

$$K = \frac{0.056^2}{(1-0.056)50} = 0.000063 \text{ mol dm}^{-3}$$

16.3 IONIC PRODUCT OF WATER

Even if water is purified by repeated distillations, the electrical conductivity never falls to zero.

This is because of the **self-ionisation** of water. This can be represented either by

$$2H_2O(l) \rightleftharpoons H_3O^+(aq) + OH^-(aq)$$
or
$$H_2O(l) \rightleftharpoons H^+(aq) + OH^-(aq)$$

Using the simpler equation

$$K_c = \frac{[H^+][OH^-]}{[H_2O]}$$

Only a few molecules of water ionise and $[H_2O]$ can be regarded as constant at constant temperature.

$$K_w = K_c \times \text{constant} = [H^+][OH^-]$$

This is called the **ionic product** of water.

At 25 °C, $K_w = 1 \times 10^{-14}$ mol^2 dm^{-6} and because, from the equation, the concentrations of H$^+$ and OH$^-$ are equal:

$$[H^+] = [OH^-] = 1 \times 10^{-7} \text{ mol dm}^{-3}$$

In any aqueous solution the product of the concentration of H$^+$ and OH$^-$ is 1×10^{-14} mol^2 dm^{-6}. In a neutral solution both $[H^+]$ and $[OH^-]$ equal 1×10^{-7} mol dm^{-3}.

The ionic product is useful in A-level questions. If either the $[OH^-]$ or $[H^+]$ is known, the other one can be calculated. For example, a solution contains $[OH^-] = 10^{-1}$ mol dm^{-3}, find $[H^+]$. Since $[H^+][OH^-] = 1 \times 10^{-14}$ mol^2 dm^{-6} and $[OH^-] = 10^{-1}$ mol dm^{-3}, $[H^+] = 10^{-13}$ mol dm^{-3}.

16.4 pH

A solution which is neutral contains

$$[H^+] = [OH^-] = 10^{-7} \text{ mol dm}^{-3}$$

If a solution is acidic

$$[H^+] > [OH^-]$$

and if the solution is alkaline

$$[H^+] < [OH^-]$$

The concentrations of the ions are all very small, for example, a weak acid might have $[H^+] = 6.28 \times 10^{-6}$ mol dm^{-3}.

The system of pH is designed to simplify these values by removing the awkward negative indices.

pH is defined as $-\log_{10}[H^+]$.

A solution with $[H^+] = 10^{-7}$ mol dm^{-3} has a pH = 7. This is a neutral solution.

Solutions that are acidic have a pH less than 7. A solution of hydrochloric acid (0.1 mol dm^{-3}) ionises to produce 0.1 mol dm^{-3} of H^+ ions (10^{-1} mol dm^{-3}). The pH of this solution is 1 (i.e. $-\log_{10} 10^{-1}$). A solution with $[H^+] = 6.28 \times 10^{-6}$ mol dm^{-3} has a pH of 5.20.

Solutions in which $[OH^-]$ is greater than $[H^+]$ are alkaline and have a pH greater than 7. A solution of sodium hydroxide (0.1 mol dm^{-3}) ionises to produce 0.1 mol dm^{-3} of OH^- (10^{-1} mol dm^{-3}) Using the ionic product of water,

$$[H^+][OH^-] = 10^{-14} \text{ mol}^2 \text{ dm}^{-6}$$
$$[H^+] = 10^{-13} \text{ mol dm}^{-3}$$
$$pH = -\log_{10}[H^+] = 13$$

16.5 COMPARING THE STRENGTH OF WEAK ACIDS AND BASES

For a weak acid HA in water, the equilibrium in the solution will be

$$HA + H_2O \rightleftharpoons H_3O^+ + A^-$$

The equilibrium constant K_c is given by

$$K_c = \frac{[H_3O^+][A^-]}{[HA][H_2O]}$$

In a dilute solution $[H_2O]$ is large and effectively constant, so

$$\frac{[H_3O^+][A^-]}{[HA]} = K_c \times \text{constant} = K_a$$

K_a (called the **acid dissociation constant**) is the measure of the strength of an acid. For example, for methanoic acid $K_a = 1.6 \times 10^{-4}$ mol dm^{-3}; it is obvious that the ionisation of this acid is small, and many organic acids have even smaller values.

All K_a values are very small and it is convenient to record the strengths of acids as pK_a values. (This is similar to the use of pH for recording $[H^+]$.)

$$pK_a = -\log_{10} K_a$$

The important thing to remember is that the **smaller** the value of pK_a, the larger is the value of K_a and the **stronger** is the acid.

The equilibrium that exists when a base is added to water is

$$B + H_2O \rightleftharpoons BH^+ + OH^-$$

Again $[H_2O]$ is approximately constant, so

$$K_b = \frac{[BH^+][OH^-]}{[B]}$$

where K_b is the **base dissociation constant**. It is a measure of the strength of a base and, for convenience, it is usually expressed as a pK_b value. The **smaller** the value of pK_b the **stronger** is the base.

16.6 INDICATORS AND ACID –ALKALI TITRATIONS

Most indicators for acid–alkali titrations are weak acids or bases. Phenolphthalein is a weak acid and it dissociates

$$H_2O + HA \rightleftharpoons H_3O^+ + A^-$$
$$\textit{colourless} \qquad\qquad \textit{pink}$$

HA exists in acid solution and A^- in alkaline solution. If acid is added to the equilibrium mixture, the equilibrium moves to the left and the solution turns colourless. Addition of alkali removes H_3O^+ ions and moves the equilibrium to the right, turning the solution pink.

Methyl orange is a weak base which dissociates

$$BOH \rightleftharpoons B^+ + OH^-$$
$$\textit{yellow} \quad \textit{red}$$

BOH exists in alkaline solution and B^+ in acid solution. For a substance to be a good indicator, the two forms (HA and A^- for phenolphthalein and BOH and B^+ for methyl orange) must be different colours.

The weak acids and bases which act as indicators have varying K_a and K_b values and, in consequence, they change colour at different characteristic pH values.

Table 16.1 lists the common indicators, their colour change and the pH range in which the colour change occurs.

Table 16.1 *Colour changes of some common indicators*

Indicator	Acid solution	Approximate pH	Alkali solution
methyl orange	orange	4	yellow
methyl red	red	5	yellow
litmus	red	7	blue
phenolphthalein	colourless	9	red

In choosing the indicator for an acid–alkali titration it is important to consider the pH at which the indicator changes colour.

Fig. 16.1 shows curves of pH during titrations of the four types of acid–alkali titrations.

(a) Strong acid–strong base

e.g. $$NaOH(aq) + HCl(aq) \rightarrow NaCl(aq) + H_2O(l)$$

0.1 M sodium hydroxide solution is added to 25 cm^3 of 0.1 M hydrochloric acid. Initially, the pH of the solution is 1 and the pH increases as alkali is added. When 25.0 cm^3 of sodium hydroxide solution are added the solution is exactly neutral (pH 7) and further addition of sodium hydroxide solution gives a pH greater than 7 as all the acid is used up and the alkali is in excess. A suitable indicator changes colour on the vertical portion of the graph (between 3 and 11). On the vertical portion, there is a rapid change in pH with addition of a small amount of alkali. Any of the indicators in Table 16.1 would be suitable.

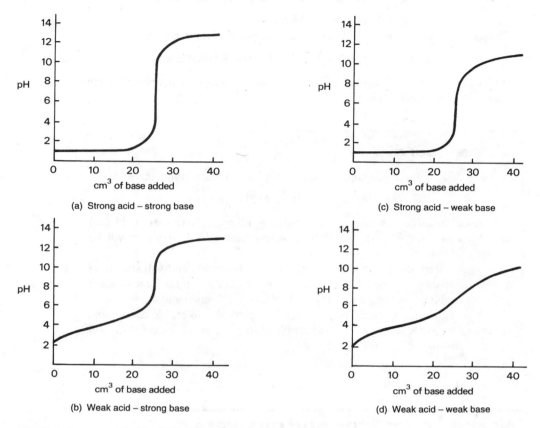

Fig. 16.1 Four types of acid–alkali titrations

(b) Weak acid–strong base

e.g. $CH_3COOH(aq) + NaOH(aq) \rightarrow CH_3COONa(aq) + H_2O(l)$

0.1 M ethanoic acid has a pH between 2 and 3 (not 1 as with a strong acid because it is not completely ionised). On addition of 0.1 M sodium hydroxide the curve in (b) is obtained. The vertical portion is between about 7 and 10 and phenolphthalein is the best indicator to use.

(c) Strong acid–weak base

e.g. $HCl(aq) + NH_3(aq) \rightarrow NH_4Cl(aq)$

This time the vertical portion of the graph is between about 3 and 7 and methyl orange or methyl red is suitable.

(d) Weak acid–weak base

e.g. $CH_3COOH(aq) + NH_3(aq) \rightarrow CH_3COONH_4(aq)$

There is no vertical portion on the graph. There is no sharp change in pH and no indicator is suitable.

It is possible to use different indicators for the same titration to detect different end points. For example, the reaction of sodium carbonate with dilute hydrochloric acid has the following overall equation

$$Na_2CO_3(aq) + 2HCl(aq) \rightarrow 2NaCl(aq) + H_2O(l) + CO_2(g)$$

This is detected by methyl orange or methyl red.

Phenolphthalein, however, will detect the end point of the reaction

$$Na_2CO_3(aq) + HCl(aq) \rightarrow NaHCO_3(aq) + NaCl(aq)$$

This end point requires only half of the volume of acid compared to that with methyl orange or methyl red as indicator.

Chapter roundup

A strong acid, such as hydrochloric acid, is completely ionised in aqueous solution.

$$HCl(aq) \rightarrow H^+(aq) + Cl^-(aq)$$

A solution of concentration $1.0 \, mol \, dm^{-3}$ would contain $1.0 \, mole \, dm^{-3} \, H^+(aq)$ and $1.0 \, mol \, dm^{-3} \, Cl^-(aq)$. Similarly, a strong base added to water will be completely ionised.

The concept of pH takes on a mathematical dimension and you should be able to calculate pH values. A useful thing to remember is that the ionic product of water enables you to calculate $[H^+]$ when $[OH^-]$ is known and vice versa.

The use of pH, pK_a and pK_b is a mathematical ploy to enable us to quote figures such as 1×10^{-5} in a standard positive form, i.e. in this case 5. You will use pK_a and pK_b in Chapter 39.

Worked questions and answers

1 For each of the following reactions, underline the substance on the left-hand side which is behaving as an acid, and the substance on the right-hand side which is its conjugate base:

$$\text{(a) } H_2O + HCl \rightarrow H_3O^+ + Cl^-$$
$$\text{(b) } CH_3COOH + OH^- \rightarrow CH_3COO^- + H_2O$$
$$\text{(c) } H_2SO_4 + HNO_3 \rightarrow HSO_4^- + H_2NO_3^+$$
$$\text{(d) } CH_3COOH + HNO_3 \rightarrow CH_3COOH_2^+ + NO_3^-$$

Tutorial note

Underline: (a) HCl and Cl^-

(b) CH_3COOH and CH_3COO^-

(c) H_2SO_4 and HSO_4^-

(d) HNO_2 and NO_3^-

2 Explain why the pH of 0.1 M hydrochloric acid is 1 but 0.1 M ethanoic acid has a pH of approximately 3.

Calculate the pH of

(a) hydrochloric acid ($0.01 \, mol \, dm^{-3}$)

(b) ammonia solution ($0.1 \, mol \, dm^{-3}$)

$$(K_b \text{ for ammonia} = 1.8 \times 10^{-5})$$

Tutorial note

A solution of hydrochloric acid (0.1 mol dm^{-3}) is fully ionised.

$$HCl + H_2O \rightarrow H_3O^+ + Cl^-$$

The solution of ethanoic acid is only partially ionised.

$$CH_3COOH + H_2O \rightleftharpoons CH_3COO^- + H_3O^+$$

The number of H_3O^+ ions in solution is greater in hydrochloric acid than in ethanoic acid.

(a) 0.01 mol dm^{-3} hydrochloric acid. The acid is completely ionised and the concentration of H^+ ions is 0.01 mol dm^{-3} (10^{-2} mol dm^{-3}).

$$pH = -\log_{10}[H^+] = 2$$

(b) $NH_3 + H_2O \rightleftharpoons NH_4^+ + OH^-$

$$K_b = \frac{\left[NH_4^+\right]\left[OH^-\right]}{\left[NH_3\right]}$$

If ammonia solution is 0.1 mol dm^{-3} and assuming no ionisation, $[NH_3] = 10^{-1}$ mol dm^{-3}. This has reduced to $(10^{-1} - x)$ mol dm^{-3} because x mol dm^{-3} have dissociated. Concentrations of NH_4^+ and OH^- are equal from the equation

$$K_b = \frac{x^2}{\left(10^{-1} - x\right)} = 1.8 \times 10^{-5}$$

It is useful here to use the approximation that since x is small, $(10^{-1} - x)$ is approximately equal to 10^{-1}. This will save you having to solve an awkward quadratic equation.

$$x^2 = 1.8 \times 10^{-6}$$
$$x = 1.34 \times 10^{-3} \text{ mol dm}^{-3} = [OH^-]$$

Using the ionic product of water

$$[H^+][OH^-] = 10^{-14} \text{ mol}^2 \text{ dm}^{-6}$$
$$[H^+] = 7.46 \times 10^{-12} \text{ mol dm}^{-3}$$
$$pH = -\log_{10}[H^+]$$
$$= 12 - \log_{10}7.46$$
$$= 11.13$$

Question bank

1 (a) (i) What is a Brønsted–Lowry acid?

(ii) What is a Brønsted–Lowry base?

(iii) In the equilibrium below, indicate by writing beneath each species whether it is an acid (A) or a base (B).

$$H_2O(l) + NH_4^+(aq) \rightleftharpoons NH_3(g) + H_3O^+(aq)$$

$$H_2O(l) + HSO_4^-(aq) \rightleftharpoons SO_4^{2-}(aq) + H_3O^+(aq)$$

$$CH_3CO_2H(l) + HClO_4(l) \rightleftharpoons CH_3CO_2H_2^+(aq) + ClO_4^-(aq)$$

(b) Aminoethanoic acid (glycine) is the simplest amino acid and has the formula $H_2NCH_2CO_2H$. Give the formula of the organic species formed when aminoethanoic acid is added to
(i) aqueous sodium hydroxide;
(ii) dilute hydrochloric acid.

(c) Show, by means of an equation, how two aminoethanoic acid molecules react to form a peptide link.

(d) The pH of tears is maintained at 7.4 by the use of a buffer solution consisting of proteins.
(i) Explain the term buffer solution.
(ii) Name a suitable mixture, other than one of proteins, which can act as buffer system.
(iii) Calculate the hydrogen ion concentration of tears.

(ULEAC 1990)

Points

This question links with 16.4, 17.2 and 36.3.

CHAPTER 17

SALT HYDROLYSIS, BUFFER SOLUTIONS, SOLUBILITY PRODUCT

Units in this chapter

Chapter objectives

At first sight this chapter contains three apparently unconnected ideas which could be considered in separate chapters. However, on closer examination all three topics are closely related to ionic equilibria.

Before attempting this chapter you should have studied Chapters 15 and 16. You will know that

$$\text{acid} + \text{base} \rightarrow \text{salt} + \text{water}$$

Many students consider that aqueous solutions of salts are always neutral. This is reinforced by the fact that sodium chloride (common salt) may be the first salt they encounter and it is neutral. In fact, salt solutions may be strongly acidic, slightly acidic, neutral, slightly alkaline or strongly alkaline. Aluminium chloride solution, for example, is extremely acidic.

Since an equilibrium is very unstable and can be easily disturbed, how can you maintain the pH of a solution if it is slightly contaminated? The usual method is to prepare a buffer solution which maintains its pH if contaminated. A buffer solution consists of either:

❶ a weak acid and a salt of the weak acid; or

❷ a weak alkali and a salt of the weak alkali.

The exact pH of the solution will depend upon the relative concentrations of the two components.

When aqueous solutions are mixed, an insoluble product may be precipitated, e.g.

$$CaCl_2(aq) + Na_2SO_4(aq) \rightarrow CaSO_4(s) + 2NaCl(aq)$$

If dilute solutions of calcium chloride and sodium sulphate are mixed together, no precipitate is formed, but a white precipitate is formed if concentrated solutions are mixed. A precipitate is formed if the product of the concentrations of the ions exceeds a certain value called the **solubility product**. It is important to remember that this applies at a constant temperature.

17.1 SALT HYDROLYSIS

The first task here is to recognise that a question is a salt hydrolysis question.

When a salt is dissolved in water, the resulting solution may be acid, alkaline or neutral. This is because the salt may have reacted to some extent with the water. This hydrolysis produces an acid and an alkali but they may not be of equal strength. There are four types of salt that should be considered.

Salt of a strong acid and a strong base

An example is sodium chloride. Sodium chloride is completely ionised in solution to form $Na^+(aq)$ and $Cl^-(aq)$. $H_3O^+(aq)$ and $OH^-(aq)$ are also present from the ionisation of a few of the water molecules. There is no interaction between the sodium and chloride ions and the water and as a result the concentrations of $H_3O^+(aq)$ and $OH^-(aq)$ are the same and the solution is exactly neutral.

Salt of a strong acid and a weak base

Examples are ammonium chloride and iron(III) chloride. In a solution of ammonium chloride, ammonium ions in the solution react with the solvent to produce additional $H_3O^+(aq)$ ions.

$$NH_4Cl(s) \rightarrow NH_4^+(aq) + Cl^-(aq)$$
and
$$NH_4^+(aq) + H_2O(l) \rightleftharpoons NH_3(aq) + H_3O^+(aq)$$

The resulting solution is acidic because of an excess of $H_3O^+(aq)$ ions over $OH^-(aq)$ ions.

A solution of iron(III) chloride in water is appreciably acidic. It will react rapidly with magnesium to produce hydrogen. The explanation for the acidity of the solution will be found in 28.8. Similarly, the explanation of the acidity of a solution of aluminium chloride will be found in 23.4.

Salt of a weak acid and a strong base

An example is sodium ethanoate. The ionisation of sodium ethanoate produces $CH_3COO^-(aq)$ and $Na^+(aq)$. The resulting solution is alkaline, however, because of reaction between the ethanoate ions and the water to produce an excess of $OH^-(aq)$ ions.

$$CH_3COONa(s) \rightarrow CH_3COO^-(aq) + Na^+(aq)$$
$$CH_3COO^-(aq) + H_2O(l) \rightleftharpoons CH_3COOH(aq) + OH^-(aq)$$

Salt of a weak acid and a weak base

An example is ammonium ethanoate. Ammonium ethanoate is ionised in solution to produce $NH_4^+(aq)$ and $CH_3COO^-(aq)$ ions. Both of these ions react with water.

$$NH_4^+(aq) + H_2O(l) \rightleftharpoons NH_3(aq) + H_3O^+(aq)$$
$$CH_3COO^-(aq) + H_2O(l) \rightleftharpoons CH_3COOH(aq) + OH^-(aq)$$

Whether the final solution is slightly acidic, slightly alkaline or neutral depends upon the position of the two equilibria. In fact this solution is almost neutral.

17.2 BUFFER SOLUTIONS

A **buffer solution** is a solution of constant pH. The pH of the solution will not change appreciably if the solution is contaminated with traces of acid or alkali.

An acidic buffer solution (i.e. with pH less than 7) is prepared by mixing together definite amounts of a weak acid and the sodium or potassium salt of the same acid, e.g. ethanoic acid and sodium ethanoate.

An alkaline buffer (i.e. with pH greater than 7) is prepared by mixing a weak base and a soluble salt of the base, e.g. ammonia solution and ammonium chloride.

The most frequent mistake at A level is to fail to appreciate that a weak acid or base is required to make a buffer solution. Statements such as 'hydrochloric acid and sodium chloride can be used to make a buffer solution' are common but wrong.

The mixture of ethanoic acid and sodium ethanoate acts as a buffer as follows:

$$CH_3COOH(aq) + H_2O(l) \rightleftharpoons CH_3COO^-(aq) + H_3O^+(aq)$$
$$CH_3COONa(s) \rightarrow CH_3COO^-(aq) + Na^+(aq)$$

The resulting mixture contains a large concentration of ethanoate ions, most of which come from the sodium ethanoate.

If $H_3O^+(aq)$ ions are added, the equilibrium in the first equation is disturbed and moves to the left in order to reduce the $H_3O^+(aq)$ concentration. This is in accordance with Le Chatelier's principle and the concentration of $H_3O^+(aq)$ (i.e. the acidity) remains unchanged.

If $OH^-(aq)$ ions are added, they remove the $H_3O^+(aq)$ ions from the solution.

$$H_3O^+(aq) + OH^-(aq) \rightarrow 2H_2O(l)$$

The equilibrium in the first equation is disturbed by the removal of $H_3O^+(aq)$. The equilibrium moves to the right to produce more $H_3O^+(aq)$ and restore the pH of the solution.

The mixture of ammonia solution and ammonium chloride acts as a buffer solution:

$$NH_3(aq) + H_2O(l) \rightleftharpoons NH_4^+(aq) + OH^-(aq)$$
$$NH_4Cl(s) \rightarrow NH_4^+(aq) + Cl^-(aq)$$

This buffer solution contains a large concentration of $NH_4^+(aq)$ ions. Most of these ions come from the ammonium chloride which is completely ionised.

If $OH^-(aq)$ ions are added, the equilibrium in the first equation moves to the left in accordance with Le Chatelier's principle (see 15.5). This reduces the concentration of the $OH^-(aq)$ and restores the original pH.

If $H_3O^+(aq)$ ions are added, they remove $OH^-(aq)$ from the solution. The equilibrium moves to the right to produce more $OH^-(aq)$.

Quantitative approach to buffer solutions

If we consider the simple ionisation of ethanoic acid

$$CH_3COOH(aq) \rightleftharpoons CH_3COO^-(aq) + H^+(aq)$$

Applying the law of equilibrium (see 15.2)

$$K_a = \frac{[CH_3COO^-][H^+]}{[CH_3COOH]} \text{ or } [H^+] = K_a \frac{[CH_3COOH]}{[CH_3COO^-]}$$

$$pH = -\log_{10}[H^+] = -\log_{10}K_a - \log_{10}\frac{[CH_3COOH]}{[CH_3COO^-]}$$

NB ❶ The ratio $\dfrac{[CH_3COOH]}{[CH_3COO^-]}$ is the ratio of concentration of acid to base.

❷ The pH of a buffer solution depends upon the ratio of concentration of acid to base and not on the *actual* concentrations.

❸ When $[CH_3COOH]$ and $[CH_3COO^-]$ are equal, pH = $-\log_{10}K_a$.

K_a can be found by measuring the pH of a solution when a solution of an acid has been half neutralised by a strong base.

17.3   SOLUBILITY PRODUCT

The ideas of equilibrium can be applied to the equilibrium between an almost insoluble solid and its ions in solution. This leads to the concept of **solubility product** which explains the conditions under which precipitation from a solution will occur.

For example, silver chloride AgCl is a sparingly soluble salt.

$$AgCl(s) \rightleftharpoons Ag^+(aq) + Cl^-(aq)$$

An equilibrium is established when silver chloride is added to water. Using the ideas of equilibria (Chapter 15), the following expression can be obtained

$$K_s = [Ag^+(aq)][Cl^-(aq)]$$

[AgCl(s)] remains constant at constant temperature, as long as any solid remains in contact with the solution.

$$K_s = [Ag^+][Cl^-] = 2 \times 10^{-10} \ mol^2 \, dm^{-6}$$

where K_s is called the **solubility product**. The solubility product is the maximum value of the ionic product of Ag^+ and Cl^- ions that can exist in solution without precipitation occurring. If the product of the ionic concentrations exceeds this maximum value precipitation will occur.

Another common example is silver chromate(VI), Ag_2CrO_4, whose solubility product is

$$K_s = [Ag^+]^2 [CrO_4^{2-}] = 3 \times 10^{-12} \ mol^3 \, dm^{-9}$$

For the sparingly soluble electrolyte A_xB_y the equilibrium is:

$$A_xB_y (aq) \rightleftharpoons xA^{y+} (aq) + yB^{x-}(aq)$$

and the solubility product is

$$K_s = [A^{y+}]^x [B^{x-}]^y$$

The most frequent mistake with solubility product is to try to apply it to solids that are readily soluble. For example, when dry hydrogen chloride is bubbled through a saturated solution of sodium chloride, sodium chloride crystals precipitate out. Many candidates would state that the solubility product of sodium chloride had been exceeded and precipitation occurs. This statement is incorrect as the solubility product of sodium chloride is meaningless, since sodium chloride is so soluble.

The observation is explained by the **common ion effect**. The equation for the solubility of sodium chloride is

$$NaCl(s) \rightleftharpoons Na^+(aq) + Cl^-(aq)$$

Addition of a large concentration of chloride ions (from the hydrogen chloride) moves the equilibrium to the left and sodium chloride precipitates.

Solubility product can be used to calculate the solubility of a sparingly soluble solid in water. For example, the solubility product of iron(III) hydroxide $Fe(OH)_3$ at 25 °C is $8 \times 10^{-40} \ mol^4 \, dm^{-12}$. Calculate the solubility of iron(III) hydroxide in a saturated solution at 25 °C ($A_r(Fe) = 56.0$, $A_r(O) = 16.0$, $A_r(H) = 1.0$). Relative molecular mass of iron(III) hydroxide = $56 + (3 \times (16 + 1)) = 107$

$$Fe(OH)_3 \rightleftharpoons Fe^{3+} + 3OH^-$$
$$K_s = [Fe^{3+}][OH^-]^3 = 8 \times 10^{-40} \ mol^4 \, dm^{-12}$$

Now $3[Fe^{3+}] = [OH^-]$
Substitute

$$\begin{aligned} K_s &= [Fe^{3+}] (3[Fe^{3+}])^3 \\ &= 27 \, [Fe^{3+}]^4 = 8 \times 10^{-40} \end{aligned}$$

$$[Fe^{3+}]^4 = 0.3 \times 10^{-40}$$
$$[Fe^{3+}] = 0.74 \times 10^{-10} \text{ mol dm}^{-3}$$

Mass of iron(III) hydroxide dissolving per dm^3 $= 0.74 \times 10^{-10} \times 107$
$= 7.9 \times 10^{-9}$ g

Chapter roundup

The three topics in this chapter are closely linked and can occur in a practical situation, e.g. if you do not follow the instructions in a qualitative exercise you may not get a precipitate which should form, or you may wrongly assume that an acid is present because the pH is less than 7. You may have the salt of a strong acid and a weak base, e.g. ammonium sulphate.

There are clues about each topic to enable you to recognise the questions being asked.

➊ If the question is about salt hydrolysis it will mention aqueous solutions being acidic or alkaline. It probably will not use the words 'salt hydrolysis'.

➋ If the question is about buffer solutions it will mention constant pH or the solution being contaminated.

➌ If the question is about solubility product it will mention precipitation occurring or not occurring when solutions are mixed.

Worked questions and answers

1 (a) Write an expression for the solubility product of lead(II) chloride.
  (b) The solubility product of lead(II) chloride at 25 °C is 1.6×10^{-5} mol^3 dm^{-9}.
    (i) What is the solubility in mol dm^{-3} of lead(II) chloride in water at the same temperature?
    (ii) How many moles of chloride ion must be added to a solution of lead(II) nitrate containing 1 mol dm^{-3} at 25 °C in order to cause a precipitate of lead(II) chloride? Assume that there is no change in volume on adding the chloride ion.

Tutorial note

(a) $K_s = [Pb^{2+}][Cl^-]^2$
(b) (i) In the saturated solution $\qquad$ $2[Pb^{2+}] = [Cl^-]$
    Substitute in the equation $\qquad$ $K_s = [Pb^{2+}](2[Pb^{2+}])^2$
    $$4[Pb^{2+}]^3 = 1.6 \times 10^{-5}$$
    $$[Pb^{2+}]^3 = 4 \times 10^{-6}$$
    $$[Pb^{2+}] = 1.59 \times 10^{-2} \text{ mol dm}^{-3}$$
    (ii) Concentration of Pb^{2+} ions in solution = 1 mol dm^{-3}
Substitute $\qquad$ $1.6 \times 10^{-5} = 1 \times [Cl^-]^2$
    $$[Cl^-] = 4 \times 10^{-3} \text{ mol dm}^{-3}$$

2 In what proportions must solutions of ammonia and ammonium chloride (both 0.1 mol dm^{-3}) be mixed to obtain a buffer solution of pH 10.0 (K_a for the ammonium ion is 6×10^{-10} mol dm^{-3})?

Tutorial note

NH_4^+ (aq) $\rightleftharpoons$ NH_3 (aq) + H^+ (aq)
Acid $\qquad\qquad$ Base

$$pH = -\log_{10}K_a - \log_{10}\frac{[NH_4^+]}{[NH_3]} \qquad 10.0 = -\log_{10}6 \times 10^{-10} - \log_{10}\frac{[NH_4^+]}{[NH_3]}$$

$$\log_{10}\frac{[NH_4^+]}{[NH_3]} = -0.8 \qquad \frac{[NH_4^+]}{[NH_3]} = 0.16$$

$0.16 \, dm^3$ of ammonium chloride ($0.1 \, mol \, dm^{-3}$) need to be mixed with $1.0 \, dm^3$ of $0.1 \, mol \, dm^{-3}$ ammonia to give a solution of pH 10.0.

CHAPTER 18

FURTHER OXIDATION AND REDUCTION

Units in this chapter

Chapter objectives

In Chapter 6 we extended our understanding of oxidation and reduction by using the idea of electron transfer. Oxidation involves electron loss and reduction electron gain. We also introduced the concept of oxidation state to allow us to recognise when oxidation and reduction were occurring. Before attempting this chapter go back and revise Chapter 6.

In Chapter 13 we introduced free energy change and you should appreciate that for a reaction to take place ΔG has got to be negative.

At GCSE level you will probably have studied the **reactivity series**. This is a list of metals in order of decreasing reactivity. In this chapter you will meet the **electrochemical series**, which is a very similar list of metals, this time using the order of redox potentials – a measure of how easily electrons are lost into solution.

18.1 ELECTROCHEMICAL CELLS

When a metal rod is dipped into a solution of metal ions an equilibrium is set up. There is a tendency for the metal to form positive metal ions and go into solution. There is also a tendency for metal ions in solution to gain electrons from the metal and be deposited. This can be summarised as:

$$M(s) \rightleftharpoons M^{n+}(aq) + ne^-$$

Whether the metal acquires an overall positive or negative charge depends upon the position of the equilibrium. This depends upon the particular metal. With reactive metals the equilibrium lies well to the right-hand side.

A metal dipping into a metal salt solution is called a **half cell**. Combining two half cells together can produce an **electrochemical cell**. An electrochemical cell is shown in Fig. 18.1.

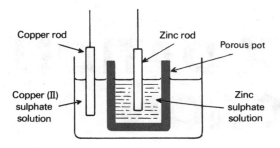

Fig. 18.1 An electrochemical cell

A zinc rod dips into a solution of zinc sulphate and a copper rod dips into a solution of copper(II) sulphate. The porous pot allows ions to move without the solutions mixing freely. This cell is called the **Daniell cell**.

In the Daniell cell the following reactions take place

$$Zn(s) \rightarrow Zn^{2+}(aq) + 2e^-$$
$$Cu^{2+}(aq) + 2e^- \rightarrow Cu(s)$$

The overall equation is obtained by addition.

$$Zn(s) + Cu^{2+}(aq) \rightarrow Zn^{2+}(aq) + Cu(s)$$

The chemicals possess a certain amount of chemical energy that is converted into electrical energy in the cell. The cell stops working when either the zinc rod or the copper(II) sulphate solution is used up.

The zinc ions go into solution. The electrons that are released flow through the external circuit to the copper electrode and are used to deposit the copper.

The maximum potential difference between the two electrodes is known as the **electromotive force** (emf). If both solutions have concentrations of 1 mol dm^{-3}, the emf of the Daniell cell is 1.1 V. The maximum potential difference is obtained when there is a large resistance in the external circuit so that a negligible current flows. The emf of a cell cannot be measured with an ordinary voltmeter because the resistance is insufficient. It is usually measured with a high resistance voltmeter or a potentiometer.

18.2 ELECTRODE POTENTIALS

The potential difference between a metal and a solution of its ions is dependent upon the materials used, the temperature and the concentration of the solution. The conditions are standardised with the temperature at 25 °C and the concentration of metal ions at 1 mol dm^{-3}. The **electrode potential** E is the potential difference in volts between the metal and the solution of metal ions. The standard electrode potential (represented by $E^\ominus$) is the electrode potential that exists when the solution of metal ions has a concentration of 1 mol dm^{-3} and the temperature is 25 °C. The potential difference is measured relative to the standard hydrogen electrode.

The standard electrode potentials $E^\ominus$ for some common metals are given in Table 18.1. Do not try to remember these values, they will be given on the examination paper. Do remember that, by convention, the *reduced* form (i.e. *after* gain of electrons) is put on the *right* of the equation for which $E^\ominus$ is given, so that an *electropositive* metal has a *negative* $E^\ominus$.

It is not possible to measure the potential difference between a metal and its ions in solution directly. It is possible, however, to measure the potential difference between two electrodes. The hydrogen electrode is used as a standard reference electrode and its standard electrode potential is arbitrarily taken as zero.

The standard electrode potential of a metal M is obtained by setting up two half cells, one with a rod of M dipping into a solution (concentration 1 mol dm^{-3}) of a salt of M and the other a hydrogen electrode (Fig. 18.2).

Table 18.1 *Standard electrode potentials for some common metals*

	$E^{\ominus}$/volts	
$K^+ + e^- \rightarrow K$	−2.92	
$Na^+ + e^- \rightarrow Na$	−2.71	
$Mg^{2+} + 2e^- \rightarrow Mg$	−2.37	Increasing
$Zn^{2+} + 2e^- \rightarrow Zn$	−0.76	tendency
$Fe^{2+} + 2e^- \rightarrow Fe$	−0.44	of electrode
$2H^+ + 2e^- \rightarrow H_2$	0.00 standard	to release
$Cu^{2+} + 2e^- \rightarrow Cu$	+0.34	electrons
$Ag^+ + e^- \rightarrow Ag$	+0.80	

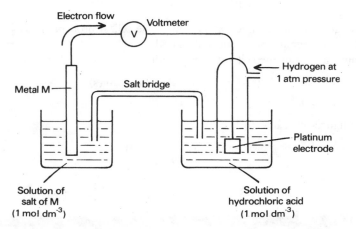

Fig. 18.2 Cell to obtain the standard electrode potential of the metal M

Note that the arrow in the circuit from the metal M to the platinum electrode is the direction of flow of electrons when the standard electrode potential is negative. If the standard electrode potential is positive the flow of electrons is in the opposite direction. Remember that the conduction in the external circuit is electronic, but in the solution and salt bridge it is ionic.

The salt bridge replaces the porous pot in Fig. 18.1. It consists of an agar jelly with added potassium chloride (or potassium nitrate). It allows charge to pass through it to complete the circuit, but limits diffusion of the solutions. The voltage of the cell measured with a potentiometer or a high resistance voltmeter is taken to be the electrode potential of the metal.

Although a hydrogen electrode is taken as standard, it is not easy to set up. In practice a **calomel electrode** is often used as a secondary reference electrode. It consists of mercury in contact with solid mercury(I) chloride and a solution of potassium chloride saturated with the mercury(I) salt.

18.3 WORKING OUT THE EMF OF A CELL

In the Daniell cell (see 18.1), the maximum voltage is 1.1 V. The cell can be represented by a cell diagram. In this case it is:

$$Zn(s) \mid Zn^{2+}(aq) \vdots Cu^{2+}(aq) \mid Cu(s)$$

This means that a zinc rod is dipped into a solution of zinc ions and this solution is connected by a salt bridge to a solution of copper(II) ions with a copper rod dipping into it.

By convention, the more negative electrode is put on the left-hand side. The emf of the cell is given by:

$$E_{cell} = E_{rhs} - E_{lhs} \qquad \text{(rhs – right-hand side,}$$
$$\text{lhs – left-hand side)}$$

In the case of the Daniell cell

$$E_{rhs} = 0.34 \text{ V } (Cu^{2+}(aq) + 2e^- \rightarrow Cu(s))$$
$$E_{lhs} = -0.76 \text{ V } (Zn^{2+}(aq) + 2e^- \rightarrow Zn(s))$$
$$E_{cell} = 0.34 - (-0.76) \text{ V}$$
$$= 0.34 + 0.76 \text{ V}$$
$$= +1.10 \text{ V}$$

(NB If you get a negative value for the emf of the cell, it probably means you have written the cell diagram the wrong way round.)

Calculate the emf of the cell with the cell diagram

$$Fe(s) \mid Fe^{2+}(aq) \vdots Ag^+(aq) \mid Ag(s)$$

Emf of the cell = $E_{rhs} - E_{lhs}$
Using the figures in Table 18.1

$$emf = 0.80 - (-0.44)$$
$$= +1.24 \text{ V}$$

18.4 REDOX POTENTIALS

The equation

$$Zn^{2+}(aq) + 2e^- \rightarrow Zn(s)$$

is a reduction process since electrons are gained (Chapter 6). The standard electrode potential (-0.76 V) is a measure of the relative willingness of zinc metal to be reduced or oxidised.

For copper

$$Cu^{2+}(aq) + 2e^- \rightarrow Cu(s) \ E^\ominus = 0.34 \text{ V}$$

This process therefore takes place more readily for copper than for zinc. The more positive the $E^\ominus$ value the more readily this process takes place.

There are three types of half cell.

1 A metal dipping into a solution of its ions, e.g. zinc dipping into a solution of zinc sulphate.

2 A gas in contact with an inert electrode, e.g. hydrogen in contact with a platinum electrode in the hydrogen electrode.

3 An inert metal in contact with a solution containing ions in two different oxidation states, e.g. a platinum electrode dipping into a solution containing $Fe^{2+}(aq)$ and $Fe^{3+}(aq)$ ions.

It is possible to extend Table 18.1 by including nonmetals. The standard redox potentials are measured by forming a half cell of one of the three types above and measuring the voltage with reference to the hydrogen electrode. The standard redox potentials for some nonmetals are given in Table 18.2.

Table 18.2 *Standard redox potentials for some nonmetals*

	$E^{\ominus}$ / V
$\frac{1}{2}I_2 + e^- \rightarrow I^-$	+0.54
$\frac{1}{2}Cl_2 + e^- \rightarrow Cl^-$	+1.36
$\frac{1}{2}F_2 + e^- \rightarrow F^-$	+2.85

18.5   THE ELECTROCHEMICAL SERIES

The arrangement of elements in order of their standard electrode potentials (Tables 18.1 and 18.2) leads to the **electrochemical series**. The element with the greatest negative $E^{\ominus}$ value is placed at the top of the list.

You may have met the electrochemical series at GCSE, or it may have been called the **reactivity series**, although the two are not exactly the same. The electrochemical series is useful for a number of reasons. Usually we restrict it only to metals.

① The order of reactivity of metals decreases down the series. For nonmetals the reactivity increases down the series (Table 18.3).

Table 18.3 *Order of reactivity for metals and nonmetals*

	Metals	Nonmetals	
Decreasing reactivity ↓	potassium sodium magnesium zinc iron copper silver		
		iodine bromine chlorine fluorine	**Increasing reactivity** ↓

② The electrochemical series can be used to predict reactions. For example, if iron is added to copper(II) sulphate solution, a reaction takes place producing iron(II) sulphate and copper.

$$Fe(s) + CuSO_4(aq) \rightarrow FeSO_4(aq) + Cu(s)$$

The cell can be represented by:

$$Fe(s) \mid Fe^{2+}(aq) \vdots Cu^{2+}(aq) \mid Cu(s)$$

Using the information in Table 18.1:

$$Fe \rightarrow Fe^{2+} + 2e^- \qquad E^{\ominus} = +0.44 \text{ V}$$
$$Cu^{2+} + 2e^- \rightarrow Cu \qquad E^{\ominus} = +0.34 \text{ V}$$

Adding the $E^{\ominus}$ values, $E^{\ominus}$ for the cell = +0.78 V. The reaction will occur if the $E^{\ominus}$ value is positive.

③ The electrochemical series explains why a piece of iron can be protected by galvanising, i.e. coating with a layer of zinc. If the surface is scratched so that water (containing dissolved carbon dioxide to produce an electrolyte) is in contact with both metals, an electrochemical cell is set up:

$$Zn(s) \mid Zn^{2+}(aq) \vdots Fe^{2+}(aq) \mid Fe(s)$$

This represents a cell with an $E^{\ominus}$ value of $+\,0.32$ V; the corrosion of iron is the reverse and is therefore unfavourable.

④ The electrochemical series can predict the products of electrolysis.

⑤ The electrochemical series is related to the methods available for extracting metals from metal ores.

18.6 THE FEASIBILITY OF A REACTION

If a chemical reaction is to take place spontaneously, the **standard free energy change** $\Delta G^{\ominus}$ must be negative (Chapter 13). There is an equation which relates $\Delta G^{\ominus}$ to the standard redox potential $E^{\ominus}$.

$$\Delta G^{\ominus} = -nFE^{\ominus}$$

where n is the number of electrons transferred and F is the Faraday constant. For a reaction to be feasible, $E^{\ominus}$ should be positive.

A positive E value does not give any indication of the speed of a reaction. If E is greater than about $+0.4$ V it can be assumed that the reaction will take place in the direction indicated, although it might take an infinitely long time.

18.7 NERNST EQUATION APPLIED TO THE DANIELL CELL

The variation of electrode potential with concentration is given by the Nernst equation

$$E = E^{\ominus} + \frac{2.3RT}{zF}\ln[\text{ion}]$$

where E is electrode potential, $E^{\ominus}$ is standard electrode potential, R is the gas constant, T is absolute temperature, z is the number of electrons transferred, F is the Faraday constant and [ion] is the concentration of the ionic species.

In the Daniell cell

$$E_{\text{cell}} = E_{\text{Cu}} - E_{\text{Zn}} = E_{\text{Cu}}^{\ominus} - E_{\text{Zn}}^{\ominus} - \frac{2.3RT}{zF}\ln[\text{Zn}^{2+}] + \frac{2.3RT}{zF}\ln[\text{Cu}^{2+}]$$

$$= E_{\text{cell}}^{\ominus} - \frac{2.3RT}{zF}\ln\frac{[\text{Zn}^{2+}]}{[\text{Cu}^{2+}]} \qquad \text{NB } K_{\text{c}} = \frac{[\text{Zn}^{2+}]}{[\text{Cu}^{2+}]}$$

If the cell is short-circuited by connecting the zinc and copper rods, the emf falls to zero and the cell reaction reaches equilibrium, i.e. $E_{\text{cell}} = 0$

$$E_{\text{cell}}^{\ominus} = \frac{RT}{zF}\ln K_{\text{c}} \qquad K_{\text{c}} = 10^{37}$$

Chapter roundup

There is frequent confusion between ionisation energy and redox potential. Perhaps these two equations will help to show you the difference.

Ionisation energy $\qquad Mg(g) \rightarrow Mg^{2+}(g) + 2e^-$

Redox potential $\qquad Mg(s) \rightarrow Mg^{2+}(aq) + 2e^-$

Redox potentials can be used together to calculate the emf of a cell.

Worked questions and answers

1 Use the equations

$$Fe^{3+} + e^- \rightarrow Fe^{2+} \qquad E^\ominus = +0.77 \text{ V}$$
$$Ag^+ + e^- \rightarrow Ag \qquad E^\ominus = +0.80 \text{ V}$$

to predict whether iron(III) ions are reduced by silver under standard conditions.

Tutorial note

The equation for the reaction is

$$Fe^{3+} + Ag \rightarrow Fe^{2+} + Ag^+$$

If the $E^\ominus$ value for the cell $Pt \mid Fe^{2+}, Fe^{3+} : Ag^+ \mid Ag$ is positive then the reaction is feasible.

$$E^\ominus{}_{cell} = E_{rhs} - E_{lhs}$$
$$= +0.77 - (+0.80) \text{ V}$$
$$= -0.03 \text{ V}$$

The reaction does not take place. For the reverse reaction the $E^\ominus$ value is $+ 0.03$ V and the reaction is feasible.

2 The reaction between peroxodisulphate ions and iodide ions in aqueous solution is represented by the equation

$$S_2O_8^{2-}(aq) + 2I^-(aq) \rightarrow 2SO_4^{2-}(aq) + I_2(aq)$$

This reaction is catalysed by Fe^{3+} ions but not by Cr^{3+}. Using the following standard electrode potentials, suggest a possible mechanism for this catalytic action

$$Fe^{3+}(aq) \ Fe^{2+}(aq) = +0.77 \text{ V}$$
$$S_2O_8^{2-}(aq) \ 2SO_4^{2-}(aq) = +2.01 \text{ V}$$
$$I_2(aq) \ 2I^-(aq) = +0.54 \text{ V}$$

What can be predicted about the standard electrode potential $Cr^{3+}(aq) \ Cr^{2+}(aq)$ in view of the fact that the Cr^{3+} ion does not catalyse the reaction?

Tutorial note

Possible mechanism in two stages:

❶ $\qquad 2Fe^{3+}(aq) + 2I^-(aq) \rightarrow I_2(aq) + 2Fe^{2+}(aq)$

❷ $\qquad S_2O_8^{2-}(aq) + 2Fe^{2+}(aq) \rightarrow 2Fe^{3+}(aq) + 2SO_4^{2-}(aq)$

The $E^\ominus$ values for stages 1 and 2 are +0.23 and +1.24 V, respectively. In both stages the $E^\ominus$ values are positive and therefore both stages are feasible and the mechanism is possible.

The fact that Cr^{3+} does not catalyse the reaction suggests that in a two stage mechanism one of the $E^\ominus$ values is negative (and this stage is, therefore, not feasible).

$$2I^-(aq) \rightarrow I_2(aq) + 2e^- \qquad\qquad E^\ominus = -0.54 \text{ V}$$

The $E^\ominus$ value for Cr^{3+} (aq) Cr^{2+} (aq) must be less negative than –0.54 V if the reaction is to be feasible. It is in fact –0.41 V and so no reaction takes place (you are not expected to remember this value).

3 The reaction between zinc powder and nickel(II) sulphate can be represented by:

$$Zn(s) + Ni^{2+}(aq) \rightarrow Zn^{2+}(aq) + Ni(s)$$

(a) Calculate the mass of nickel which could be formed if 1.308 g of zinc was added to excess nickel(II) sulphate solution (Ni = 59, Zn = 65.4).

(b) Draw a labelled diagram of the apparatus which could be used to measure the emf of the cell

$$Zn(s) \mid Zn^{2+}(aq) \vdots Ni^{2+}(aq) \mid Ni(s)$$

(c) Calculate $E^\ominus$ for the cell using Table 18.1 and

$$Ni^{2+} + 2e^- \rightarrow Ni \qquad\qquad E^\ominus = -0.25 \text{ V}$$

(d) Calculate $\Delta G^\ominus$ for the reaction given $F = 96\,500$ C mol^{-1}

(e) ΔS_{system} can be calculated at 298 K using $\Delta G^\ominus$, $\Delta H^\ominus$ and an equation in 13.13.
   (i) What is the equation?
   (ii) How would you attempt to find $\Delta H^\ominus$ by experiment?

Tutorial note

(a) 1 mol of Zn produces 1 mol Ni
   1.308 g of Zn = 1.308/65.4 = 0.02 mol Zn
   0.02 mol Ni = 0.02 × 59 = 1.18 g Ni

(b)

(c) $Ni^{2+} + 2e^- \rightarrow Ni \quad E^\ominus = -0.25$ V
      $Zn \rightarrow Zn^{2+} + 2e^- \quad E^\ominus = +0.76$ V
      $E^\ominus$ for cell = +0.51 V

(d) $\Delta G^\ominus = nFE^\ominus \qquad n = 2$ because 2 electrons transferred
   $\Delta G^\ominus = -2 \times 96\,500 \times 0.51 = 98\,430$ J mol^{-1} or 98.43 kJ mol^{-1}

(e) (i) $\Delta G = \Delta H - T\Delta S_{system}$
   (ii) Add slight excess of zinc powder to 100 cm^3 of 0.2 mol dm^{-3} nickel(II) sulphate solution (0.02 mole $NiSO_4$). Measure temperature rise, taking all precautions to minimise temperature loss. Calculate from results.

CHAPTER 19

VOLUMETRIC CALCULATIONS

Units in this chapter

Chapter objectives

Most candidates in an A-level Chemistry examination will have to carry out one or more volumetric calculations. These are calculations where volumes of solution are mixed together until they both completely react with no reactants left over. Often this point, called the **end point**, is detected using an indicator, but it could be detected in other ways, e.g. by pH meter, electrical conductivity measurement, energy changes, etc. From the results concentrations of solutions can be calculated.

Often these calculations occur in practical papers or assessments. Many candidates are frightened of them. They put down a formula and substitute numbers in it and hope for the best. This leads to as many wrong answers as right answers.

The key to these questions is usually to write a balanced, symbolic equation that gives the ratio of the reacting particles. Before attempting this chapter look back to Chapter 3.

19.1 VOLUMETRIC CALCULATIONS

Volumetric calculations are required for theory papers and often on practical papers. These calculations involve reactions between reacting volumes of solutions. When attempting this type of question it is important to ensure that you have a balanced equation for the reaction, e.g.

$$2NaOH(aq) + H_2SO_4(aq) \rightarrow Na_2SO_4(aq) + 2H_2O(l)$$

From the equation, 2 moles of sodium hydroxide react with 1 mole of sulphuric acid. If $25\,cm^3$ of sodium hydroxide solution ($0.1\,mol\,dm^{-3}$, although this may still be shown as 0.1 molar or 0.1 M) is neutralised by $20\,cm^3$ of sulphuric acid, we can use this equation to find the concentration of the sulphuric acid in $mol\,dm^{-3}$.

Sodium hydroxide

$1000\,cm^3$ of sodium hydroxide ($0.1\,mol\,dm^{-3}$) contain 0.1 mole of sodium hydroxide.

25 cm³ of 0.1 mol dm⁻³ sodium hydroxide contains $\dfrac{0.1 \times 25}{1000}$ mole

$$= 0.0025 \text{ mole}$$

From the equation,

2 moles of sodium hydroxide react with 1 mole of sulphuric acid

0.0025 mole NaOH reacts with 0.00125 mole H_2SO_4

Sulphuric acid

0.00125 mole of sulphuric acid is present in 20 cm³ of solution.

$\dfrac{0.00125 \times 1000}{20}$ mole of sulphuric acid would be present in 1000 cm³.

Molar concentration of sulphuric acid = 0.0625 mol dm⁻³.

All calculations can be worked out in a similar way. This method of working is far better than simply substituting in the equation

$$n_2 V_1 M_1 = n_1 V_2 M_2$$

where n_1 = number of moles of sulphuric acid in the equation = 1

V_1 = volume of sulphuric acid used = 20 cm³

M_1 = molar concentration of sulphuric acid – unknown

n_2 = number of moles of sodium hydroxide in the equation = 2

V_2 = volume of sodium hydroxide solution used = 25 cm³

M_2 = molar concentration of sodium hydroxide = 0.1 mol dm⁻³.

If you substitute the figures in the equation you will get the correct answer, but the problem comes when you make a mistake. The examiner has difficulty in awarding marks if you make a mistake in substituting in an equation. In the first method of calculation, marks can be awarded at each stage even if an error is made.

19.2 TYPES OF VOLUMETRIC CALCULATION

There are three types of volumetric analysis question which appear on theory papers.

1 Acid–base titration

The one above between sodium hydroxide and sulphuric acid is an example.

2 Redox titrations

These can be of two types but in both cases they involve transfer of electrons.

❶ Reactions involving acidified potassium manganate(VII) or potassium dichromate(VI).

❷ The reaction of iodine solution with sodium thiosulphate(VI). In some cases the iodine for titration is liberated from acidified potassium iodide solution by an oxidising agent such as potassium manganate(VII), potassium iodate(V) or copper(II) sulphate.

3 Precipitation titrations

The usual example here is the reaction of silver nitrate solution with chloride ions to precipitate silver chloride. The end point is usually detected with potassium chromate(VI) solution as indicator.

The following question section gives examples of some of these volumetric calculations.

> ## Chapter roundup
>
> Carefully look at the calculations at the end of this chapter. Try to see how the equation gives the ratio of the reacting species and how it is used in the calculation.

Worked questions and answers

1 (a) Give a half-equation for the oxidation of the ethanedioate ion, $C_2O_4^{2-}(aq)$, to carbon dioxide $CO_2(g)$.

(b) Give a half-equation for the reduction of the manganate(VII) ion, $MnO_4^-(aq)$, to manganese(II) ions, $Mn^{2+}(aq)$, in acidic conditions.

(c) Calculate the volume of an acidified solution of 0.02 M potassium manganate(VII), $KMnO_4$, which would be needed to oxidise 100 cm^3 of a saturated solution of magnesium ethanedioate, MgC_2O_4.

Solubility of magnesium ethanedioate at 20 °C is 9.3×10^{-3} mol dm^{-3}.

(Nuffield)

Tutorial note

(a) $C_2O_4^{2-}(aq) \rightarrow 2CO_2(g) + 2e^-$

(b) $MnO_4^-(aq) + 8H^+(aq) + 5e^- \rightarrow Mn^{2+}(aq) + 4H_2O(l)$

(c) $5C_2O_4^{2-}(aq) + 2MnO_4^-(aq) + 16H^+(aq) \rightarrow 10CO_2(g) + 8H_2O(l) + 2Mn^{2+}(aq)$

100 cm^3 of saturated MgC_2O_4 solution at 20 °C contains 9.3×10^{-4} mol.

From the equation

$$5 \text{ mol of } C_2O_4^{2-} \text{ reacts with 2 mol } MnO_4^-$$

$$9.3 \times 10^{-4} \text{ mol } C_2O_4^{2-} \equiv \frac{2 \times 9.3 \times 10^{-4}}{5} \text{ mol } MnO_4^-$$

$$1000 \text{ } cm^3 \text{ of } 0.02 \text{ M } MnO_4^- \text{ contain } 0.02 \text{ mol } MnO_4^-$$

$$\frac{1000 \times 2 \times 9.3 \times 10^{-4}}{0.02 \times 5} \text{ } cm^3 \text{ of } 0.02 \text{ M } MnO_4^- \text{ contain } \frac{2 \times 9.3 \times 10^{-4}}{5} \text{ mol}$$

Answer: 18.6 cm^3

This question would be more difficult if iron(II) ethanedioate had been used. Then both Fe^{2+} and $C_2O_4^{2-}$ would be oxidised.

2 A solution of arsenic(III) oxide containing 0.248 g required 50 cm^3 of acidified potassium manganate(VII) solution (0.02 mol dm^{-3}) for complete oxidation. What is the oxidation state of arsenic in the product? ($A_r(O) = 16$, $A_r(As) = 75$)

Tutorial note

$$As^{3+}(aq) \rightarrow As^{n+}(aq) + (n-3)e^-$$
$$MnO_4^-(aq) + 8H^+(aq) + 5e^- \rightarrow Mn^{2+}(aq) + 4H_2O(l)$$

$$5As^{3+}(aq) + (n-3)MnO_4^-(aq) + 8(n-3)H^+(aq) \rightarrow (n-3)Mn^{2+}(aq)$$
$$+ 4(n-3)H_2O(l) + 5As^{n+}(aq)$$

Number of moles $As_2O_3 = \dfrac{0.248}{150 + 48} = 0.00125$

Number of moles $As^{3+} = 0.0025$

50 cm^3 of potassium manganate(VII) (0.02 mol dm^{-3}) contain

$$\frac{50 \times 0.02}{1000} \text{ mole} = 0.001 \text{ mole potassium manganate(VII)}$$

From this information,
0.0025 mole As^{3+} reacts with 0.001 mole MnO_4^-
2.5 moles As^{3+} react with 1 mole MnO_4^-

In the equation, ratio $\dfrac{2.5}{1} = \dfrac{5}{n-3}$

Oxidation state of arsenic in the product = +5

Question bank

1 (a) Write a balanced equation for the reaction between iron(II) ions and manganate(VII) ions in acidified aqueous solution.
   (b) Calculate the volume of potassium manganate(VII) of concentration 0.02 mol dm⁻³ required to react exactly with 25.0 cm³ of iron(II) solution of concentration 0.08 mol dm⁻³.

Points

(a) For the equation refer to 6.4.
(b) It is important to get the relationship

$$5Fe^{2+} \equiv 1MnO_4^-$$

Then calculate the number of moles of iron(II) and manganate(VII), and finally the volume of 0.02 mol dm⁻³ potassium manganate(VII) containing this number of moles.
Answer: 20 cm³

2 Hydrogen peroxide is a colourless liquid with the formula H_2O_2. Its solution can be used as an antiseptic.
   (a) Work out the structural formula for the hydrogen peroxide molecule and draw it below.
   (b) A hospital technician was checking the concentration of a hydrogen peroxide solution. She titrated 25.0 cm³ portions of the solution against an acidified potassium permanganate solution.
   The reaction taking place during the titration is:
   $2MnO_4^-(aq) + 6H^+(aq) + 5H_2O_2(aq) \rightarrow 2Mn^{2+}(aq) + 8H_2O(l) + 5O_2(g)$
   (purple)   (colourless)
   The technician's results are shown in the table below:

Titration	1	2	3
Titre volume/cm³	16.5	15.8	15.8

   (i) How would the technician know that the end point of the titration had been reached?
   (ii) Why would the technician ignore the results of the first titration when calculating the mean titre volume?
   (iii) The concentration of the potassium permanganate was 0.101 mol dm⁻³.
   Use the technician's results to calculate the concentration of the hydrogen peroxide solution.
(Show your working clearly)

(SEB 1994)

Points

A possible structure of hydrogen peroxide is

The concentration of the hydrogen peroxide is 0.40 mol dm⁻³.

CHAPTER 20

RADIOACTIVITY

Units in this chapter

Chapter objectives

Radioactivity used to appear on O-level Chemistry and Physics courses. With the introduction of GCSE, radioactivity was dropped from many syllabuses. Now, with the new GCSE syllabuses based on the National Curriculum, radioactivity has reappeared.

In Chapter 1 we looked at atomic structure and we saw that protons and neutrons are closely packed in the nucleus and electrons orbit the nucleus. For most simple atoms the nucleus remains intact and only changes in electron numbers and arrangement occur during chemical reactions. However, in some atoms the nucleus breaks down and radiation occurs. The three types of radiation are α, β and γ radiation.

By the end of the chapter you should be able to write equations that summarise changes in atomic structure, e.g.

$$\ce{^2_1H} + \ce{^3_1H} \rightarrow \ce{^4_2He} + \ce{^1_0n}$$

Remember that the sums of the superscripts (mass numbers) on the left-hand side and the right-hand side should be the same.

$$2 + 3 = 4 + 1$$

Similarly with subscripts (atomic numbers)

$$1 + 1 = 2 + 0$$

You should also be able to calculate the half-life of a radioactive species from given results.

20.1 RADIOACTIVITY

Radioactivity is the spontaneous decay of unstable atoms with the emission of either α (alpha), β (beta) or γ (gamma) radiation. It was first observed by Becquerel who found that a uranium salt blackened a photographic plate wrapped in paper. The radiation coming from the radioactive source passed through the paper to expose the plate. The properties of α, β and γ radiation are as follows.

❶ α rays are composed of a stream of fast-moving helium nuclei (He^{2+}). They are deflected by a magnetic field because of their positive charge. They have a very limited penetrating power, being unable to penetrate even thin metal foil.

❷ β rays are composed of a stream of fast-moving electrons. They are greatly deflected by a magnetic field. They will penetrate a thin metal foil but are stopped by lead.

❸ γ rays are electromagnetic waves with very short wavelength. They are not deflected by a magnetic field as they are uncharged. They are more penetrating than α or γ rays, being able to pass through lead.

The effects of a magnetic field on α, β and γ radiation are summarised in Fig. 20.1.

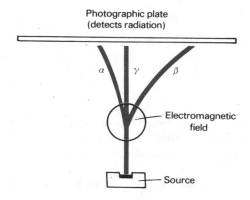

Fig. 20.1 Effects of a magnetic field on α, β and γ radiation

20.2 THE CONSEQUENCES OF α, β AND γ EMISSIONS

A radioactive isotope may decay with the emission of α, β or γ rays. If an atom loses an α particle, the particle produced will contain two protons and two neutrons less than the original atom, e.g.

$$^{238}_{92}U \xrightarrow{-\alpha} {}^{234}_{90}Th$$

A uranium-238 atom has a mass number of 238 and an atomic number of 92. On emission of an α particle, the resulting atom is an atom of thorium-234 (mass number 234, atomic number 90). Thorium is two places to the left of uranium in the Periodic Table.

The loss of a β particle from a radioactive nucleus can be explained by a change which takes place first in the nucleus. A *neutron* changes into a *proton plus an electron* and it is this electron which is lost. The resulting atom contains one less neutron and one more proton than the original atom. The mass number is unchanged but the atomic number is increased by one, e.g.

$$^{234}_{90}Th \xrightarrow{-\beta} {}^{234}_{91}Pa$$

A thorium-234 atom changes to a protactinium-234 atom. Protactinium is one place to the right of thorium in the Periodic Table.

There are no definite changes in atomic structure during γ emission.

20.3 HALF-LIFE OF RADIOACTIVE ISOTOPES

The **half-life** ($t_{\frac{1}{2}}$) of a radioactive isotope is the time taken for half the unstable nuclei in the sample to decay. It is independent of the original mass, unaffected by changes in temperature and cannot be catalysed. It can also be defined as the time required for the reactivity to drop to half its original value. Radioactive decay is a first-order process.

The half-life is characteristic of a particular isotope and may vary from a fraction of a second to millions of years.

The half-life is best determined graphically by plotting radioactive count against time (Fig. 20.2). Readings of radioactive count are taken with a Geiger counter at intervals. If a convenient reading is taken (say 2000) and the lines AB and BC drawn, then the lines DE and EF are drawn at a value which is half of the original reading. The time difference between F and C is called the half-life.

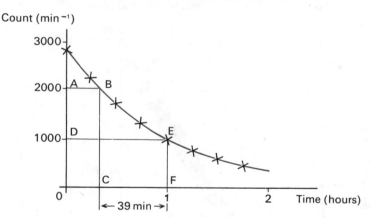

Fig. 20.2 Radioactive decay and half-life

20.4 ARTIFICIAL NUCLEAR REACTIONS

It is possible to carry out reactions which change one element into another. Usually one substance is bombarded by α particles, protons, neutrons or even heavier atoms such as carbon,

e.g. bombarding sodium atoms with neutrons

$$^{23}_{11}\text{Na} + ^{1}_{0}\text{n} \rightarrow ^{23}_{10}\text{Ne} + ^{1}_{1}\text{H}$$

Neutrons from an atomic reactor are particularly useful for bombarding other atoms because they are neutral and are not repelled.

e.g. bombarding beryllium atoms with α particles

$$^{9}_{4}\text{Be} + ^{4}_{2}\text{He} \rightarrow ^{12}_{6}\text{C} + ^{1}_{0}\text{n}$$

bombarding nitrogen atoms with neutrons

$$^{14}_{7}\text{N} + ^{1}_{0}\text{n} \rightarrow ^{14}_{6}\text{C} + ^{1}_{1}\text{H}$$

Carbon-14 is formed in this process. It is present in all living material. The detection of the amount of carbon-14 remaining in a sample is used for dating objects.

Bombarding californium with boron atoms gives

$$^{250}_{98}\text{Cf} + ^{11}_{5}\text{B} \rightarrow ^{257}_{103}\text{Lr} + 4^{1}_{0}\text{n}$$

This process produces unstable radioactive **isotopes** of elements, such as lawrencium, which do not exist naturally on earth.

In equations of this type it is important that the total atomic numbers on both sides are equal and also the sum of the mass numbers. In the equation for the production of lawrencium-257, the mass numbers add up to 261 and the atomic numbers add up to 103:

20.5 STABLE ISOTOPES

Fig. 20.3 shows a graph of the numbers of protons and neutrons in stable isotopes. Each point on the graph represents a stable isotope and you will notice a certain band of stability in which all of these isotopes are located. For atoms containing less than about 20 protons, the numbers of protons and neutrons are approximately the same (i.e. the band is close to the line representing 1:1 neutron:proton ratio). For more complicated atoms, the isotopes have a greater neutron:proton ratio.

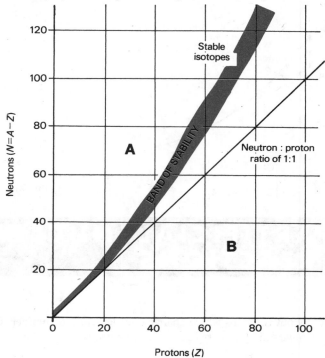

Fig. 20.3 Numbers of protons and neutrons in stable isotopes

Isotopes not lying within the band of stability will decay until they form products which lie within this band. Nuclei which are in area A achieve stability by the emission of β particles. Emission of a β particle reduces the number of neutrons by one and increases the number of protons by one. β decay has moved the point closer to the band of stability. A series of β decay processes would produce a nucleus within this band.

Nuclei in area B are neutron-deficient and can achieve stability by converting a proton into a neutron.

$$_1^1H \rightarrow {}_0^1n + {}_{+1}^0e$$

The positively charged electron, called a **positron**, is unstable and forms γ radiation. Again the point is moving closer to the band of stability. This process can also be achieved by K-electron capture where a nucleus in region B captures an orbital electron from the first shell and converts a proton into a neutron.

$$_1^1H + {}_{-1}^0e \rightarrow {}_0^1n$$

20.6 MASS DEFECT

There is always a discrepancy between the total mass of the protons and neutrons in a nucleus and the actual mass of the nucleus. For example, for a stable $^{16}_{8}O$ atom, which contains eight protons, eight electrons and eight neutrons,

$$\text{mass of 8p, 8n and 8e} = (8 \times 1.0073) + (8 \times 1.0087) + (8 \times 0.0005)$$
$$= 16.132 \text{ amu (atomic mass units)}$$

Actual mass of oxygen atom (determined by mass spectroscopy) = 15.995 amu

$$\text{Difference} = 0.137 \text{ amu}$$

The difference in mass is the net loss on forming a particular isotope from its constituent particles, and is called the **mass defect**. The mass is converted into energy according to Einstein's equation where

$$E = mc^2$$

(E, energy produced; m, loss of mass; c, velocity of light)
This energy, called the **binding energy**, is lost on forming the atom.
    For comparison, the mass defect for a radioactive $^{13}_{8}O$ isotope can be found.
    Mass of 8p, 5n, 8e = $(8 \times 1.0073) + (5 \times 1.0087) + (8 \times 0.0005)$ amu
$$= 13.106 \text{ amu}$$

$$\text{Actual mass} = 13.025 \text{ amu}$$
$$\text{Mass defect} = 0.081 \text{ amu}$$

The mass defect and hence the binding energy for a radioactive isotope is much less than for the stable isotope. This applies generally.
    Fig. 20.4 shows a graph of the binding energy per nucleon against mass number.

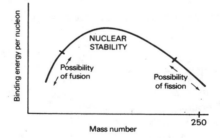

Fig. 20.4 Graph of binding energy per nucleon against mass number

(A **nucleon** is a particle in the nucleus, either proton or neutron.) From the graph it is clear that the most stable elements are the ones with intermediate mass numbers.
    Isotopes with small mass numbers have nuclei which are relatively unstable. The **fusion** of these nuclei together to form a larger nucleus releases a vast amount of energy, e.g.

$$^{2}_{1}H + ^{3}_{1}H \rightarrow ^{4}_{2}He + ^{1}_{0}n$$

This process requires a temperature of several million degrees in order to operate, but it occurs in the sun and is the source of energy in the sun. It also takes place in a hydrogen bomb.
    Isotopes with a large mass number again have unstable nuclei. These nuclei can break up in a series of stages, in a process called **fission**, to produce smaller nuclei which are relatively stable, e.g.

$$^{235}_{92}U + ^{1}_{0}n \rightarrow ^{236}_{92}U \rightarrow ^{143}_{56}Ba + ^{90}_{36}Kr + 3^{1}_{0}n$$

This process produces two smaller nuclei, when a uranium-235 nucleus is struck by a neutron. These smaller nuclei are relatively stable and a large amount of energy is released. Fission processes are the basis of the atomic bomb and (more usefully) of electric power generation in nuclear power stations.

Chapter roundup

There are generally few questions on radioactivity but when they occur they are usually straightforward.

Worked questions and answers

1 The disintegration rates (measured on a Geiger counter) at 25 °C of a 10 g sample of radioactive sodium-24 at various times are given in Table 20.1.

Table 20.1 *Disintegration rates*

Time (hour)	Rate of disintegration (counts sec^{-1})
0	670
2	610
5	530
10	420
20	270
30	170

(a) Plot a graph of disintegration against time. From the graph determine the half-life of sodium-24.

(b) On the graph, sketch the curve that would be obtained if a 5 g sample of sodium-24 had been used.

(c) What is the effect of an increase in temperature on this process?

Tutorial note

(a) The graph is shown in Fig. 20.5. The half-life of sodium-24 is approximately $15\frac{1}{2}$ hours.

(b) If half the mass is used, the counts per second are halved. At time $15\frac{1}{2}$ hours the reading will be 168 (half the original value of 335).

(c) Increasing temperature has no effect on the rate of disintegration of the radioactive isotope.

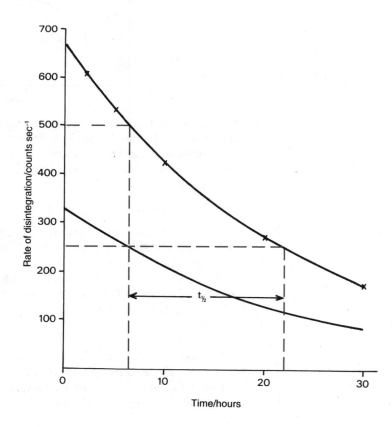

Fig. 20.5

Question bank

1 The radioisotope of hydrogen, called tritium (^3_1H), can be used in the dating of stored wines. It has a half-life of 12.3 years.
   (a) Write a balanced nuclear equation for the β decay of tritium.
   (b) A sample of tritium from a wine has a mass of 0.003 g.
      How many tritium atoms will be present in the sample after 36.9 years?
(SEB 1991)

Points

It is fairly easy to work out the mass remaining after three half-lives. It is not 0.001 g as some candidates will answer.

0.003 g	0.0015 g	0.00075 g	0.000375 g
1	2	3	half-lives

Then remember that 6×10^{23} atoms of tritium will weigh 3 g and you are almost there!

CHEMICAL PERIODICITY

Units in this chapter

Chapter objectives

In Chapter 2 we looked at the Periodic Table and periodicity. In this chapter you will see that the periodicity shown in physical properties can also be seen in chemical properties. We will look at the properties of oxides, hydrides and chlorides.

Before looking at this chapter you should look at Chapter 2 again. Also, for this chapter and Chapters 22–28, it would be useful to have a copy of the Periodic Table close at hand.

21.1 OXIDES

Formula	Na_2O Na_2O_2	MgO	Al_2O_3	SiO_2	P_4O_6 P_4O_{10}	SO_2 SO_3	Cl_2O
State at 20 °C	--------------- solid -------------------- // ----- gas -------
Structure	-------- giant lattices ----------- // ------ molecules -----------
Bonding	-- ionic ----- // -------------- covalent ----------------------
Type of oxide	-- basic ---- //amphoteric //----------- acidic -------------

In any period the oxides change gradually from ionic and basic on the left-hand side (Groups I and II) to covalent and acidic on the right-hand side (Group VII). Also a change occurs from a giant lattice structure to a molecular structure.

The ionic oxides of sodium and magnesium are discussed in 22.1. These oxides are alkaline when tested with Universal indicator.

Aluminium oxide is insoluble in water but, being amphoteric, it reacts with acid or alkali

$$Al_2O_3(s) + 3H_2SO_4(aq) \rightarrow Al_2(SO_4)_3(aq) + 3H_2O(l)$$
$$Al_2O_3(s) + 2OH^-(aq) + 3H_2O(l) \rightarrow 2Al(OH)_4^-(aq)$$

The oxides of silicon and phosphorus are discussed in 24.6 and 25.6 respectively. The structures of P_4O_6 and P_4O_{10} are shown in Fig. 21.1.

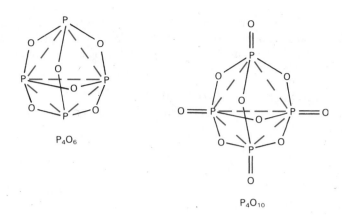

Fig. 21.1 Structures of P$_4$O$_6$ and P$_4$O$_{10}$

There are other polymorphic forms of P$_4$O$_{10}$. You will notice that the structures of the two molecules are similar and based upon a tetrahedron. Each phosphorus atom in P$_4$O$_{10}$ is bonded to an extra oxygen atom. Because these P—O bonds are shorter, it is believed that they are double bonds.

Both oxides of sulphur are acidic, but as usual the oxide containing the greater proportion of oxygen, i.e. SO$_3$, is more strongly acidic.

Dichlorine oxide reacts with water to produce chloric(I) acid.

$$Cl_2O(g) + H_2O(l) \rightarrow 2HOCl(aq)$$

Other oxides of chlorine are possible: chlorine dioxide ClO$_2$ (a yellow gas); chlorine hexoxide Cl$_2$O$_6$ (a red liquid); and chlorine heptoxide Cl$_2$O$_7$ (a colourless liquid) . They are all unstable and explosive. They dissolve in water to give acidic solutions.

21.2 HYDRIDES

Formula	NaH	MgH$_2$	(AlH$_3$)$_n$	SiH$_4$	PH$_3$	H$_2$S	HCl
State at 20 °C	- - - - - - solid - - - - - - - - - - - - - - // - - - - - - - - - - - - - - - - -					gas - - - - - - - - - - - - -	
Structure	- - - - - - giant lattice - - - - - - - - - // - - - - - - - - - - - - - - - - -					molecular - - - - - - - - -	
Bonding	- - ionic - - - - - - - - - // - covalent - - - - - - - - - - - - - - - - -						

The hydrides of sodium and magnesium are formed when hydrogen is passed over heated sodium or magnesium

$$2Na(l) + H_2(g) \rightarrow 2NaH(s)$$
$$Mg(s) + H_2(g) \rightarrow MgH_2(s)$$

These hydrides are white solids containing H$^-$ ions. An H$^-$ ion is formed when a hydrogen atom accepts an electron.

Sodium hydride and magnesium hydride react with cold water to form hydrogen.

$$NaH(s) + H_2O(l) \rightarrow NaOH(aq) + H_2(g)$$
$$MgH_2(s) + H_2O(l) \rightarrow MgO(s) + 2H_2(g)$$

Electrolysis of molten ionic hydrides produces hydrogen at the positive electrode (anode)

$$2H^-(l) \rightarrow H_2(g) + 2e^-$$

This is unusual because hydrogen is usually produced at the cathode.

Aluminium hydride is rather less stable and less studied, but it also reacts with water to produce hydrogen.

Silane, SiH_4, unlike methane, CH_4, dissolves in water and undergoes slow hydrolysis. This is possible because silicon can use its $3d$ orbitals to give a maximum covalency of six but carbon, with no d orbitals available, has a maximum covalency of 4.

orthosilicilic acid

Phosphine, PH_3, is slightly soluble in water, giving an almost neutral solution. It reacts with acids to form salts, e.g.

$$PH_3 + HCl \rightarrow PH_4^+ Cl^-$$

Hydrogen chloride is neutral when it is absolutely dry. Under these conditions the bonding is covalent

H – Cl

When added to water, ionisation occurs accompanied by an evolution of energy

$$HCl(g) + H_2O(l) \rightarrow H_3O^+(aq) + Cl^-(aq)$$

21.3 CHLORIDES

Formula	NaCl	$MgCl_2$	$AlCl_3$	$SiCl_4$	PCl_3	PCl_5	S_2Cl_2	SCl_2
State at 20 °C	s	s	s	l	l	s	l	l
Structure	- giant lattice - - // - - - - - - - - - - molecular -							
Bonding	- ionic - - - - - - // - - - covalent - - - - - - - - - - - // ionic // - - - - - covalent - -							
Reaction with moist air	- none - - - - - - // - - - fumes producing HCl -							

Anhydrous chlorides are produced by heating an element in dry chlorine, e.g.

$$2Al(s) + 3Cl_2(g) \rightarrow 2AlCl_3(s) \text{ (see 23.3)}$$
$$P_4(s) + 6Cl_2(g) \rightarrow 4PCl_3(l)$$

Where two chlorides are possible, the reaction with chlorine produces the higher oxidation state, e.g.

$$2Fe(s) + 3Cl_2(g) \rightarrow 2FeCl_3(s) \qquad \text{iron(III) chloride}$$

Iron(II) chloride is produced by the reaction of iron with dry hydrogen chloride, e.g.

$$Fe(s) + 2HCl(g) \rightarrow FeCl_2(s) + H_2(g)$$

Sodium chloride dissolves in water without hydrolysis. Magnesium chloride and aluminium chloride undergo some hydrolysis when dissolved in water

$$MgCl_2(s) + 2H_2O(l) \rightleftharpoons Mg(OH)_2(s) + 2HCl(aq)$$
$$AlCl_3(s) + 3H_2O(l) \rightleftharpoons Al(OH)_3(s) + 3HCl(aq)$$

The hydrolysis of silicon and phosphorus chlorides will be found in 24.7 and 25.7.

Chapter roundup

You should see regular changes in the properties of oxides, hydrides and chlorides across any Period in the Periodic Table. For example, oxides change from being ionic solids which are basic to covalent gases which are acidic. During your lessons you will probably study the Periodic Table Group by Group. This is to emphasise similarities within any Group. In your revision it is useful to study the properties of the elements and their compounds across a Period. I would suggest that you start with Period 3 (Na–Ar) because there are more familiar elements in this Period.

Worked questions and answers

1 (a) (i) When 0.203 g of hydrated magnesium chloride, $MgCl_m \cdot nH_2O$, was dissolved in water and titrated with 0.1 M silver nitrate ($AgNO_3$) solution, 20.0 cm³ of the latter were required. A sample of the hydrated chloride lost 53.2% of its mass when heated in a stream of hydrogen chloride, leaving a residue of anhydrous magnesium chloride. From these figures calculate the values of m and n.

(ii) Is the value of m, calculated in (i), what you would have expected? Explain your answer.

(b) When the hydrated chloride was heated in air instead of hydrogen chloride, the loss of mass was greater than 53.2% and both HCl and H_2O were evolved.

(i) What reaction do you think might have occurred and what was the solid product?

(ii) Why was the stream of hydrogen chloride used in (a)?

(c) (i) What types of chemical bond exist in hydrated magnesium chloride? Indicate the particles involved in each type.

(ii) What is the type of bonding in sulphur dichloride, SCl_2?

(iii) Compare the physical properties of anhydrous magnesium chloride with those of sulphur dichloride, restricting your answer to two properties.

$$(A_r(H) = 1, A_r(O) = 16, A_r(Mg) = 24, A_r(Cl) = 35.5)$$

(ULEAC)

Tutorial note

(a) (i) Mass of anhydrous magnesium chloride $= \dfrac{46.8}{100} \times 0.203 \text{ g} = 0.095 \text{ g}$

Number of moles of silver ions reacting $= \dfrac{20 \times 0.1}{1000} = 0.002$

$$Cl^- + Ag^+ \rightarrow AgCl \text{ (reacting ratio 1:1)}$$

The sample of magnesium chloride contains 0.002 mole of chloride ions. 95 g of anhydrous magnesium chloride contains 2 moles of chloride ions. The value of $m = 2$.

Percentage of water in sample = 53.2%

46.8 g of anhydrous magnesium chloride combine with 53.2 g water
0.492 mole of anhydrous magnesium chloride combines
with 2.95 moles H_2O
1 mole of anhydrous magnesium chloride combines with 6 moles H_2O,
$n = 6$

(ii) Yes. Group II. Two electrons in s^2 orbital to be lost forming Mg^{2+} ion.

(b) (i) Hydrolysis. Magnesium oxide.

(ii) $MgCl_2 \cdot 6H_2O \rightleftharpoons MgO + 2HCl + 5H_2O$

HCl gas ensures equilibrium moves to the left and prevents hydrolysis.

(c) (i) Covalent – between atoms in water molecule.
Ionic – between Mg^{2+} and Cl^- ions.
Coordinate bonding between water molecules and Mg^{2+} and Cl^- ions.
(ii) Covalent.
(iii) High melting point of $MgCl_2$.
Solubility of $MgCl_2$ in water without extensive hydrolysis.

Question bank

1 This question concerns the properties of inorganic chlorides.
   (a) Element X forms a chloride which is a volatile liquid (*density = 1.41; boiling temperature = 58 °C*) which is violently hydrolysed by water to give a white turbidity and an acidic solution.
   (i) State and explain what you can deduce about the element X and the nature of its bonding in its chloride.
   (ii) At its boiling temperature, 0.1000 g of the chloride occupied 15.98 cm³ at 1.01×10^5 Pa and, when the same amount of the chloride was hydrolysed, the chloride ion liberated required 23.50 cm³ of a 0.1000 mol dm⁻³ silver nitrate solution for complete reaction:
$$Ag^+(aq) + Cl^-(aq) \rightarrow AgCl(s)$$
   Hence calculate the relative molecular mass of the chloride and deduce a formula for it. Then using the Periodic Table, give an identity for X itself.
   (b) Element Y forms a white crystalline chloride (*density = 2.15; melting temperature = 772 °C*) which dissolves readily in water without decomposition to produce a neutral solution which conducts electricity well.
   (i) State and explain what you can deduce about element Y and the nature of the bonding in its chloride.
   (ii) Element Y is denser than water (*density = 1.55*), but reacts readily with it. Thus 0.1000 g of Y liberates 55.89 cm³ of hydrogen gas measured at 273 K and 1.01×10^5 Pa. Calculate the number of moles of hydrogen thus produced and deduce the relative atomic mass of Y. Hence, using the Periodic Table, identify Y, explaining your reasoning.
   (c) Element Z forms a chloride which is a white solid. This forms a dimer which undergoes reversible thermal dissociation, and is also hydrolysed by water. Suggest an identity for Z, giving a brief explanation of your reasoning, and indicate the nature of the bonding in the chloride.
   (1 mole of a gas occupies 2.24×10^4 cm³ at 273 K and 1.01×10^5 Pa.)
(WJEC 1994)

Points

Look back to Chapter 4.
(a) The element Y is silicon and the bonding in $SiCl_4$ is covalent. In (ii) correct the volume of the chloride to stp and then using the fact that 1 mole of gas occupies 2.24×10^4 cm³ at stp, calculate the molar mass of the chloride (170 g). 23.50 cm³ of 0.1000 mol dm⁻³ contains 0.00235 moles of chloride ion, which has come from the 0.1000 g sample of the chloride. The sample contains 0.000588 moles of X chloride (0.1 ÷ 170). 1 mole of the chloride produces 4 moles of chloride ion on hydrolysis. 170 – (4 × 35.5) = 28. In the Periodic Table this identifies the element as silicon.
(b) Y is calcium. 55.89 ÷ 22 400 = 0.0025 moles of hydrogen. Density greater than 1 suggests Group II rather than Group I:
$$Y + 2H_2O \rightarrow Y(OH)_2 + H_2$$
   Number of moles of Y = 0.0025. Relative atomic mass = 0.1 ÷ 0.0025 = 40.
(c) A possible element is aluminium (see 23.3).

THE *s*-BLOCK ELEMENTS

Units in this chapter

22.1 *The s-block elements*
22.2 *Compounds of the s-block elements*

Chapter objectives

The *s*-block elements are the reactive metals of Groups I and II. These are called the alkali metals (Group I) and the alkaline earth metals (Group II). In some syllabuses these two Groups are studied together and in others separately.

Other chapters which are linked with the *s*-block elements are Chapters 2, 4 and 13. In particular, many questions on *s*-block elements link with questions on the Born–Haber cycle (see 13.10).

22.1 THE *s*-BLOCK ELEMENTS

The elements in Groups I and II are:

Group I		Group II	
lithium	Li	beryllium	Be
sodium	Na	magnesium	Mg
potassium	K	calcium	Ca
rubidium	Rb	strontium	Sr
caesium	Cs	barium	Ba
francium	Fr	radium	Ra

Francium and radium are very rare radioactive elements and they will not be included in the study which follows.

The elements in Group I (**alkali metals**) all contain a single electron in the outer *s* orbital, e.g.

Li $1s^2 2s^1$
Na $1s^2 2s^2 2p^6 3s^1$
K $1s^2 2s^2 2p^6 3s^2 3p^6 4s^1$

In all compounds, Group I metals show only an oxidation state of +1, which corresponds to the loss of a single electron from the *s* orbital, e.g.

$$\text{sodium atom Na} \rightarrow \text{sodium ion Na}^+ + e^-$$
$$1s^2 2s^2 2p^6 3s^1 \qquad 1s^2 2s^2 2p^6$$

The elements in Group II (**alkaline earth metals**) all contain two electrons in the outer *s* orbital, e.g.

$$\text{Be} \quad 1s^2 2s^2$$
$$\text{Mg} \quad 1s^2 2s^2 2p^6 3s^2$$
$$\text{Ca} \quad 1s^2 2s^2 2p^6 3s^2 3p^6 4s^2$$

With Group II metals, the oxidation state +2 exists in all compounds. This corresponds to the loss of the two electrons in the outer *s* orbital, e.g.

$$\text{magnesium atom Mg} \rightarrow \text{magnesium ion Mg}^{2+} + 2e^-$$
$$1s^2 2s^2 2p^6 3s^2 \qquad 1s^2 2s^2 2p^6$$

In each Group the ionisation energies decrease and the chemical reactivities increase down the Group. The ionisation energies are:

Li	520 kJ mol^{-1}	Be	2700 kJ mol^{-1}
Na	500 kJ mol^{-1}	Mg	2240 kJ mol^{-1}
K	420 kJ mol^{-1}	Ca	1690 kJ mol^{-1}
Rb	400 kJ mol^{-1}	Sr	1650 kJ mol^{-1}
Cs	380 kJ mol^{-1}	Ba	1500 kJ mol^{-1}

(NB First ionisation energies are given for Group I elements and the sum of first and second ionisation energies for Group II.)

The decrease in ionisation energies down the Group can be explained by the increasing atomic radius and increased shielding down the Group.

The difference in reactivity can be seen in the reactions of these metals with cold water. Lithium reacts slowly with cold water to produce the alkali lithium hydroxide and hydrogen.

$$2\text{Li(s)} + 2\text{H}_2\text{O(l)} \rightarrow 2\text{LiOH(aq)} + \text{H}_2\text{(g)}$$

Potassium reacts rapidly with cold water and the hydrogen produced ignites spontaneously and burns with a pinkish-purple flame.

$$2\text{K(s)} + 2\text{H}_2\text{O(l)} \rightarrow 2\text{KOH(aq)} + \text{H}_2\text{(g)}$$

In Group II, beryllium does not react with water. Magnesium reacts very slowly with hot water but rapidly with steam.

$$\text{Mg(s)} + \text{H}_2\text{O(g)} \rightarrow \text{MgO(s)} + \text{H}_2\text{(g)}$$

(Magnesium hydroxide decomposes at high temperatures into magnesium oxide.) Calcium, strontium and barium react with cold water, e.g.

$$\text{Ca(s)} + 2\text{H}_2\text{O(l)} \rightarrow \text{Ca(OH)}_2\text{(aq)} + \text{H}_2\text{(g)}$$

The alkali metals and barium are usually stored in oil to prevent reaction with water and air.

The elements in Groups I and II react with chlorine on heating to produce the chlorides, e.g.

$$2\text{Na(s)} + \text{Cl}_2\text{(g)} \rightarrow 2\text{NaCl(s)}$$

A variety of oxides are produced when these metals burn in oxygen. For Group I metals, the common oxide of formula M_2O is formed by all, but the more reactive metals form additional oxides. Sodium forms a peroxide and potassium, rubidium and caesium form a **peroxide** and a **superoxide**.

$$\text{Li} \rightarrow \text{Li}_2\text{O}$$
$$\text{Na} \rightarrow \text{Na}_2\text{O} \rightarrow \text{Na}_2\text{O}_2$$
$$\text{K} \rightarrow \text{K}_2\text{O} \rightarrow \text{K}_2\text{O}_2 \rightarrow \text{KO}_2$$
$$\text{Rb} \rightarrow \text{Rb}_2\text{O} \rightarrow \text{Rb}_2\text{O}_2 \rightarrow \text{RbO}_2$$
$$\text{Cs} \rightarrow \text{Cs}_2\text{O} \rightarrow \text{Cs}_2\text{O}_2 \rightarrow \text{CsO}_2$$

Group II metals all form a typical oxide of formula MO but, in addition, strontium and barium form peroxides.

$$\text{Be} \rightarrow \text{BeO}$$
$$\text{Mg} \rightarrow \text{MgO}$$
$$\text{Ca} \rightarrow \text{CaO}$$

$$Sr \rightarrow SrO \rightarrow SrO_2$$
$$Ba \rightarrow BaO \rightarrow BaO_2$$

Lithium and the Group II metals burn in nitrogen to form the nitrides, e.g.

$$6Li(s) + N_2(g) \rightarrow 2Li_3N(s)$$

22.2 COMPOUNDS OF THE s-BLOCK ELEMENTS

Oxides

The oxides of Group I react rapidly when added to water to form strongly alkaline solutions, e.g.

$$Na_2O(s) + H_2O(l) \rightarrow 2NaOH(aq)$$

Lithium, however, does not form a strongly alkaline solution.

The tendency for Group II oxides to form alkaline solutions when added to water is less, e.g.

$$CaO(s) + H_2O(l) \rightarrow Ca(OH)_2(aq)$$

The basic strengths of the resulting solutions from both Groups increase down the Group. The ionic radii of the metal ions increase down each Group. There is, therefore, less attraction between the M^+ or M^{2+} ion and the OH^- ion.

The hydroxides of Group II metals and lithium hydroxide decompose on heating to form the oxide, e.g.

$$Ca(OH)_2(s) \rightarrow CaO(s) + H_2O(l)$$

Hydroxides of Group I metals (apart from lithium) are not decomposed by heating.

Hydrides

The hydrides produced by passing hydrogen over heated Group I and II metals are ionic hydrides (see 21.2).

Chlorides

The chlorides of Group I and II metals are generally ionic. They are white, crystalline solids with high melting points. They are poor conductors of electricity when solid but undergo electrolysis when molten or dissolved in water.

The solid chlorides have ionic crystal lattices which can be broken by melting or dissolving in water.

Beryllium chloride is different from the other chlorides of Group II. Beryllium is more electronegative (or less electropositive) than the other elements of the Group. As a result it shows the greatest tendency to covalent bonding (see 4.2). Beryllium chloride is a solid but is a poor conductor of electricity when molten. It is soluble in organic solvents and is hydrolysed when heated in aqueous solution.

Carbonates and hydrogencarbonates

Carbonates of Group I metals dissolve in water to form an alkaline solution. The solubility of lithium carbonate is much less than that of the other Group I carbonates. Only lithium carbonate is decomposed by heating.

$$Li_2CO_3(s) \rightarrow Li_2O(s) + CO_2(g)$$

Group II metal carbonates are insoluble in water and are decomposed by heating into the oxide and carbon dioxide.

$$CaCO_3(s) \rightarrow CaO(s) + CO_2(g)$$

Hydrogencarbonates are formed by passing carbon dioxide through a solution of the carbonate or a suspension of the carbonate in water, e.g.

$$Na_2CO_3(aq) + H_2O(l) + CO_2(g) \rightarrow 2NaHCO_3(s)$$
$$CaCO_3(s) + H_2O(l) + CO_2(g) \rightarrow Ca(HCO_3)_2(aq)$$

The hydrogencarbonates of Group I metals can be isolated as solids which decompose on heating. On the other hand, the hydrogencarbonates of Group II metals decompose before they can be isolated.

Salts of Group I and II metals

Salts of Group II elements generally decompose more readily than salts of Group I elements, e.g. the decomposition of carbonates. Also nitrates of Group II elements and lithium decompose to form the oxide while the nitrates of Group I elements, apart from lithium, only partially decompose to form the **nitrite** (nitrate(III)).

$$2Ca(NO_3)_2(s) \rightarrow 2CaO(s) + 4NO_2(g) + O_2(g)$$
$$2NaNO_3(s) \rightarrow 2NaNO_2(s) + O_2(g)$$
$$4LiNO_3(s) \rightarrow 2Li_2O(s) + 4NO_2(g) + O_2(g)$$

Salts of Group I metals are generally soluble in water. Some salts of lithium, however, are insoluble, e.g. Li_2CO_3 and LiF. This can be explained by the high lattice energies of these compounds caused by the small size of the lithium ion. The hydration energy produced when the substance dissolves is much less than the lattice energy. For example,

lithium fluoride

lattice energy = 1022 kJ mol^{-1} hydration energy = −833 kJ mol^{-1}

lattice energy > hydration energy ∴ insoluble.

sodium fluoride

lattice energy = 902 kJ mol^{-1} hydration energy = −912 kJ mol^{-1}

lattice energy < hydration energy ∴ soluble.

Salts of Group II metals are generally less soluble, particularly if the salt contains ions with a 2 − charge. This is due to the increased lattice energies. Sulphates decrease in solubility down the Group. This is due to decreasing hydration energies down the Group.

Many salts of alkali metals and alkaline earth metals give characteristic colours in a flame test. If one of the chlorides is mixed with concentrated hydrochloric acid, and some of the mixture introduced into a hot flame, a flame colouration is produced. Examples are: lithium − red; sodium − orange; potassium − pinkish purple (lilac); calcium − brick red; barium − apple green.

Chapter roundup

The s-block elements (Groups I and II) are generally reactive metals. There are similarities in electronic structure which account for the similarities in chemical reactivity. The alkali metals are characterised by a single electron in the outer s orbital. This can be lost easily

$$M \rightarrow M^+ + e^-$$

The ease of loss of this electron (shown by the ionisation energy) increases down the Group. The metals, therefore, become steadily more reactive down the Group.

With the alkaline earth metals, there are two electrons in the outer s orbital. These can also be lost easily.

$$M \rightarrow M^{2+} + 2e^-$$

Again the ease of loss of these electrons increases down the Group and so the reactivity increases.

In 2.7 we considered how elements in different groups that were diagonally related could have similar properties. The diagonal relationship occurs because the elements concerned have similar electronegativities and the atoms of the elements have similar atomic radii. Lithium (Group I) and magnesium (Group II) are frequently quoted in examples of diagonal relationships.

Worked questions and answers

1 Table 22.1 shows the atomic and ionic radii of the Group II metals.

Table 22.1 *Atomic and ionic radii of the Group II metals*

Element	Atomic radius/nm	Ionic radius/nm
beryllium	0.112	0.030
magnesium	0.160	0.065
calcium	0.197	0.094
strontium	0.215	0.110
barium	0.221	0.134

(a) Explain why the atomic radius is larger than the ionic radius in each case.
(b) Explain why the atomic radius increases from beryllium to barium.
(c) The ions K^+ and Ca^{2+} have identical electron arrangements, yet the ionic radius of K^+ is larger than that of Ca^{2+}.
   (i) What is the electron arrangement in these two ions?
   (ii) Explain the difference in ionic radii of the two ions.
(d) Give one reaction for magnesium, calcium and barium which shows the difference in reactivity between these three elements. Explain briefly why this difference exists.
(e) Describe clearly how to prepare good specimens of:
   (i) magnesium sulphate $MgSO_4 \cdot 7H_2O$ from magnesium carbonate;
   (ii) barium sulphate $BaSO_4$ from barium carbonate.

Tutorial note

(a) E.g. magnesium atom $1s^2 2s^2 2p^6 3s^2$ magnesium ion $1s^2 2s^2 2p^6$
   The ionic radius of magnesium is smaller than the atomic radius because of the removal of the $3s$ electrons. Electron orbitals in the third shell ($3s$, $3p$, $3d$) extend further than orbitals in the second shell.
   In each case the number of protons in the nucleus is the same (12) and the shielding is unchanged.
(b) The atomic radius increases from beryllium to barium because extra electron shells are added. Although the nuclear charge increases, there is also an increase in shielding.
(c) The electron arrangement in K^+ and Ca^{2+} is $1s^2 2s^2 2p^6 3s^2 3p^6$. There are the same number of filled electron orbitals and the same amount of shielding. The difference is due to the different numbers of protons in the ions.

K – 19 protons, Ca – 20 protons.

The extra nuclear charge produces extra nuclear attraction, drawing the electrons slightly closer to the nucleus.

(d) The reactions of magnesium, calcium and barium with water (see 22.1). In chemical reactions the atoms of all of these elements lose two electrons to form ions.

$$M(s) \rightarrow M^{2+}(aq) + 2e^-$$

These two electrons are lost most easily from barium because the atoms of barium are larger than those of magnesium or calcium. The ionisation energies (first and second) of barium are less than those of calcium and magnesium.

(e) This part could appear also on a GCSE paper and would often be badly done on either GCSE or A-level scripts because of lack of detail.
In (i) a soluble salt is prepared but in (ii) an insoluble salt is prepared.
(i) Since a sulphate is prepared, sulphuric acid must be used.
Write and balance the equation.

$$MgCO_3(s) + H_2SO_4(aq) \rightarrow MgSO_4(aq) + H_2O(l) + CO_2(g)$$

Add powdered magnesium carbonate in small portions to warm, dilute sulphuric acid. When some magnesium carbonate remains unreacted, filter to remove excess magnesium carbonate. (Candidates often believe that when magnesium carbonate remains, the solution is saturated. This is not a dissolving process but a reacting one. The addition of magnesium carbonate uses up the dilute sulphuric acid. When all the acid is used up, some magnesium carbonate remains unreacted.)

The solution consists now of magnesium sulphate dissolved in water. The solution is evaporated until a small volume of solution remains and this is left to cool and crystallise. If the solution is heated to dryness $MgSO_4 \cdot 7H_2O$ crystals will decompose to produce anhydrous magnesium sulphate.

$$MgSO_4 \cdot 7H_2O \rightleftharpoons MgSO_4 + 7H_2O$$

(ii) Barium carbonate is insoluble in water and must be reacted with a dilute acid (but not sulphuric acid) to produce a solution containing barium ions.

$$BaCO_3(s) + 2HCl(aq) \rightarrow BaCl_2(aq) + H_2O(l) + CO_2(g)$$

Then add dilute sulphuric acid to precipitate barium sulphate.

$$BaCl_2(aq) + H_2SO_4(aq) \rightarrow BaSO_4(s) + 2HCl(aq)$$

Ionic equation: $\quad Ba^{2+}(aq) + SO_4^{2-}(aq) \rightarrow BaSO_4(s)$

The precipitate is filtered off, washed with distilled water to remove soluble impurities and dried.

Question bank

1 (a) The table gives data concerning the Group I elements (Li–Cs).

Element	Atomic number	Ionisation energy/kJ mol^{-1}	Atomic radius/nm
Li	3	519	0.152
Na	11	494	0.168
K	19	418	0.231
Rb	37	402	0.244
Cs	55	376	0.262

(i) Complete the electronic configuration of potassium.

$1s^2 \ldots$

(ii) Explain the trend in ionisation energies going down Group I from Li to Cs.

(iii) Write an equation for the reaction of rubidium with water and explain why great care should be taken when carrying out this reaction.

(b) The concentration of hydroxide ions in a solution remaining after the reaction of sodium and water may be found by titrating the solution with aqueous hydrochloric acid.

(i) Name an indicator suitable for use in the titration.

(ii) A solution is found to have a concentration of hydroxide ions of 1.0×10^{-2} mol dm^{-3}. Calculate the pH of the solution.

$$([H^+][OH^-] = 1 \times 10^{-14} \text{ mol}^2 \text{ dm}^{-6})$$

(c) Give a simple laboratory test to show that a substance is a compound of sodium. Give the result of the test.

(AEB 1981)

Points

This question ranges over several chapters of this book (Chapters 1, 2, 16 and 17). In (b)(i) any acid–alkali indicator is suitable as the titration is between a strong acid and a strong alkali. The pH of the solution in (b)(ii) is 12. In (c) the examiner is expecting you to use a flame test and give an orange flame as the result.

2 (a) (i) Give a **brief** account of the **trends** in the chemical behaviour shown by the elements of Group II (Mg to Ba), dealing specifically with the following aspects;

(1) the reactions of the elements with water,

(2) the reactivity of the oxides with water,

(3) the solubilities of the hydroxides and sulphates.

(ii) Like all Group II carbonates, both $CaCO_3$ and $MgCO_3$ are only sparingly soluble in water, and on addition of carbonate ion, CO_3^{2-}, to sea water the precipitation of $CaCO_3$ begins when $[CO_3^{2-}] = 5.00 \times 10^{-7}$ mol dm^{-3}, and that of $MgCO_3$ when $[CO_3^{2-}] = 5 \times 10^{-4}$ mol dm^{-3}.

State what can be deduced qualitatively about the relative solubilities of $CaCO_3$ and $MgCO_3$, and support your conclusion by calculating **both** K_s values. (Ignore possible dilution effects.)

(Sea water is 1.00×10^{-2} mol dm^{-3} with respect to Ca^{2+} and 5.00×10^{-2} mol dm^{-3} with respect to Mg^{2+}.)

(WJEC 1994)

Points

This question emphasises trends in Group II. The reactivity of elements increases down the group. The sulphates decrease in solubility.

Part (ii) of this question refers to solubility product (17.3). From the data, magnesium carbonate is more soluble than calcium carbonate. The K_s values for $CaCO_3$ and $MgCO_3$ are 5×10^{-9} mol^2 dm^{-6} and 2.5×10^{-5} mol^2 dm^{-6}, respectively.

GROUP III

Units in this chapter

Chapter objectives

The elements in Groups III, IV, V, VI, VII and 0 are sometimes called the *p*-block elements since the highest energy orbitals occupied are *p* orbitals. In contrast to the *s*-block elements, questions are rarely asked about the *p*-block elements as a whole, and so these elements will be considered Group by Group in Chapters 23–27.

In considering the Periodic Table, it is often noted that the first element in any Group is not completely typical of that Group. In Group III, the first element, boron, is nonmetallic, but the other elements, aluminium, gallium, indium and thallium, are metallic. Of these elements, only aluminium is really available to A-level students and so we will confine ourselves largely to this element alone.

23.1 ALUMINIUM

The electron arrangement of an aluminium atom is $1s^2 2s^2 2p^6 3s^2 3p^1$. The oxidation state of aluminium in compounds is +3.

Aluminium can undergo ionic or covalent bonding. For ionic bonding the two electrons in the $3s$ orbital and the one electron in the $3p$ orbital are lost to form the Al^{3+} ion. The ionisation energy for aluminium (i.e. for the loss of 3 electrons) is extremely high (5080 kJ mol^{-1}). The resulting Al^{3+} ion is extremely small and highly polarising (see 4.3). The simple Al^{3+} ion is present only in the fluoride and oxide and even here the bonds will be partially covalent. The hydrated ion $[Al(H_2O)_6]^{3+}$ exists in aqueous solution since the hydration energy evolved compensates for the high ionisation energy.

As an alternative to ionic bonding, an electron may be promoted from the $3s$ orbital to an empty $3p$ orbital, so there can be three covalent bonds. When aluminium forms covalent compounds, e.g. $AlCl_3$, there is still a vacant p orbital on the aluminium atom. The noble gas structure of argon is not achieved. Aluminium chloride can accept an electron pair from a suitable source, e.g. ammonia, to form

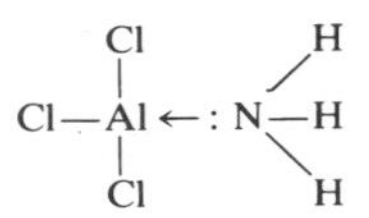

$$
\begin{array}{ccc}
 & Cl & H \\
 & | & | \\
Cl-Al & \leftarrow :N-H \\
 & | & | \\
 & Cl & H
\end{array}
$$

Aluminium is acting here as a Lewis acid (see 16.1).

Aluminium is a dull-grey metal. It has a low density for a metal, but it is very malleable and ductile. It is not as reactive as would be expected from its position in the electrochemical series. For example, aluminium reacts with moderately concentrated hydrochloric acid.

$$2Al(s) + 6HCl(aq) \rightarrow 2AlCl_3(aq) + 3H_2(g)$$

The reaction is very slow at first due to the thin layer of aluminium oxide on the surface which prevents reaction while the film remains. When the oxide film is removed by wiping with mercury, the aluminium oxidises rapidly in air. The oxide coating may be thickened and coloured by an electrolytic process called **anodising**.

Aluminium shows nonmetallic properties. It reacts exothermically with sodium hydroxide solution to produce hydrogen and sodium aluminate.

$$2Al(s) + 2OH^-(aq) + 6H_2O(l) \rightarrow 2[Al(OH)_4]^-(aq) + 3H_2(g)$$

DeVarda's alloy, used to reduce nitrate ions to ammonia, is an alloy whose main component is aluminium. It reacts with sodium hydroxide solution more slowly than aluminium.

Aluminium is a strong reducing agent because of its affinity for oxygen. For example, the **Thermit reaction**, used to weld railway track, involves

$$Fe_2O_3(s) + 2Al(s) \rightarrow 2Fe(s) + Al_2O_3(s)$$

23.2 ALUMINIUM EXTRACTION

Aluminium is extracted from the ore **bauxite**, $Al_2O_3.2H_2O$. Before extraction the ore is purified. The ore is heated with sodium hydroxide solution under pressure. The aluminium oxide reacts to form the aluminate ion which remains in solution. The solid impurities are removed by filtration.

$$Al_2O_3(s) + 2OH^-(aq) + 3H_2O(l) \rightarrow 2[Al(OH)_4]^-(aq)$$

Some freshly prepared aluminium hydroxide is added to 'seed' the solution of sodium aluminate and precipitate aluminium hydroxide.

$$[Al(OH)_4]^-(aq) \rightarrow Al(OH)_3(s) + OH^-(aq)$$

The aluminium hydroxide is heated to produce aluminium oxide.

$$2Al(OH)_3(s) \rightarrow Al_2O_3(s) + 3H_2O(l)$$

Aluminium is manufactured by the electrolysis of pure aluminium oxide dissolved in molten cryolite (Na_3AlF_6). The electrodes are carbon. The electrode reactions are:

$$\text{Cathode } (-) \quad Al^{3+} + 3e^- \rightarrow Al$$
$$\text{Anode}(+) \quad 2O^{2-} \rightarrow O_2 + 4e^-$$

The carbon anode is burned away and has to be frequently replaced.

23.3 HALIDES OF ALUMINIUM

Aluminium chloride is prepared by heating aluminium in dry chlorine or dry hydrogen chloride.

$$2Al(s) + 3Cl_2(g) \rightarrow 2AlCl_3(s)$$
$$2Al(s) + 6HCl(g) \rightarrow 2AlCl_3(s) + 3H_2(g)$$

Hydrated aluminium chloride $AlCl_3.6H_2O$ can be prepared by crystallising the solution remaining from the reaction of excess aluminium with hydrochloric acid. Anhydrous aluminium chloride cannot be prepared by heating hydrated aluminium chloride because this causes hydrolysis.

$$2AlCl_3.6H_2O(s) \rightarrow Al_2O_3(s) + 6HCl(g) + 9H_2O(l)$$

Relative molecular mass determinations of aluminium chloride when dissolved in benzene or in the vapour state indicate that aluminium chloride exists as double molecules, i.e. Al_2Cl_6.

By receiving two electrons from a chlorine atom to form a dative bond, the octet of aluminium is completed. The arrangement of atoms around each aluminium atom is tetrahedral. These double molecules exist in the vapour state up to 400 °C, when they start to dissociate.

$$Al_2Cl_6 \rightleftharpoons 2AlCl_3$$

The anhydrous aluminium trihalides (except trifluoride) are hydrolysed by water, and they fume in contact with moist air.

$$AlCl_3(s) + 3H_2O(l) \rightleftharpoons Al(OH)_3(s) + 3HCl(g)$$

23.4   SOLUTIONS OF ALUMINIUM SALTS IN WATER

Aluminium salts in aqueous solutions contain the $[Al(H_2O)_6]^{3+}$ ion. This complex cation is acidic because Al^{3+} is highly polarising, which weakens the O—H bonds.

$$[Al(H_2O)_6]^{3+}(aq) + H_2O(l) \rightleftharpoons [Al(H_2O)_5(OH)]^{2+}(aq) + H_3O^+(aq)$$
$$[Al(H_2O)_5OH]^{2+}(aq) + H_2O(l) \rightleftharpoons [Al(H_2O)_4(OH)_2]^+(aq) + H_3O^+(aq)$$
$$[Al(H_2O)_4(OH)_2]^+(aq) + H_2O(l) \rightleftharpoons [Al(H_2O)_3(OH)_3](s) + H_3O^+(aq)$$

Addition of dilute ammonia solution (a weak base) removes H_3O^+ ions and moves the equilibria to the right. This precipitates hydrated aluminium hydroxide. Aluminium hydroxide is **amphoteric**, i.e. reacts with acids and alkalis.

$$[Al(H_2O)_2(OH)_4]^- \xleftarrow{\text{addition of OH}^-} [Al(H_2O)_3(OH)_3] \xrightarrow{\text{addition of H}_3O^+} [Al(H_2O)_4(OH)_2]^+$$

Chapter roundup

Aluminium is a metal which, as the oxide and hydroxide show, is amphoteric.

Worked questions and answers

1 The extraction and refining of aluminium can be described using a flow diagram.

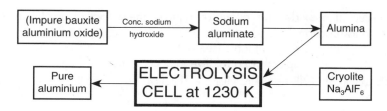

(a) Give the formulae for (i) alumina and (ii) sodium aluminate.

(b) Despite being the third most abundant element in the earth's crust, aluminium was not produced on a large scale until the nineteenth century. Suggest a reason for this.

(c) What are the positive electrodes in the electrolysis cell made of and why do they have to be replaced at regular intervals?

(d) Write an ion–electron equation for the reaction occurring at the negative electrode in the electrolysis cell.

(e) What mass of aluminium could theoretically be produced if a current of 289 500 A flows through the electrolysis cell for two minutes?

(f) Why is it possible to carry out the electrolysis at 1230 K if alumina normally melts at about 2300 K?

(g) Aluminium has a standard reduction electrode potential of –1.70 V.
(i) What does this suggest about the 'reactivity' of aluminium?
(ii) In the light of your answer give a reason why aluminium is used to make window frames. Consider the following data concerning the compounds aluminium chloride and magnesium chloride.

	Aluminium chloride	Magnesium chloride
action of heat	sublimes at 453 K	melts at 1690 K
relative molecular mass (vapour phase)	267	95
action with water	reacts (hydrolysed)	dissolves

Using the above data:

(h) Deduce the type of bonding in (i) aluminium chloride and (ii) magnesium chloride.

(i) Give the formula for aluminium chloride in the vapour phase.

(j) Write a balanced equation for the reaction between aluminium chloride and water.

(SEB)

Tutorial note

(a) (i) Al_2O_3 (ii) $NaAl(OH)_4$

(b) Many aluminium ores contain only a small percentage of aluminium. It is very expensive to extract aluminium from its ores.

(c) Carbon. They are oxidised in the oxygen which is produced at the anode.

(d) $Al^{3+} + 3e^- \rightarrow Al$

(e) Quantity of electricity used $= \dfrac{289\,500 \times 2 \times 60}{96\,500}$ Faradays

$= 360$ Faradays

27 g of aluminium is produced by 3 Faradays

$\dfrac{27 \times 360}{3}$ g of aluminium produced by 360 Faradays

Answer 3240 g

(f) Alumina is not melted but dissolved in molten cryolite.

(g) (i) See Table 18.1. The very negative electrode potential suggests that aluminium is a reactive metal.

(ii) Aluminium oxide forms a tough coating on the surface of the aluminium. This prevents reaction.

(h) (i) Covalent (see 4.2); (ii) Ionic (see 4.1).

(i) Al_2Cl_6. This corresponds to a relative molecular mass of 267.

(j) $AlCl_3(s) + 3H_2O(l) \rightleftharpoons Al(OH)_3(s) + 3HCl(g)$

Question bank

1 (a) Give an account of the manufacture of aluminium, explaining carefully the principles involved and the reasons for the conditions used. No account of the purification of bauxite is required.

(b) Give equations for the reactions which occur when aluminium is heated in (i) dilute hydrochloric acid and (ii) aqueous potassium hydroxide.

(c) Aluminium fluoride melts at 1040 °C; it is soluble in water but not in organic solvents.
Aluminium chloride melts under pressure at 190 °C; it is soluble in organic solvents. Determination of the relative molecular mass M_r in the vapour at 200 °C gives $M_r = 267$.
(i) What may be deduced about the structures of the fluoride and chloride in the solid state?
(ii) Deduce the structure of the chloride in the vapour at 200 °C. What may happen at higher temperatures?

(Oxford 1989)

GROUP IV

Units in this chapter

Chapter objectives

This Group frequently appears in questions at A level. Often these involve comparison of the elements in the Group. The reason for this is that the elements in this Group are familiar to candidates and this makes comparison easier.

As we descend the Group there is a clearly defined change from nonmetal to metal.

24.1 THE ELEMENTS OF GROUP IV

Within Group IV the transition down the Group from nonmetal to metal is clearer than in other Groups.

The elements in Group IV are:

carbon	C	$1s^2 2s^2 2p^2$
silicon	Si	$1s^2 2s^2 2p^6 3s^2 3p^2$
germanium	Ge	$1s^2 2s^2 2p^6 3s^2 3p^6 3d^{10} 4s^2 4p^2$
tin	Sn	$1s^2 2s^2 2p^6 3s^2 3p^6 3d^{10} 4s^2 4p^6 4d^{10} 5s^2 5p^2$
lead	Pb	$1s^2 2s^2 2p^6 3s^2 3p^6 3d^{10} 4s^2 4p^6 4d^{10} 5s^2 5p^6 4d^{10} 6s^2 6p^2$

All of these elements contain electron arrangements with $s^2 p^2$ in the outer energy level. They could achieve noble gas electron arrangements by losing these four electrons or by gaining four electrons. The ionisation energies for losing four electrons are:

C	6200 kJ mol^{-1}
Si	4400 kJ mol^{-1}
Ge	4400 kJ mol^{-1}
Sn	3900 kJ mol^{-1}
Pb	4100 kJ mol^{-1}

There is no possibility of gaining sufficient energy to produce M^{4+} ions.

Carbon and silicon are nonmetals while tin and lead are metals. Germanium has properties intermediate between metal and nonmetal and is called a **metalloid**.

24.2 OXIDATION STATES IN GROUP IV

There are two oxidation states seen within the Group. The oxidation state of +4 decreases in stability down the Group. It corresponds to the formation of four covalent bonds, e.g.

$$\begin{array}{c} & H \\ & | \\ H - & C - H \\ & | \\ & H \end{array}$$

For this to occur, one electron is promoted from the s orbital to the empty p orbital, i.e. $s^2p^2 \to sp^3$. Four identical bonds arrange tetrahedrally by this sp^3 hybridisation.

The other oxidation state is +2. This increases in stability down the Group and becomes noticeable from germanium downwards. For lead, the +2 oxidation state is more stable than the +4. In the +2 oxidation state only the two electrons in the p orbital are lost. The remaining ion has a 2+ charge and retains the pair of s electrons. The reluctance of these two electrons to engage in bond formation is called the **inert pair effect**.

With germanium and tin, the oxidation state +4 is the more stable. Germanium(II) and tin(II) compounds are strong reducing agents, e.g.

$$SnCl_2(aq) + 2HgCl_2(aq) \to SnCl_4(aq) + Hg_2Cl_2(aq)$$
$$SnCl_2(aq) + Hg_2Cl_2(aq) \to 2Hg(l) + SnCl_4(aq)$$

With lead, however, the +2 oxidation state is more stable than the +4. Lead(IV) compounds, therefore, act as oxidising agents. For example, when concentrated hydrochloric acid is warmed with lead(IV) oxide

$$PbO_2(s) + 4HCl(aq) \to PbCl_2(s) + 2H_2O(l) + Cl_2(g)$$

24.3 THE ALLOTROPY OF GROUP IV ELEMENTS

Allotropy (or **polymorphism**) is the existence of two or more forms of the same element in the same physical state. The three allotropes of carbon are diamond, graphite (see 10.4) and the fullerenes. Silicon and germanium do not show allotropy but both have structures similar to diamond.

A chance discovery in 1985 led to the identification of a new allotrope of carbon. In fact, a new family of closed carbon clusters has been identified and called fullerenes. Two fullerenes, C_{60} and C_{70}, can be prepared by electrically evaporating graphite electrodes in helium gas at low pressure. They dissolve in benzene to produce a red solution. The solution can be removed from the solid soot by decanting. The two fullerenes can be separated by column chromatography.

The diagram shows C_{60} – sometimes called buckminsterfullerene after R. Buckminster Fuller, the American engineer who designed the geodesic dome that resembles the structure of the fullerene. Fullerenes react with fluorine to form fluorides, which may turn out to be superlubricants. So far, one fluoride $C_{60}F_{60}$ has been produced.

There are three allotropes of tin. Each allotrope is stable over a definite temperature range.

grey tin		**white tin**		**rhombic tin**
or α-tin		or β-tin		or γ-tin
stable below 13 °C	$\rightleftarrows$	stable between 13 °C and 161 °C	$\rightleftarrows$	stable between 161 °C and melting point
diamond structure		*metal structure*		*metal structure*

Lead does not show allotropy but has a metal structure.

Carbon and tin are examples of the two types of allotropy. Carbon is said to show **monotropy** because although more than one allotrope can exist under particular conditions one is more stable than the others at all temperatures. Diamond and graphite both exist at room temperature and pressure, but graphite is more stable than diamond.

Tin is an example of **enantiotropy** because each allotrope exists over a definite temperature range.

24.4 REACTIONS OF THE ELEMENTS WITH ACIDS AND ALKALIS

Carbon reacts with hot oxidising acids such as concentrated nitric and sulphuric acids, e.g.

$$C(s) + 2H_2SO_4(l) \rightarrow CO_2(g) + 2H_2O(l) + 2SO_2(g)$$

Silicon is not attacked by any acid except hydrofluoric acid.

$$Si(s) + 6HF(l) \rightarrow H_2SiF_6(l) + 2H_2(g)$$
$$\textit{hexafluorosilicic}$$
$$\textit{acid}$$

Germanium, tin and lead react with nitric acid.

$$3Ge(s) + 4HNO_3(l) \xrightarrow{conc.} 3GeO_2(s) + 4NO(g) + 2H_2O(l)$$
$$3Sn(s) + 4HNO_3(l) \xrightarrow{conc.} 3SnO_2(s) + 4NO(g) + 2H_2O(l)$$
$$Pb(s) + 4HNO_3(l) \xrightarrow{conc.} Pb(NO_3)_2(aq) + 2NO_2(g) + 2H_2O(l)$$

Carbon does not react with alkali. Silicon reacts with dilute sodium hydroxide solution to produce sodium silicate(IV).

$$Si(s) + 2OH^-(aq) + H_2O(l) \rightarrow SiO_3^{2-}(aq) + 2H_2(g)$$

Germanium and tin react with hot concentrated sodium hydroxide solution to form a germanate(IV) and stannate(IV) respectively.

$$Ge(s) + 2OH^-(aq) + H_2O(l) \rightarrow GeO_3^{2-}(aq) + 2H_2(g)$$
$$Sn(s) + 2OH^-(aq) + H_2O(l) \rightarrow SnO_3^{2-}(aq) + 2H_2(g)$$

Lead reacts with hot concentrated sodium hydroxide solution to produce the plumbate(II) (plumbite).

$$Pb(s) + 2OH^-(aq) \rightarrow PbO_2^{2-}(aq) + H_2(g)$$

This illustrates the greater stability of the +2 oxidation state down the Group.

24.5 CATENATION

Catenation is the ability of an element to form bonds between its own atoms to form chains. Carbon can form long chains, e.g. alkanes (Chapter 29). The tendency to catenation decreases markedly down the Group (see 24.8).

The strength of the C—C bond is due to the small size of the carbon atom and the closeness of the bonding electrons to the two nuclei.

Silicon–oxygen bonds are much stronger than silicon–silicon bonds, and these bonds are the basis of the structures of silicates and silicones, e.g.

$$\left[\begin{matrix} & CH_3 & \\ -Si & -O- \\ & CH_3 & \end{matrix} \right]_n$$

24.6 OXIDES

All of the elements form dioxides. The stability of these dioxides decreases down the Group.

Carbon dioxide can be prepared by burning carbon in excess oxygen. Alternatively, it can be produced by treating a metal carbonate with a dilute acid, or by heating most carbonates and hydrogencarbonates, e.g.

$$CaCO_3(s) + 2HCl(aq) \rightarrow CaCl_2(aq) + H_2O(l) + CO_2(g)$$

Carbon dioxide is an acidic oxide, dissolving in water to form the weak acid carbonic acid.

$$H_2O(l) + CO_2(g) \rightleftharpoons H_2CO_3(aq)$$

Carbon dioxide is composed of discrete molecules. These molecules have the structure:

$$O{=}C{=}O$$

The carbon–oxygen bonds are, however, shorter than expected. This suggests that two resonance structures are possible

$$^+O{\equiv}C{-}O^- \leftrightarrow O^-{-}C{\equiv}O^+$$

Silicon(IV) oxide (silicon dioxide) is produced by the hydrolysis of silicon(IV) chloride or silicon(IV) fluoride. It occurs, with various degrees of impurity, as sand.

$$SiCl_4(l) + 2H_2O(l) \rightarrow SiO_2(s) + 4HCl(g)$$

Silicon(IV) oxide is an acidic oxide. It reacts with alkali to form silicate(IV).

$$SiO_2(s) + 2OH^-(aq) \rightarrow SiO_3^{2-}(aq) + H_2O(l)$$

Silicon(IV) oxide has a giant structure (see Fig. 4.2).

Germanium(IV) oxide, tin(IV) oxide and lead(IV) oxide are **amphoteric oxides**. For example, tin(IV) oxide reacts with acids and alkalis.

Lead(IV) oxide cannot be prepared by heating lead in oxygen. It is prepared by heating dilead(II) lead(IV) oxide (red lead) with dilute nitric acid.

$$Pb_3O_4(s) + 4HNO_3(aq) \rightarrow 2Pb(NO_3)_2(aq) + PbO_2(s) + 2H_2O(l)$$

The elements also form monoxides. The monoxides are more important with elements lower in the Group. Carbon monoxide is produced when carbon is burned in a limited supply of oxygen.

$$2C(s) + O_2(g) \rightarrow 2CO(g)$$

It can also be prepared by dehydration of methanoic acid (formic acid) or its salts with warm, concentrated sulphuric acid.

$$HCOOH(l) \rightarrow H_2O(l) + CO(g)$$

Carbon monoxide is only very slightly soluble in water and the solution does not show acidic properties. Carbon monoxide does react with sodium hydroxide solution at 150 °C and under high pressures to form sodium methanoate.

$$NaOH(aq) + CO(g) \rightarrow HCOONa(aq)$$

Carbon monoxide is a good reducing agent. It is produced in the blast furnace (see 28.8) and reduces iron(III) oxide to iron.

$$Fe_2O_3(s) + 3CO(g) \rightarrow 2Fe(l) + 3CO_2(g)$$

Carbon monoxide combines with chlorine in the presence of ultraviolet light to form carbonyl chloride (phosgene)

$$CO(g) + Cl_2(g) \rightarrow COCl_2(g)$$

The structure of carbon monoxide is a resonance hybrid of two structures.

$$C=O \leftrightarrow C\equiv O \quad \left[\overset{x}{\underset{x}{\cdot}} C\overset{x}{\underset{x}{\cdot}} O^x_x \right]$$

The resulting structure contains a lone pair of nonbonding electrons on the carbon atom. This can form coordinate bonds with d-block elements (see 28.5).

Silicon(II) oxide is an unstable and unimportant oxide. Germanium(II) oxide is also unstable and tends to disproportionate on heating.

$$2GeO(s) \rightarrow GeO_2(s) + Ge(s)$$

Both tin(II) oxide and lead(II) oxide are amphoteric. They react with acids to form tin(II) and lead(II) salts. With alkalis they form stannate(II) (stannite) and plumbate(II) (plumbite).

Dilead(II) lead(IV) oxide (red lead) is a mixed oxide behaving as if it is a mixture of two parts of lead(II) oxide and one part of lead(IV) oxide. For example, with concentrated hydrochloric acid

$$2PbO(s) + 4HCl(aq) \rightarrow 2PbCl_2(s) + 2H_2O(l)$$
$$PbO_2(s) + 4HCl(aq) \rightarrow PbCl_2(s) + 2H_2O(l) + Cl_2(g)$$

$$Pb_3O_4(s) + 8HCl(aq) \rightarrow 3PbCl_2(s) + 4H_2O(l) + Cl_2(g)$$

24.7 HALIDES

Germanium, tin and lead form dihalides which are solid and show some ionic character in the bonding. Tin(II) chloride can be prepared by reacting tin with concentrated hydrochloric acid.

$$Sn(s) + 2HCl(aq) \rightarrow SnCl_2(aq) + H_2(g)$$

Lead(II) chloride is prepared by adding dilute hydrochloric acid to lead(II) nitrate solution.

$$Pb(NO_3)_2(aq) + 2HCl(aq) \rightarrow PbCl_2(s) + 2HNO_3(aq)$$

Lead(II) chloride precipitates as a white solid. It is soluble in hot water but insoluble in cold water.

Tin(II) chloride and lead(II) chloride form complex ions with concentrated hydrochloric acid, e.g.

$$PbCl_2 + 2Cl^- \rightarrow [PbCl_4]^{2-}$$

Germanium(II) and tin(II) halides are reducing agents because the oxidation state +4 is the more stable.

All of the elements form tetrahalides. The tetrahalides are more important higher up the Group. The tetrabromide and tetraiodide of lead do not exist. All of the tetrahalides apart from lead(IV) fluoride are volatile and show covalent bonding.

Tetrachloromethane (carbon tetrachloride) is prepared by passing chlorine through boiling carbon disulphide, e.g.

$$CS_2(l) + 3Cl_2(g) \rightarrow CCl_4(l) + S_2Cl_2(l)$$

Alternatively, it can be prepared by the reaction of excess chlorine with methane in the presence of ultraviolet light (see 29.2).

Tetrachlorides, tetrabromides and tetraiodides of silicon, germanium and tin are prepared by the reaction of chlorine, bromine or iodine with the heated element, e.g.

$$Si(s) + 2Cl_2(g) \rightarrow SiCl_4(l)$$

Lead(IV) chloride cannot be prepared by a similar method as this leads to lead(II) chloride. Lead(IV) chloride is prepared by the reaction of cold, concentrated hydrochloric acid with lead(IV) oxide.

$$PbO_2(s) + 4HCl(aq) \rightarrow PbCl_4(l) + 2H_2O(l)$$

If the temperature rises above 0 °C, the lead(IV) oxide oxidises the hydrochloric acid to chlorine. Complex ions such as $[SnCl_6]^{2-}$ and $[PbCl_4]^{2-}$ can be prepared by adding concentrated hydrochloric acid to tin(IV) chloride or lead(II) chloride accordingly.

All of the tetrachlorides are covalent liquids. All (except tetrachloromethane) fume in moist air because they are hydrolysed by water.

$$SiCl_4(l) + 2H_2O(l) \rightarrow SiO_2(s) + 4HCl(g)$$

During the hydrolysis of silicon(IV) chloride there is an intermediate stage when the water molecules are forming bonds with the silicon as the chloride ions are leaving. At this stage the silicon atom is using $3s$, $3p$ and $3d$ orbitals.

For tetrachloromethane, no reaction takes place because this kind of intermediate is not possible. The carbon atom does not have the opportunity to hybridise s, p and d orbitals because $2d$ orbitals do not exist. The nonavailability of d orbitals at the lower energy levels is a major reason for the fact that the first element in each Group behaves oddly.

24.8 HYDRIDES

Carbon forms a wide range of hydrides and these are collectively called hydrocarbons (Chapter 29). The existence of so many hydrides is due to the strong bonds that can be formed between carbon atoms (see 24.5).

Carbon–carbon double and triple bonds are also possible. Other elements in Group IV do not form multiple bonds.

Silicon forms a limited number of hydrides similar to alkanes. They range from SiH_4 to Si_6H_{14} and are called **silanes. Germanes** range from GeH_4 to Ge_3H_8 and tin hydrides are only SnH_4 and Sn_3H_8. The hydride PbH_4 is extremely unstable. The stability of the hydrides decreases down the Group.

Chapter roundup

The regular change in properties within this Group can be seen in the stabilities of the oxidation states +2 and +4, the ability of the atoms to form chains (catenation), and the properties of the chlorides, oxides and hydrides.

Worked questions and answers

1 The elements in Group IV of the Periodic Table are carbon (6), silicon (14), germanium (32), tin (50) and lead (85). (The numbers in brackets are the atomic numbers.)
   (a) Give the electron arrangements of silicon and germanium.
   (b) Explain why the total energy for the process shown is greatest for the element carbon.

$$M(g) \rightarrow M^{2+}(g) + 2e^-$$

   (c) Why are compounds containing the M^{4+} or M^{4-} ions comparatively rare in this Group? Which of these elements is most likely to form these compounds?
   (d) What is 'catenation'? Which of these elements has the greatest tendency for catenation?

Tutorial note

(a) Si $1s^22s^22p^63s^23p^2$
    Ge $1s^22s^22p^63s^23p^63d^{10}4s^24p^2$
(b) The process is the sum of the first and second ionisations of M. Carbon has the greatest total ionisation energy for this process and the value decreases down the Group.

   The ionisation energies are greatest for carbon because the electrons being removed are much closer to the nucleus and, therefore, there are greater forces of attraction between these electrons and the nucleus. This explains the fact that C^{2+} ions are never formed and the stability of ions with a 2+ charge increases down the Group.

(c) Compounds containing M^{4+} ions are rare because of the large amount of energy which would be required to remove four electrons (sum 1st, 2nd, 3rd and 4th ionisation energies).

   For M^{4-} ions four electrons would have to be accepted. The steps

$$M^- + e^- \rightarrow M^{2-}$$
$$M^{2-} + e^- \rightarrow M^{3-}$$
$$M^{3-} + e^- \rightarrow M^{4-}$$

are all very unfavourable since considerable electrostatic repulsion would have to be overcome.

Lead (Pb) is most likely to form an M^{4+} ion (cf. ionisation energies, see 24.1). Similarly lead will also be most likely to gain electrons to form an M^{4-} ion as the repulsion of electrons in the larger ion will be less than for the other elements in the Group.

NB Neither Pb^{4+} nor Pb^{4-} is actually formed.

(d) Catenation is the formation of chains of atoms (see 24.5). Carbon is better at catenation because the C—C bond is much stronger than Si—Si, etc.

Question bank

1 Give an account of the chemistry of the Group IV elements (carbon to lead) using the following headings as a guide to answering.

(a) The variety of oxidation states possible and the relative stabilities of these oxidation states.

(b) The properties of carbon and carbon compounds which are different from those of silicon and its compounds.

(c) The changes in ionic and covalent character of the compounds of these elements.

Points

In this question the examiner is asking for a comparison of the Group IV elements. Too many candidates reproduce a poorly written set of Group IV notes without concentrating on the specific points mentioned. The content of Chapter 24 is sufficient. The following is a brief guide to the content but a good essay style is important in this question.

(a) Oxidation state +2 and +4. +2 increases in stability and +4 decreases in stability down the Group.

Give examples.

(b) Differences between the elements and compounds of the elements include:
- allotropy of carbon
- reaction of carbon with hot, concentrated, oxidising acids
- silicon reacts with alkalis
- carbon dioxide is a gas, silicon(IV) oxide is a solid
- hydrolysis of silicon tetrachloride.

(c) Compounds in oxidation state +4 are covalent and +2 are ionic (CO is an exception). Give examples and relate to physical properties, e.g. solubility in water.

GROUP V

Units in this chapter

Chapter objectives

In this chapter there are three elements which might appear in questions at A level – nitrogen, phosphorus and, to a lesser extent, bismuth. Again, down the Group there is an increase in metallic character.

25.1 NITROGEN

Nitrogen is the first member of Group V and has an electron arrangement of $1s^2 2s^2 2p^3$. A nitrogen atom contains a single electron in each $2p$ orbital.

Nitrogen can form bonds in three ways.

❶ It can form three covalent bonds by overlap with orbitals on other atoms – each bond contains one pair of shared electrons.

❷ Nitrogen can accept three electrons to form nitride N^{3-} ions.

❸ Molecules containing a nitrogen atom often contain a pair of nonbonding electrons. These electrons can be donated to another particle to form a coordinate bond, e.g.

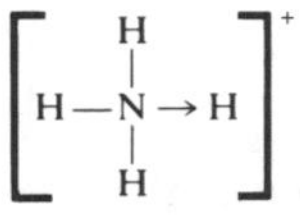

$$\left[\begin{array}{c} H \\ | \\ H-N \rightarrow H \\ | \\ H \end{array} \right]^{+} \quad \text{ammonium ion}$$

Nitrogen can show a range of oxidation states. These are shown in Table 25.1 with examples.

Table 25.1 Oxidation states of nitrogen

Oxidation state	Example
−3	NH_3 ammonia
−2	N_2H_4 hydrazine
−1	NH_2OH hydroxylamine
0	N_2 nitrogen
+1	N_2O dinitrogen monoxide
+2	NO nitrogen monoxide
+3	NO_2^- nitrite (nitrate(III))
+4	N_2O_4 dinitrogen tetroxide
+5	NO_3^- nitrate (nitrate(V))

Nitrogen is a colourless, odourless and tasteless gas, and is particularly unreactive at room temperature. It reacts with reactive metals to form nitrides (Chapter 22) and with hydrogen to form ammonia (Chapter 15). The unreactivity of nitrogen can be explained by the high dissociation energy (945 kJ mol⁻¹) owing to the strong triple bond between the two nitrogen atoms.

Nitrogen can be produced in the laboratory by the action of heat on ammonium nitrite (ammonium nitrate(III)). Ammonium nitrite is prepared by mixing ammonium chloride and sodium nitrite (sodium nitrate(III)).

$$NH_4Cl(s) + NaNO_2(s) \rightarrow NH_4NO_2(s) + NaCl(s)$$
$$NH_4NO_2(s) \rightarrow N_2(g) + 2H_2O(g)$$

Industrially, nitrogen is obtained by the fractional distillation of liquid air. Nitrogen (boiling point −196 °C) boils off first, followed by oxygen (boiling point −183 °C). Much of the nitrogen produced is used for making ammonia (see 40.2).

The oxides of nitrogen have been frequently discussed in newspapers and other media because they are present in car exhaust gases. Sometimes they are represented as NO_x. When exhaust gases pass through a converter containing a platinum catalyst, the oxides of nitrogen are broken down.

oxides of nitrogen + carbon monoxide → nitrogen + carbon dioxide

There are several different oxides of nitrogen.

Dinitrogen monoxide (nitrous oxide) N₂O

This is sometimes called 'laughing gas'. It can be prepared by heating a mixture of ammonium chloride and sodium nitrate (which produces the unstable ammonium nitrate *in situ*).

$$NH_4Cl(s) + NaNO_3(s) \rightarrow NH_4NO_3(s) + NaCl(s)$$
$$NH_4NO_3(s) \rightarrow N_2O(g) + 2H_2O(g)$$

N_2O can be confused in a practical situation with oxygen because both relight a glowing splint. However, you are unlikely to come across it.

Nitrogen monoxide NO

This oxide of nitrogen is produced by the reaction of copper with dilute nitric acid.

$$3Cu(s) + 8\ HNO_3(aq) \rightarrow 3Cu(NO_3)_2(aq) + 4H_2O(l) + 2NO(g)$$

Nitrogen monoxide is a colourless gas but it immediately oxidises on contact with air to produce nitrogen dioxide.

$$2NO(g) + O_2(g) \rightarrow 2NO_2(g)$$

Molecules of nitrogen monoxide are **paramagnetic**, i.e. they contain an unpaired electron. This electron can be easily lost or regained.

$$NO \rightarrow NO^+ + e^- \qquad NO^+ + e^- \rightarrow NO$$

Nitrogen dioxide NO$_2$

This is produced by heating lead(II) nitrate crystals.

$$2Pb(NO_3)_2(s) \rightarrow 2PbO(s) + 4NO_2(g) + O_2(g)$$

On cooling, nitrogen dioxide dimerises to form a pale yellow liquid called dinitrogen tetroxide.

$$2NO_2 \rightleftharpoons N_2O_4$$

In NO$_2$ the molecules are paramagnetic but there are no unpaired electrons in N$_2$O$_4$. Hence, N$_2$O$_4$ is **diamagnetic**.

Nitrogen dioxide dissolves in water to form a mixture of nitric(III) acid (sometimes called nitrous acid) and nitric(V) acid.

$$2NO_2(g) + H_2O(l) \rightarrow HNO_2(aq) + HNO_3(aq)$$

25.2 NITROGEN TRICHLORIDE

Nitrogen forms only a single chloride (compare with phosphorus in 25.7). Nitrogen trichloride is formed when excess chlorine reacts with ammonia:

$$4NH_3(g) + 3Cl_2(g) \rightarrow NCl_3(l) + 3NH_4Cl(s)$$

It is a covalent liquid composed of NCl$_3$ molecules. It is liable to explode.

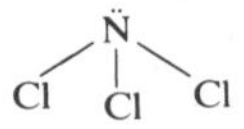

Nitrogen trichloride is readily hydrolysed to ammonia and chloric(I) acid (hypochlorous acid):

$$NCl_3(l) + 3H_2O(l) \rightarrow NH_3(g) + 3HOCl(aq)$$

25.3 HYDRIDES OF NITROGEN

The most important hydride of nitrogen is ammonia NH$_3$. Ammonia is prepared in the laboratory by heating a mixture of an ammonium compound and an alkali. For example,

$$NH_4Cl(s) + NaOH(s) \rightarrow NaCl(s) + H_2O(g) + NH_3(g)$$

or $$NH_4^+ + OH^- \rightarrow NH_3 + H_2O$$

Ammonia is also produced by the action of water on metal nitrides, e.g.

$$N^{3-}(s) + 3H_2O(l) \rightarrow 3OH^-(aq) + NH_3(g)$$

Ammonia is produced industrially by the Haber process (see 40.2).

The structure of the ammonia molecule is shown in Chapter 5. The lone pair of electrons on the nitrogen atom has a profound effect on the properties of ammonia. Because nitrogen is a highly electronegative element, hydrogen bonds can be formed with other ammonia molecules and water molecules.

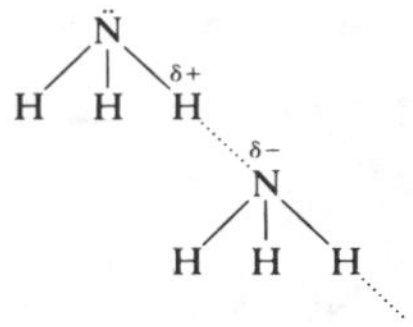

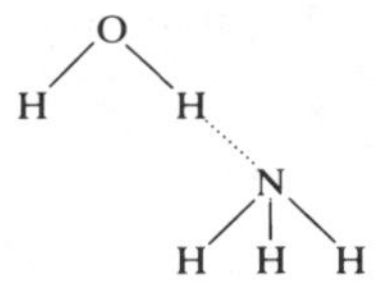

The hydrogen bonds formed with water molecules explain the high solubility of ammonia in water.

Ammonia can also use its lone pair of electrons to remove a proton (H^+ ion) from a water molecule. In doing this, ammonia is acting as a Lewis base.

$$NH_3 + H_2O \rightleftharpoons NH_4^+ + OH^-$$

Ammonia solution (sometimes called ammonium hydroxide, although this is not strictly correct) is a weak base and will precipitate certain metal hydroxides, e.g.

$$CuSO_4(aq) + 2OH^-(aq) \rightarrow Cu(OH)_2(s) + SO_4^{2-}(aq)$$
$$\text{copper(II) hydroxide – blue ppt.}$$

Some metal hydroxide precipitates redissolve in excess ammonia solution to form soluble complexes, e.g.

$$Cu(OH)_2(s) + 4NH_3(aq) + 2H_2O(l) \rightarrow [Cu(NH_3)_4(H_2O)_2]^{2+}(aq) + 2OH^-(aq)$$
$$\text{deep blue solution}$$

Hydrazine NH_2NH_2 is the other hydride of nitrogen. It is much less stable than ammonia. Hydrazine is to NH_3 as hydrogen peroxide is to H_2O.

25.4 NITRIC ACID

Nitric acid (nitric(V) acid), HNO_3, is prepared industrially from ammonia. A mixture of ammonia and air is passed over a heated platinum catalyst at 900 °C. The reactions are

$$4NH_3(g) + 5O_2(g) \rightarrow 4NO(g) + 6H_2O(g)$$

On cooling

$$2NO(g) + O_2(g) \rightarrow 2NO_2(g)$$

The gases are then passed through water.

$$4NO_2(g) + O_2(g) + 2H_2O(l) \rightarrow 4HNO_3(l)$$

In the laboratory, nitric acid is prepared by the action of concentrated sulphuric acid on potassium nitrate.

$$KNO_3(s) + H_2SO_4(l) \rightarrow HNO_3(g) + KHSO_4(s)$$

With cold, very dilute nitric acid, magnesium reacts to form magnesium nitrate and hydrogen.

$$Mg(s) + 2HNO_3(aq) \rightarrow Mg(NO_3)_2(aq) + H_2(g)$$

In other reactions with metals, nitric acid acts as an oxidising agent and oxides of nitrogen are formed. The products depend upon the conditions. For example, copper and dilute nitric acid give

$$3Cu(s) + 8HNO_3(aq) \rightarrow 3Cu(NO_3)_2(aq) + 4H_2O(l) + 2NO(g)$$

while copper and concentrated nitric acid give

$$Cu(s) + 4HNO_3(l) \rightarrow Cu(NO_3)_2(aq) + 2H_2O(l) + 2NO_2(g)$$

Nitric acid oxidises iron(II) compounds to iron(III).

$$2HNO_3(aq) + 6H_3O^+(aq) + 6Fe^{2+}(aq) \rightarrow 6Fe^{3+}(aq) + 10H_2O(l) + 2NO(g)$$

The following ionic half-equations represent the oxidising properties of nitric acid.

$$4HNO_3 + 2e^- \rightarrow 2NO_3^- + 2H_2O + 2NO_2$$
$$8HNO_3 + 6e^- \rightarrow 6NO_3^- + 4H_2O + 2NO$$
$$2HNO_3 + 6H_3O^+ + 6e^- \rightarrow 10H_2O + 2NO$$
$$10HNO_3 + 8e^- \rightarrow 9NO_3^- + 3H_2O + NH_4^+$$

The equations in 25.4 should be examined in the light of these half-equations to see how electrons are transferred in the redox processes.

25.5 PHOSPHORUS

Phosphorus has an electron arrangement of $1s^2\,2s^2\,2p^6\,3s^2\,3p^3$ and each of the $3p$ orbitals contains a single electron.

Phosphorus can form bonds in the same three ways as nitrogen. It can form three covalent bonds, gain three electrons to form P^{3-} ions, and form coordinate bonds with electron–deficient species. Phosphorus does not form ionic and coordinate bonds as readily as nitrogen.

Phosphorus can also form five covalent bonds by using the $3d$ orbitals. An electron is promoted from the $3s$ orbital to one of the $3d$ orbitals, giving five unpaired electrons.

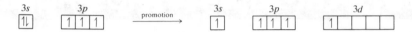

Hybridisation produces five orbitals which can form five covalent bonds by overlap with orbitals of suitable energy in five other atoms. Nitrogen is unable to form five covalent bonds by overlap with five other atoms because there are no available $2d$ orbitals. This explains why nitrogen forms one chloride, NCl_3, but phosphorus forms two, PCl_3 and PCl_5.

Phosphorus can show allotropy (polymorphism) – compare with nitrogen (see 25.1). The properties of the two common allotropes are summarised in Table 25.2.

Table 25.2 Two common allotropes of phosphorus

White phosphorus	Red phosphorus
whitish-yellow waxy solid	red powder
stored under water	stored dry
composed of P_4 molecules	macromolecular structure
low melting point	high melting point
soluble in organic solvents	insoluble in organic solvents
ignites at 30 °C in air	ignites above 300 °C in air
reacts with chlorine at room temperature	reacts with chlorine on heating
reacts with sodium hydroxide solution to form phosphine	no reaction with sodium hydroxide solution

The P_4 tetrahedra in white phosphorus also exist in the phosphorus vapour.

25.6 OXIDES OF PHOSPHORUS

Two oxides of phosphorus exist, corresponding to the oxidation states +3 and +5.

Phosphorus(III) oxide is made by burning phosphorus in a limited amount of oxygen.

$$P_4(s) + 3O_2(g) \rightarrow P_4O_6(s)$$

Phosphorus(V) oxide is the product of the reaction between phosphorus and excess oxygen.

$$P_4(s) + 5O_2(g) \rightarrow P_4O_{10}(s)$$

(It was originally believed that these two oxides had formulae of P_2O_3 and P_2O_5 but relative molecular mass studies in the solution and vapour states confirmed formulae of P_4O_{10} and P_4O_6.)

Phosphorus(III) and phosphorus(V) oxides are acidic oxides that react with water to form acids.

$$P_4O_6(s) + 6H_2O(l) \rightarrow 4H_3PO_3(aq) \quad \text{phosphonic acid (phosphorous acid)}$$

$$P_4O_{10}(s) + 6H_2O(l) \rightarrow 4H_3PO_4(aq) \quad \text{phosphoric(V) acid (orthophosphoric acid)}$$

25.7 CHLORIDES OF PHOSPHORUS

There are two chlorides of phosphorus: PCl_3 and PCl_5. Phosphorus trichloride is prepared when phosphorus reacts with a limited amount of chlorine and phosphorus pentachloride when phosphorus reacts with excess chlorine.

$$P_4(s) + 6Cl_2(g) \rightarrow 4PCl_3(l)$$
$$P_4(s) + 10Cl_2(g) \rightarrow 4PCl_5(s)$$

In the solid state phosphorus pentachloride is ionic.

$$[PCl_4]^+ \, [PCl_6]^-$$

The structures of phosphorus trichloride and phosphorus pentachloride are given in Chapter 5.

On heating, phosphorus pentachloride dissociates.

$$PCl_5 \rightleftharpoons PCl_3 + Cl_2$$

Both chlorides of phosphorus are hydrolysed by water and fume in moist air:

$$PCl_3(l) + 3H_2O(l) \rightarrow H_3PO_3(aq) + 3HCl(g)$$
$$\text{phosphonic acid (phosphorous acid)}$$

Phosphorus pentachloride reacts in two stages.

$$PCl_5(s) + H_2O(l) \rightarrow POCl_3(l) + 2HCl(g)$$
$$\text{phosphorus trichloride oxide (phosphorus oxychloride)}$$
$$POCl_3(l) + 3H_2O(l) \rightarrow H_3PO_4(aq) + 3HCl(g)$$
$$\text{phosphoric(V) acid (orthophosphoric acid)}$$

25.8 HYDRIDES OF PHOSPHORUS

Phosphine PH_3 can be prepared by the action of sodium hydroxide on phosphonium iodide.

$$PH_4I(s) + NaOH(s) \rightarrow NaI(s) + H_2O(g) + PH_3(g)$$

(NB This is similar to the preparation of ammonia in 25.3.)

A more common method is to boil white phosphorus with a concentrated aqueous solution of sodium hydroxide.

$$P_4(s) + 3NaOH(aq) + 3H_2O(l) \rightarrow 3NaH_2PO_2(aq) + PH_3(g)$$
$$\text{sodium phosphinate}$$

(NB Disproportionation occurs here: $4P(0) \rightarrow P(-III) + 3P(+I)$.)

The reaction does not take place with red phosphorus. An impurity in the phosphine is the unstable hydride diphosphine P_2H_4, which is spontaneously inflammable.

Phosphine is less basic than ammonia. It is only slightly soluble in water and the following equilibrium lies well over to the left:

$$PH_3 + H_2O \rightleftharpoons PH_4^+ + OH^-$$

The phosphorus atom is larger than the nitrogen atom. Ammonia is better at donating its pair of nonbonding electrons.

The boiling points of NH_3 and PH_3 are 33 °C and −90 °C respectively. Because phosphine molecules have a higher relative molecular mass than ammonia molecules, the boiling point of phosphine should be higher than that of ammonia. This assumption neglects the hydrogen bonding (see 4.5) which is present in ammonia but not in phosphine. Phosphorus is not electronegative enough for hydrogen bonding to exist. The lack of hydrogen bonding also explains the low solubility of phosphine in water.

25.9 PHOSPHORIC(V) ACID H₃PO₄

This acid is a very deliquescent crystalline solid and exists as a viscous solution owing to a large amount of hydrogen bonding. It is tribasic and three endpoints should be detected (see 16.6).

$$NaOH(aq) + H_3PO_4(aq) \rightarrow NaH_2PO_4(aq) + H_2O(l)$$
$$\text{(indicator: methyl orange)}$$
$$NaOH(aq) + NaH_2PO_4(aq) \rightarrow Na_2HPO_4(aq) + H_2O(l)$$
$$\text{(indicator: phenolphthalein)}$$
$$NaOH(aq) + Na_2HPO_4(aq) \rightarrow Na_3PO_4(aq) + H_2O(l)$$

The last endpoint cannot be detected because PO_4^{3-} is a strong base and hydrolyses in solution (see 17.1).

25.10 BISMUTH

Bismuth is more metallic than nitrogen or phosphorus. It forms Bi^{3+} ions by the loss of the three electrons in the p orbitals. It shows the **inert pair effect** (see 24.2). Bismuth reacts with dilute nitric acid to produce bismuth(III) nitrate.

$$Bi(s) + 6HNO_3(aq) \rightarrow Bi(NO_3)_3(aq) + 3H_2O(l) + 3NO_2(g)$$

The hydride of bismuth BiH_3, called bismuthine, is much less stable and more difficult to form than ammonia or phosphine.

Bismuth in the +5 oxidation state is a very powerful oxidising agent.

Chapter roundup

In this chapter the most common examination point concerns why it is possible to get PCl_3 and PCl_5 but only possible to get NCl_3. This is because of the availability of d orbitals in the third energy level but not in the second.

Worked questions and answers

1 (a) Explain in outline how compounds of nitrogen in oxidation states +2, –3 and +4 could be prepared from nitric acid.

(b) The overall equation for the preparation of iodine monochloride is

$$N_2H_6O\,(aq) + IO_3^-\,(aq) + 2H_3O^+\,(aq) + Cl^-\,(aq) \rightarrow N_2\,(g) + ICl\,(g) + 6H_2O\,(l)$$

During this reaction the oxidation states of all elements except nitrogen and iodine are unchanged. Using the equation, give the oxidation states of nitrogen in reactants and products.

Tutorial note

(a) Three nitrogen compounds with oxidation states +2, –3 and +4 are nitrogen monoxide (NO), ammonia (NH_3) and nitrogen dioxide (NO_2).

Nitrogen monoxide is prepared by the reaction of copper with dilute nitric acid.

Ammonia can be prepared by adding sodium hydroxide solution and aluminium powder (or De Varda's alloy, see 23.1). Nitrogen is reduced from oxidation state +5 to –3.

$$HNO_3 + 8[H] \rightarrow NH_3 + 3H_2O$$

Nitrogen dioxide is prepared by the action of copper on concentrated nitric acid.

(b) Oxidation state of iodine changes from +5 to +1. In the products nitrogen is in oxidation state zero (element). In the compound N_2H_6O, nitrogen must be in oxidation state –2.

GROUP VI

Units in this chapter

Chapter objectives

At first sight there may not appear to be much similarity between oxygen, a very reactive gas, and sulphur, a yellow, less reactive solid. There also appears to be little similarity between water (H_2O) and hydrogen sulphide (H_2S), an unpleasant smelling gas. In the case of water and hydrogen sulphide the similarities are masked by the presence of hydrogen bonding in water (Chapter 4).

The industrial manufacture of sulphuric acid by the Contact process is included in illustrative question 2 at the end of the chapter.

26.1 OXYGEN

Oxygen (electron arrangement $1s^2 2s^2 2p^4$) can form two covalent bonds or gain two electrons to form O^{2-} ions.

Oxygen is the product in several common reactions:

❶ catalytic decomposition of hydrogen peroxide (laboratory preparation)

$$2H_2O_2(aq) \rightarrow 2H_2O(l) + O_2(g)$$

❷ thermal decomposition of oxygen-rich compounds, e.g.
potassium manganate(VII)

$$2KMnO_4(s) \rightarrow K_2MnO_4(s) + MnO_2(s) + O_2(g)$$

potassium chlorate(VII)

$$2KClO_3(s) \rightarrow 2KCl(s) + 3O_2(g)$$

potassium nitrate

$$2KNO_3(s) \rightarrow 2KNO_2(s) + O_2(g)$$

❸ electrolysis of aqueous solutions

$$4OH^-(aq) \rightarrow 2H_2O(l) + O_2(g) + 4e^-$$

❹ action of a peroxide on water, e.g.

$$2Na_2O_2(s) + 2H_2O(l) \rightarrow 4NaOH(aq) + O_2(g)$$

Industrially, oxygen is prepared by the fractional distillation of liquid air.

Oxygen is an extremely electronegative element. Most elements, apart from the noble gases, combine with oxygen to form oxides. Elements which combine with oxygen (or with fluorine in Group VII) tend to show their maximum oxidation state, e.g. Cl_2O_7 dichlorine heptoxide – chlorine shows a maximum oxidation state of +7. The stability of the high oxidation state is due to the high electronegativity and small size of the oxygen atom.

26.2 CLASSIFICATION OF OXIDES

Oxides can be divided into six groups, though the boundaries between some of these groups are rather arbitrary.

(i) Basic oxides

These are metal oxides containing the O^{2-} ion. The oxidation state of a metal in a basic oxide is low. A basic oxide reacts with an acid to form a salt and water only, e.g.

$$CuO(s) + H_2SO_4(aq) \rightarrow CuSO_4(aq) + H_2O(l)$$

ionic equation $\qquad O^{2-}(s) + 2H_3O^+(aq) \rightarrow 3H_2O(l)$

Basic oxides of metals high in the electrochemical series react with water to form soluble hydroxides or alkalis, e.g.

$$CaO(s) + H_2O(l) \rightarrow Ca(OH)_2(s)$$

ionic equation $\qquad O^{2-}(s) + H_2O(l) \rightarrow 2OH^-(s)$

(ii) Acidic oxides

Acidic oxides are oxides of nonmetals or d-block elements in high oxidation states, e.g.

SO_3, sulphur(VI) oxide, dissolves in water to form an acid.

$$SO_3(s) + H_2O(l) \rightarrow H_2SO_4(aq)$$

Chromium(VI) oxide dissolves in water to form chromic(VI) acid.

$$CrO_3(s) + H_2O(l) \rightarrow H_2CrO_4(aq)$$

These acidic oxides are usually simple molecules with mainly covalent bonding. Oxides dissolving in water to form an acid are called **acid anhydrides**.

Where an element forms a number of different oxides with different oxidation states, the higher the oxidation state the more acidic the oxide is, e.g.

SO_3 oxidation state of sulphur is +6
SO_2 oxidation state of sulphur is +4
SO_3 is more strongly acidic than SO_2

Acidic oxides react with basic oxides to form **salts**.

(iii) Amphoteric oxides

These are oxides which can behave as acidic or basic oxides depending upon the conditions. They are usually oxides of the less electropositive metals, e.g. zinc, aluminium, lead.

1 $$ZnO(s) + 2HCl(aq) \rightarrow ZnCl_2(aq) + H_2O(l)$$
2 $$ZnO(s) + 2OH^-(aq) + H_2O(l) \rightarrow Zn(OH)_4^{2-}(aq)$$

In equation 1 zinc oxide is acting as a basic oxide and in 2 as an acidic oxide.

(iv) Neutral oxides

A neutral oxide does not react either with an acid or an alkali to form a salt. Examples are nitrogen oxide (NO), and dinitrogen oxide (N_2O).

(v) Mixed oxides

Mixed oxides behave as if they were composed of mixtures of simple oxides, e.g. dilead(II) lead(IV) oxide, Pb_3O_4, behaves as if it is a mixture of lead(II) oxide, PbO (2 parts), and lead(IV) oxide, PbO_2 (1 part).

(vi) Peroxides

Peroxides are higher oxides of electropositive metals and contain O_2^{2-} ions. They are strong oxidising agents. When acidified with cold, dilute acid, hydrogen peroxide is produced, e.g.

$$Na_2O_2(s) + H_2SO_4(aq) \rightarrow Na_2SO_4(aq) + H_2O_2(aq)$$

ionic equation $$O_2^{2-}(s) + 2H_3O^+(aq) \rightarrow H_2O_2(aq) + 2H_2O(l)$$

26.3 TRIOXYGEN (OZONE)

Oxygen gas is composed of diatomic molecules O_2. Trioxygen is an unstable allotrope of oxygen where the molecules contain three oxygen atoms, i.e. O_3.

Trioxygen is a nonlinear molecule which is a resonance hybrid of two resonance structures.

In trioxygen the two oxygen–oxygen bonds are of equal length.

Trioxygen occurs naturally in the upper atmosphere. The trioxygen in the so-called **'ozone layer'** absorbs most of the ultraviolet radiation approaching the earth. There is concern about the destruction of the trioxygen by fluorocarbons from aerosol propellants.

Trioxygen can be produced by passing a high electrical discharge through dry oxygen.

$$3O_2(g) \rightleftharpoons 2O_3(g)$$

Only about 10% of the oxygen is converted to trioxygen, which is very unstable.

The strong oxidising properties of trioxygen in acid solution can be represented by:

$$O_3(g) + 2H_3O^+(aq) + 2e^- \rightarrow O_2(g) + 3H_2O(l)$$

The two important reactions of trioxygen for examination purposes are:

1 the reaction with alkenes to split carbon–carbon double bonds (called **ozonolysis**, see 29.5); and

❷ oxidation of a sulphide to a sulphate

$$PbS(s) + 4O_3(g) \rightarrow PbSO_4(s) + 4O_2(g)$$

lead(II) sulphide   lead(II) sulphate
black   white

ionic equation: $$S^{2-}(s) + 4O_3(g) \rightarrow SO_4^{2-}(s) + 4O_2(g)$$

26.4 WATER

Water is a hydride of oxygen and its properties should be compared with the properties of the hydride of sulphur – hydrogen sulphide.

Many of the physical properties of water differ from those expected, including:

❶ maximum density at 4 °C;

❷ high boiling point;

❸ high enthalpies of fusion and vaporisation; and

❹ high dielectric constant (relative permittivity).

The main reasons for these differences are:

❶ Water is highly polarised. Because of the high electronegativity of oxygen there is a partial separation of charges in the molecule.

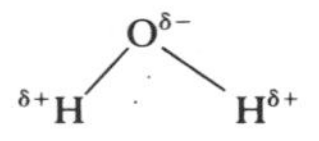

$$\overset{\delta+}{H} \diagdown \overset{O^{\delta-}}{} \diagup \overset{\delta+}{H}$$

This can cause solvation of ions in solution (Fig. 4.1).

❷ As a result of the presence of these partial charges, hydrogen bonding can exist between water molecules, and between water molecules and polar molecules such as alcohols (Chapter 4).

Water is composed of H_2O molecules but very few molecules are dissociated into ions.

$$2H_2O(l) \rightleftharpoons H_3O^+(aq) + OH^-(aq)$$

Many substances are split up by water and this is called **hydrolysis** (see 24.7, 34.2).

26.5 HYDROGEN PEROXIDE H_2O_2

Hydrogen peroxide is an unstable hydride of oxygen containing the O—O grouping. The bond between the two oxygen atoms is weak and this accounts for its instability. It is prepared in the laboratory by the action of dilute sulphuric acid on barium peroxide. The temperature must be maintained at around 0 °C to prevent decomposition of the hydrogen peroxide.

$$BaO_2(s) + H_2SO_4(aq) \rightarrow BaSO_4(s) + H_2O_2(aq)$$

The barium sulphate is removed by filtration.

Industrially, 2-butylanthraquinone is reduced to 2-butylanthraquinol using a catalyst and hydrogen. The 2-butylanthraquinol is oxidised by oxygen to regenerate the 2-butylanthraquinone and produce hydrogen peroxide.

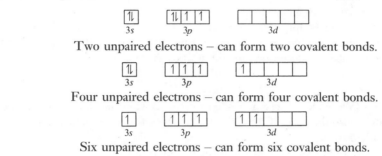

Hydrogen peroxide can act as an oxidising agent or as a reducing agent depending upon the conditions (Chapter 6).

26.6 SULPHUR

Sulphur can exist in two solid allotropes (polymorphs). These allotropes are α-sulphur (**rhombic sulphur**) and β-sulphur (**monoclinic sulphur**).

In addition to forming two covalent bonds and ions with a 2− charge, sulphur can also form compounds where it forms four or six covalent bonds, i.e. where the oxidation states of sulphur are +4 and +6. It achieves this by promotion of electrons from $3s$ or $3p$ orbitals into $3d$ orbitals.

Two unpaired electrons – can form two covalent bonds.

Four unpaired electrons – can form four covalent bonds.

Six unpaired electrons – can form six covalent bonds.

Examples of compounds of sulphur with oxidation states +4 and +6 are:

SO_3 sulphur(VI) oxide +6
SO_2 sulphur dioxide   +4

The oxidation state of +6 is only achieved with fluorine and oxygen in fluorides and oxides.

Sulphur reacts with most metals to form sulphides which are much less ionic than the corresponding oxides, e.g.

$$Zn(s) + S(s) \rightarrow ZnS(s)$$

Sulphur does not react with water or dilute acids. With hot, concentrated sulphuric acid, sulphur is oxidised to sulphur dioxide.

$$S(s) + 2H_2SO_4(l) \rightarrow 3SO_2(g) + 2H_2O(l)$$

26.7 OXIDES OF SULPHUR

There are two simple oxides of sulphur, namely:

sulphur dioxide – SO_2
sulphur(VI) oxide (sulphur trioxide) – SO_3

Sulphur dioxide is a pungent gas produced by the action of hot, concentrated sulphuric acid on copper.

$$Cu(s) + 2H_2SO_4(l) \rightarrow CuSO_4(aq) + 2H_2O(l) + SO_2(g)$$

It can also be produced by burning sulphur or warming a sulphite (sulphate(IV)) with a dilute acid.

$$Na_2SO_3(s) + 2HCl(aq) \rightarrow 2NaCl(aq) + H_2O(l) + SO_2(g)$$

The structure of sulphur dioxide is

It is an acidic oxide, dissolving in water to form a weak acid called sulphurous acid (sulphuric(IV) acid). This partially ionises in solution:

$$H_2SO_3(aq) + H_2O(l) \rightleftharpoons HSO_3^-(aq) + H_3O^+(aq)$$
$$H_2SO_3(aq) + 2H_2O(l) \rightleftharpoons SO_3^{2-}(aq) + 2H_3O^+(aq)$$

Sulphurous acid and moist sulphur dioxide act as a reducing agent. As a result of this process sulphur is oxidised from oxidisation state +4 to +6.

$$SO_3^{2-}(aq) + 3H_2O(l) \rightarrow SO_4^{2-}(aq) + 2H_3O^+(aq) + 2e^-$$

When sulphur dioxide is bubbled through a purple solution of potassium manganate(VII), the purple solution is decolourised.

Sulphur(VI) oxide (sulphur trioxide) cannot be produced directly by burning sulphur in oxygen. It can be produced by passing a mixture of sulphur dioxide and oxygen over a heated platinum or vanadium(V) oxide catalyst.

$$2SO_2(g) + O_2(g) \rightleftharpoons 2SO_3(g)$$

The sulphur(VI) oxide collects in a cooled receiver as white, needle-shaped crystals. This reaction is also the basis of the **Contact process for** manufacturing sulphuric acid (see worked question 2).

The structure of sulphur(VI) oxide in the gaseous state is

The molecule is planar.

Sulphur(VI) oxide reacts exothermically with water to produce sulphuric acid (sulphuric(VI) acid).

$$SO_3(s) + H_2O(l) \rightarrow H_2SO_4(aq)$$

26.8 SULPHURIC ACID (SULPHURIC(VI) ACID)

Sulphuric acid is produced when sulphur(VI) oxide reacts with water. The reactions of sulphuric acid include the following.

(i) Acidic properties

Sulphuric acid in aqueous solution ionises as follows:

$$H_2SO_4(aq) + H_2O(l) \rightleftharpoons H_3O^+(aq) + HSO_4^-(aq)$$
$$H_2SO_4(aq) + 2H_2O(l) \rightleftharpoons 2H_3O^+(aq) + SO_4^{2-}(aq)$$

Neutralising sulphuric acid with alkali can produce sulphates and hydrogensulphates.

(ii) Dehydration reactions

Concentrated sulphuric acid acts as a dehydrating agent. It removes water or the elements of water from carbohydrates.

$$C_6H_{12}O_6(s) \xrightarrow{\text{conc. } H_2SO_4} 6C(s) + 6H_2O(g)$$

(iii) As an oxidising agent

Hot concentrated sulphuric acid acts as an oxidising agent usually producing sulphur dioxide.

$$2H_3O^+(aq) + H_2SO_4(l) + 2e^- \rightarrow 4H_2O(l) + SO_2(g)$$

Hydrogen fluoride and hydrogen chloride are not oxidised by sulphuric acid. Hydrogen bromide is oxidised by concentrated sulphuric acid to bromine.

$$2H_2O(l) + 2HBr(aq) \rightarrow Br_2(g) + 2H_3O^+(aq) + 2e^-$$
$$\underline{2H_3O^+(aq) + H_2SO_4(l) + 2e^- \rightarrow 4H_2O(l) + SO_2(g)}$$

$$2HBr(aq) + H_2SO_4(l) \rightarrow Br_2(g) + 2H_2O(l) + SO_2(g)$$

Hydrogen iodide is oxidised even more thoroughly by concentrated sulphuric acid. The sulphuric acid is reduced in this case partly to hydrogen sulphide because hydrogen iodide is an even stronger reducing agent than hydrogen bromide.

$$H_2SO_4(l) + 8H_3O^+(aq) + 8e^- \rightarrow H_2S(g) + 12H_2O(l)$$
$$\underline{8I^-(aq) \rightarrow 4I_2(aq) + 8e^-}$$

$$H_2SO_4(l) + 8H_3O^+(aq) + 8I^-(aq) \rightarrow H_2S(g) + 12H_2O(l) + 4I_2(aq)$$

(iv) Sulphonation

Sulphuric acid is used as a sulphonating agent (see 29.9).

The structure of sulphuric acid is

26.9 HALIDES OF SULPHUR

When chlorine is passed over heated molten sulphur, disulphur dichloride is formed.

$$2S(l) + Cl_2(g) \rightarrow S_2Cl_2(l)$$

Disulphur dichloride is an amber liquid which combines with more chlorine at 0 °C to form sulphur dichloride.

$$S_2Cl_2(l) + Cl_2(g) \rightarrow 2SCl_2(l)$$

Fluorine reacts with sulphur to form sulphur hexafluoride.

$$S(s) + 3F_2(g) \rightarrow SF_6(s)$$

Chapter roundup

Usually questions on this Group are about individual elements or their compounds, rather than a Group comparison. The elements in Group VI have a p^4 configuration in the outer energy level.

Worked questions and answers

1 (a) Give the electron arrangement for a sulphur atom.
   (b) For each of the following species give the oxidation state of sulphur, the shape of the molecule and the distribution of electrons.
      (i) SO_2
      (ii) H_2S
      (iii) SO_4^{2-}
   (c) Describe in outline how substances containing sulphur in oxidation states +6 and 0 could be obtained from sulphur dioxide.

Tutorial note

(a) $1s^2 2s^2 2p^6 3s^2 3p^4$
(b) (i) Oxidation state +4. The shape and distribution of electrons is shown in 26.7.
   (ii) Oxidation state –2. (iii) Oxidation state +6.

(c) A compound with sulphur in oxidation state +6 is sulphur(VI) oxide (sulphur trioxide).
   Pass a mixture of sulphur dioxide and oxygen over a heated platinum catalyst. Collect the sulphur(VI) oxide in a receiver cooled in ice.

$$2SO_2(g) + O_2(g) \rightleftharpoons 2SO_3(s)$$

Sulphur is in oxidation state zero in elemental sulphur. Plunge burning magnesium into a gas jar of sulphur dioxide.

$$2Mg(s) + SO_2(g) \rightarrow 2MgO(s) + S(s)$$

Or mix SO_2 with damp H_2S.

$$2H_2S(g) + SO_2(g) \rightarrow 2H_2O(l) + 3S(g)$$

2 (a) The important step in the Contact process is the following reversible reaction:

$$2SO_2(g) + O_2(g) \rightleftharpoons 2SO_3(g) \quad \Delta H = -98 \text{ kJ mol}^{-1}$$

Describe the manufacture of sulphuric acid, explaining carefully, and making use of the information given, the reasons for the chemical and physical conditions used.
   (b) Why is it important to recycle the gases after the absorption of sulphur trioxide?

Tutorial note

(a) There are three stages in the manufacture of sulphuric acid.
   (i) Oxidation of sulphur-containing minerals

e.g. $$S(s) + O_2(g) \rightarrow SO_2(g)$$
$$4FeS_2(s) + 11O_2(g) \rightarrow 2Fe_2O_3(s) + 8SO_2(g)$$

The sulphur dioxide is purified to remove impurities which would poison the catalyst.

(ii) The oxidation of sulphur dioxide to produce sulphur trioxide (equation given in the question).

The conditions are low temperature to increase the yield of sulphur trioxide (Le Chatelier's Principle). However, low temperatures would cause the reaction to be very slow. Temperatures about 450 °C and vanadium(V) oxide catalyst. High pressure increases yield of sulphur trioxide as there are fewer molecules on the right-hand side of equation.

(iii) Absorption of sulphur trioxide in concentrated sulphuric acid to produce oleum which, on dilution with the correct volume of water, produces concentrated sulphuric acid.

$$SO_3(g) + H_2SO_4(l) \rightarrow H_2S_2O_7(l)$$
$$H_2S_2O_7(l) + H_2O \rightarrow 2H_2SO_4(l)$$

(b) Sulphur is the most expensive raw material. It is important not to lose any expensive sulphur dioxide. Sulphur dioxide also causes acid rain problems if it escapes into the atmosphere.

3 (a) (i) 'Ozone is an allotrope of oxygen'. Explain what is meant by an allotrope and give one other example of allotropy.

(ii) For ozone describe
   (1) two of its reactions,
   (2) its structure and bonding.

(iii) What is the 'ozone layer' and why is it in the news?

(b) Choose three oxides, one basic, one amphoteric and one acidic, and discuss
   (i) their structure and bonding,
   (ii) their acid–base behaviour.

(Oxford 1994)

Tutorial note

(a) (i) See 24.3.

(ii) See 26.3.

(iii) In the upper atmosphere ozone has been produced by the action of UV light on oxygen gas.

$$3O_2 \rightleftharpoons 2O_3$$

The ozone in this layer is able to absorb harmful UVB radiation.

This ozone is being depleted by nitrogen oxide, NO, the hydroxyl free radical, OH•, and chlorine free radicals, Cl•. Chlorine free radicals are produced by the decomposition of CFCs (chlorofluorocarbons).

(b) (i) and (ii) See 26.1, 26.2.

CHAPTER 27

GROUP VII

Units in this chapter

Chapter objectives

The elements of Group VII (called the halogens) probably show as clear a gradation of physical and chemical properties as any Group of the Periodic Table. They are a family of nonmetals which show decreasing chemical reactivity down the Group. In most reactions the halogen atom gains an electron to form a halide ion.

$$X + e^- \rightarrow X^-$$

Halogens are good oxidising agents and you should look back at Chapters 6 and 18 before looking at this chapter. In organic chemistry halogens are used for halogenation, i.e. the introduction of a halogen into an organic molecule. Often this involves a free radical chain reaction (see 14.4 and 38.3). Halogen free radicals are single halogen atoms.

27.1 THE ELEMENTS OF GROUP VII

The elements in Group VII are shown in Table 27.1.

Table 27.1 *The elements of Group VII*

Element	Symbol	Appearance	Electron arrangement
fluorine	F	pale greenish-yellow gas	[He] $2s^2 2p^5$
chlorine	Cl	greenish-yellow gas	[Ne] $3s^2 3p^5$
bromine	Br	dark red liquid	[Ar] $3d^{10} 4s^2 4p^5$
iodine	I	grey-black solid	[Kr] $4d^{10} 5s^2 5p^5$

Astatine is a further member of the halogen family. It is very rare because it is intensely radioactive. It is estimated that there is only 0.029 g of astatine in the earth's crust.

All of the halogen atoms are one electron short of a noble gas arrangement, e.g.

fluorine $1s^2 2s^2 2p^5$ neon $1s^2 2s^2 2p^6$

Halogen atoms can combine by ionic and covalent bonding. The halogen atoms can gain one electron to form negatively charged halide ions, e.g.

$$Cl + e^- \rightarrow Cl^-$$

A halogen atom can also form a covalent bond by overlap of the p orbital containing one electron with a partially filled orbital on another atom.

Ionic halides are formed with electropositive metals, e.g. sodium chloride. Ionic halides are high melting point solids which are soluble in water. Covalent halides are formed between a halogen and a nonmetal or a less electropositive metal.

Fluorine exhibits a maximum covalency of one. The other elements can exhibit covalencies of three, five or seven corresponding to the promotion of electrons into the available d orbitals.

For example, iodine can show higher covalencies

One unpaired electron – forms one covalent bond, e.g. ICl.

One electron promoted into a $5d$ orbital

Three unpaired electrons – forms three covalent bonds, e.g. ICl_3.

Two electrons promoted into $5d$ orbitals

Five unpaired electrons – forms five covalent bonds, e.g. ICl_5.

Three electrons promoted into $5d$ orbitals

Seven unpaired electrons – forms seven covalent bonds, e.g. ICl_7.

All halogens are composed of diatomic molecules. Within the molecule, the two halogen atoms are joined by a single covalent bond. The enthalpies of atomisation of these elements are:

fluorine	79.1 kJ mol^{-1}
chlorine	121.1 kJ mol^{-1}
bromine	112.0 kJ mol^{-1}
iodine	106.6 kJ mol^{-1}

From chlorine to iodine, the strength of the bond between the halogen atoms decreases. Fluorine has a much weaker bond than might be expected and this is because of the extra repulsion caused by the close proximity of the two fluorine nuclei and the repulsion between nonbonding electrons on both atoms.

The halogen elements have the highest electron affinities of all the elements. They are:

fluorine	-332 kJ mol^{-1}
chlorine	-364 kJ mol^{-1}
bromine	-342 kJ mol^{-1}
iodine	-295 kJ mol^{-1}

Again, the electron affinity of fluorine is less than might be expected.

The electronegativities of these elements decrease down the Group. The high electronegativity of fluorine is the reason for the existence of hydrogen bonding in hydrogen fluoride. It also explains why fluorine (like oxygen in Group VI, Chapter 26) causes elements to show their maximum oxidation state.

Since iodine is the least electronegative, it is more inclined to show metallic properties. It is possible to form compounds of iodine containing the I^+ ion, e.g. I^+CNO^-.

All of the halogens are oxidising agents. Fluorine is the strongest of all chemical oxidising agents.

$$\tfrac{1}{2}F_2 + e^- \rightarrow F^-$$

Despite the fact that the electron affinity of fluorine is less than that of chlorine, the dissociation energy of the fluorine molecule is also less. The difference in oxidising power between the halogens is shown by the standard electrode potentials $E^\ominus$:

fluorine/fluoride	+2.87 V
chlorine/chloride	+1.36 V
bromine/bromide	+1.09 V
iodine/iodide	+0.54 V

The difference in oxidising power between the halogens explains their displacement reaction. If chlorine is bubbled through a colourless solution of potassium iodide, the solution turns brown due to the liberation of iodine.

$$Cl_2(g) + 2I^-(aq) \rightarrow 2Cl^-(aq) + I_2(aq)$$

Chlorine is a stronger oxidising agent than iodine.

27.2 THE PROPERTIES OF THE HALOGENS

(i) Reactions with water

Fluorine reacts vigorously with cold water to form hydrogen fluoride and oxygen.

$$2F_2(g) + 2H_2O(l) \rightarrow 4HF(g) + O_2(g)$$

In addition to these products, traces of trioxygen, hydrogen peroxide and oxygen difluoride F_2O are detected.

Chlorine reacts less readily with water. A solution of chlorine in water (chlorine water) is acidic due to the formation of hydrochloric acid and chloric(I) acid (hypochlorous acid).

$$Cl_2(g) + H_2O(l) \rightleftharpoons HCl(aq) + HOCl(aq)$$

When this solution is exposed to strong sunlight the chloric(I) acid decomposes to produce oxygen.

$$2HOCl(aq) \rightarrow 2HCl(aq) + O_2(g)$$

It is this available oxygen which accounts for the bleaching properties of chlorine.

Bromine is much less soluble in water than chlorine. The reaction of bromine with water is similar to that of chlorine but to a lesser extent.

Iodine is only very sparingly soluble in water. Iodine dissolves better in other solvents. The colour of an iodine solution depends upon the solvent. With solvents containing oxygen (e.g. ethers, alcohols) the solution is brown. Hydrocarbons and tetrachloromethane solutions are violet in colour. Iodine dissolves in an aqueous solution of potassium iodide to form a brown solution containing a complex ion.

$$I_2(aq) + I^-(aq) \rightleftharpoons I_3^-(aq)$$

(ii) Reactions with alkalis

Fluorine reacts with an aqueous solution of potassium hydroxide. With a cold, dilute potassium hydroxide solution, oxygen difluoride (fluorine monoxide) is produced.

$$2KOH(aq) + 2F_2(g) \rightarrow 2KF(aq) + F_2O(g) + H_2O(l)$$

With hot, concentrated potassium hydroxide solution, a different reaction takes place to produce oxygen.

$$4KOH(aq) + 2F_2(g) \rightarrow 4KF(aq) + O_2(g) + 2H_2O(l)$$

Chlorine and bromine also react with aqueous potassium hydroxide solution, with the products again depending upon the conditions. With cold, dilute potassium hydroxide solution, potassium chloride and potassium chlorate(I) (potassium hypochlorite) are formed.

$$Cl_2(g) + 2OH^-(aq) \rightarrow Cl^-(aq) + ClO^-(aq) + H_2O(l)$$

With hot, concentrated potassium hydroxide, the chlorate(I) or bromate(I) disproportionates.

$$6OH^-(aq) + 3Cl_2(g) \rightarrow 5Cl^-(aq) + ClO_3^-(aq) + 3H_2O(l)$$
$$\text{chlorate(V)}$$

The reaction of iodine with potassium hydroxide solution is reversible.

$$2KOH(aq) + I_2(s) \rightleftharpoons KI(aq) + KIO(aq) + H_2O(l)$$

27.3 HYDROGEN HALIDES

The hydrogen halides can all be prepared by direct combination. The laboratory preparations of the halides differ. Hydrogen chloride and hydrogen fluoride are prepared by the action of concentrated sulphuric acid on sodium chloride or calcium fluoride.

$$NaCl(s) + H_2SO_4(l) \rightarrow NaHSO_4(s) + HCl(g)$$
$$CaF_2(s) + H_2SO_4(l) \rightarrow CaSO_4(s) + 2HF(g)$$

The reaction between a bromide or iodide and concentrated sulphuric acid does not produce the corresponding hydrogen halide since hydrogen bromide and hydrogen iodide reduce sulphuric acid (see 26.8).

Hydrogen bromide and hydrogen iodide are prepared by the hydrolysis of phosphorus tribromide or phosphorus triiodide.

$$PBr_3(l) + 3H_2O(l) \rightarrow H_3PO_3(aq) + 3HBr(aq)$$
$$PI_3(s) + 3H_2O(l) \rightarrow H_3PO_3(aq) + 3HI(aq)$$

Hydrogen fluoride is a liquid at room temperature and pressure while the other hydrogen halides are gases. The boiling points are:

HF	20 °C
HCl	−85 °C
HBr	−67 °C
HI	−35 °C

The anomalous boiling point of hydrogen fluoride is due to hydrogen bonding (see 4.5) between hydrogen fluoride molecules.

Hydrogen bonding exists in the liquid and in the vapour up to about 90 °C. Solutions of the hydrogen halides in water are acidic. All except aqueous hydrogen fluoride are strong acids, e.g.

$$HCl(aq) + H_2O(l) \rightarrow H_3O^+(aq) + Cl^-(aq)$$

Hydrogen fluoride is a weak acid due to the dissociation:

$$2HF(aq) + H_2O(l) \rightleftharpoons H_3O^+(aq) + HF_2^-(aq)$$

(NB 2 moles of hydrogen fluoride produce 1 mole of $H_3O^+(aq)$ ions.)

27.4 HALIDES

The halides formed by electropositive metals are ionic while halides of nonmetals and less electropositive metals are covalent. Where an element forms two chlorides, the one with the other element in the higher oxidation state is more covalent, e.g. $SnCl_4$ (oxidation state of tin +4) is more covalent than $SnCl_2$ (oxidation state +2).

In the series lithium fluoride, lithium chloride, lithium bromide, lithium iodide the bonding is predominantly ionic for lithium fluoride but there is a tendency towards covalency across the series. This is due to the increasing size of the halogen ion.

Anhydrous halides are prepared by passing dry halogen vapour over the heated element, e.g.

$$2Fe(s) + 3Cl_2(g) \rightarrow 2FeCl_3 \qquad \text{iron(III) chloride}$$

NB The reaction of iron with dry hydrogen chloride produces iron(II) chloride.

$$Fe(s) + 2HCl(g) \rightarrow FeCl_2(s) + H_2(g)$$

Most ionic halides are not hydrolysed by water and can be produced by reacting a metal, metal oxide, metal hydroxide or metal carbonate with a hydrogen halide, followed by evaporation and crystallisation, e.g.

$$NaOH(aq) + HCl(aq) \rightarrow NaCl(aq) + H_2O(l)$$

Metal halides containing water of crystallisation are often hydrolysed on heating. It is not possible to produce an anhydrous metal halide by heating the hydrated metal halide. This process can be carried out by heating the hydrated halide in an atmosphere of hydrogen halide.

Insoluble metal halides can be produced by mixing two suitable solutions, e.g. lead(II) iodide is precipitated when solutions of lead(II) nitrate and potassium iodide are mixed.

$$Pb(NO_3)_2(aq) + 2KI(aq) \rightarrow PbI_2(s) + 2KNO_3(aq)$$
ionic equation: $\qquad Pb^{2+}(aq) + 2I^-(aq) \rightarrow PbI_2(s)$

The yellow lead(II) iodide is removed by filtration and washed and dried.

The silver halides are produced by adding silver nitrate solution to a solution of halide ions.

$$Ag^+(aq) + X^-(aq) \rightarrow AgX(s) \quad \text{where X represents a halogen.}$$

Silver fluoride is soluble in water because the fluoride ion has a particularly high hydration energy owing to its small size. The other halides precipitate as follows:

silver chloride	AgCl	white precipitate
silver bromide	AgBr	cream precipitate
silver iodide	AgI	pale yellow precipitate

The precipitates can also be distinguished by their solubilities in ammonia solution. Silver chloride is readily soluble, forming the diammine silver(I) ion.

$$AgCl(s) + 2NH_3(aq) \rightarrow [Ag(NH_3)_2]^+(aq) + Cl^-(aq)$$

Silver bromide is partially soluble and silver iodide virtually insoluble.

Calcium chloride, bromide and iodide are soluble in water but calcium fluoride is insoluble due to its high lattice energy. This is caused by the small sizes of the calcium and fluoride ions and the double charge on the calcium ion.

Chapter roundup

You should have seen the gradation of physical and chemical properties within the halogens. Perhaps the gradation in chemical properties is best seen in the reactions of the halogens with hydrogen and in the displacement reactions (see 27.1).

Worked questions and answers

1 The halogen family includes chlorine, bromine and iodine. This question concerns these three elements and their compounds.
   (a) (i) Write an ionic equation for the reaction which takes place when chlorine is bubbled through a solution of potassium iodide.
      (ii) Using this as an example, explain the terms oxidation and reduction.
   (b) Explain why, although hydrogen chloride can be prepared by warming a mixture of sodium chloride and concentrated sulphuric acid, a similar method cannot be used for preparing hydrogen iodide.
   (c) Disproportionation occurs when chlorine reacts with a hot aqueous sodium hydroxide solution.
      (i) What is meant by 'disproportionation'?
      (ii) Write an equation for the reaction.

Tutorial note

(a) (i) $$Cl_2(g) + 2I^-(aq) \rightarrow 2Cl^-(aq) + I_2(aq)$$
   (ii) Oxidation and reduction are in Chapter 6. Chlorine molecules gain electrons to form chloride ions and are reduced. Iodide ions lose electrons to form iodine molecules and are oxidised.
(b) See 26.8.
(c) (i) Disproportionation: a reaction in which a single substance reacts to form two products. One product is obtained by the oxidation of the original substance and the other by reduction. Other examples will be found in Chapters 6 and 18.
   (ii) When chlorine reacts with cold alkali

$$Cl_2(g) + 2OH^-(aq) \rightarrow Cl^-(aq) + ClO^-(aq) + H_2O(l)$$

On heating the chlorate(I) disproportionates

$$3ClO^-(aq) \rightarrow ClO_3^-(aq) + 2Cl^-(aq)$$

Question bank

1 Chlorine (0.12 mol) was made to react with aqueous NaOH at a temperature which allowed both of the following reactions to occur.

$$Cl_2 + 2NaOH \rightarrow NaOCl + H_2O + NaCl$$
$$3Cl_2 + 6NaOH \rightarrow NaClO_3 + 3H_2O + 5NaCl$$

Immediately all of the chlorine reacted it was found that the solution contained 0.16 mol of NaCl.
Calculate the amount of $NaClO_3$ produced.

(Oxford 1989)

Points

In answering this question, let x = number of moles of chlorine reacting in the second equation and $(0.12 - x)$ = number of moles of chlorine reacting in the first. Using the equation, calculate the number of moles of sodium chloride produced, i.e. $(0.12 - x)$ and $5x/3$. These added together should give the total, i.e. 0.16. Solve this equation and get $x = 0.06$. Therefore, number of moles of $NaClO_3$ from the equation = 0.02.

THE *d*-BLOCK ELEMENTS

Units in this chapter

Chapter objectives

The first row *d*-block elements (sometimes called transition metals) are a series of metals from scandium to zinc, positioned in the Periodic Table between Groups II and III. As you have seen, the position of an element in the Periodic Table is closely linked with its electron arrangement (Chapters 1 and 2).

Calcium has an electron arrangement of $1s^2 2s^2 2p^6 3s^2 3p^6 4s^2$. The two electrons which go into the 4*s* orbital do so because it is of slightly lower energy than the 3*d* orbital (Fig. 1.3). The next orbitals to be filled are the five 3*d* orbitals, each of which can hold two electrons. The 3*d* orbitals are smaller than the 4*s* orbital and so addition of electrons to the 3*d* orbitals as we move from calcium across to zinc does not have much effect on chemical properties. Remember that the chemical properties are determined largely by the outer electron arrangements. The *d*-block elements therefore represent a family of metals with largely similar properties and we usually consider them together.

Questions on the *d*-block elements are common and usually divide into two types.

❶ Questions about the general properties of the *d*-block elements.

❷ Specific questions about individual *d*-block elements and their compounds.

Many textbooks and notes from your teacher will be detailed about individual properties and reactions. I have therefore concentrated on the general properties of the *d*-block elements. When you understand these properties spend some time going back and looking at other sources of information. Hopefully they will make more sense to you then.

28.1 THE *d*-BLOCK ELEMENTS

The elements in the first row of the *d*-block and their electron arrangements appear in Table 28.1.

Table 28.1 *The first row d-block elements*

Element	Symbol	Atomic number	Electron arrangement
scandium	Sc	21	$1s^2\ 2s^2\ 2p^6\ 3s^2\ 3p^6\ 3d^1\ 4s^2$
titanium	Ti	22	$1s^2\ 2s^2\ 2p^6\ 3s^2\ 3p^6\ 3d^2\ 4s^2$
vanadium	V	23	$1s^2\ 2s^2\ 2p^6\ 3s^2\ 3p^6\ 3d^3\ 4s^2$
chromium	Cr	24	$1s^2\ 2s^2\ 2p^6\ 3s^2\ 3p^6\ 3d^5\ 4s^1$
manganese	Mn	25	$1s^2\ 2s^2\ 2p^6\ 3s^2\ 3p^6\ 3d^5\ 4s^2$
iron	Fe	26	$1s^2\ 2s^2\ 2p^6\ 3s^2\ 3p^6\ 3d^6\ 4s^2$
cobalt	Co	27	$1s^2\ 2s^2\ 2p^6\ 3s^2\ 3p^6\ 3d^7\ 4s^2$
nickel	Ni	28	$1s^2\ 2s^2\ 2p^6\ 3s^2\ 3p^6\ 3d^8\ 4s^2$
copper	Cu	29	$1s^2\ 2s^2\ 2p^6\ 3s^2\ 3p^6\ 3d^{10}4s^1$
zinc	Zn	30	$1s^2\ 2s^2\ 2p^6\ 3s^2\ 3p^6\ 3d^{10}4s^2$

NB The electrons are being added to $3d$ orbitals but the irregularities at chromium and copper exist because half filled orbitals and fully filled orbitals are slightly more stable.

The *d*-block elements from scandium to zinc are silvery metals (apart from copper). They all (except zinc) have high melting points and high densities because the atoms are strongly bonded together and closely packed. Zinc has a low melting point because it has full $3d$ and $4s$ orbitals, and these electrons are not used in the same way in bonding the atoms together. The *d*-block elements are good conductors of electricity because the $3d$ and $4s$ electrons are free to move through the structure.

These elements readily form alloys. For example, brass is an alloy of copper and zinc. Since the atoms are similar in size and chemical nature, they can be incorporated in each other's lattices.

Across the first row of the *d*-block elements there is a slight decrease in atomic and ionic radii. Moving from scandium to titanium, there is an additional proton in the nucleus. The extra electron goes into an existing $3d$ orbital causing no increase in radius. Due to the extra nuclear attraction, the radius is slightly smaller.

The first ionisation energy is approximately the same but increasing slightly across the series due to extra nuclear attraction.

The $E^{\ominus}$ values (i.e. M^{2+}/M) for the *d*-block elements, except copper, are negative. From this it can be concluded that these elements will react with dilute hydrochloric acid or sulphuric acid to produce hydrogen, e.g.

$$Mn(s) + H_2SO_4(aq) \rightarrow MnSO_4(aq) + H_2(g)$$
$$\text{manganese(II)}$$
$$\text{sulphate}$$

The *d*-block elements form **interstitial compounds** with hydrogen, carbon and other small atoms. The small atoms fit into spaces in the lattices of the *d*-block elements. Steel is an interstitial compound with carbon atoms in spaces in the iron lattice.

The *d*-block elements are much less reactive than the alkali and alkaline earth metals, i.e. the *s*-block elements.

The *d*-block elements have certain characteristic properties. These include:

❶ formation of compounds in a wide variety of oxidation states;

❷ formation of coloured compounds;

❸ existence of paramagnetism; and

❹ formation of coordination compounds.

Each of these will be considered in 28.2–28.5.

28.2 VARIABLE OXIDATION STATES

When a first row d-block element loses electrons to form positive ions, the $4s$ electrons are lost first, followed by the $3d$ electrons. In no case are electrons lost from the $3p$ orbitals.

Table 28.2 lists the common oxidation states of the first row of d-block elements. The most common oxidation state for each element is given in bold type.

Table 28.2 *Common oxidation states of the first row d-block elements*

Element	Oxidation states	Examples
scandium	+**3**	Sc_2O_3
titanium	+2, +3, +**4**	TiO, Ti_2O_3, TiO_2
vanadium	+2, +3, +**4**, +5	VO, V_2O_3, VO_2, V_2O_5
chromium	+2, +**3**, +6	CrO, Cr_2O_3, CrO_3
manganese	+**2**, +3, +4, +6, +7	MnO, Mn_2O_3, MnO_2, K_2MnO_4, $KMnO_4$
iron	+2, +**3**	FeO, Fe_2O_3
cobalt	+**2**, +3	CoO, Co_2O_3
nickel	+**2**, +3, +4	NiO, Ni_2O_3, NiO_2
copper	+1, +**2**	Cu_2O, CuO
zinc	+**2**	ZnO

The maximum oxidation states for scandium, titanium, vanadium, chromium and manganese increase to a peak. For these elements, the maximum oxidation state corresponds to the use of all $3d$ and $4s$ electrons. An oxidation state greater than the number of $3d$ and $4s$ electrons would involve electrons from the $3p$ orbitals which are of much lower energy.

For any element, the higher oxidation states give rise to covalent compounds.

The existence of a variety of oxidation states for each element explains the catalytic properties of the d-block elements. For example, the decomposition of hydrogen peroxide with manganese(IV) oxide can occur in two stages. The manganese(IV) oxide is oxidised by hydrogen peroxide to manganese(VII) oxide. The manganese(VII) oxide then decomposes to reform manganese(IV) oxide and produce oxygen.

28.3 FORMATION OF COLOURED COMPOUNDS

Hydrated d-block metal ions are coloured where the $3d$ orbitals contain unpaired electrons. Light of a certain colour is absorbed when electrons move from one d-orbital to another. For example, hydrated copper(II) ions absorb red light when certain electrons move from one orbital to another and so the residual blue light is transmitted. This gives hydrated copper(II) compounds their characteristic blue colour.

Table 28.3 lists the colours of some hydrated ions of d-block metals.

Where $3d^0$ or $3d^{10}$ arrangements exist ($3d$ orbitals either empty or completely full) the solution of the ion is colourless.

Table 28.3   Colours of some hydrated ions of d-block elements

Hydrated ion	Electron arrangement of ion	Colour
Sc^{3+}	[Ar] $3d^0$	colourless
Ti^{3+}	[Ar] $3d^1$	violet
V^{3+}	[Ar] $3d^2$	green
Cr^{3+}	[Ar] $3d^3$	green
Mn^{3+}	[Ar] $3d^4$	violet
Mn^{2+}	[Ar] $3d^5$	pale pink
Fe^{3+}	[Ar] $3d^5$	yellow
Fe^{2+}	[Ar] $3d^6$	green
Co^{2+}	[Ar] $3d^7$	pink
Ni^{2+}	[Ar] $3d^8$	green
Cu^{2+}	[Ar] $3d^9$	blue
Zn^{2+}	[Ar] $3d^{10}$	colourless

Note: [Ar] represents $1s^2 2s^2 2p^6 3s^2 3p^6$.

Table 28.4   Unpaired electrons in ions of first row d-block elements

Ion	Electron arrangement of ion						Number of unpaired electrons
Sc^{3+}	[Ar] $3d^0$						0
Ti^{3+}	[Ar] $3d^1$	1					1
V^{3+}	[Ar] $3d^2$	1	1				2
Cr^{3+}	[Ar] $3d^3$	1	1	1			3
Mn^{3+}	[Ar] $3d^4$	1	1	1	1		4
Fe^{3+}	[Ar] $3d^5$	1	1	1	1	1	5
Co^{3+}	[Ar] $3d^6$	1↑	1	1	1	1	4
Co^{2+}	[Ar] $3d^7$	1↑	1↑	1	1	1	3
Ni^{2+}	[Ar] $3d^8$	1↑	1↑	1↑	1	1	2
Cu^{2+}	[Ar] $3d^9$	1↑	1↑	1↑	1↑	1	1
Zn^{2+}	[Ar] $3d^{10}$	1↑	1↑	1↑	1↑	1↑	0

28.4 PARAMAGNETISM

Those d-block metal ions that contain unpaired electrons show **paramagnetism**. The movement of an unpaired, negatively charged electron produces a small magnetic field. If a particle containing unpaired electrons is subjected to an external magnetic field, there is a positive interaction which is called paramagnetism. This causes the lines of force to become more concentrated and a measurable paramagnetic moment can be obtained. An extreme case of this is **ferromagnetism**.

A substance containing no unpaired electrons is repelled by the magnetic field and is said to be **diamagnetic**.

Table 28.4 shows the unpaired electrons in some ions of first row d-block elements.

Fig. 28.1 shows a graph of the relative paramagnetic moments of ions in the first row against the number of unpaired electrons.

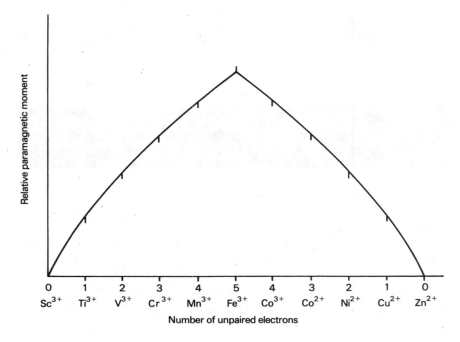

Fig. 28.1 Relative paramagnetic moments of ions in the first row aainst number of unpaired electrons

28.5 FORMATION OF COORDINATION COMPOUNDS

A **coordination compound** is formed when a number of molecules or negatively charged ions combine with a central d-block atom or ion to form a molecule or complex ion. The molecules or ions which bond onto the central metal ion or atom are called **ligands** and the type of bonding involved is **coordinate** (or dative) bonding (see 4.4). For example, when a copper(II) compound such as anhydrous copper(II) sulphate is dissolved in water a hexaaquacopper(II) ion is formed.

$$Cu^{2+} + 6H_2O(l) \rightarrow$$

The water molecules are the ligands. Each water molecule acts as a Lewis base (see 16.1), donating a pair of electrons to form a coordinate bond. Energy is evolved during this process due to the formation of six new bonds.

Another example of a complex ion is the hexacyanoferrate(II) ion. When potassium cyanide solution is added to a solution of iron(II) sulphate, a precipitate of iron(II) cyanide is produced which redissolves to form a solution containing hexacyanoferrate(II) ions.

$$FeSO_4(aq) + 2KCN(aq) \rightarrow Fe(CN)_2(s) + K_2SO_4(aq)$$

$$Fe(CN)_2(s) + 4CN^-(aq) \rightarrow$$

hexacyanoferrate(II) ion

The hexacyanoferrate(II) ion was previously called the ferrocyanide ion. This should be distinguished from the hexacyanoferrate(III) or ferricyanide ion which is similar in structure but contains iron in oxidation state +3.

In these complex ions the cyanide (CN^-) ions are the ligands. In the hexaaquacopper(II) ion the resulting complex ion is positively charged but in hexacyanoferrate(II) and hexacyanoferrate(III) the resulting ions are negatively charged. The resulting complexes can be neutral, e.g. $Ni(CO)_4$ tetracarbonylnickel(0), or positively charged (called **cationic complexes**) or negatively charged (called **anionic complexes**).

Fe^{2+} ions contain six electrons in the $3d$ subshell, and require 12 more electrons to achieve the noble gas electron arrangement of krypton. Twelve electrons are supplied by accepting six lone pairs. In all complexes a similar tendency to achieve a noble gas electron arrangement exists, but this is not always achieved.

The properties of a complex ion are different from the simple ions from which it is composed. For example, it is impossible to obtain positive tests for Fe^{2+} and CN^- ions in the hexacyanoferrate(II) complex. Instead, there are distinct tests for the hexacyanoferrate(II) ion. When copper(II) sulphate solution is added to a solution containing hexacyanoferrate(II) ions, a brown precipitate of copper hexacyanoferrate(II) is produced.

$$2Cu^{2+}(aq) + Fe(CN)_6^{4-}(aq) \rightarrow Cu_2Fe(CN)_6(s)$$

Ligands such as H_2O, NH_3 and Cl^- form only a single coordinate bond with a central metal ion. They are said to be **unidentate**. Some ligands are able to form two or more coordinate bonds to the central metal ion. They are said to be **polydentate**. Some ligands such as EDTA can form as many as six coordinate bonds with the central metal ion. The resulting complexes are called **chelates** *or* **chelated complexes**.

Some polydentate ligands are

ethanedioate
ion

butanedione dioxime
(dimethylglyoxime)

EDTA

There is a system for naming complexes. Negatively charged ligands end in '-o', e.g. chloro- Cl^-, cyano- CN^-.

Neutral ligands include water and ammonia. The name **aqua-** is used for water and **ammine** for ammonia. (NB It is important to distinguish ammine from amine. Amines (Chapter 35) are organic derivatives obtained by replacing hydrogens of ammonia with alkyl and aryl groups.)

If the complex ion is negatively charged (anionic complex) the name ends in '-ate', e.g. hexacyanoferrate(II). (NB Some metals are given the Latin name, e.g. iron – ferrate, lead – plumbate, silver – argentate.)

The number in Roman numerals is the oxidation state of the central metal ion. In hexacyanoferrate(II), the central metal ion is Fe^{2+} in oxidation state +2.

Where the complex is positively charged or neutral, the name does not end in -ate, e.g. tetracarbonylnickel(0) and hexaaquacopper(II).

The shape of a complex is determined by the coordination number of the central metal atom or ion. The coordination number is the number of ligands which will bond to a central metal atom or ion. In hexacyanoferrate(II) and hexaaquacopper(II) ions the coordination number is 6 but in tetracarbonylnickel(0) the coordination number is 4. The common coordination numbers are 2, 4 and 6.

Coordination number 2

The complex is linear, e.g. dichlorocuprate(I) $[CuCl_2]^-$.

$$[Cl \rightarrow Cu \leftarrow Cl]^-$$

The central ion is *sp* hybridised.

Coordination number 4

The usual shape for the complex ion is tetrahedral, e.g. tetracarbonylnickel(0).

The central atom is *sp*³ hybridised.

In cases where the central metal ion has a d^8 arrangement, the shape is square planar, e.g. tetracyanonickelate(II).

The central ion is *dsp²* hybridised.

Coordination number 6

The coordination number 6 is extremely common and the octahedral shape is preferred, e.g. hexacyanoferrate(II), with d^2sp^3 hybridisation of the central ion.

Ligands may change during a reaction and, rarely, the coordination number may change, e.g.

$$[Co(H_2O)_6]^{2+}(aq) + 4Cl^-(aq) \rightleftharpoons [CoCl_4]^{2-}(aq) + 6H_2O(l)$$

octahedral	tetrahedral
pink	blue
hexaaquacobalt(II) ion	tetrachlorocobaltate(II)

In this case the water ligands are replaced by chloride ligands and the coordination number changes from 6 to 4.

In 28.6–28.11 some of the d-block elements will be considered separately. As you work through these sections you will see some of the above principles in operation.

28.6 CHROMIUM

Chromium is a hard, bluish-white metal used to electroplate steel (e.g. bicycle handlebars) because it is shiny and prevents corrosion.

It reacts with steam at red heat to produce chromium(III) oxide.

$$2Cr(s) + 3H_2O(g) \rightarrow Cr_2O_3(s) + 3H_2(g)$$

Chromium reacts slowly with dilute hydrochloric acid to produce chromium(II) chloride.

$$Cr(s) + 2HCl(aq) \rightarrow CrCl_2(aq) + H_2(g)$$

Chromium can be extracted from chromium(III) oxide by heating a mixture of chromium(III) oxide and aluminium powder.

$$Cr_2O_3(s) + 2Al(s) \rightarrow Al_2O_3(s) + 2Cr(s)$$

Chromium has an electron arrangement $[Ar]3d^54s^1$. There are three possible oxidation states (+2, +3 and +6).

Chromium(II)

This is an unstable oxidation state and is readily oxidised to chromium(III). Chromium(II) oxide, CrO, is a basic oxide.

Chromium(III)

Chromium(III) is the most common oxidation state of chromium. If a chromium(III) salt contains water of crystallisation the crystals are usually violet.

In a solution of a chromium(III) salt, the hexaaquachromium(III) ion $[Cr(H_2O)_6]^{3+}$ exists. This complex ion readily loses protons owing to the high charge density of the Cr^{3+} ion (see 23.4).

$$[Cr(H_2O)_2(OH)_4]^- \xleftarrow{\text{addn of OH}^-} [Cr(H_2O)_3(OH)_3] \xrightarrow{\text{addn of H}_3O^+} [Cr(H_2O)_4(OH)_2]^+$$

The action of ammonia solution on a chromium(III) salt solution is different. The chromium(III) hydroxide dissolves in excess ammonia solution to form a yellow solution of hexaamminechromium(III) ions, $[Cr(NH_3)_6]^{3+}$.

Chromium(III) salts are oxidised to chromium(VI) by warming with hydrogen peroxide in an alkaline solution.

$$2Cr^{3+}(aq) + 5H_2O_2(aq) \rightarrow 2CrO_4^{2-}(aq) + 10H^+(aq) + O_2(g)$$

chromate(VI)
yellow

Chromium(VI)

Chromium(VI) compounds are strong oxidising agents. The two common chromium(VI) compounds are potassium chromate(VI) (K_2CrO_4 containing the CrO_4^{2-} ions) and potassium dichromate(VI) ($K_2Cr_2O_7$ containing $Cr_2O_7^{2-}$ ions).

The chromate(VI) and dichromate(VI) ions are both in the same oxidation state and are readily interconverted. If an acid is added to a yellow chromate(VI) solution, the orange dichromate(VI) is produced.

$$2CrO_4^{2-}(aq) + 2H_3O^+(aq) \rightleftharpoons Cr_2O_7^{2-}(aq) + 3H_2O(l)$$

Addition of an alkali to a dichromate(VI) solution produces the chromate(VI). The structures of the two ions are

chromate(VI)   dichromate(VI)

NB The arrangement of oxygens around each chromium atom is approximately tetrahedral.

The dichromate(VI) ion is a strong oxidising agent in acid solution (see 6.2). The dichromate(VI) ion does not, however, oxidise hydrogen chloride to chlorine (cf. manganate(VII)).

Chromium(VI) oxide is an acidic oxide. It is produced as bright red, needle-shaped crystals when concentrated sulphuric acid is added to concentrated solutions of chromate(VI) or dichromate(VI).

$$CrO_4^{2-}(aq) + 2H_2SO_4(l) \rightarrow CrO_3(s) + 2HSO_4^{2-}(aq) + H_2O(l)$$
$$Cr_2O_7^{2-}(aq) + 2H_2SO_4(l) \rightarrow 2CrO_3(s) + 2HSO_4^-(aq) + H_2O(l)$$

This chromium(VI) oxide dissolves in water to form chromic(VI) acid ('chromic acid').

$$CrO_3(s) + H_2O(l) \rightarrow H_2CrO_4(aq)$$

28.7 MANGANESE

Manganese is a hard, grey metal. It reacts readily with hot water and dilute hydrochloric acid.

$$Mn(s) + 2HCl(aq) \rightarrow MnCl_2(aq) + H_2(g)$$

(Some candidates confuse manganese (Mn – a dense metal in the *d*-block) and magnesium (Mg – a less dense metal in Group II).)

Manganese has an electron arrangement $[Ar]3d^54s^2$ and can exist in oxidation states +2, +3, +4, +6 and +7.

Manganese(II)

Manganese(II) is the most stable oxidation state corresponding to a $3d^5$ electron arrangement, i.e. 1 electron in each *d* orbital. Manganese(II) oxide is a basic oxide. Solutions of manganese(II) ions in water are pale pink owing to the presence of $[Mn(H_2O)_6]^{2+}$ ions.

Manganese(III)

This is an unstable oxidation state existing only in complexes. In acid solution manganese(III) disproportionates.

$$2Mn(III) \rightarrow Mn(IV) + Mn(II)$$

Manganese(IV)

Manganese(IV) exists only in insoluble compounds (e.g. manganese(IV) oxide) and complexes.

Manganese(IV) oxide is a brown-black covalent oxide with feebly amphoteric properties. It is an oxidising agent, oxidising concentrated hydrochloric acid to chlorine.

$$MnO_2(s) + 4HCl(aq) \rightarrow MnCl_2(aq) + 2H_2O(l) + Cl_2(g)$$

Manganese(VI)

The manganese(VI) oxidation state is unstable. The manganate(VI) ion (**manganate**) is produced when manganese(IV) oxide is fused with a strong oxidising agent such as potassium chlorate(V).

$$3MnO_2(s) + KClO_3(l) + 6KOH(l) \rightarrow 3K_2MnO_4(l) + KCl(l) + 3H_2O(g)$$
$$\text{potassium}$$
$$\text{manganate(VI)}$$

Potassium manganate(VI) is a green salt. In neutral or acid solution, it disproportionates to form manganese(IV) oxide and manganate(VII) (**permanganate**).

$$3MnO_4^{2-}(aq) + 2H_2O(l) \rightarrow 2MnO_4^-(aq) + MnO_2(s) + 4OH^-(aq)$$

Potassium manganate(VI) is produced when potassium manganate(VII) is heated.

$$2KMnO_4(s) \rightarrow K_2MnO_4(s) + MnO_2(s) + O_2(g)$$

The structure of the manganate(VI) ion is

$$\begin{bmatrix} \overset{\displaystyle \ddot{O}}{\underset{\displaystyle \ddot{O}}{\overset{\|}{O}-Mn-\ddot{O}}} \end{bmatrix}^{2-}$$

Manganese(VII)

Manganese(VII) exists in the oxide Mn_2O_7 which is strongly acidic. Manganate(VII) can be produced directly from manganese(II) by warming with a strong oxidising agent, e.g. sodium bismuthate $NaBiO_3$. The manganate(VII) (permanganate) ion is produced by acidification of manganate(VI) ions, or by passing chlorine through a solution of potassium manganate(VI).

$$2MnO_4^{2-}(aq) + Cl_2(g) \rightarrow 2MnO_4^-(aq) + 2Cl^-(aq)$$

Potassium manganate(VII) is a powerful oxidising agent in inorganic and organic chemistry (see 6.2).

28.8 IRON

Extraction of iron

Iron exists in the earth's crust in ores such as **haematite** Fe_2O_3, **magnetite** Fe_3O_4 and **iron pyrites** FeS_2. Iron is obtained by reducing the ores in a blast furnace. The blast furnace is loaded with a charge of iron ore, coke and limestone through the top of the furnace. The furnace is heated by blasts of hot air into the base. Various reactions take place in the furnace.

1 The burning of the coke in the air produces temperatures in excess of 1500 °C.

$$C(s) + O_2(g) \rightarrow CO_2(g)$$

2 The reduction of carbon dioxide to carbon monoxide.

$$CO_2(g) + C(s) \rightarrow 2CO(g)$$

3 The reduction of iron ore takes place in the furnace. At the top of the furnace

$$Fe_2O_3(s) + 3CO(g) \rightarrow 2Fe(l) + 3CO_2(g)$$
$$Fe_2O_3(s) + CO(g) \rightarrow 2FeO(s) + CO_2(g)$$

and lower in the furnace where the temperature is higher

$$FeO(s) + C(s) \rightarrow Fe(l) + CO(g)$$

4 The limestone is added to the furnace to remove impurities of silicon(IV) oxide in the ore. The calcium carbonate decomposes to form calcium oxide.

$$CaCO_3(s) \rightarrow CaO(s) + CO_2(g)$$

5 The calcium oxide reacts with the silicon(IV) oxide to form calcium silicate (**slag**).

$$CaO(s) + SiO_2(s) \rightarrow CaSiO_3(l)$$

The slag floats on top of the molten iron and both can be tapped off separately. The iron produced is called pig iron and contains about 4% carbon plus other impurities such as phosphorus, silicon and manganese.

Most of the pig iron is converted into steel. The molten iron is loaded into a furnace and a blast of hot air or oxygen is blown through the iron to burn off the impurities. Calculated quantities of carbon and other elements are then added to give steel of the desired composition.

Steel is basically iron with 0.5–1.5% carbon added. The properties of steel depend upon the percentage of carbon and other elements added. Steel containing 1.5% carbon is very hard. Steel containing chromium and nickel is called stainless steel and shows resistance to corrosion.

Rusting of iron

The rusting of iron requires the presence of water and oxygen. The product, rust, is essentially a hydrated iron(III) oxide. The rusting process is accelerated by carbon dioxide and electrolytes such as salt.

Rusting can be prevented by mechanical means such as painting and oiling which prevent the metal from coming into contact with oxygen and water. Rusting can also be prevented by sacrificial protection and coating with metals.

Properties of iron and its compounds

Iron is a grey metal which rusts in contact with moist air. It reacts with steam to produce iron(II) diiron(III) oxide (ferrosoferric oxide).

$$3Fe(s) + 4H_2O(g) \rightleftharpoons 3Fe_3O_4(s) + 4H_2(g)$$

It reacts with dilute hydrochloric and sulphuric acids to produce hydrogen.

$$Fe(s) + 2H_3O^+(aq) \rightarrow Fe^{2+}(aq) + H_2(g) + 2H_2O(l)$$

Compounds and complexes of iron exist in oxidation states +2 and +3. Since an iron atom has an electron arrangement $[Ar]3d^64s^2$, the electron arrangements in the two oxidation states are $[Ar]3d^6$ (Fe(II)) and $[Ar]3d^5$ (Fe(III)). Iron(III) is more stable than iron(II) because of the stability of the d^5 arrangement.

Both iron(II) and iron(III) ions form hexaaquacomplexes in aqueous solution.

$$\begin{bmatrix} & OH_2 & \\ & | & \\ H_2O \rightarrow Fe & \leftarrow OH_2 \\ H_2O \nearrow & \uparrow & \\ & OH_2 & \end{bmatrix}^{2+} \rightarrow \begin{bmatrix} & OH_2 & \\ & | & \\ H_2O \rightarrow Fe & \leftarrow OH_2 \\ H_2O \nearrow & \uparrow & \\ & OH_2 & \end{bmatrix}^{3+}$$

very pale green
hexaaquairon(II)

yellow
hexaaquairon(III)

The hexaaquairon(II) complex is relatively stable in acid solution, but in neutral or alkaline solution it is oxidised by air to hexaaquairon(III).

The hexaaquairon(III) complex is acidic in solution because of hydrolysis.

$$[Fe(H_2O)_6]^{3+}(aq) + H_2O(l) \rightleftharpoons [Fe(H_2O)_5(OH)]^{2+}(aq) + H_3O^+(aq)$$

It is important to know how to distinguish iron(II) and iron(III) by chemical tests. One method of distinguishing them is by the action of an aqueous solution of sodium hydroxide. With iron(II) salts, a green precipitate of iron(II) hydroxide is formed which slowly turns brown owing to oxidation.

$$Fe^{2+}(aq) + 2OH^-(aq) \rightarrow Fe(OH)_2(s)$$

Iron(III) hydroxide is formed as a reddish brown precipitate when sodium hydroxide solution is added to a solution of an iron(III) salt.

$$Fe^{3+}(aq) + 3OH^-(aq) \rightarrow Fe(OH)_3(s)$$

Another method of distinguishing the two is to use a solution of potassium thiocyanate (KCNS). A blood-red complex is formed with iron(III), and no colouration with iron(II).

When potassium hexacyanoferrate(II) (potassium ferrocyanide) is added to a solution containing iron(III) ions, a dark blue or Prussian blue precipitate is formed. This is a good test for iron(III) ions as iron(II) does not form this precipitate.

$$K^+(aq) + [Fe(CN)_6]^{4+}(aq) + Fe^{3+}(aq) \rightarrow KFe[Fe(CN)_6](s)$$

potassium iron(III)
hexacyanoferrate(II)

A similar precipitate is formed, however, if potassium hexacyanoferrate(III) (potassium ferricyanide) is added to a solution containing iron(II) ions. This occurs in two steps. The iron(II) ions are oxidised to iron(III) ions while the potassium hexacyanoferrate(III) is reduced to potassium hexacyanoferrate(II). Then the precipitation occurs as before.

$$Fe^{2+}(aq) + [Fe(CN)_6]^{3-}(aq) \rightarrow Fe^{3+}(aq) + [Fe(CN)_6]^{4+}(aq)$$
$$K^+(aq) + [Fe(CN)_6]^{4+}(aq) + Fe^{3+}(aq) \rightarrow KFe[Fe(CN)_6]$$

The distinction between a **complex** or **coordinate compound** and a **double salt** is also important. Iron(II) ammonium sulphate, $FeSO_4.(NH_4)_2SO_4.7H_2O$, is a double salt. It is prepared by mixing solutions of iron(II) sulphate and ammonium sulphate in the correct proportions. The solution is then crystallised. Only one type of crystal is obtained: it contains Fe^{2+}, SO_4^{2-}, and NH_4^+ ions and water molecules. The double salt behaves as you would expect, each ion being detectable. Potassium aluminium sulphate (called alum), $KAl(SO_4)_2.12H_2O$, is another double salt.

A complex salt such as $K_4[Fe(CN)_6]$, potassium hexacyanoferrate(II), does not give all of the tests for the metal present. In this case, addition of sodium hydroxide solution would not precipitate iron(II) hydroxide.

28.9 COBALT

Cobalt does not react with air or water at room temperature. It reacts very slowly with dilute hydrochloric and sulphuric acids.

$$Co(s) + 2HCl(aq) \rightarrow CoCl_2(aq) + H_2(g)$$
cobalt(II)
chloride

The electron arrangement of cobalt is $[Ar]3d^74s^2$. It can form compounds in oxidation states +2 and +3. The +3 oxidation state is stable in complexes, and cobalt(III), which reduces readily to cobalt(II), is a strong oxidising agent.

In aqueous solution cobalt(II) compounds exist as hexaaquacobalt(II) ions $[Co(H_2O)_6]^{2+}$. This solution is pink. On addition of sodium hydroxide solution, a blue precipitate of cobalt(II) hydroxide is formed which does not dissolve in excess sodium hydroxide solution.

$$[Co(H_2O)_6]^{2+}(aq) + 2OH^-(aq) \rightarrow [Co(H_2O)_4(OH)_2](s) + 2H_2O(l)$$

Addition of ammonia solution to a solution of hexaaquacobalt(II) ions precipitates cobalt(II) hydroxide, which dissolves in excess ammonia solution to form a hexaammine complex.

$$[Co(H_2O)_6]^{2+}(aq) + 6NH_3(aq) \rightarrow [Co(NH_3)_6]^{2+}(aq) + 6H_2O(l)$$
hexaamminecobalt(II) ion
pale yellow

On passing air through this solution or by adding hydrogen peroxide, the cobalt in the complex is oxidised from +2 to +3.

$$[Co(NH_3)_6]^{2+}(aq) \rightarrow [Co(NH_3)_6]^{3+}(aq) + e^-$$

In the hexaamminecobalt(III) ion, the central cobalt ion has achieved the noble gas electron arrangement of krypton. For this reason it is more stable than hexaamminecobalt(II).

When concentrated hydrochloric acid is added to a solution of cobalt(II) chloride, the solution turns blue owing to the formation of the tetrachlorocobaltate(II) ion.

octahedral   tetrahedral

One reason given for this change in coordination number is that the chloride ion is larger than the water molecule, and only four chloride ions will fit around the central cobalt ion.

28.10 NICKEL

Nickel as a metal resembles cobalt in its chemical properties. Nickel has an electron arrangement of $[Ar]3d^84s^2$ and can form compounds in oxidation states +2, +3 and +4. Of these, +2 is by far the most stable.

Nickel can form complexes in oxidation state 0, e.g. tetracarbonylnickel(0).

In this complex, nickel has received eight electrons, sufficient to give nickel the electron arrangement of krypton. Tetracarbonylnickel(0) is a key compound in the production of metallic nickel.

Aqueous solutions of nickel(II) salts contain the hexaaquanickel(II) ion $[Ni(H_2O)_6]^{2+}$(aq), and this solution is green. On addition of sodium hydroxide solution a green precipitate of nickel(II) hydroxide is formed.

$$[Ni(H_2O)_6]^{2+}(aq) + 2OH^-(aq) \rightarrow Ni(H_2O)_4(OH)_2(s) + 2H_2O(l)$$

Addition of ammonia solution to an aqueous solution of a nickel(II) salt precipitates nickel(II) hydroxide, which redissolves to form the bluish violet $[Ni(NH_3)_6]^{2+}$(aq) complex.

Square planar complexes are known with nickel(II) as the central ion. An example is tetracyanonickelate(II), $[Ni(CN)_4]^{2-}$(aq).

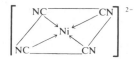

A common test for nickel(II) ions in solution is the addition of a solution of butanedione dioxime (dimethylglyoxime) in slightly alkaline conditions. This produces a pink precipitate.

28.11 COPPER

A copper atom has an electron arrangement of $[Ar]\,3d^{10}4s^1$. Sometimes questions make a comparison between copper and, for example, the alkali metal potassium ($[Ar]4s^1$). Both contain a single electron in a $4s$ orbital. However, in copper there are extra protons in the nucleus and the poor screening of the $3d$ orbitals decreases the radius of the atom. As a result, the first ionisation energy of copper is much greater than that of potassium. Copper is, therefore, much less reactive than potassium.

There are two common oxidation states of copper, +1 and +2. The +2 oxidation state is more stable than the +1 because the higher charge produced gives stronger bonding and this compensates for the extra energy required to remove an electron from the $3d$ orbital in addition to the electron from the $4s$ orbital.

Copper(I)

Copper(I) is unstable in aqueous solution and exists only

❶ at high temperatures,

❷ when insoluble and precipitated, and

❸ in complexes.

In aqueous solution, copper(I) compounds disproportionate, e.g. a solution of copper(I) sulphate.

$$Cu_2SO_4(aq) \rightarrow Cu(s) + CuSO_4(aq)$$
$$Cu(I) \rightarrow Cu(0) + Cu(II)$$

The copper(I) ion can be stabilised in solution by adding concentrated hydrochloric acid to form a complex.

$$CuCl(s) + Cl^-(aq) \rightarrow [CuCl_2]^-(aq)$$
dichlorocuprate(I)

Copper(I) chloride is prepared by boiling copper(II) chloride with copper and concentrated hydrochloric acid. The tetrachlorocuprate(II) ion is reduced to the dichlorocuprate(I) ion.

$$[Cu(H_2O)_6]^{2+}(aq) + 4Cl^-(aq) \rightarrow [CuCl_4]^{2-}(aq) + 6H_2O(l)$$
$$[CuCl_4]^{2-}(aq) + Cu(s) \rightarrow 2[CuCl_2]^-(aq)$$

When this solution is poured into water a white precipitate of copper(I) chloride is formed.

$$[CuCl_2]^-(aq) \rightarrow CuCl(s) + Cl^-(aq)$$

Copper(I) iodide is precipitated as a white precipitate (coloured by the iodine also formed) when potassium iodide solution is added to copper(II) sulphate solution.

$$2CuSO_4(aq) + 4KI(aq) \rightarrow 2CuI(s) + 2K_2SO_4(aq) + I_2(aq)$$
ionic equation: $\quad 2Cu^{2+}(aq) + 4I^-(aq) \rightarrow 2CuI(s) + I_2(aq)$

Some of the iodide ions reduce the copper(II) to copper(I). The iodide ions are oxidised to iodine. This is an extremely important reaction for A-level students. It frequently appears and many candidates in ignorance write

$$CuSO_4 + 2KI \rightarrow CuI_2 + K_2SO_4$$

This reaction between copper(II) and iodide ions can be used in volumetric analysis to estimate the concentration of copper(II) by titration of the resulting solution with standard sodium thiosulphate solution.

Copper(I) oxide, Cu_2O, is precipitated as a red precipitate when an alkaline solution of copper(II) sulphate is reduced by glucose (or an aldehyde) on warming. This is Fehling's test. The copper(II) ions are complexed with 2,3-dihydroxybutanedioates (tartrates) to prevent precipitation of copper(II) hydroxide.

$$2Cu^{2+}(aq) + 2OH^-(aq) + 2e^- \rightarrow Cu_2O(s) + H_2O(l)$$

Copper(II)

This is the more stable oxidation state of copper. Solutions of copper(II) ions in water are blue owing to the presence of the hexaaquacopper(II) ion $[Cu(H_2O)_6]^{2+}$.

Copper(II) hydroxide is precipitated as a pale blue precipitate when sodium hydroxide solution or ammonia solution is added to an aqueous solution of hexaaquacopper(II) ions.

$$[Cu(H_2O)_6]^{2+}(aq) + 2OH^-(aq) \rightarrow [Cu(H_2O)_4(OH)_2](s) + 2H_2O(l)$$

The copper(II) hydroxide does not dissolve in excess sodium hydroxide solution but it does dissolve in ammonia solution to form the tetraamminecopper(II) ions. A solution of tetramminecopper(II) ions is deep blue.

$$[Cu(H_2O)_4(OH)_2](s) + 4NH_3(aq) \rightarrow [Cu(NH_3)_4(H_2O)_2]^{2+}(aq) + 2OH^-(aq)$$
$$+ 2H_2O(l)$$

28.12 ISOMERISM OF COMPLEX IONS

There are inorganic examples of geometric and structural isomers involving complex ions. In 7.7 there is an example of optical isomerism using chromium complex ions with three bidendate ethanedioate ligands.

Chapter roundup

The study of the *d*-block elements can be a very large study and, in some ways, resembles organic chemistry. Remember the four characteristic properties of the *d*-block elements:

❶ the formation of compounds in a wide range of oxidation states;

❷ the formation of coloured compounds;

❸ the existence of paramagnetism; and

❹ the formation of coordinate bonds.

Worked questions and answers

1 Properties of chromyl chloride: formula CrO_2Cl_2; boiling point 116 °C; red liquid, hydrolysed rapidly in contact with water.

Chromyl chloride is prepared by distilling a mixture of potassium dichromate(VI), sodium chloride and concentrated sulphuric acid. The equation is:

$$K_2Cr_2O_7(s) + 4NaCl(s) + 3H_2SO_4(l) \rightarrow 2CrO_2Cl_2(l) + 3H_2O(l) + 2Na_2SO_4(s) + K_2SO_4(s)$$

(a) Write the simplest ionic equation for the reaction taking place.

(b) What change in oxidation state of chromium, if any, occurs during the reaction?

(c) (i) Draw a labelled diagram of apparatus suitable for preparing a sample of chromyl chloride in the laboratory. Include in your diagram:

❶ a suitable means of mixing the reagents safely; and

❷ a method of removing chromyl chloride from the final mixture.

(ii) What precautions could be taken to prevent chromyl chloride hydrolysing during the preparation?

(d) CrO_2Cl_2

                $\downarrow$ + H_2O / steamy fumes produced

                solution

                $\downarrow$ neutralise with NaOH(aq)

      yellow   add silver
      solution $\xrightarrow{\hspace{3cm}}$ red precipitate
              nitrate

Name (i) the steamy fumes when water is added to chromyl chloride;

       (ii) the yellow solution; and

       (iii) the red precipitate

Tutorial note

(a) $Cr_2O_7^{2-} + 4Cl^- + 6H^+ \rightarrow 2CrO_2Cl_2 + 3H_2O$

(b) No change – oxidation state +6 throughout.

(c) (i)

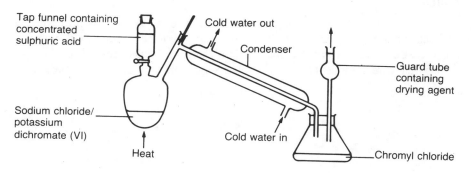

(ii) Dry reagents, dry apparatus in oven before use, guard tubes containing drying agent to prevent water entering.

(d) (i) Hydrogen chloride, HCl.

(ii) Chromate ions, CrO_4^{2-}, or sodium chromate, Na_2CrO_4.

(iii) Silver chromate, Ag_2CrO_4.

Question bank

1 (a) The atomic number of iron is 26. Give the electron configuration of iron(II) and iron(III) ions. Describe how you would convert iron(III) ions to iron(II) ions and how you would show, by a suitable chemical test, that the conversion had taken place.

(b) One of the most important properties of the *d*-block elements (transition metals) is their ability to form complex ions. Using a suitable example describe the bonding in such an ion.

(c) Outline the industrial manufacture of a *d*-block element with reference to the chemical and physicochemical principles and the economic consideration involved in the production.

(ULEAC 1990)

Points

This question can be answered with reference to iron throughout. In (a) reduce iron(III) to iron (II) by adding zinc and hydrochloric acid, which produce the reducing agent hydrogen. To test the solution add

❶ sodium hydroxide solution – dirty green precipitate of iron(II) hydroxide or red-brown precipitate of iron(III) hydroxide, *or*

❷ potassium thiocyanate – red colouration with iron(III) and no colouration with iron(II).

In (c) there are ten marks available. You should refer to the Ellingham diagram (Fig. 40.2) and economic considerations could include the quality and availability of ores, energy costs, possible uses of products, removal of impurities, etc.

2 Identify element A and write an equation for each reaction involved.

A is a solid with a lustrous, silver appearance and a high melting temperature. It is used, by electroplating, as a protective and decorative coating. A dissolves slowly in dilute hydrochloric acid to give a blue solution B. A rapid oxidation to give a green solution C occurs when oxygen is passed into B.

Further oxidation is possible if C is made alkaline with aqueous potassium hydroxide and then hydrogen peroxide added. The resulting solution is yellow but turns orange when acidified without any change in the oxidation state of A.

(Oxford 1989)

Points

This question relies on you being able to recognise A. With A being relatively unreactive and forming so many coloured compounds it must be a *d*-block element. Often the best clues come at the end. Certainly this is the case here. The chromate–dichromate clue in the last sentence should tell you that the element is chromium.

HYDROCARBONS

Units in this chapter

Chapter objectives

In Chapter 7 we had an introduction to organic chemistry. In this chapter we will consider different hydrocarbons. Hydrocarbons are compounds of carbon and hydrogen only. We can divide hydrocarbons into aliphatic hydrocarbons (alkanes, alkenes, alkynes, cycloalkanes, cycloalkenes, etc.) and aromatic hydrocarbons (benzene, methylbenzene, etc.).

29.1 ALKANES

Alkanes are a series of hydrocarbons which all have molecular formulae which fit the general formula C_nH_{2n+2} The simplest alkanes are shown in Table 29.1.

Table 29.1 *Some examples of alkanes*

CH_4	methane	C_6H_{14}	hexane
C_2H_6	ethane	C_7H_{16}	heptane
C_3H_8	propane	C_8H_{18}	octane
C_4H_{10}	butane	C_9H_{20}	nonane
C_5H_{12}	pentane	$C_{10}H_{22}$	decane

Any group of compounds which fits the general formula, the members of the group differing only by different numbers of CH_2 units, is called a **homologous series**. Within a homologous series the compounds have the same chemical properties and there are trends in physical properties such as increasing melting and boiling points. These increases are due to increasing relative molecular masses and van der Waals forces (see 4.6).

In addition to the alkanes in Table 29.1, other isomers are possible with alkanes containing more than three carbon atoms. This isomerism is due to branching of chains. The possible isomers of C_5H_{12} are

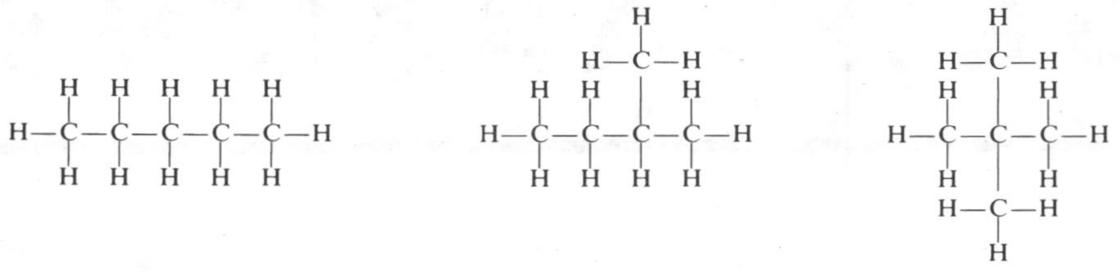

pentane
boiling point
36°C

2-methylbutane
boiling point
28°C

2,2 dimethylpropane
boiling point
9°C

These three isomers have identical relative molecular mass but differ in boiling point. van der Waals forces are greater between longer petane molecules. This causes a higher boiling point.

Alkanes are called **saturated** hydrocarbons because all the bonds are single bonds (C—H and C—C). Hydrocarbons with C=C or C≡C bonds are termed **unsaturated**.

Alkanes are found in natural gas and crude petroleum. Natural gas is largely methane, and petroleum is a mixture of alkanes up to about C_{40}, with other hydrocarbons present. Crude petroleum was produced over millions of years by the effect of pressure and temperature on decaying marine life. It is refined by fractional distillation into different fractions with different boiling points, chemical compositions and uses.

Aviation spirit – solvents	$C_5H_{12} – C_7H_{16}$
Petrol	$C_6H_{14} – C_{11}H_{24}$
Paraffin	$C_{12}H_{26} – C_{16}H_{34}$
Fuel oil	$C_{13}H_{28} – C_{18}H_{38}$
Lubricating oils	$C_{19}H_{40} – C_{40}H_{82}$

The remaining fractions are used for heavy oils, greases and waxes.

29.2 REACTIONS OF ALKANES

Alkanes are comparatively unreactive and there are few chemical reactions of importance.

(i) Combustion of alkanes

Many of the uses of alkanes rely upon their ready combustion or oxidation. The products depend upon the amount of oxygen available.

Unlimited supply of oxygen
Complete combustion of alkanes produces carbon dioxide and water, e.g.

$$2C_2H_6(g) + 7O_2(g) \rightarrow 4CO_2(g) + 6H_2O(l)$$

Limited supply of oxygen
Carbon monoxide and water are produced. Carbon monoxide is very poisonous, which explains the danger of running a car engine in an enclosed space, e.g.

$$2C_2H_6(g) + 5O_2(g) \rightarrow 4CO(g) + 6H_2O(l)$$

(ii) Chlorination of alkanes

A mixture of methane and chlorine subjected to ultraviolet light undergoes a series of substitution reactions. The mechanism of this reaction is important and is discussed in 38.3.

$$CH_4 + Cl_2 \rightarrow CH_3Cl + HCl$$
chloromethane
$$CH_3Cl + Cl_2 \rightarrow CH_2Cl_2 + HCl$$
dichloromethane
$$CH_2Cl_2 + Cl_2 \rightarrow CHCl_3 + HCl$$
trichloromethane
$$CHCl_3 + Cl_2 \rightarrow CCl_4 + HCl$$
tetrachloromethane

In practice, a complex mixture of all possible products will be produced.

(iii) Cracking of hydrocarbons

Higher fractions can be cracked into shorter chain molecules by passing over a heated catalyst. The products of cracking include alkenes, which are suitable for making polymers (Chapter 36).

29.3 ALKENES

Alkenes are a homologous series of hydrocarbons containing a double bond. They all have molecular formulae which fit a general formula C_nH_{2n}.

The simplest members of the homologous series are

ethene C_2H_4

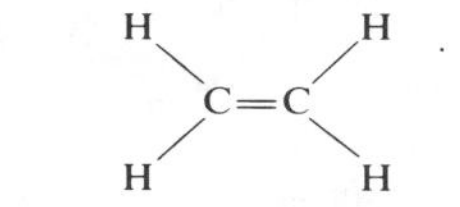

propene C_3H_6

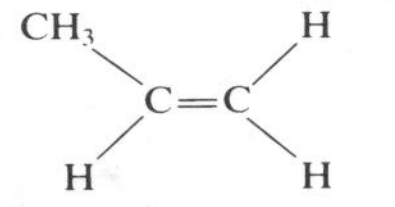

but-1-ene

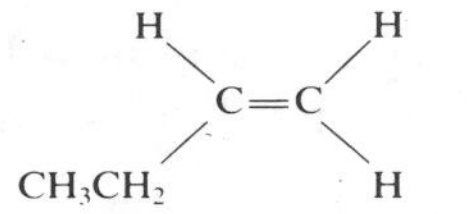

but-2-ene

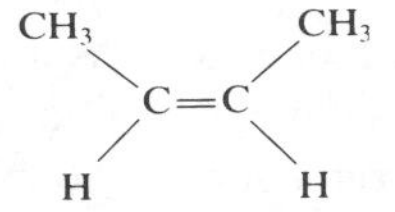

Alkenes are obtained by cracking alkanes derived from petroleum. In the laboratory, alkenes can be prepared by dehydration of alcohols or by dehydrohalogenation of haloalkanes (alkyl halides).

29.4 LABORATORY PREPARATION OF ALKENES

Ethene is prepared by the dehydration of ethanol.

$$CH_3CH_2OH \rightarrow CH_2{=}CH_2 + H_2O$$

The dehydration can be carried out by adding concentrated sulphuric acid added slowly in excess to ethanol. The flask containing the mixture is cooled during this step to reduce charring. Ethene is produced when this mixture is heated to 170 °C.

$$CH_3CH_2OH + H_2SO_4 \rightarrow CH_3CH_2OSO_2OH + H_2O$$
$$CH_3CH_2OSO_2OH \rightarrow CH_2{=}CH_2 + H_2SO_4$$

The mechanism for this process is discussed in Chapter 38.

With excess ethanol present and at a lower temperature, ethoxyethane (an ether) is produced.

$$CH_3CH_2OSO_2OH + CH_3CH_2OH \rightarrow CH_3CH_2OCH_2CH_3$$

Less charring is obtained if concentrated phosphoric(V) acid is used. Alternatively the dehydration can be carried out by passing the ethanol vapour over heated aluminium oxide at about 350 °C.

Alkenes can also be produced by dehydrohalogenation of haloalkanes by refluxing with a solution of potassium hydroxide in ethanol. The mechanism for this reaction will be found in Chapter 38. It is an elimination reaction.

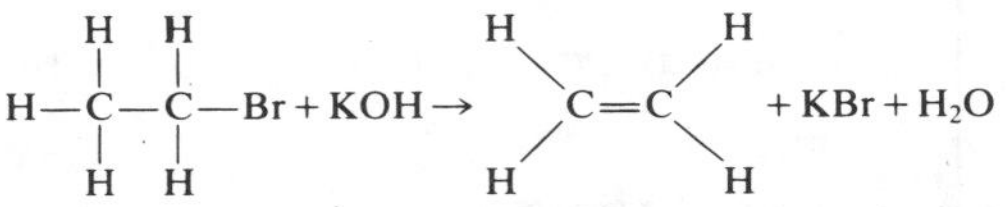

29.5 REACTIONS OF ALKENES

Most of the reactions of alkenes involve addition reactions to the carbon–carbon double bond. The mechanism called electrophilic addition is discussed in 38.4.

(i) Hydrogenation

When an alkene is mixed with hydrogen and passed over a platinum catalyst at room temperature or a nickel catalyst at between 140 and 200 °C, an addition reaction takes place to form the corresponding alkane

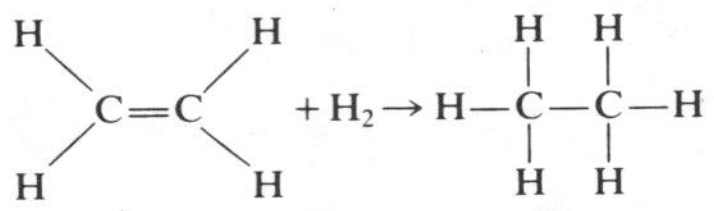

This process is important in the 'hardening' of vegetable and animal oils to produce solid fats used to make margarine. The oils are unsaturated and addition of hydrogen removes the double bonds.

(ii) Hydration of alkenes

This is the reverse of the method used to produce ethene in the laboratory from ethanol and concentrated sulphuric acid. It is widely used to produce ethanol from ethene. The ethene is passed into almost concentrated sulphuric acid and then water is added to decompose the product.

$$CH_2{=}CH_2 + H_2SO_4 \rightarrow CH_3CH_2OSO_2OH \overset{+H_2O}{\rightarrow} CH_3CH_2OH + H_2SO_4$$

(iii) Addition of a halogen

Chlorine and bromine are readily added to an alkene to form a dichloro- or dibromo-compound.

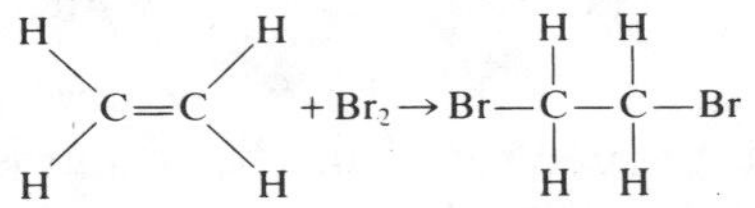

A solution of bromine in hexane or tetrachloromethane is used as a test for unsaturation. It is decolourised without heating when added to a compound containing a double or triple bond.

If bromine water (a solution of bromine in water) is used the solution is decolourised, but a slightly different product is obtained.

$$\underset{H}{\overset{H}{>}}C=C\underset{H}{\overset{H}{<}} + Br_2/H_2O \rightarrow H-\overset{\overset{H}{|}}{\underset{\underset{Br}{|}}{C}}-\overset{\overset{H}{|}}{\underset{\underset{OH}{|}}{C}}-H + HBr$$
2-bromoethanol

The mechanisms for these reactions are given in 38.4.

(iv) Addition of hydrogen halides

Hydrogen halides can be added to alkenes to produce haloalkanes.

$$\underset{H}{\overset{H}{>}}C=C\underset{H}{\overset{H}{<}} + HBr \rightarrow H-\overset{\overset{H}{|}}{\underset{\underset{H}{|}}{C}}-\overset{\overset{H}{|}}{\underset{\underset{H}{|}}{C}}-Br$$
ethene   bromoethane

Ethene is a symmetrical alkene because the same types of atoms are bonded to both carbon atoms. If an asymmetrical alkene – one where one carbon atom is bonded to a different atom – is used, two products are possible.

$$\underset{H}{\overset{CH_3}{>}}C=C\underset{H}{\overset{H}{<}} + HBr \rightarrow Br-\overset{\overset{CH_3}{|}}{\underset{\underset{H}{|}}{C}}-\overset{\overset{H}{|}}{\underset{\underset{H}{|}}{C}}-H$$
2-bromopropane

$$\underset{H}{\overset{CH_3}{>}}C=C\underset{H}{\overset{H}{<}} + HBr \rightarrow H-\overset{\overset{CH_3}{|}}{\underset{\underset{H}{|}}{C}}-\overset{\overset{H}{|}}{\underset{\underset{H}{|}}{C}}-Br$$
1-bromopropane

When the reaction is carried out, the product is 2-bromopropane rather than 1-bromopropane. This is predicted by Markownikoff's rule (see 38.4). If the reaction is carried out in the presence of peroxides, 1-bromopropane is produced.

(v) Oxidation of alkenes

❶ Alkenes burn in air or oxygen to form similar products to those from alkanes (see 29.2), e.g.

$$C_2H_4(g) + 3O_2(g) \rightarrow 2CO_2(g) + 2H_2O(l) \quad \text{excess oxygen}$$
$$C_2H_4(g) + 2O_2(g) \rightarrow 2CO(g) + 2H_2O(l) \quad \text{limited oxygen}$$

Combustion usually occurs with a slightly smoky flame caused by the greater proportion of carbon compared with alkanes.

❷ The reaction of alkenes with trioxygen (ozone) is important as it is the basis of the technique called **ozonolysis**. When trioxygen is passed into a solution of an alkene in an inert solvent, an ozonide is formed. When the ozonide is hydrolysed by boiling with water, aldehydes or ketones are produced (Chapter 32).

$$>C=C< + O_3 \rightarrow \underset{\underset{O}{ozonide}}{>\overset{O-O}{C}\diagup \diagdown C<} \overset{H_2O}{\longrightarrow} >C=O \quad O=C<$$

An example of a question using ozonolysis will be found in the questions at the end of this chapter.

❸ Alkenes are oxidised by an alkaline solution of potassium manganate(VII) (permanganate). The oxidation does not require heating and results in the formation of a diol or glycol.

$$H_2C=CH_2 + H_2O + [O] \rightarrow H-\underset{OH}{\underset{|}{C}}H_2-\underset{OH}{\underset{|}{C}}H_2-H$$

ethane-1,2-diol
(ethylene glycol)

Ethane-1,2-diol is the major ingredient of antifreeze used in car cooling systems, and is also used in making Terylene. The decolourisation of an alkaline potassium manganate(VII) solution is another test for unsaturation.

When an alkene is treated with peroxotrifluoroethanoic acid, the corresponding alkene oxide or epoxide is formed.

ethene + $CF_3-C\overset{O}{\underset{O-O-H}{}}$ → ethene oxide + $CF_3-C\overset{O}{\underset{OH}{}}$ trifluoroethanoic acid

Alkene oxides are useful organic intermediates. For example, warming ethene oxide with very dilute hydrochloric acid produces ethane-1,2-diol.

ethene oxide + H_2O → $H-\underset{OH}{\underset{|}{C}}H_2-\underset{OH}{\underset{|}{C}}H_2-H$

Alkene oxides can also be produced by passing a mixture of alkene and oxygen over a heated silver catalyst at 300 °C.

(vi) Polymerisation of alkenes

See Chapter 36.

29.6 ALKYNES

The homologous series of alkynes has the general formula C_nH_{2n-2}. All alkynes contain a triple bond between two carbon atoms. The simplest alkyne is called ethyne (sometimes called acetylene). It has a molecular formula of C_2H_2 and a structural formula of $H-C\equiv C-H$.

Laboratory preparation of alkynes

Ethyne can be prepared by the action of cold water on calcium dicarbide (calcium carbide).

$$CaC_2(s) + 2H_2O(l) \rightarrow Ca(OH)_2(s) + C_2H_2(g)$$

(This equation is frequently written by candidates as

$$CaC_2(s) + H_2O(l) \rightarrow CaO(s) + C_2H_2(g)$$

By writing this the candidate fails to appreciate that calcium oxide reacts with water.)

Calcium dicarbide is manufactured by heating calcium oxide and carbon strongly in an electric furnace.

$$CaO(s) + 3C(s) \rightarrow CaC_2(s) + CO(g)$$

Other alkynes cannot be prepared by a similar method. The usual method is to reflux a dihaloalkane with a solution of potassium hydroxide in ethanol. A dehydrohalogenation reaction takes place to produce the alkyne. Two molecules of hydrogen halide are eliminated.

$$CH_3-\underset{Br}{\underset{|}{CH}}-\underset{Br}{\underset{|}{CH}}_2 + 2KOH \rightarrow CH_3-C\equiv CH + 2KBr + 2H_2O$$
propyne

Reactions of alkynes

Alkynes undergo addition reactions similar to those of alkenes. These reactions are electrophilic addition reactions (see 38.4). It is also possible for the terminal hydrogen atoms to be substituted.

(i) Addition of hydrogen

A mixture of hydrogen and alkyne is passed over a platinum catalyst at room temperature, or a nickel catalyst at 250 °C. The reaction takes place in two stages.

$$
H-C\equiv C-H \xrightarrow{+H_2} \quad \substack{H \\ \diagdown} C=C \substack{\diagup H \\ } \xrightarrow{+H_2} H-C-C-H
$$

ethyne   ethene   ethane

The reaction usually goes directly to the alkane, and the alkene is not isolated. The reaction can be stopped at the alkene stage by adding poisons to the catalyst which prevent the second stage.

(ii) Addition of bromine

$$
H-C\equiv C-H + Br_2 \rightarrow \quad C=C \quad \quad C=C \quad + Br_2 \rightarrow Br-C-C-Br
$$

Br   Br   Br   Br   Br   Br
1,2-dibromoethene   1,1,2,2-tetrabromoethane

When an alkyne is passed into a solution of bromine dissolved in an inert solvent, the bromine is decolourised.

(iii) Addition of hydrogen bromide

$$
H-C\equiv C-H + HBr \rightarrow \quad C=C \quad \quad C=C \quad + HBr \rightarrow H-C-C-Br
$$

H   Br   H   Br   H   Br
bromoethene   1,1-dibromoethane
(vinyl bromide)

(See Markownikoff's rule, 38.4.)

(iv) Substitution reactions of alkynes

Ethyne differs from ethene because the hydrogen atoms in ethyne are slightly acidic. If ethyne is passed into an ammoniacal solution of silver nitrate, a white precipitate of silver dicarbide (silver acetylide) is produced.

$$ H-C\equiv C-H + 2[Ag(NH_3)_2]^+ \rightarrow Ag^+(C\equiv C)^{2-}Ag^+ + 2H^+ + 4NH_3 $$

This reaction can be used to distinguish ethyne from ethene.

(v) Reactions of ethyne with dilute sulphuric acid

When ethyne is passed into warm, dilute sulphuric acid in the presence of a catalyst, a reaction takes place to produce ethanal.

$$
H-C\equiv C-H + H_2O \rightarrow CH_3-C\substack{\diagup O \\ \diagdown H}
$$

ethanal

(vi) Conversion of ethyne to benzene

When ethyne gas is passed through a copper tube at about 300 °C a reaction takes place. On cooling the gas, a colourless liquid condenses. This liquid is **benzene**, produced by joining three molecules of ethyne together.

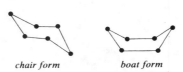

benzene

The copper tube acts as a catalyst.

29.7 CYCLOALKANES

It is possible to produce saturated hydrocarbons with a ring structure. These compounds, like alkenes, fit the general formula C_nH_{2n}. They do *not*, however, behave at all like alkenes. An example of a cycloalkane is cyclohexane. This molecule is not planar but can exist in two readily interconvertible forms. These forms are the chair and boat forms.

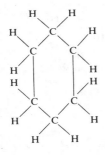

chair form   *boat form*

In these two forms the bond angles are close to the tetrahedral angle. Neither of these two forms can be isolated and the chair form, which allows the hydrogen atoms to be further apart, predominates.

The chemical reactions of cycloalkanes closely resemble those of the alkanes.

29.8 AROMATIC HYDROCARBONS

The most important aromatic hydrocarbon is benzene, C_6H_6. A benzene molecule consists of a planar ring of six carbon atoms. All of the carbon–carbon bond lengths are the same at 0.139 nm. Since the bond lengths in carbon–carbon single and double bonds are 0.154 nm and 0.132 nm respectively, it can be concluded that these bonds in benzene are intermediate between single and double bonds.

Benzene may be considered to be a resonance hybrid of a number of extreme structures such as the Kekulé formulae.

Neither of these extreme structures actually exists.

The modern approach to the structure of benzene explains why the carbon–carbon bonds are all the same length. It also explains the planar nature of the molecule, the bond angles and the fact that benzene does not decolourise a solution of bromine.

Each carbon atom is sp^2 hybridised, forming three sp^2 hybrid orbitals in the same plane but at angles of 120°. One of these sp^2 orbitals on each carbon atom overlaps with the 1s orbital of a hydrogen atom and the other two sp^2 orbitals overlap with sp^2 orbitals of other carbon atoms. This forms a planar hexagonal framework with one p orbital on each carbon atom unused and at right angles to the ring. These remaining p orbitals can overlap to form a ring of negative charge above and below the ring (Fig. 29.1).

Fig. 29.1

It is usual to represent a benzene ring in a simplified way. The most common method is

Do not forget that this molecule has six carbon atoms and six hydrogen atoms.
  Other aromatic hydrocarbons include

methylbenzene   naphthalene

29.9 REACTIONS OF BENZENE

(i) Addition reactions of benzene

Because the benzene ring structure is so stable, addition reactions, which would result in the destruction of this system, do not readily take place.

If a mixture of hydrogen and benzene is passed over a nickel catalyst at 200 °C, a series of reactions takes place to form cyclohexane.

Chlorine and benzene react to form an addition product when the mixture of vapours is subjected to ultraviolet light. The product is 1,2,3,4,5,6–hexachlorocyclohexane.

1,2,3,4,5,6-hexachlorocyclohexane
benzene hexachloride

(ii) Substitution reactions of benzene

Benzene undergoes a range of substitution reactions. These reactions are examples of electrophilic substitutions and the mechanisms are discussed in Chapter 38.

Nitration of benzene
When benzene is refluxed with a mixture of concentrated nitric and sulphuric acids, nitrobenzene is produced.

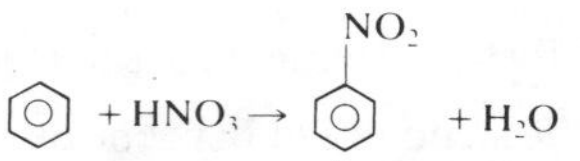

nitrobenzene

If the temperature rises above 55 °C further reaction is possible.

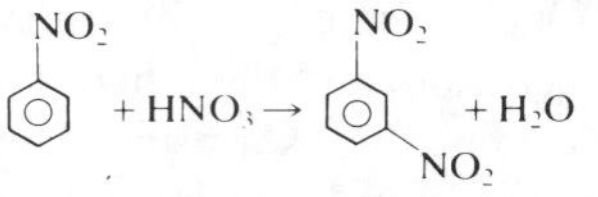

1,3-dinitrobenzene

Sulphonation of benzene
Refluxing benzene with concentrated sulphuric acid for 24 hours produces a benzenesulphonic acid. The reaction is, however, reversible.

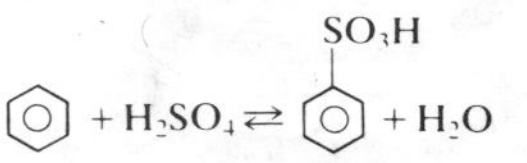

benzenesulphonic acid

Halogenation of benzene
Benzene undergoes substitution reactions with chlorine and bromine. The reaction takes place on heating the mixture out of contact with strong light and in the presence of catalysts called 'halogen carriers'. Suitable halogen carriers are aluminium chloride, iron(III) chloride and iodine.

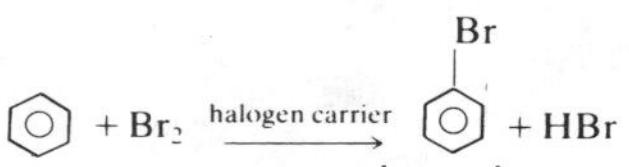

bromobenzene

Friedel–Crafts reactions
There are two types of Friedel–Crafts reaction.

❶ Alkylation
Benzene is refluxed with a haloalkane in the presence of aluminium chloride, e.g.

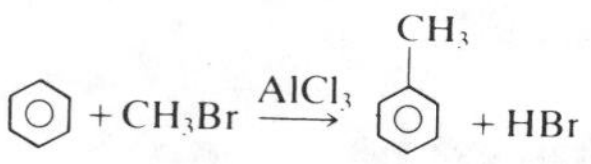

It is difficult to stop the reaction at this stage. Further substitutions take place, e.g.

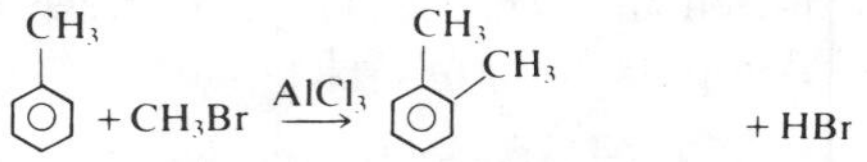

1,2-dimethylbenzene

❷ Acylation
A similar reaction takes place when benzene is refluxed with an acyl chloride in the presence of aluminium chloride. The product of the reaction is a ketone, e.g.

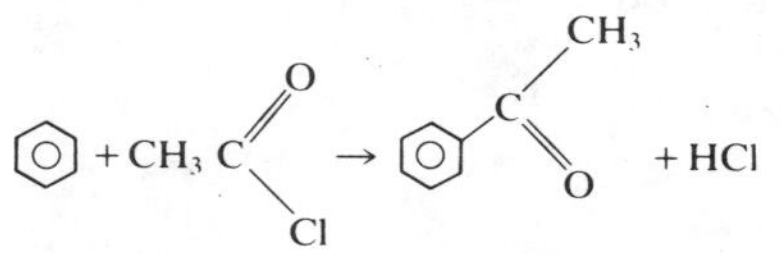

ethanoyl chloride   phenylethanone

A substituent in the benzene ring may speed up or slow down similar reactions. If the substituent is electron-supplying, e.g. CH_3, the reaction is faster. If the substituent is electron-withdrawing the reaction is slower (see 38.6).

29.10 REACTIONS OF METHYLBENZENE

Since methylbenzene contains a benzene ring, it will undergo the usual electrophilic substitutions of benzene, i.e. nitration, sulphonation, halogenation and Friedel–Crafts reactions. (Note: the reactions are *quicker* with methylbenzene than benzene.)

Methylbenzene also contains a CH_3 side-chain which, since it is a saturated hydrocarbon chain, undergoes reactions typical of alkanes.

The reaction of chlorine with methylbenzene depends upon the conditions. In the dark, on refluxing the mixture with a halogen carrier, a mixture of chloromethyl-benzenes is produced.

If the mixture is subjected to ultraviolet light, free radical substitution reactions in the side-chain take place.

(chloromethyl) benzene   (dichloromethyl) benzene   (trichloromethyl) benzene

Chapter roundup

All hydrocarbons burn in air in a similar way to produce carbon dioxide and water (if excess air is used) or carbon monoxide and water (if limited air is used).

Alkanes are quite unreactive, with substitution reactions being slow even with reactive halogens. Alkenes and alkynes readily undergo addition reactions with halogens. Aromatic hydrocarbons undergo substitution by halogen on the ring in the presence of a halogen carrier. If there is a side-chain on the aromatic ring with a CH_3 or CH_3CH_2 group, substitution by halogen in the side-chain can occur in the presence of ultraviolet light.

Worked questions and answers

1 Dehydration of an alcohol X with a formula C_4H_9OH produces a hydrocarbon Y, C_4H_8. When Y is treated with trioxygen (ozone), and the product hydrolysed, only one product Z is obtained.
Identify X, Y and Z.

Tutorial note

There are three possible structural isomers of Y.

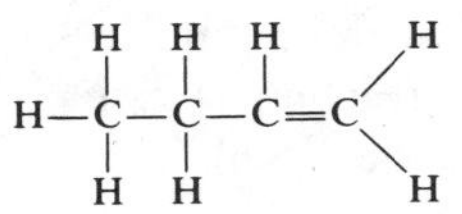

A 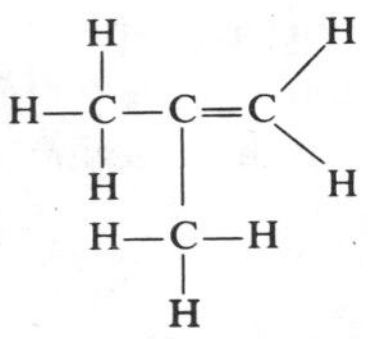   B 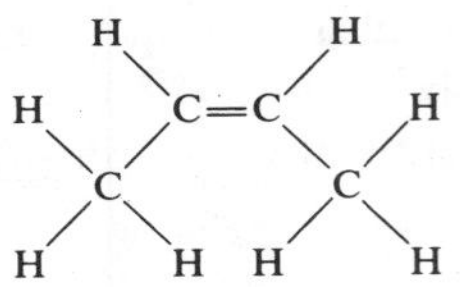   C

Ozonolysis of A would produce 2 products, CH_3CH_2CHO and HCHO.
Ozonolysis of B would produce 2 products, CH_3COCH_3 and HCHO.
Ozonolysis of C would produce only 1 product, CH_3CHO, because C is symmetrical about the carbon–carbon double bond.

The product Z is therefore $CH_3 \!-\! C\!\!<^H_{=O}$ ethanal.

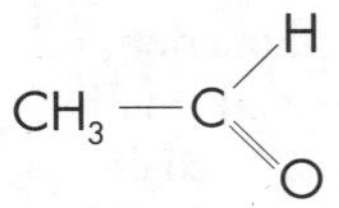

C (but-2-ene) is therefore compound Y.
Working backwards, X is butan-2-ol.

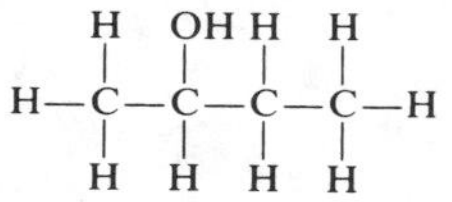

2 A hydrocarbon X, C_4H_6 (0.50 g), was shaken with hydrogen and palladium until uptake of hydrogen ceased; 415 cm^3 of hydrogen (measured at stp) were absorbed. Reaction with mercury(II) sulphate in dilute sulphuric acid yielded Y, C_4H_8O; Y gave a positive iodoform reaction. Polymerisation of X gave Z, $C_{12}H_{18}$. What are the structures of X, Y and Z?

($A_r(H) = 1$, $A_r(C) = 12$), $A_r(O) = 16$; 1 mole of gas at stp occupies 22 400 cm^3)

(Oxford and Cambridge)

Tutorial note

It is important to use the information given in the question.

$$415 \text{ cm}^3 \text{ of hydrogen at stp} = \frac{415}{22\ 400} \text{ mole of hydrogen molecules}$$

$$= 0.018 \text{ mole of hydrogen molecules.}$$

Relative molecular mass of X = 54 (i.e. $12 \times 4 + 6$)

$$\text{Number of moles of X} = \frac{0.5}{54} = 0.009$$

0.009 mole of X reacts with 0.018 mole of hydrogen molecules. 1 mole of X reacts with 2 moles of hydrogen molecules. X therefore contains either two double bonds or one triple bond.

The reaction of X with dilute sulphuric acid in the presence of mercury(II) sulphate and polymerisation suggest an alkyne.

X is $CH_3C\!\equiv\!CCH_3$, but-2-yne

This reacts with dilute sulphuric acid to produce a compound Y which gives a positive iodoform test.

Y is therefore $CH_3\!-\!\underset{\underset{O}{\|}}{C}\!-\!CH_2CH_3$, butanone

Polymerisation of X leads to a substituted benzene compound, Z.

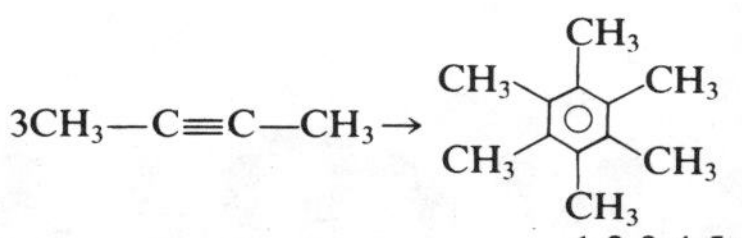

$$3CH_3-C\equiv C-CH_3 \rightarrow$$

1,2,3,4,5,6-hexamethylbenzene

Question bank

1 Many alkenes are manufactured by the thermal cracking of hydrocarbons, e.g.

$$C_5H_{12} \rightarrow C_2H_5\cdot + (CH_3)_2CH\cdot \quad (i)$$
$$2(CH_3)_2CH\cdot \rightarrow CH_3CH{=}CH_2 + A \quad (ii)$$

(a) State and explain the type of decomposition occurring in (i).
(b) Draw a structure for C_5H_{12} consistent with (i) and explain your reasoning.
(c) Write down the structure of A in equation (ii).

(Oxford 1989)

Points

For (a) refer to 38.1.

(b)

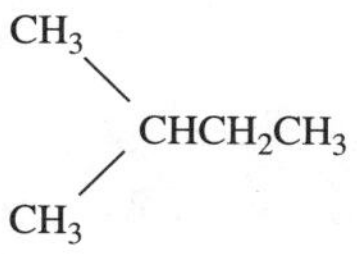

CH₃
\
  CHCH₂CH₃
/
CH₃

(c) $CH_3CH_2CH_3$

CHAPTER 30

ORGANOHALOGEN COMPOUNDS

Units in this chapter

Chapter objectives

We have seen in Chapters 27 and 29 that the halogens are reactive elements and they form a large number of organic compounds. There is a big difference in properties between a halogen atom attached to a carbon chain and one attached to an aromatic ring. This chapter concentrates on halogen atoms in different molecular environments.

You should appreciate that where bromine is used, it could equally well be any other halogen atom.

30.1 COMMON COMPOUNDS OF ORGANOHALOGEN

Common organohalogen compounds include

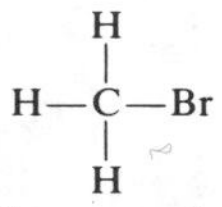

bromomethane 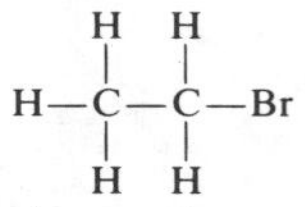   bromoethane 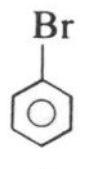   bromobenzene    1-iodo-4-methylbenzene

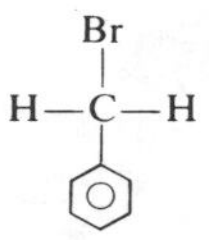

(bromomethyl)benzene 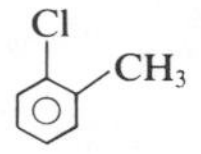   1-chloro-2-methylbenzene 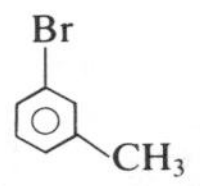   1-bromo-3-methylbenzene

Bromomethane and bromethane are examples of haloalkanes (sometimes called halogenoalkanes or alkyl halides). They are useful organic chemicals because they can readily be converted into other products. The halogen atom of the haloalkane is readily displaced.

When a halogen atom is attached directly to an aromatic ring the halogen is difficult to displace. (Bromomethyl)benzene reacts in a similar way to a haloalkane since the bromine atom is not directly attached to the benzene ring.

You should realise having studied Chapter 7 that some of the organohalogen compounds shown have the same molecular formula and are structural isomers. Structural isomers in this chapter are (bromomethyl)benzene, 1-bromo-2-methylbenzene, 1-bromo-3-methylbenzene and 1-bromo-4-methylbenzne. They all have the formula C_7H_7Br. Now try to name possible isomers of $C_7H_6Cl_2$. You will find the answers in the chapter roundup.

30.2 PREPARATION OF ORGANOHALOGEN COMPOUNDS

❶ Addition of a hydrogen halide molecule to an alkene, e.g.

❷ From an alcohol using a hydrogen halide or phosphorus halide, e.g.

$$CH_3CH_2OH + HCl \rightleftharpoons CH_3CH_2Cl + H_2O$$
ethanol   chloroethane

$$CH_3CH_2OH + PCl_5 \rightarrow CH_3CH_2Cl + POCl_3 + HCl$$
chloroethane phosphorus
trichloride
oxide

Preparing a haloalkane from the corresponding alcohol is often the most convenient method.

The reaction of alcohol with hydrogen halide is most suitable for chlorides and bromides. This reaction is reversible and is usually carried out, for example, by bubbling dry hydrogen chloride gas into the alcohol in the presence of a catalyst of anhydrous zinc chloride.

The halide of phosphorus can be prepared *in situ*, e.g. by mixing red phosphorus and iodine together to produce phosphorus triiodide.

$$3CH_3OH + PI_3 \rightarrow 3CH_3I + H_3PO_3$$
methanol   iodomethane phosphonic acid
(phosphorous acid)

Sulphur dichloride oxide (thionyl chloride) is useful for producing a chloroalkane. If halides of phosphorus are used, the task of separating the haloalkane from the phosphorus compound remains. This may require fractional distillation. If sulphur dichloride oxide is used the other products are gases and escape from the solution.

$$CH_3CH_2OH + SOCl_2 \rightarrow CH_3CH_2Cl + SO_2 + HCl$$
ethanol + sulphur → chloroethane + sulphur + hydrogen
dichloride oxide   dioxide   chloride

Aryl halides are prepared by different methods.

❶ From benzene. Halogenation of benzene can be used to prepare aryl halides (29.9 and 38.5). These reactions take place when the benzene and halogen are mixed and the mixture heated out of contact with light in the presence of a halogen carrier.

$$\text{C}_6\text{H}_6 + \text{Br}_2 \rightarrow \text{C}_6\text{H}_5\text{Br} + \text{HBr}$$

❷ Via a diazonium salt (see 35.4). A diazonium salt is warmed with a copper(I) halide and concentrated hydrogen halide or copper to produce an aryl halide, e.g.

$$\text{C}_6\text{H}_5\text{N}_2^+\text{Cl}^- \rightarrow \text{C}_6\text{H}_5\text{Cl} + \text{N}_2$$

Warming a diazonium salt with potassium iodide solution produces an iodo compound.

(Bromomethyl)benzene is prepared by the action of ultraviolet light on a mixture of bromine and methylbenzene. This is a free radical substitution reaction.

$$\text{C}_6\text{H}_5\text{CH}_3 + \text{Br}_2 \rightarrow \text{C}_6\text{H}_5\text{CH}_2\text{Br} + \text{HBr}$$

In order to minimise the possibility of further substitution taking place, the methylbenzene is present in excess.

30.3 REACTIONS OF HALOALKANES

Haloalkanes react readily with a variety of reagents to undergo nucleophilic substitution reactions (mechanism in 38.5). Iodoalkanes react more rapidly than bromoalkanes which react more rapidly than chloroalkanes (see 38.5).

Some of the common reactions include the following.

(i) Reaction with potassium hydroxide

Potassium hydroxide in aqueous solution reacts with haloalkanes on refluxing to produce an alcohol. These reactions are substitution reactions, e.g.

$$\underset{\text{ethanol}}{\text{CH}_3\text{CH}_2\text{Br} + \text{OH}^- \rightarrow \text{CH}_3\text{CH}_2\text{OH} + \text{Br}^-}$$

A different reaction takes place if a haloalkane is refluxed with a solution of potassium hydroxide dissolved in ethanol. The reaction is an elimination reaction and produces an alkene, e.g.

$$\underset{\text{ethene}}{\text{CH}_3\text{CH}_2\text{Br} + \text{OH}^- \rightarrow \text{CH}_2{=}\text{CH}_2 + \text{Br}^- + \text{H}_2\text{O}}$$

Potassium hydroxide is preferred to the cheaper sodium hydroxide in this reaction since it is more soluble in ethanol.

When a haloalkane is heated with moist silver(I) oxide, hydrolysis occurs similarly to the reaction with aqueous potassium hydroxide solution, e.g.

$$2\text{CH}_3\text{CH}_2\text{Br} + \text{Ag}_2\text{O} + \text{H}_2\text{O} \rightarrow 2\text{AgBr} + 2\text{CH}_3\text{CH}_2\text{OH}$$

(ii) Reaction of a haloalkane with potassium cyanide

A haloalkane is converted to a nitrile (or cyanide) by refluxing the haloalkane with a solution of potassium cyanide in ethanol.

$$CH_3CH_2Br + KCN \rightarrow CH_3CH_2CN + KBr$$
$$\text{propanenitrile}$$

This reaction is an important step in increasing the number of carbon atoms in a molecule (called **ascending the homologous series**; see 37.1).

(iii) Reaction of a haloalkane with ammonia

When a solution of a haloalkane in ethanol is heated with ammonia in a sealed vessel an amine is produced, but the reaction does not stop there. For example,

$$CH_3CH_2Br + NH_3 \rightarrow CH_3CH_2NH_2 + HBr$$
$$\text{ethylamine}$$
$$CH_3CH_2NH_2 + CH_3CH_2Br \rightarrow (CH_3CH_2)_2NH + HBr$$
$$\text{diethylamine}$$
$$(CH_3CH_2)_2NH + CH_3CH_2Br \rightarrow (CH_3CH_2)_3N + HBr$$
$$\text{triethylamine}$$
$$(CH_3CH_2)_3N + CH_3CH_2Br \rightarrow (CH_3CH_2)_4N^+Br^-$$
$$\text{tetraethylammonium bromide.}$$

Tetraethylammonium bromide is a quaternary ammonium salt. Quaternary ammonium salts are widely used as household fabric softeners.

The amines produced are bases and the reaction products of the above reaction will include salts, e.g.

$$CH_3CH_2NH_2 + HBr \rightarrow CH_3CH_2NH_3^+Br^-$$
$$\text{ethylammonium bromide}$$

(iv) Reaction of a haloalkane with the sodium salt of a carboxylic acid

Refluxing a haloalkane with the sodium salt of a carboxylic acid produces an ester.

$$CH_3CH_2Br + CH_3COONa \rightarrow CH_3COOCH_2CH_3 + NaBr$$
$$\text{bromoethane} + \text{sodium} \rightarrow \text{ethyl ethanoate} + \text{sodium}$$
$$\text{ethanoate} \qquad\qquad\qquad\qquad \text{bromide}$$

A similar reaction can be carried out by heating a haloalkane with the silver salt of a carboxylic acid

$$CH_3COOAg + CH_3CH_2Br \rightarrow CH_3COOCH_2CH_3 + AgBr$$

(v) Reaction of a haloalkane with an alkoxide

Sodium ethoxide is an alkoxide produced by reacting sodium and ethanol.

$$2Na + 2CH_3CH_2OH \rightarrow 2CH_3CH_2O^-Na^+ + H_2$$
$$\text{sodium} + \text{ethanol} \rightarrow \text{sodium ethoxide} + \text{hydrogen}$$

An ether is produced when this solution of sodium ethoxide in ethanol is refluxed with a haloalkane.

$$CH_3Br + CH_3CH_2O^-Na^+ \rightarrow CH_3CH_2OCH_3 + NaBr$$
$$\text{bromomethane} + \text{sodium ethoxide} \rightarrow \text{methoxyethane} + \text{sodium bromide}$$

This method of producing an ether is called the **Williamson ester synthesis.**

(vi) Formation of Grignard reagents

Haloalkanes can be converted into unstable compounds called **Grignard reagents**. These Grignard reagents are useful for converting one organic compound into another.

A Grignard reagent is prepared by adding magnesium turnings to a solution of a haloalkane in dry ethoxyethane. The mixture is refluxed and all water is excluded.

$$CH_3CH_2Br + Mg \rightarrow CH_3CH_2MgBr$$

Grignard reagents can be used in a variety of reactions.

❶ Hydrolysis of Grignard reagent with a dilute acid.

$$CH_3CH_2MgBr + H^+ \rightarrow CH_3CH_3 + Mg^{2+} + Br^-$$

❷ Reaction with methanal followed by refluxing with a dilute acid.

$$CH_3CH_2MgBr + H-C\underset{H}{\overset{O}{\Big\langle}} \rightarrow \left[CH_3CH_2-\underset{H}{\overset{OMgBr}{\underset{|}{\overset{|}{C}}}}-H \right] \rightarrow CH_3CH_2-\underset{H}{\overset{OH}{\underset{|}{\overset{|}{C}}}}-H$$

Propan-1-ol
(primary alcohol)

❸ Reaction with an aldehyde (other than methanal) followed by refluxing with a dilute acid.

$$CH_3CH_2MgBr + CH_3-C\underset{H}{\overset{O}{\Big\langle}} \rightarrow \left[CH_3-\underset{H}{\overset{OMgBr}{\underset{|}{\overset{|}{C}}}}-CH_2CH_3 \right] \rightarrow CH_3-\underset{H}{\overset{OH}{\underset{|}{\overset{|}{C}}}}-CH_2CH_3$$

ethanal

butan-2-ol (secondary alcohol)

❹ Reaction with a ketone followed by refluxing with a dilute acid.

$$CH_3CH_2MgBr + CH_3-C\underset{CH_3}{\overset{O}{\Big\langle}} \rightarrow \left[CH_3-\underset{CH_3}{\overset{OMgBr}{\underset{|}{\overset{|}{C}}}}-CH_2CH_3 \right] \rightarrow CH_3-\underset{CH_3}{\overset{OH}{\underset{|}{\overset{|}{C}}}}-CH_2CH_3$$

propanone

2-methylbutan-2-ol
(tertiary alcohol)

❺ Reaction with carbon dioxide followed by refluxing with a dilute acid.

$$CH_3CH_2MgBr + O{=}C{=}O \rightarrow \left[CH_3CH_2-\underset{O}{\overset{OMgBr}{\underset{\|}{\overset{|}{C}}}} \right] \rightarrow CH_3CH_2-\underset{O}{\overset{OH}{\underset{\|}{\overset{|}{C}}}}$$

propanoic acid
(carboxylic acid)

30.4 REACTIONS OF ARYL HALIDES

Whereas nucleophilic substitution reactions occur readily with haloalkanes, aryl halides only undergo substitution reactions with the greatest of difficulty. For example,

chlorobenzene   phenol

For this reaction to occur the reactants must be heated to 300 °C under great pressure. For all practical purposes substitution of the halogen in the ring does not take place under laboratory conditions.

An explanation for this lack of reactivity is the overlap between a pair of electrons in a p orbital on the halogen atom and the overlapping p orbitals in the benzene ring system (called π orbitals) (Fig. 30.1).

The halogen atom, chlorine in this case, is strongly held, as shown by the bond length.

C–Cl in chloroalkanes = 0.177 nm

C–Cl in chlorobenzene = 0.169 nm

Overlap between p orbital on chlorine atom and π orbital in benzene ring system

Fig. 30.1 Structure of chlorobenzene

30.5 REACTIONS OF (BROMOMETHYL)BENZENE

The bromine atom in (bromomethyl)benzene is not attached to a carbon atom of the benzene ring. There is no possibility of overlap between a bromine p orbital and the π orbital system of the benzene ring. The bromine atom is therefore more readily lost as a bromide ion, and (bromomethyl)benzene undergoes reactions similar to those of haloalkanes, e.g. on refluxing with aqueous sodium hydroxide solution.

Chapter roundup

When halogen atoms are attached to a carbon chain or to a nonaromatic ring such as a cyclohexane, the halogen is readily removed. This makes such compounds useful intermediates in organic reactions.

If attached to an aromatic ring, halogen atoms are very difficult to displace. This is because there is an overlap between the p orbital of the halogen and the π orbital of the ring.

The possible isomers of $C_7H_6Cl_2$ are:

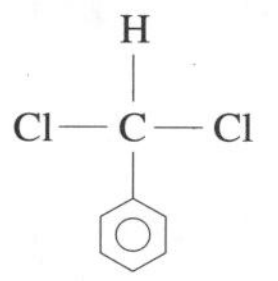

(dichloromethyl)benzene

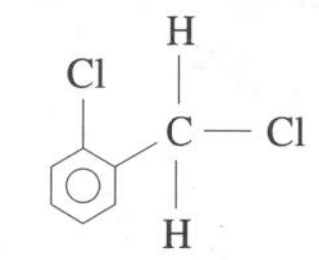

1–chloro–2–(chloromethyl)benzene

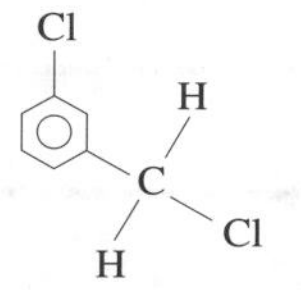

1–chloro–3–(chloromethyl)benzene

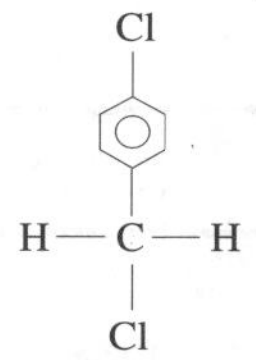

1–chloro–4–(chloromethyl)benzene

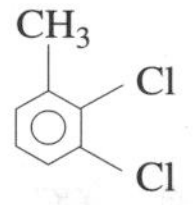

1,2–dichloro–3–methylbenzene

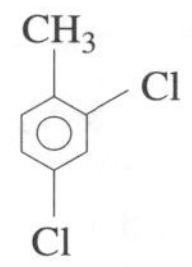

1,3–dichloro–4–methylbenzene

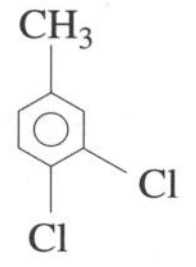

1,2–dichloro–4–methylbenzene

Also
1,3–dichloro–2–methylbenzene
1,3–dichloro–5–methylbenzene
1,4–dichloro–2–methylbenzene

Worked questions and answers

1 Hydrolysis of a compound A (formula $C_7H_6Cl_2$) was carried out by refluxing with excess potassium hydroxide solution. The resulting solution was acidified with dilute nitric acid and excess silver nitrate added to precipitate the chloride ions

as silver chloride. 0.718 g of silver chloride was formed from 0.805 g of A.
(a) Calculate the number of chlorine atoms present in each molecule of A which are liberated by hydrolysis.
(b) Suggest an explanation for the result obtained in (a).
(c) Give a possible structure for A.

$$(A_r(H) = 1, A_r(C) = 12, A_r(Cl) = 35.5, A_r(Ag) = 108)$$

Tutorial note

(a) Relative molecular mass of A = $(7 \times 12) + (6 \times 1) + (35.5 \times 2)$
$$= 161$$

Number of moles of A used = $\dfrac{0.805}{161}$ = 0.005

Number of moles of silver chloride produced = $\dfrac{0.718}{108 + 35.5}$
$$= 0.005$$

∴ 0.005 mole of silver chloride liberated from 0.005 mole of A.
Only one of the two chlorine atoms in the molecule is liberated during hydrolysis.

(b) An explanation is that one chlorine atom is attached to the benzene ring while the other is attached to a side-chain.

(c) Possible structures for A are

Question bank

1 (a) Give two examples of catalysis in organic chemistry. For each example, name the catalyst and the reactants and write an equation for the reaction.
(b) Under appropriate conditions, trichloroethanal reacts with chlorobenzene to produce the pesticide DDT.
(i) Classify this type of reaction.
(ii) If one mole of the product is refluxed with excess aqueous sodium hydroxide, acidified with aqueous nitric acid and then treated with excess aqueous silver nitrate, what mass of silver chloride would you expect to obtain?
(iii) What would you expect to observe if trichloroethanal was warmed with aqueous, ammoniacal silver nitrate?
(iv) What type of reaction has occurred in (b) (iii)?
(c) The pesticide DDT has been restricted in its use
(i) Give two reasons why this restriction has been imposed.
(ii) Suggest an alternative method to DDT for the control of harmful insects.
(AEB 1991)

Points

(a) There are plenty of examples in this book for you to use.
(b) (i) Condensation. (ii) Three of the chlorine atoms will be replaced – not the ones attached directly to the benzene rings. 430.5 g of silver chloride expected. (iii) Silver mirror (or black precipitate). (iv) Oxidation–reduction (or redox).
(c) DDT appears regularly on papers today. (i) Could include fat soluble, very stable and not broken up, building up in the food chain, kills harmful and harmless insects. (ii) Name a natural insecticide or biological control.

CHAPTER 31

ALCOHOLS, PHENOLS AND ETHERS

Units in this chapter

Chapter objectives

Alcohols consist of an aliphatic group with an OH group added. Phenols have an OH group on an aromatic ring such as benzene. As we saw with the organohalogen compounds the same group can behave differently depending upon its environment.

Alcohols can be divided into primary, secondary and tertiary and this is a most important distinction.

Alcohols and ethers are isomeric and we will see considerable differences in reactivity between them.

31.1 ALCOHOLS, PHENOLS AND ETHERS

In this chapter a comparison will be made between **alcohols** and **phenols**. Both contain a hydroxyl (OH) group, but in the alcohol the OH group is attached to a chain derived from an alkane while a phenol has an OH group attached directly to a benzene nucleus.

Examples of simple alcohols and phenols include

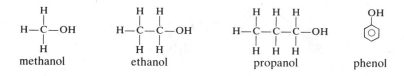

methanol   ethanol   propanol   phenol

Ethers also contain a single oxygen atom and are structural isomers of alcohols. They do not, however, resemble alcohols in properties. Simple ethers include

$$CH_3OCH_3 \qquad CH_3CH_2OCH_2CH_3 \qquad CH_3OCH_2CH_3$$
methoxymethane   ethoxyethane   methoxyethane

31.2 PRIMARY, SECONDARY AND TERTIARY ALCOHOLS

An understanding of the differences between primary, secondary and tertiary alcohols is most important. The classification depends upon the position of the OH group in the molecule, unlike the classification of amines as primary, secondary and tertiary (see Chapter 35).

In a primary alcohol, the OH group is attached to a carbon atom which is in turn attached directly to two or three hydrogen atoms. It can be represented as

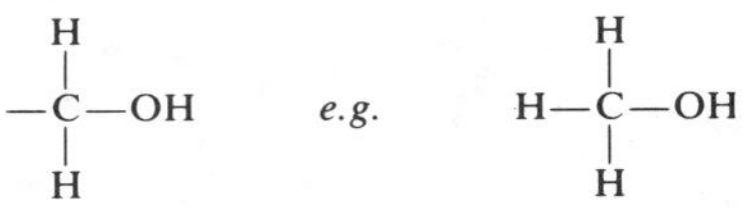

Only one hydrogen is attached to this carbon atom in a secondary alcohol:

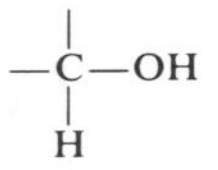

In a tertiary alcohol there are no hydrogen atoms attached to this carbon atom:

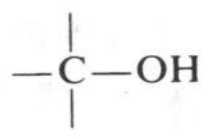

The four alcohols with a molecular formula C_4H_9OH have the following structures.

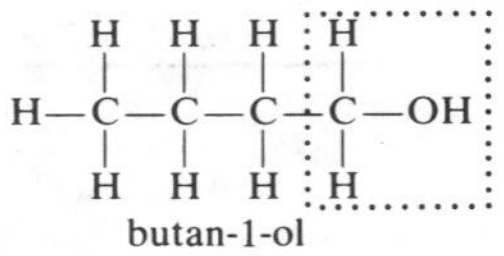

butan-1-ol
(primary alcohol)

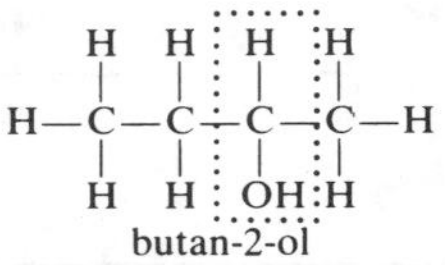

butan-2-ol
(secondary alcohol)

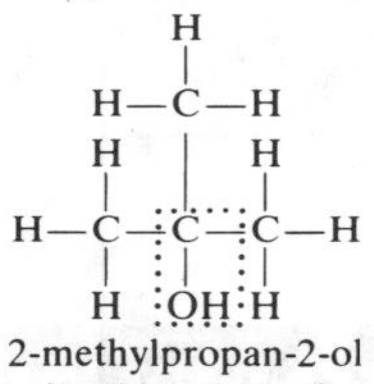

2-methylpropan-2-ol
(tertiary alcohol)

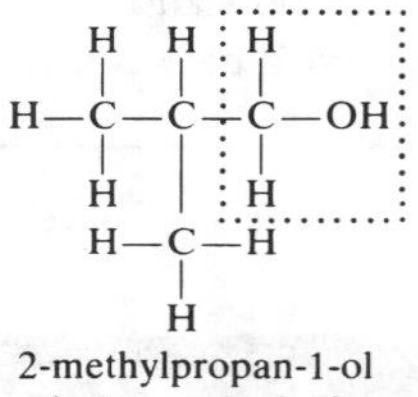

2-methylpropan-1-ol
(primary alcohol)

In 31.4 the chemical tests necessary to differentiate between primary, secondary and tertiary alcohols are given.

31.3 METHODS OF PREPARATION OF ALCOHOLS

Ethanol, C_2H_5OH, can be prepared by fermentation of starch or sugar solution in the presence of enzymes in yeast in *anaerobic* conditions (i.e. in absence of air), as in the wine–making process, e.g.

$$C_6H_{12}O_6 \xrightarrow{\text{zymase}} 2C_2H_5OH + 2CO_2$$

This process is carried out in slightly warm conditions (about 30–35 °C). Air must not be allowed to come into contact with the solution, or souring of the wine might take place. The souring involves the bacterial oxidation of the alcohol to a carboxylic acid.

$$C_2H_5OH + 2[O] \rightarrow CH_3COOH + H_2O$$

The solution resulting from anaerobic fermentation is a dilute solution of ethanol in water. This solution can be concentrated by fractional distillation (see 7.2). This does not produce 100% pure ethanol, however.

Methods of producing alcohols include the following.

① Hydrolysis of a haloalkane (see 30.3).

$$CH_3CH_2Br + OH^-(aq) \rightarrow CH_3CH_2OH + Br^-$$

② Reduction of aldehydes, ketones or carboxylic acids (see 32.6 and 33.3).

(a)

$$CH_3-\overset{H}{\underset{O}{C}} + 2[H] \rightarrow CH_3CH_2OH$$

ethanal (aldehyde)   ethanol (primary alcohol)

(b)

$$CH_3-\overset{O}{\underset{CH_3}{C}} + 2[H] \rightarrow CH_3-\overset{H}{\underset{OH}{C}}-CH_3$$

propanone   propan-2-ol
(ketone)   (secondary alcohol)

(c)

$$CH_3-\overset{O}{\underset{OH}{C}} + 4[H] \rightarrow CH_3CH_2OH + H_2O$$

ethanoic acid   ethanol
(carboxylic acid)   (primary alcohol)

The reagents necessary for these reactions are never well known by examination candidates. For the examples (a) and (b) any of the following reagents could be used: sodium and ethanol, hydrogen with platinum or nickel catalyst, lithium tetrahydridoaluminate(III) (lithium aluminium hydride), or sodium tetrahydridoborate(III) (sodium borohydride). Example (c) requires lithium tetrahydridoaluminate(III); this reaction is carried out in a solution in dry ethoxyethane.

Alcohols can also be produced by the reduction of esters with lithium tetrahydridoaluminate(III) (see 34.4).

③ Action of nitrous acid (nitric(III) acid) on a primary amine (see 35.3), e.g.

$$CH_3CH_2NH_2 + HONO \rightarrow CH_3CH_2OH + N_2 + H_2O$$

④ From the reaction of a Grignard reagent with an aldehyde or ketone (see 30.3).

Industrial methods for preparing alcohols are important. Vast quantities of the common alcohols are required by the chemical industry. Methanol is manufactured by heating carbon monoxide and hydrogen.

$$CO + 2H_2 \rightleftharpoons CH_3OH$$

The process is carried out at high pressures and between 350 °C and 400 °C in the presence of a chromium(III) oxide catalyst.

The other alcohols are obtained from alkenes. Alkenes are produced by cracking of higher fractions from petroleum refining. The alkene is reacted with concentrated sulphuric acid and the product is hydrolysed:

$$CH_3-CH=CH_2 + H_2SO_4 \rightarrow CH_3-\underset{\underset{H}{|}}{\overset{\overset{OSO_2OH}{|}}{C}}-CH_3 \qquad CH_3-\underset{\underset{H}{|}}{\overset{\overset{OSO_2OH}{|}}{C}}-CH_3 + H_2O \rightarrow CH_3-\underset{\underset{H}{|}}{\overset{\overset{OH}{|}}{C}}-CH_3 + H_2SO_4$$

propene   propan-2-ol

For industrial purposes ethanol is made from ethene, rather than by fermentation, by hydration over a phosphoric acid catalyst.

31.4 REACTIONS OF ALCOHOLS

(i) Oxidation of alcohols

Oxidation is used to distinguish primary, secondary and tertiary alcohols.

Primary alcohols are oxidised to produce aldehydes and then, on prolonged oxidation, carboxylic acids.

$$R-\underset{\underset{H}{|}}{\overset{\overset{H}{|}}{C}}-OH + [O] \rightarrow R-C{\overset{\overset{H}{\diagup}}{\diagdown_{O}}} + H_2O \qquad R-C{\overset{\overset{H}{\diagup}}{\diagdown_{O}}} + [O] \rightarrow R-C{\overset{\overset{OH}{\diagup}}{\diagdown_{O}}}$$

                           aldehyde   carboxylic acid

Secondary alcohols are oxidised to produce a ketone, and no further oxidation takes place under the stated conditions.

$$R-\underset{\underset{R'}{|}}{\overset{\overset{H}{|}}{C}}-OH + [O] \rightarrow R-C{\overset{\overset{O}{\diagup}}{\diagdown_{R'}}}$$

                                   ketone

Tertiary alcohols are only oxidised under very severe conditions, when the molecule is split. Under the conditions stated, no oxidation takes place.

There are a variety of methods available for carrying out these oxidations. One of the commonest methods is to heat the alcohol with a solution of potassium dichromate(VI) acidified with dilute sulphuric acid. During the oxidation the orange solution turns green owing to the formation of $Cr^{3+}(aq)$ ions.

$$6e^- + Cr_2O_7^{2-}(aq) + 14H^+(aq) \rightarrow 2Cr^{3+}(aq) + 7H_2O(l)$$

The aldehyde usually distils off during the oxidation as it has a lower boiling point than the corresponding alcohol.

Other suitable methods of oxidation include the following.

❶ Heating with either an acidic or an alkaline solution of potassium manganate(VII). The purple colour is removed during the oxidation and a brown precipitate of manganese(IV) oxide (manganese dioxide) may be formed if an alkaline solution is used.

❷ Passing the alcohol vapour over a heated copper catalyst, e.g.

$$CH_3CH_2OH \rightarrow CH_3CHO + H_2$$

❸ Passing a mixture of alcohol vapour and air over a heated silver catalyst, e.g.

$$2CH_3CH_2OH + O_2 \rightarrow 2CH_3CHO + 2H_2O$$

❹ Warming with concentrated nitric acid.

(ii) Reactions of alcohols with concentrated sulphuric acid

The reaction of an alcohol with concentrated sulphuric acid can lead to the formation of an alkene or an ether depending upon the conditions (see 29.4).

(iii) Reaction with sodium

Sodium (and the other members of the alkali metal family) react with an alcohol to produce hydrogen. There are parallels between this reaction and the reaction of sodium with water, but the reaction is slower.

$$2CH_3CH_2OH + 2Na \rightarrow 2CH_3CH_2O^- Na^+ + H_2$$

ethanol   sodium ethoxide

This reaction is used to dispose safely of waste scraps of alkali metals.

(iv) The triiodomethane (iodoform) reaction

This is a most important reaction for A-level candidates. Many successful answers rely upon recognising that the triiodomethane reaction will take place, and on understanding the steps in the reaction.

Only certain alcohols (and certain aldehydes and ketones) undergo this reaction. In order to give the reaction the compound must contain one of the following groups.

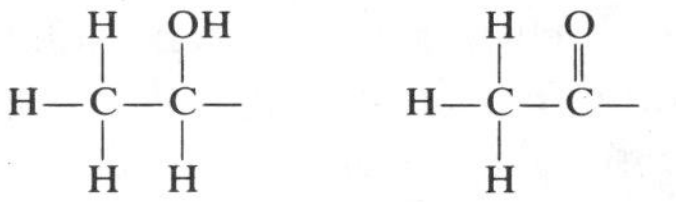

alcohols   ethanal or ketones

Methanol CH_3OH does not undergo the triiodomethane reaction. The simplest alcohol to undergo this reaction is ethanol CH_3CH_2OH.

The reaction takes place when the compound is warmed with a solution of sodium hydroxide (to produce alkaline conditions) and iodine solution. Alternatively a solution of potassium iodide and sodium chlorate(I) (hypochlorite) can be used. On warming, a yellow crystalline precipitate of triiodomethane is produced, which has an antiseptic smell.

The steps in this reaction using ethanol as the example are as follows.

1 Oxidation of alcohol with iodine:

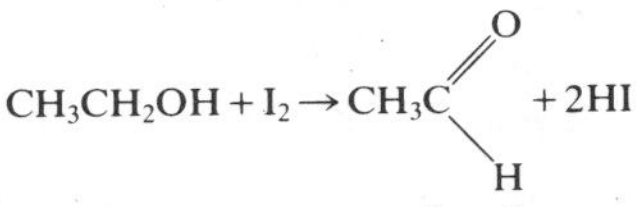

ethanal

2 Substitution of the iodine atoms into the aldehyde:

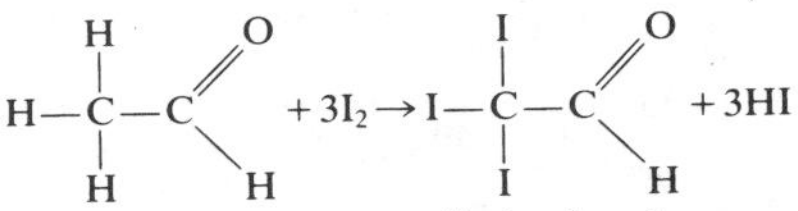

triiodoethanal

3 Hydrolysis in alkaline conditions:

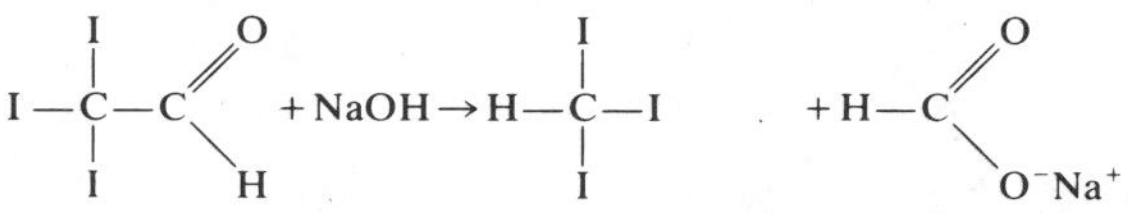

triiodomethane   sodium methanoate

If ethanal or a suitable ketone is used for this reaction, only steps 2 and 3 are necessary.

273

An overall equation for this reaction is

$$CH_3CH_2OH + 4I_2 + 6NaOH \rightarrow CHI_3 + HCOONa + 5NaI + 5H_2O$$

(v) Ester formation

See 34.4.

(vi) Reaction with phosphorus halides

See 30.2.

31.5   PREPARATION OF PHENOL

In the laboratory, phenol can be prepared from benzenesulphonic acid and from benzenediazonium chloride.

(i) From benzenesulphonic acid

Benzenesulphonic acid is prepared from benzene by sulphonation (see 29.9). The benzenesulphonic acid is neutralised with sodium hydroxide, and anhydrous sodium benzenesulphonate is fused with solid sodium hydroxide. Phenol is then produced by acidification.

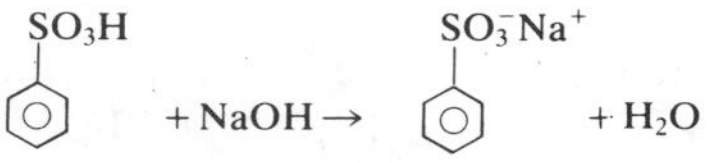

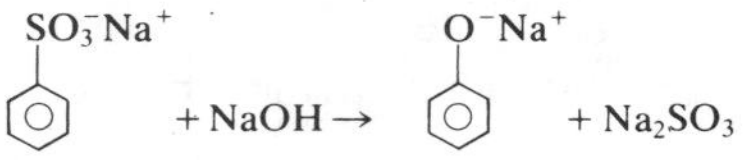

sodium phenoxide
(sodium phenate)

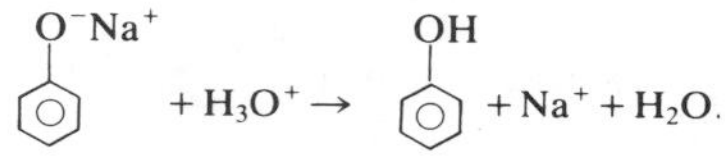

(ii) From benzenediazonium chloride

Benzenediazonium chloride is prepared by the action of nitrous acid (nitric(III) acid) on phenylamine below 5 °C (see 35.4).

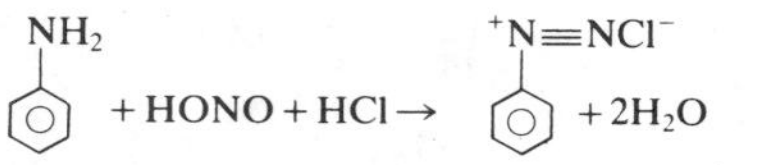

benzenediazonium chloride

An aqueous solution of benzenediazonium chloride decomposes on heating to produce phenol.

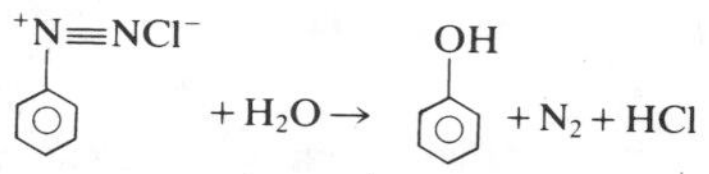

Industrially, phenol is produced from benzene. Propene and benzene vapours are mixed and passed over a heated catalyst to produce 2-phenylpropane (cumene).

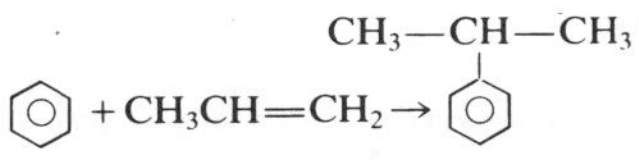

$$\text{C}_6\text{H}_6 + \text{CH}_3\text{CH}{=}\text{CH}_2 \rightarrow \underset{\text{cumene}}{\text{C}_6\text{H}_5\text{CH}(\text{CH}_3)_2}$$

Cumene is then heated with air at 180 °C.

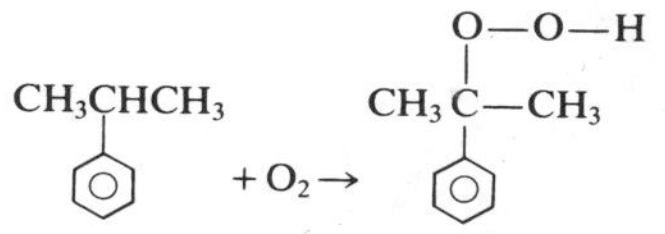

$$\underset{\text{}}{\text{C}_6\text{H}_5\text{CH}(\text{CH}_3)_2} + \text{O}_2 \rightarrow \underset{\text{cumene hydroperoxide}}{\text{C}_6\text{H}_5\text{C}(\text{CH}_3)_2\text{O}{-}\text{O}{-}\text{H}}$$

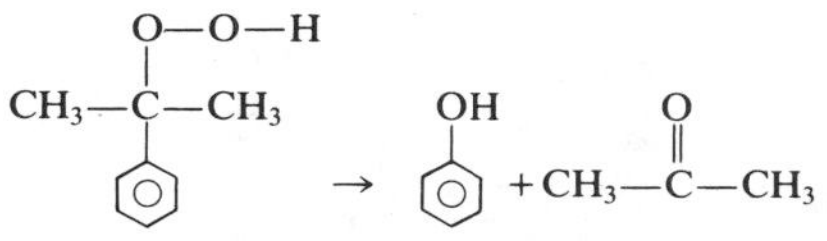

$$\underset{\text{}}{\text{CH}_3{-}\text{C}(\text{C}_6\text{H}_5){-}\text{CH}_3 \, \text{O}{-}\text{O}{-}\text{H}} \rightarrow \underset{\text{phenol}}{\text{C}_6\text{H}_5\text{OH}} + \underset{\text{propanone}}{\text{CH}_3{-}\text{C}({=}\text{O}){-}\text{CH}_3}$$

Phenol is produced by the hydrolysis of cumene hydroperoxide with dilute sulphuric acid.

31.6 REACTIONS OF PHENOL

(i) Acidic properties of phenol

Phenols are very slightly acidic. Phenol dissolves in sodium hydroxide solution to form sodium phenoxide. Alcohols do not carry out this reaction.

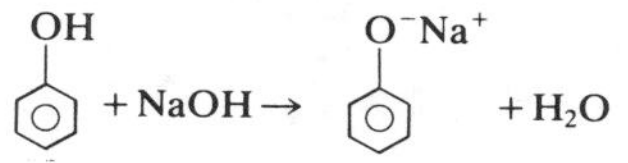

$$\text{C}_6\text{H}_5\text{OH} + \text{NaOH} \rightarrow \text{C}_6\text{H}_5\text{O}^-\text{Na}^+ + \text{H}_2\text{O}$$

Phenol is not sufficiently acidic to liberate carbon dioxide from sodium hydrogencarbonate. This distinguishes a phenol from a carboxylic acid.

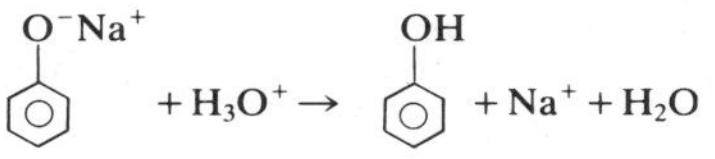

$$\text{C}_6\text{H}_5\text{O}^-\text{Na}^+ + \text{H}_3\text{O}^+ \rightarrow \text{C}_6\text{H}_5\text{OH} + \text{Na}^+ + \text{H}_2\text{O}$$

Phenol is recovered from sodium phenoxide by acidification with a dilute acid. The reasons for the acidity of phenol are discussed in Chapter 39.

(ii) Testing for phenol

Phenol contains the enol group $\underset{}{\text{C}{=}\text{C}}$ $\overset{\text{OH}}{}$. This can be tested for by adding a neutral solution of iron(III) chloride. A deep purple colouration is formed owing to the formation of a complex.

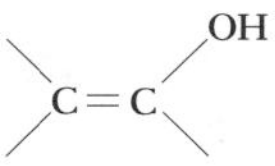

(iii) Reduction of phenol

Phenol can be reduced to benzene by heating with zinc dust at 400 °C.

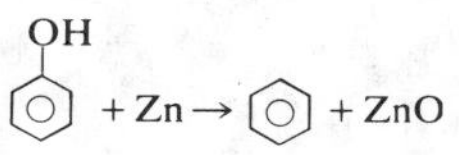

$$\text{C}_6\text{H}_5\text{OH} + \text{Zn} \rightarrow \text{C}_6\text{H}_6 + \text{ZnO}$$

(iv) Reaction with phosphorus halides

See 30.2.

(v) Ester formation (34.4)

Phenol does not produce an ester with a carboxylic acid in the presence of concentrated sulphuric acid. In this it differs from the alcohols. Phenol does, however, form an ester when treated with an acid chloride or anhydride.

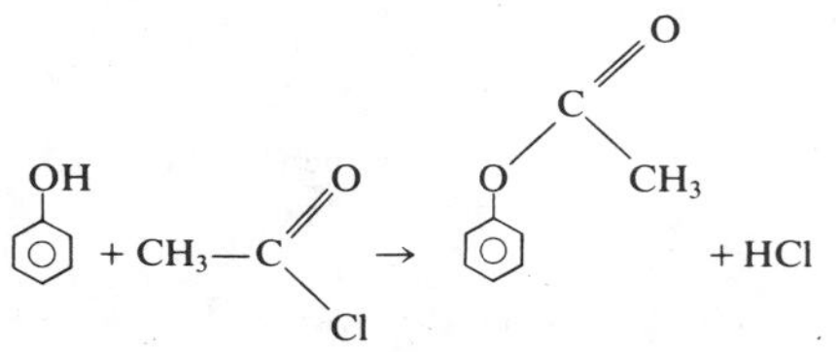

ethanoyl chloride   phenyl ethanoate

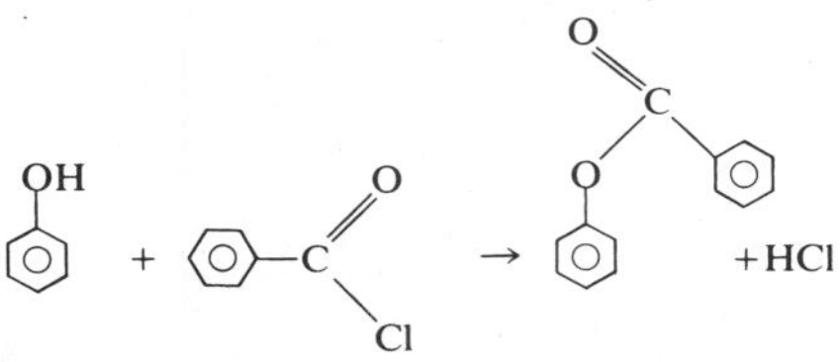

phenyl benzenecarboxylate
(phenyl benzoate)

(vi) Substitution reactions

Phenol undergoes substitution reactions into the nucleus more readily than benzene. This is because of the tendency for the pair of nonbonding electrons of the OH group to be drawn into the π electron system. The positions 2, 4 and 6 in the ring of phenol are particularly susceptible to electrophilic attack.

1 Bromination of benzene requires bromine in the presence of a halogen carrier. With phenol, however, bromination takes place immediately when bromine water is added to phenol.

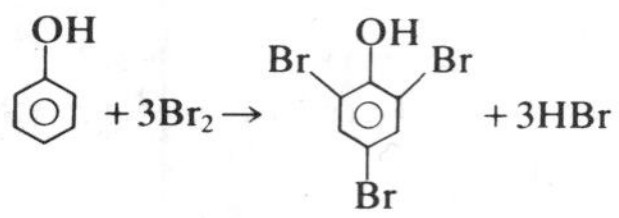

$$+ 3Br_2 \rightarrow \quad + 3HBr$$

2,4,6-tribromophenol
(white precipitate)

2 Nitration of benzene requires a mixture of concentrated nitric and sulphuric acids. Phenol is, however, nitrated with dilute nitric acid.

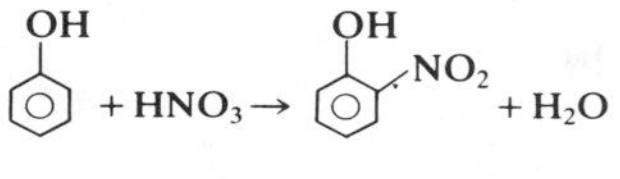

$$+ HNO_3 \rightarrow \quad + H_2O$$

2-nitrophenol

$$+ HNO_3 \rightarrow \quad + H_2O$$

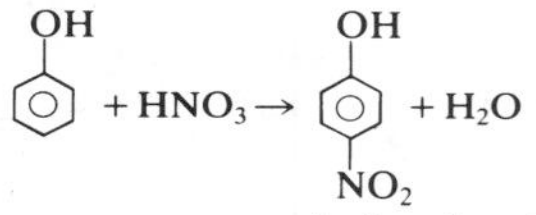

4-nitrophenol

A mixture of 2-nitrophenol and 4-nitrophenol is produced. This mixture can be separated by steam distillation.

3 With diazonium salts. The benzenediazonium ion $C_6H_5N_2^+$ is not sufficiently powerful an electrophile for substitution into benzene but it will react with an alkaline solution of phenol. An orange precipitate is formed in this coupling reaction.

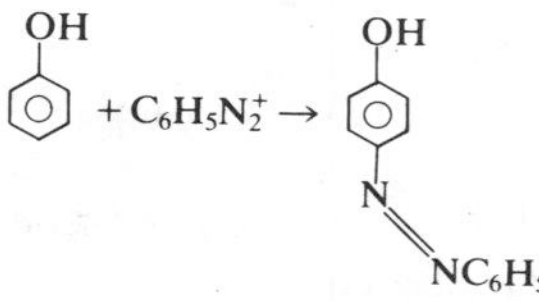

$$+ C_6H_5N_2^+ \rightarrow$$

(4-hydroxyphenylazobenzene)

31.7 TESTING FOR AN OH GROUP IN ALCOHOLS

Phosphorus pentachloride can be used to show the presence of an OH group in an alcohol. When solid phosphorus pentachloride is added to a carefully dried alcohol, fumes of hydrogen chloride are produced. If the alcohol is not dry, HCl will be generated by the water present.

$$CH_3CH_2OH + PCl_5 \rightarrow CH_3CH_2Cl + POCl_3 + HCl$$
$$\text{chloroethane}$$

Hydrogen chloride produces steamy fumes in moist air and dense white fumes with ammonia gas.

$$NH_3 + HCl \rightarrow NH_4Cl$$

Hydrogen chloride fumes are also produced if phosphorus pentachloride is added to a dry carboxylic acid.

31.8 ETHERS

Ethoxyethane can be prepared by the action of concentrated sulphuric acid on ethanol (see 29.4). Ethers can also be produced by the reaction of a haloalkane with an alkoxide (see 30.3) or by heating a haloalkane with dry silver oxide, e.g.

$$2CH_3CH_2Br + Ag_2O \rightarrow CH_3CH_2OCH_2CH_3 + 2AgBr$$

A phenoxide can be used to replace the alkoxide in the reaction with a haloalkane. This produces an ether containing an aromatic group.

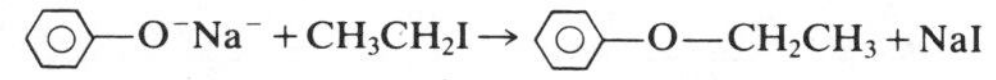

sodium phenoxide   ethoxybenzene

Chemically, ethers are much less reactive than alcohols. They do not contain a hydrogen atom attached directly to the oxygen atom.

31.9 HYDROGEN BONDING

Hydrogen bonding (see also 4.5) takes place between alcohol molecules but it is not possible with ethers.

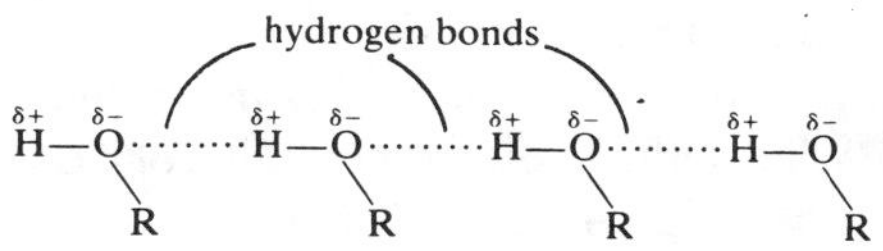

As a result, the boiling point of an alcohol is higher than the boiling point of the isomeric ether, e.g.

ethanol – boiling point   78 °C
methoxymethane – boiling point   –24 °C

Table 31.1 gives the formulae and viscosity at 20 °C of a number of alcohols.

Table 31.1 Viscosities of some alcohols at 20 °C

Alcohol	Formula	Viscosity/N s m^{-2}
propan-1-ol	$CH_3CH_2CH_2OH$	0.0023
propane-1,2-diol	$CH_3CH(OH)CH_2OH$	0.064
propane-1,2,3-triol	$CH_2(OH)CH(OH)CH_2OH$	1.07

The viscosity increases as the number of hydroxyl groups in the molecule increases. This is due to the increased amount of hydrogen bonding which is possible with the presence of the extra OH groups.

If the OH groups in propane-1,2,3-triol are modified by ester formation, the viscosity should decrease.

$$
\begin{array}{l}
\text{CH}_2\text{O}-\overset{\overset{\displaystyle O}{\|}}{\text{C}}-\text{CH}_3 \\
\text{CHO}-\overset{\overset{\displaystyle O}{\|}}{\text{C}}-\text{CH}_3 \\
\text{CH}_2\text{O}-\overset{\overset{\displaystyle O}{\|}}{\text{C}}-\text{CH}_3
\end{array}
\qquad \text{viscosity at } 20\,°C = 0.023\,\text{N s m}^{-2}
$$

Chapter roundup

A primary alcohol can be oxidised to an aldehyde and then a carboxylic acid. A secondary alcohol can be oxidised to a ketone and a tertiary alcohol cannot be oxidised. Remember to look at the carbon atom attached to the OH group and the number of hydrogen atoms attached to this carbon atom.

Phenols are slightly acidic while alcohols are completely neutral. Alcohols and phenols can be distinguished from ethers by the reaction with phosphorus pentachloride: alcohols and phenols produce fumes of hydrogen chloride and ethers do not.

Worked questions and answers

1 (a) Two isomeric compounds A and B, with the molecular formula C_3H_8O, can be oxidised to C and D respectively. C reacts with Fehling's solution to produce a red-brown precipitate E and another compound F. D has no reaction with Fehling's solution, but gives a yellow crystalline product G when treated with 2,4-dinitrophenylhydrazine solution.
   (i) Give the names and structural formulae of compounds A, B, C, D and F.
   (ii) Name the compound E.
   (iii) Draw the structural formula of G.
   (b) Describe what you would observe and name all the products formed when C is warmed with sodium dichromate(VI) solution acidified with dilute sulphuric acid. Write an equation (or equations) for the reactions taking place.
   (c) Describe how D is obtained industrially from crude petroleum.

(SUJB)

Tutorial note

This question uses information from Chapter 32 but illustrates the distinguishing features of primary and secondary alcohols.
(a) (i) Since these isomers are easily oxidised, they cannot be ethers.

$$
\begin{array}{cccc}
& \text{H} & \text{H} & \text{H} \\
& | & | & | \\
\text{H}-&\text{C}-&\text{C}-&\text{C}-\text{OH} \\
& | & | & | \\
& \text{H} & \text{H} & \text{H} \\
\end{array}
\qquad
\begin{array}{cccc}
& \text{H} & \text{H} & \text{H} \\
& | & | & | \\
\text{H}-&\text{C}-&\text{C}-&\text{C}-\text{H} \\
& | & | & | \\
& \text{H} & \text{OH} & \text{H} \\
\end{array}
$$
propan-1-ol   propan-2-ol

C reacts with Fehling's solution and must, therefore, be an aldehyde. D must be a ketone as it gives a reaction with 2,4-dinitrophenylhydrazine but not with Fehling's solution.

A must be propan-1-ol (primary alcohol) which oxidises to give the aldehyde C.

B must be propan-2-ol (secondary alcohol) which oxidises to give the ketone D.

C is CH_3CH_2C (propanal, with $=O$ and H)

D is CH_3-C-CH_3 (propanone, with $=O$)

F is CH_3CH_2C (with $=O$ and OH)

(ii) E is copper(I) oxide, Cu_2O.

(iii)

CH_3-C-CH_3 with $N-NH-$ ring $-NO_2$, NO_2 groups

(b) During the reaction the organic solution will turn green.

CH_3CH_2C (with $=O$ and H) $+ [O] \rightarrow CH_3CH_2C$ (with $=O$ and OH)
propanoic acid

$$Cr_2O_7^{2-} + 14H^+ + 6e^- \rightarrow 2Cr^{3+} + 7H_2O$$

The products are propanoic acid, chromium(III) sulphate and water.

(c) Propanone is produced from crude petroleum by fractional distillation followed by cracking to produce propene. The industrial method of obtaining phenol (31.5) produces propanone as a by-product.

Question bank

1 In some tropical countries, e.g. Brazil, ethanol is used as a motor fuel. The ethanol is obtained by the fermentation of cane sugar.

In the UK, industrial ethanol is made by the hydration of ethene which itself is a product of the petrochemical industry. Fermentation is used to produce alcoholic beverages.

(a) (i) Write a simple equation to show the production of ethanol in a fermentation reaction.

(ii) Write an equation to show the production of ethanol by the hydration of ethene.

(iii) Suggest reasons why Brazil produces ethanol for motor fuel by fermentation rather than from ethene.

(b) One type of breathalyser makes use of the reaction in which ethanol is converted into an aldehyde by specially treated potassium dichromate(VI) crystals.

(i) Name the type of reaction in which ethanol is converted into an aldehyde and give the structural formula of the aldehyde.

(ii) What colour do the potassium dichromate(VI) crystals turn when the breathalyser is used to test a person who has recently consumed a large number of alcoholic drinks?

(c) (i) Write an equation for the reaction in which ethanol burns completely in air.

(ii) Use the data below to calculate the molar enthalpy change for the combustion of ethanol.

$$\Delta H_{f, 298}/\text{kJ mol}^{-1}$$

C_2H_5OH (l)	−278.0
H_2O (l)	−286.0
CO_2 (g)	−394.0

(AEB 1989)

Points

Part (a)(i) refers to 31.3 and part (a)(ii) to 29.5.

Reasons why Brazil might produce ethanol for motor fuel by fermentation rather than from ethene could include the following.

❶ Hot, sunny climate will make plants photosynthesise well and produce plenty of material for fermentation.

❷ Lack of refinery capacity to produce ethene which would be expensive to buy.

Remember the question says *suggest*, which means you are not expected to know but will be given marks for reasonable suggestions.

In part (b) is a different way of asking the common question about the oxidation of ethanol (see 31.4). Many people know that the crystals turn green. You should know this is because the dichromate(VI) is reduced to chromium(III).

Part (c) relies on you getting the correct equation in (i).

$$C_2H_5OH + 3O_2 \rightarrow 2CO_2 + 3H_2O$$

Then in (ii) the question goes back to Chapter 13. You should get an answer of −1368 kJ mol^{-1}.

ALDEHYDES AND KETONES

Units in this chapter

Chapter objectives

Aldehydes and ketones are very important organic compounds. They both contain the carbonyl group

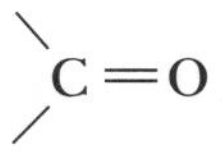

$$\text{C} = \text{O}$$

This undergoes addition reactions. They are, however, very different from addition reactions to carbon–carbon double bonds (Chapter 29).

Many questions at A level compare the properties of aldehydes and ketones.

32.1 COMMON ALDEHYDES AND KETONES

Some common aldehydes and ketones are:

Aldehydes

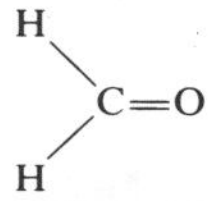

H
    C=O
H

methanal (formaldehyde)

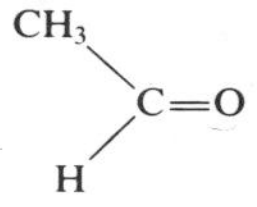

CH_3
    C=O
H

ethanal (acetaldehyde)

Ketones

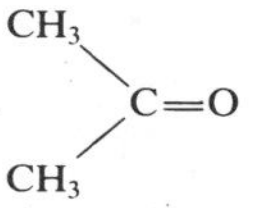

CH_3
    C=O
CH_3

propanone (acetone)

CH_3
    C=O
CH_3CH_2

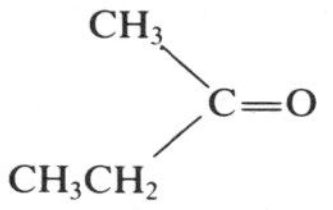

butanone

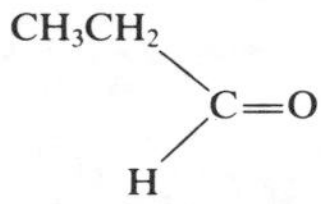

propanal

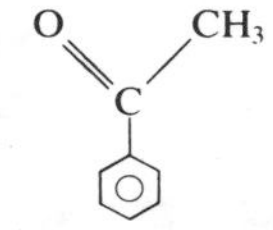

phenylethanone

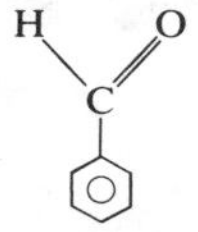

benzenecarbaldehyde (benzaldehyde)

Both aldehydes and ketones contain the $C=O$ (carbonyl) group. In an aldehyde there is a hydrogen atom attached to the carbonyl group. Aldehydes and ketones can be represented as

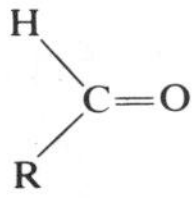

aldehyde

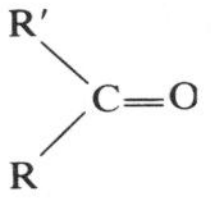

ketone

Methanal is a gas at room temperature and pressure but is used in solution in water. The other simple aldehydes are liquids under normal laboratory conditions.

32.2 PREPARATION OF ALDEHYDES AND KETONES

(i) Oxidation of alcohols

Aldehydes and ketones are usually prepared by the oxidation of alcohols using acidified potassium dichromate(VI) solution. Aldehydes are produced by the oxidation of primary alcohols, and ketones by the oxidation of secondary alcohols, e.g.

$$CH_3CH_2OH + [O] \rightarrow CH_3CHO + H_2O$$
ethanal
$$CH_3CH(OH)CH_3 + [O] \rightarrow CH_3COCH_3 + H_2O$$
propanone

Prolonged oxidation of primary alcohols leads to the formation of carboxylic acids.

(ii) Hydrolysis of certain dihalides

Hydrolysis of compounds with two halogen atoms attached to the same carbon atom by boiling with dilute acid can produce aldehydes or ketones. If the two halogen atoms are attached to a terminal (or end) carbon atom an aldehyde is produced, and if attached to a middle carbon atom a ketone is produced.

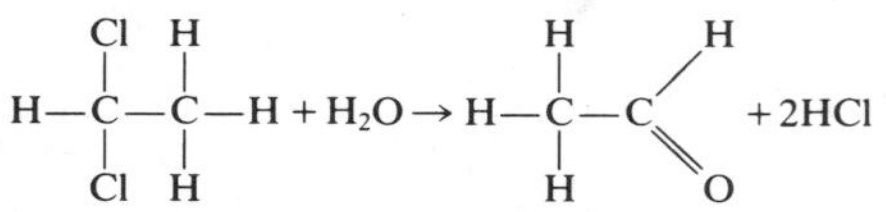

1,1-dichloroethane   ethanal

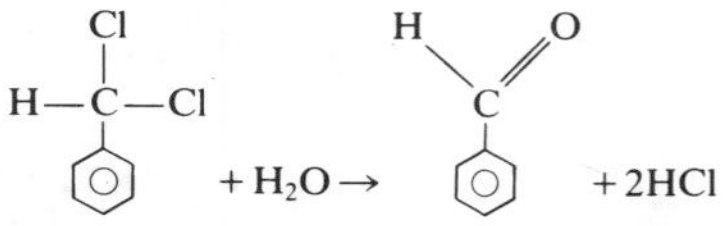

(dichloromethyl)benzene   benzenecarbaldehyde

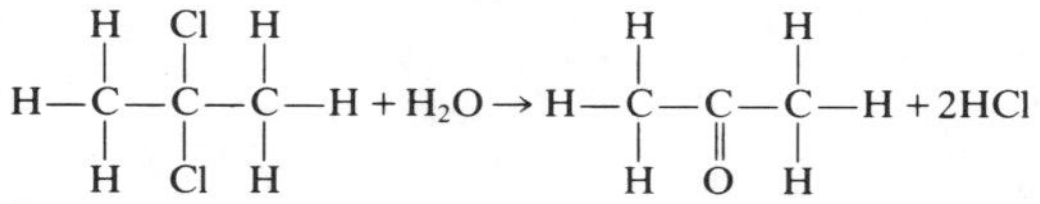

2,2-dichloropropane   propanone

There are other methods for preparing specific aldehydes and ketones. These include:

① Friedel–Crafts reaction to produce phenylethanone (see 29.9);
② hydration of ethyne to produce ethanal (see 29.6);
③ action of heat on calcium ethanoate produces propanone (see 33.5); and
④ propanone obtained as a by-product of the manufacture of phenol (see 31.5).

32.3 STRUCTURE OF THE CARBONYL GROUP

There are four electrons between the carbon and oxygen atoms in the double bond. Because oxygen is more electronegative than carbon, there is a slight electron shift towards the oxygen.

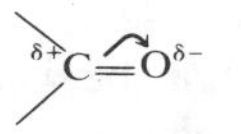

$$\underset{}{\overset{\delta^+}{>}}C \overset{\frown}{=\!\!=} O^{\delta^-}$$

This makes the carbon atom susceptible to nucleophilic attack (see 38.4).

32.4 ADDITION REACTIONS

There are a number of important addition reactions of aldehydes and ketones. In each reaction the double bond between the carbon and oxygen is converted into a single bond and an OH group is formed. Ketones undergo these reactions less readily than aldehydes, or not at all, especially if the ketone contains other than a methyl group. This is due to steric hindrance – the attacking nucleophile is unable to reach the carbonyl group. The addition reactions of aldehydes and ketones include the following.

(i) Addition of sodium hydrogensulphite

When a saturated solution of sodium hydrogensulphite is added to an aldehyde, a white crystalline addition product is formed.

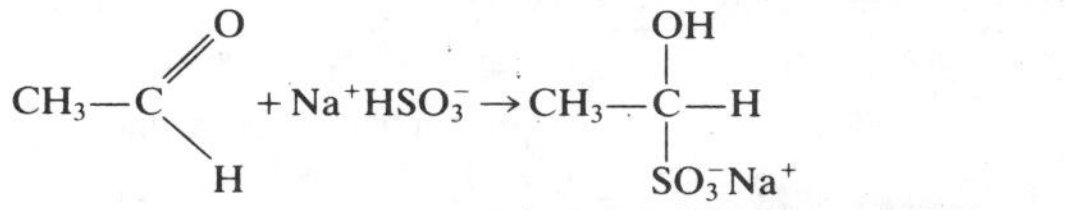

$$CH_3-\overset{\displaystyle O}{\underset{\displaystyle H}{C}} + Na^+HSO_3^- \rightarrow CH_3-\overset{\displaystyle OH}{\underset{\displaystyle SO_3^-Na^+}{\overset{\displaystyle |}{C}}}-H$$

ethanal sodium hydrogensulphite

This addition product decomposes on warming with a dilute acid to produce the original carbonyl compound. This provides a good method of purification for aldehydes.

(ii) Addition of hydrogen cyanide

Addition of hydrogen cyanide to an aldehyde or ketone produces a cyanohydrin.

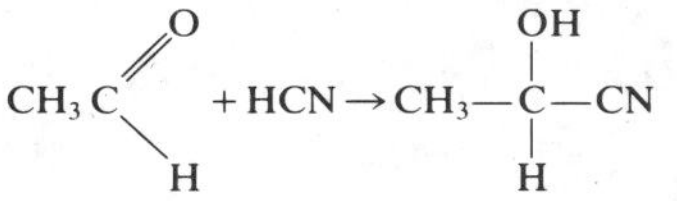

$$CH_3\overset{\displaystyle O}{\underset{\displaystyle H}{C}} + HCN \rightarrow CH_3-\overset{\displaystyle OH}{\underset{\displaystyle H}{\overset{\displaystyle |}{C}}}-CN$$

2-hydroxypropanenitrile
(ethanal cyanohydrin)

(iii) Addition of ammonia

Ammonia forms a solid addition product with aldehydes (but not with methanal). Similar compounds using ketones in place of aldehydes are unstable.

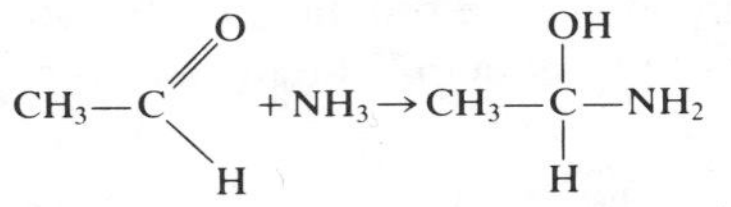

$$CH_3-C{\overset{O}{\underset{H}{\big<}}} + NH_3 \rightarrow CH_3-\overset{OH}{\underset{H}{C}}-NH_2$$

1-aminoethanol

(iv) Grignard reagents

See 30.3.

32.5 CONDENSATION REACTIONS

A **condensation reaction** is a reaction between two molecules to form a larger molecule, with the loss of a small molecule such as water or hydrogen chloride. Alternatively, a condensation reaction may be regarded as an addition reaction followed immediately by an elimination reaction. The product of the condensation reaction of an aldehyde or ketone always contains a double bond.

(i) Reaction with hydrazine, NH₂NH₂

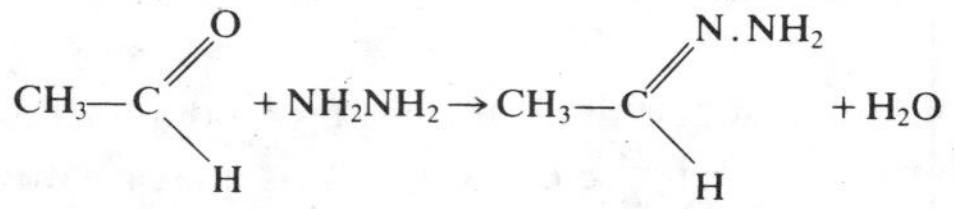

$$CH_3-C{\overset{O}{\underset{H}{\big<}}} + NH_2NH_2 \rightarrow CH_3-C{\overset{N.NH_2}{\underset{H}{\big<}}} + H_2O$$

ethanal hydrazone

$$CH_3-C{\overset{O}{\underset{CH_3}{\big<}}} + NH_2NH_2 \rightarrow CH_3-C{\overset{N.NH_2}{\underset{CH_3}{\big<}}} + H_2O$$

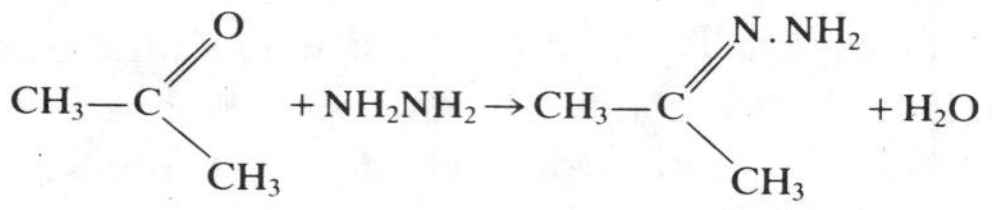

propanone hydrazone

(ii) Reaction with phenylhydrazine

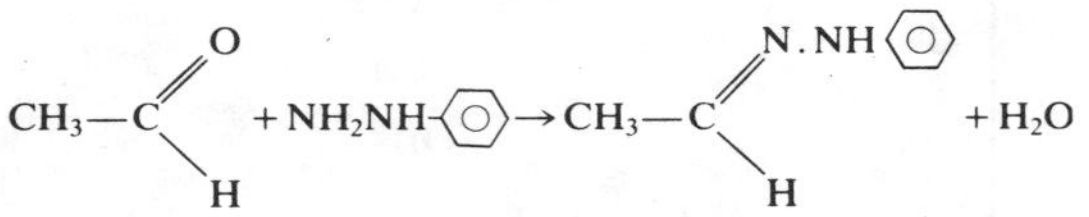

$$CH_3-C{\overset{O}{\underset{H}{\big<}}} + NH_2NH\text{—}\bigcirc \rightarrow CH_3-C{\overset{N.NH\bigcirc}{\underset{H}{\big<}}} + H_2O$$

ethanal phenylhydrazone

(iii) Reaction with 2,4-dinitrophenylhydrazine

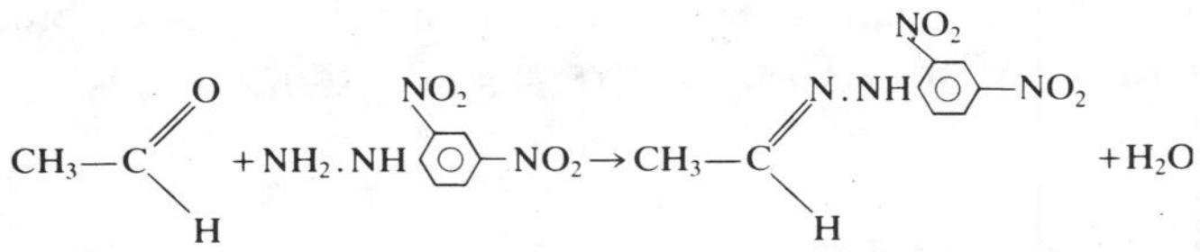

$$CH_3-C{\overset{O}{\underset{H}{\big<}}} + NH_2.NH\overset{NO_2}{\underset{}{\bigcirc}}\text{—}NO_2 \rightarrow CH_3-C{\overset{N.NH\overset{NO_2}{\bigcirc}\text{—}NO_2}{\underset{H}{\big<}}} + H_2O$$

ethanal 2,4-dinitrophenylhydrazone

(iv) Reaction with hydroxylamine, NH₂OH

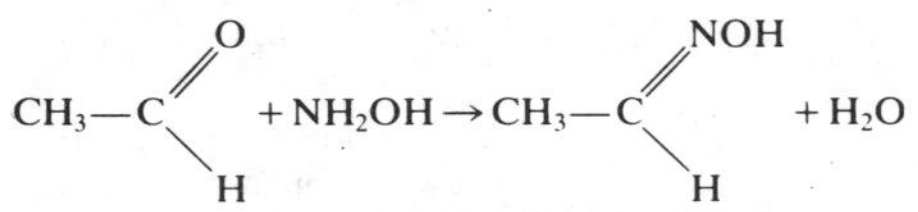

$$CH_3-C{\overset{O}{\underset{H}{\big<}}} + NH_2OH \rightarrow CH_3-C{\overset{NOH}{\underset{H}{\big<}}} + H_2O$$

ethanal oxime

The products of these condensation reactions are obtained as solids by mixing a solution of the reagent with the aldehyde or ketone. These derivatives, particularly the phenylhydrazones and the 2,4–dinitrophenylhydrazones which are less soluble and more easily precipitated, are used as a means of identifying aldehydes and ketones as the derivatives have characteristic melting points.

The mechanism for these reactions is explained in Chapter 38.

32.6 OXIDATION AND REDUCTION REACTIONS

Aldehydes and ketones can be reduced to the appropriate alcohol by using lithium tetrahydridoaluminate(III) (lithium aluminium hydride), sodium and ethanol, or sodium tetrahydridoborate(III) (sodium borohydride).

$$CH_3-C\begin{matrix}O\\\\H\end{matrix} + 2[H] \rightarrow CH_3CH_2OH$$

ethanol (primary alcohol)

$$CH_3-C\begin{matrix}O\\\\CH_3\end{matrix} + 2[H] \rightarrow CH_3CH(OH)CH_3$$

propan-2-ol (secondary alcohol)

Lithium tetrahydridoaluminate(III) is used in solution with ethoxyethane as solvent. Sodium tetrahydridoborate(III) is less reactive and is used in solution in water or ethanol.

Aldehydes can be oxidised to acids by the following methods.

❶ Passing the aldehyde vapour into a solution of dilute sulphuric acid containing a manganese(II) salt as catalyst. The solution should be heated to about 50 °C.

❷ Refluxing the aldehyde with an excess of acidified sodium dichromate(VI) solution.

Aldehydes and ketones can be distinguished by oxidation. Aldehydes are readily oxidised to carboxylic acids but ketones cannot readily be oxidised.

❶ Aldehydes readily restore the colour to Schiff's reagent. Schiff's reagent consists of a pinkish-purple solution of magenta (rosaniline) decolourised by passing sulphur dioxide through the solution. The pinkish-purple colour is restored when an aldehyde is added.

❷ Tollens' reagent is essentially a complexed solution of silver(I) ions produced by dissolving silver(I) oxide in excess ammonia. When an aldehyde is mixed with Tollens' solution and the mixture heated, a silver mirror forms on the inside of the test tube. No silver mirror is produced with a ketone.

$$Ag_2O + CH_3CHO \rightarrow CH_3COOH + 2Ag$$

❸ Fehling's and Benedict's solutions are two very similar tests for reducing sugars. Either can be employed to distinguish between an aldehyde and a ketone. Both reagents consist of a complexed solution of copper(II) ions. When one of these solutions is mixed with an aldehyde and the mixture warmed, a precipitate of copper(I) oxide is produced. The precipitate can vary considerably in colour from red to orange or even yellow. No precipitate is obtained with ketones.

$$RCHO + 2CuO \rightarrow RCOOH + Cu_2O$$

32.7 REACTIONS WITH ALKALIS

The reactions of aldehydes with alkalis are very complicated and depend upon the particular aldehyde, the concentration of the alkali and the reaction conditions.

Aliphatic aldehydes except methanal react with cold, dilute sodium hydroxide solution (or aqueous potassium carbonate solution). For example, ethanal reacts to produce 3-hydroxybutanal (aldol). This reaction is called the **aldol condensation**.

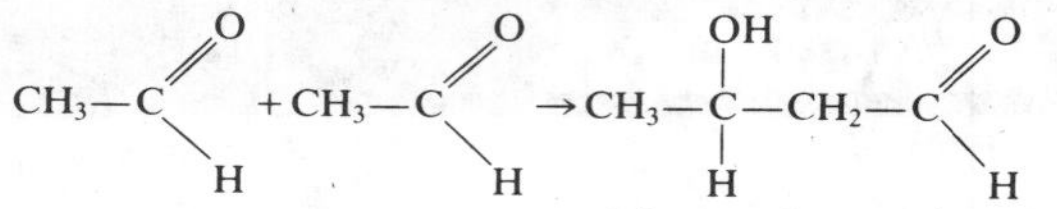

3-hydroxybutanal (aldol)

The aldol is inclined to lose water.

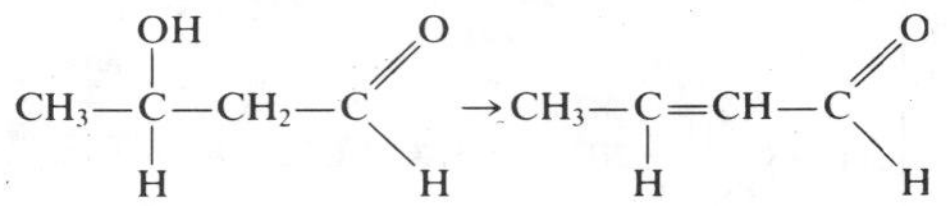

but-2-enal

Ketones do not undergo this type of condensation.

With hot, concentrated sodium hydroxide solution a complex yellow-brown resin is produced from polymerisation of the aldehyde.

Aldehydes that undergo the aldol condensation contain a hydrogen atom attached directly to the carbon atom next to the carbonyl group. This is called an α-hydrogen atom. Methanal and benzaldehyde possess no α-hydrogen atom and therefore do not undergo the aldol condensation. These aldehydes, when shaken with sodium hydroxide solution, undergo disproportionation. The products are the corresponding alcohol and the sodium salt of the corresponding acid. This is the **Cannizzaro reaction**.

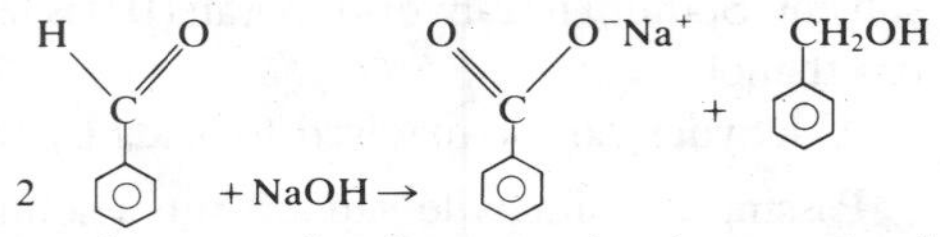

sodium benzenecarboxylate   phenylmethanol

Benzenecarboxylic acid can be obtained by acidification with a dilute acid.

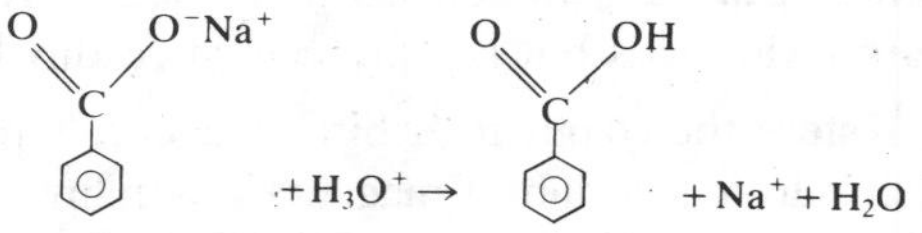

Similarly, methanal can undergo this reaction.

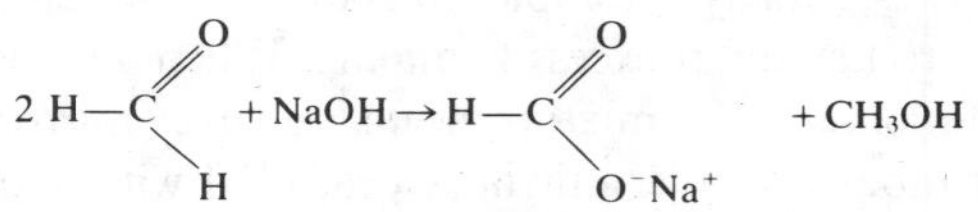

sodium methanoate methanol

32.8 COMPARISON OF ALDEHYDES AND KETONES

Table 32.1 compares the properties of a typical aldehyde and ketone.

Table 32.1 *Comparison of aldehydes and ketones*

	Aldehydes	Ketones
method of preparation	oxidation of primary alcohol	oxidation of secondary alcohol
reduction with lithium tetrahydridoaluminate(III)	primary alcohol formed	secondary alcohol formed
reaction with sodium hydrogensulphite	addition product formed	addition product formed
reaction with hydrogen cyanide	addition product formed	addition product formed
reaction with ammonia	addition product formed (not with methanal)	no addition product formed
reaction with hydrazine, phenylhydrazine, 2,4-dinitrophenylhydrazine	precipitate formed condensation reaction	precipitate formed condensation reaction
Fehling's solution	red brown precipitate	no reaction
Tollens' reagent	silver mirror	no reaction
Schiff's reagent	pinkish-purple colour restored	no reaction
triiodomethane (iodoform) reaction	yellow precipitate only formed with ethanal	yellow precipitate formed with any ketone containing $CH_3-\overset{\overset{\textstyle O}{\|\|}}{C}-$ group
polymerisation	polymerisation takes place	little tendency to polymerise

Chapter roundup

Primary alcohols can be easily oxidised to aldehydes which in turn can be oxidised to carboxylic acids. Ketones are produced by oxidising secondary alcohols but they are not further oxidised.

The presence of a carbonyl group in an aldehyde or ketone can be shown easily by reagents such as 2,4-dinitrophenylhydrazine which forms a dinitrophenylhydrazone. Aldehydes give positive tests with:

❶ Schiff's reagent;
❷ Tollens' reagent; and
❸ Fehling's (or Benedict's) reagent.

Worked questions and answers

1 Glycerol ($CH_2OHCH(OH)CH_2OH$), on heating with anhydrous magnesium sulphate, yields an acrid-smelling distillate of molecular formula C_3H_4O, which immediately decolourises bromine water and restores the colour to Schiff's reagent. Indicate a possible structure for the compound and suggest its mode of formation from glycerol.

Tutorial note

The product must contain the CHO aldehyde group as it restores the colour to Schiff's reagent. The product also contains a double or triple bond as it decolourises bromine water.

The product is therefore

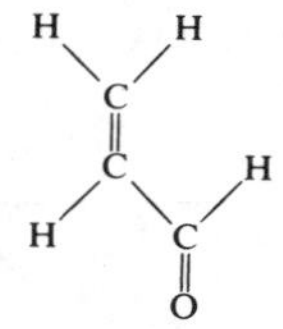

This compound is formed by the dehydration of glycerol. Anhydrous magnesium sulphate acts as the dehydrating agent.

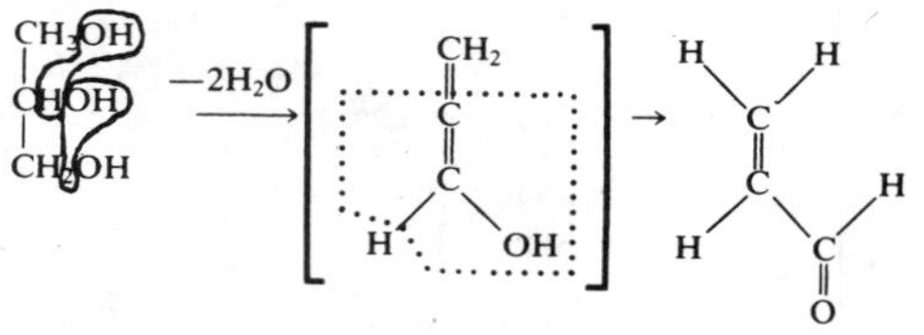

enol form rearranges

2 The reaction between ethanal and hydrogen cyanide can be represented by

$$CH_3CHO + HCN \rightarrow CH_3CH(OH)CN$$

(a) Explain how it is possible for the product to be a mixture of two isomers. (Hint: see 7.6.)

(b) Draw spatial formulae showing these two isomers.

(c) Why are the isomers present in equal quantities?

Tutorial note

(a) The product, 2-hydroxypropanenitrile, contains a chiral carbon atom. It can, therefore, exist as two optical isomers.

(b)

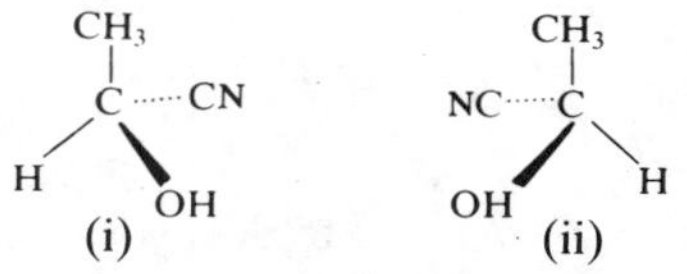

(c) The reaction involves nucleophilic attack by CN^-. The CN^- can attack either from the back or the front and the probabilities are the same. Attacking from the front produces one isomer and from the back the other.

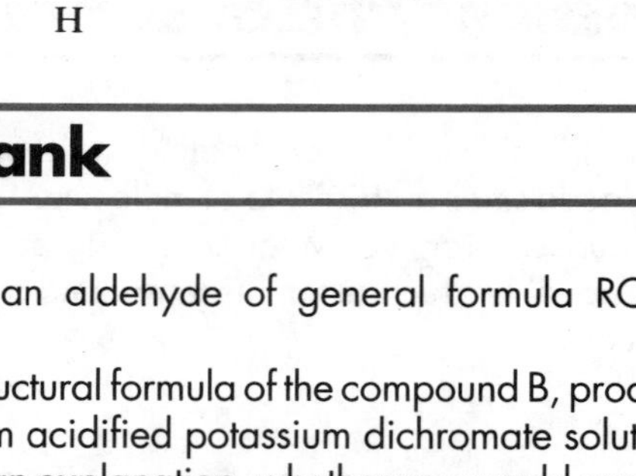

Question bank

1 Compound A is an aldehyde of general formula RCHO, where R is an alkyl group.

(a) (i) Write the structural formula of the compound B, produced by the treatment of A with warm acidified potassium dichromate solution.

(ii) State, with an explanation, whether you would expect B to have a higher or a lower boiling point than A.

(b) (i) State what reaction you would expect to occur on reacting with 2,4-dinitrophenylhydrazine.

(ii) Name the type of reaction taking place in (b)(i) above.

(iii) Explain how the product of this reaction may be used to identify carbonyl compounds such as A.

(c) (i) Write the structural formula of the compound C, which you would expect to be formed by reacting A with lithium tetrahydriodoaluminate(III) in ether.

(ii) State what type of reaction is taking place in (c)(i) above.

(iii) Suggest, with appropriate conditions, another reagent which would bring about the same transformation, A to C.

(iv) State, with an explanation, whether you would expect C to have a higher or lower boiling point than A.

(d) (i) Describe the reaction which you would expect to take place on gently warming A with diamminesilver(I) solution. State what you would expect to *observe*.

(ii) State what type of reaction is taking place in (d)(i) above.

(e) (i) Write the structural formula for the compound D which you would expect to be formed on reacting compound B with compound C.

(ii) State the appropriate conditions for the reactions in (e)(i).

(iii) State, with an explanation, whether you would expect D to have a higher or lower boiling point than B or C.

(WJEC 1990)

Points

This question very clearly states what has to be done and deals with alcohols (Chapter 31), aldehydes (Chapter 32), carboxylic acids (Chapter 33) and esters (Chapter 34). The mistake to avoid involves the reduction of the aldehyde with lithium tetrahydridoaluminate(III). The product is RCH_2OH, not ROH.

2 (a) What do you understand by the terms relative atomic mass, mass number, isotope?

(b) The mass spectrum of an organic compound which can be obtained by the oxidation of an alcohol is shown below.

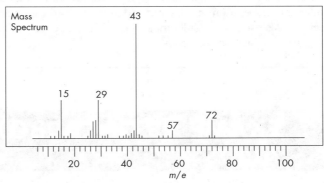

The compound has the following composition by mass

$$C = 66.7\% \quad H = 11.1\% \quad O = 22.2\%$$

Calculate the empirical formula of the compound and, by interpreting the labelled peaks on the mass spectrum, determine the structural formula of the compound.

(c) Explain the occurrence of a small peak at a mass of 73 in the mass spectrum in (b).

(d) (i) Give the name of the compound identified in (b).

(ii) Give the name and structural formula of the compound which on oxidation yields the compound identified in (b).

(ULEAC)

Points

Before attempting this question look back at Chapters 1 and 7.

The empirical formula you calculate is C_4H_8O. The peak at 72 supports a RMM of 72. Peaks correspond to CH_3^+ (15), $C_2H_5^+$ (29), $C_3H_7^+$ (43) and $C_3H_5O^+$ (57). This supports a structure of $CH_3CH_2CH_2CHO$ (butanal). The alcohol producing this on oxidation is butan-1-ol, $CH_3CH_2CH_2CH_2OH$.

The peak at 73 corresponds to the same molecular ion as 72 but with one carbon-13 instead of a carbon-12.

CHAPTER 33

CARBOXYLIC ACIDS AND THEIR SALTS

Units in this chapter

Chapter objectives

Organic acids, commonly called carboxylic acids, are weak acids, i.e. they are only partially ionised in aqueous solution (Chapter 16). In this chapter we will consider the preparation of aliphatic and aromatic carboxylic acids and their properties. We will also consider molecules where there are two carboxylic acid groups, namely dicarboxylic acids.

33.1 EXAMPLES OF CARBOXYLIC ACIDS

Carboxylic acids contain the carboxyl group, which, as its name suggests, is composed of a carbonyl group and a hydroxyl group. The carboxyl group is

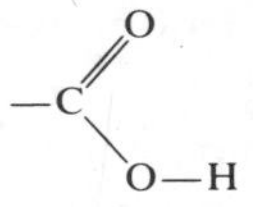

Despite having a carbonyl group within the structure, carboxylic acids do not undergo the typical addition and condensation reactions of aldehydes and ketones. This is because of the effect of the adjacent oxygen supplying electrons and making the carbon of the carbonyl group less electron deficient.

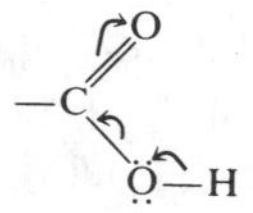

The movement of electrons away from the hydrogen atom weakens the bond between the hydrogen and oxygen atoms. The breaking away of this hydrogen to form an H^+ ion accounts for the acidity of these compounds.

Common acids include:

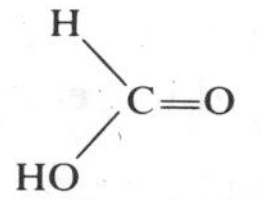

All of these acids are monobasic, i.e. they contain only one hydrogen which can be lost as an H^+ ion.

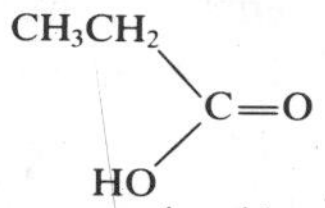

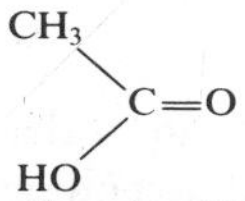

Acids are named from the corresponding hydrocarbon by removing the –e and adding –oic acid.

Hydrogen bonding has a noticeable effect on the properties of the lower acids. Because of hydrogen bonding, methanoic and ethanoic acids are more soluble in water and have higher boiling points than expected. Higher members of the homologous series, with longer carbon chains, are less influenced by hydrogen bonding and are less soluble in water.

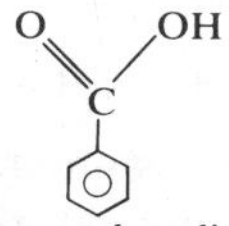

Benzenecarboxylic acid (benzoic acid) is only sparingly soluble in cold water but is more soluble in hot water.

33.2 PREPARATION OF ALIPHATIC AND AROMATIC CARBOXYLIC ACIDS

Aliphatic carboxylic acids can be prepared by the following methods.

1 Prolonged oxidation of primary alcohols or aldehydes (see 31.4), e.g.

$$CH_3CH_2OH + 2[O] \rightarrow CH_3COOH + H_2O$$
ethanoic acid

$$CH_3CH_2CHO + [O] \rightarrow CH_3CH_2COOH$$
propanoic acid

Heating with excess acidified potassium dichromate(VI) solution is one of the methods which could be used for this purpose.

2 Hydrolysis of nitriles (see 34.6). Nitriles are hydrolysed by boiling with water but are hydrolysed more quickly if the hydrolysis is carried out with a dilute acid or a dilute alkali.

Acid hydrolysis
$$CH_3CH_2CN + 2H_2O + HCl \rightarrow CH_3CH_2COOH + NH_4Cl$$
propanenitrile · · · · · · · · · · · · · · · propanoic acid

Alkaline hydrolysis
$$CH_3CH_2CN + NaOH + H_2O \rightarrow CH_3CH_2COO^-Na^+ + NH_3$$
sodium propanoate

In the latter case, the free acid is obtained by acidification of the product.

$$CH_3CH_2COO^-Na^+ + HCl \rightarrow CH_3CH_2COOH + NaCl$$

Hydrolysis of nitriles can form an important step in ascending the homologous series (see 37.1).

3 From Grignard reagents (see 30.3). The Grignard reagent is poured onto solid carbon dioxide and the product is hydrolysed by refluxing with a dilute acid.

methyl magnesium bromide ethanoic acid

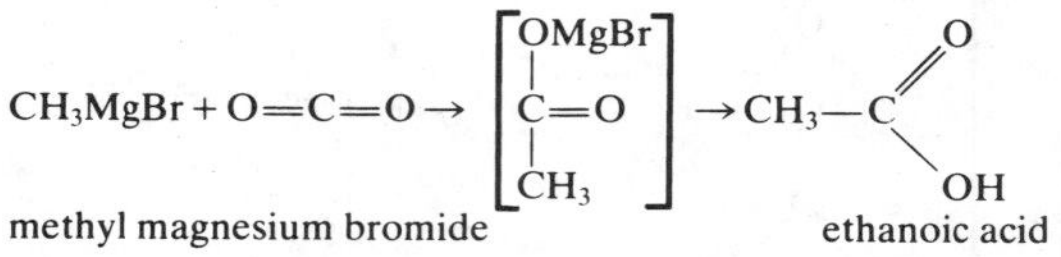

NB The product contains one more carbon atom than the Grignard reagent used. This is another method, therefore, of ascending the homologous series (see 37.1).

4 By hydrolysis of esters (see 34.4). Naturally occurring esters present in fats and oils can be used as sources of certain carboxylic acids.

Aromatic carboxylic acids can be obtained by oxidation of side-chains with strong oxidising agents, e.g. alkaline or acidified potassium manganate(VII) or acidified potassium dichromate(VI).

methylbenzene benzenecarboxylic acid

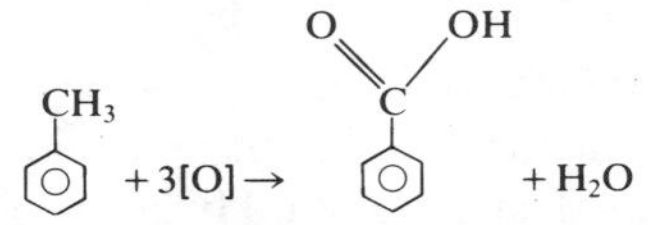

33.3 REACTIONS OF CARBOXYLIC ACIDS

(i) Acidic properties

Carboxylic acids are weak acids, e.g.

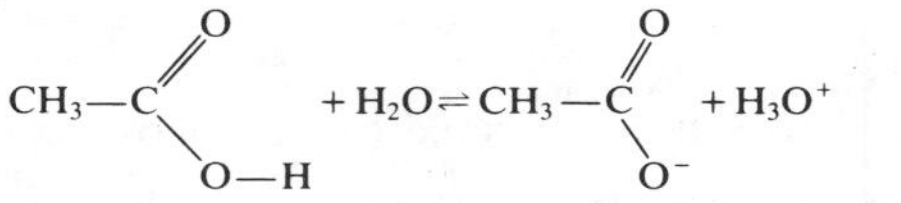

Carboxylic acids liberate carbon dioxide from a carbonate, e.g.

sodium ethanaoate

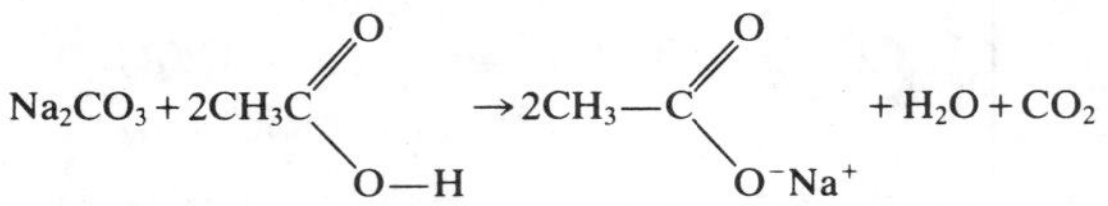

(ii) Reduction

Carboxylic acids are reduced by lithium tetrahydridoaluminate(III) (lithium aluminium hydride) in dry ethoxyethane to produce a primary alcohol, e.g.

ethanoic acid ethanol

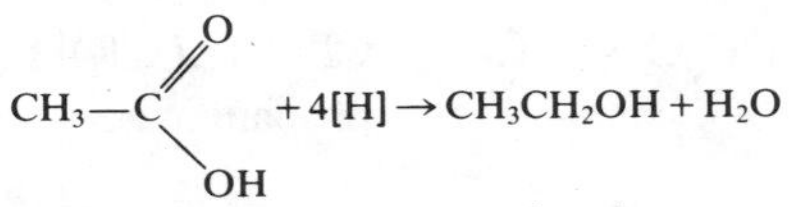

It is not possible to reduce a carboxylic acid to an aldehyde directly.

(iii) Reaction with phosphorus pentachloride and sulphur dichloride oxide (thionyl chloride)

The products of these reactions include an acid chloride and hydrogen chloride, e.g.

$$CH_3-C\overset{O}{\underset{O-H}{}} + PCl_5 \rightarrow CH_3-C\overset{O}{\underset{Cl}{}} + POCl_3 + HCl$$

ethanoic acid + phosphorus pentachloride → ethanoyl chloride
+ phosphorus trichloride oxide
+ hydrogen chloride

The formation of hydrogen chloride is used to test for the presence of an OH group.

$$\overset{}{\underset{}{\bigcirc}}-C\overset{O}{\underset{OH}{}} + SOCl_2 \rightarrow \overset{}{\underset{}{\bigcirc}}-C\overset{O}{\underset{Cl}{}} + SO_2 + HCl$$

benzenecarbonyl chloride
(benzoyl chloride)

Hydrogen chloride is produced with alcohols (see 30.2) and carboxylic acids.

(iv) Halogenation of the side-chain

Chlorine or bromine substitute in the alkyl group to form chloro- or bromo-substituted acids. The reaction takes place when the acid and halogen are mixed and subjected to strong light or a catalyst of iodine or red phosphorus. NB Unlike the chlorination of alkanes, this is a *controllable* reaction.

$$CH_3-C\overset{O}{\underset{O-H}{}} + Cl_2 \rightarrow CH_2ClC\overset{O}{\underset{O-H}{}} + HCl$$

chloroethanoic acid

$$CH_2Cl\,C\overset{O}{\underset{O-H}{}} + Cl_2 \rightarrow CHCl_2C\overset{O}{\underset{O-H}{}} + HCl$$

dichloroethanoic acid

$$CHCl_2C\overset{O}{\underset{O-H}{}} + Cl_2 \rightarrow CCl_3C\overset{O}{\underset{O-H}{}} + HCl$$

trichloroethanoic acid

Where a carboxylic acid with a longer carbon chain is used, the substitution occurs at the α carbon atom

$$CH_3CH_2CH_2COOH + Cl_2 \rightarrow CH_3CH_2CHClCOOH$$

2-chlorobutanoic acid

(v) Ester formation

When a mixture of carboxylic acid and alcohol are refluxed in the presence of concentrated sulphuric acid, an ester is formed.

$$CH_3-C\overset{O}{\underset{O-H}{}} + CH_3CH_2OH \rightleftharpoons CH_3-C\overset{O}{\underset{OCH_2CH_3}{}} + H_2O$$

Acid + Alcohol ⇌ Ester + Water

ethanoic acid + ethanol ⇌ ethyl ethanoate + water

33.4 METHANOIC ACID AS A REDUCING AGENT

The first member of any homologous series often shows atypical properties, i.e. shows some properties that are not shown by other members of the series. This is certainly true with methanoic acid.

Methanoic acid, unlike other carboxylic acids, is easily oxidised by refluxing with acidified potassium manganate(VII) solution.

$$HCOOH + [O] \rightarrow H_2O + CO_2$$

Methanoic acid produces a silver mirror with Tollens' reagent and a brown precipitate with Fehling's solution.

Methanoic acid, unlike any other carboxylic acid, contains an aldehyde group within its structure and this explains its reducing properties.

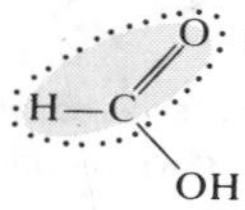

Concentrated sulphuric acid dehydrates methanoic acid to produce carbon monoxide.

$$HCOOH \xrightarrow{-H_2O} CO$$
$$\text{carbon monoxide}$$

33.5 SALTS OF CARBOXYLIC ACIDS

There are several reactions of salts of carboxylic acids that are important. Salts are ionised and contain the carboxylate ion.

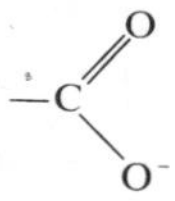

(i) Heating the sodium salt of a carboxylic acid with soda lime

Soda lime is a safer alternative to sodium hydroxide. When soda lime is heated with the sodium salt of a carboxylic acid, an alkane is produced.

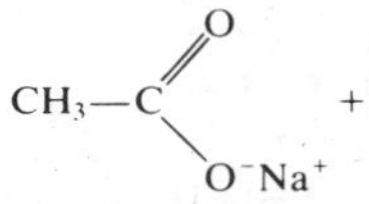

(ii) Heating calcium ethanoate

When dry calcium ethanoate is heated strongly, a poor yield of propanone is produced. Despite the poor yield, this reaction figures frequently in A-level questions.

(iii) Heating a mixture of calcium methanoate and the calcium salt of another carboxylic acid

When the mixture of two calcium salts is heated, an aldehyde is produced in very poor yield.

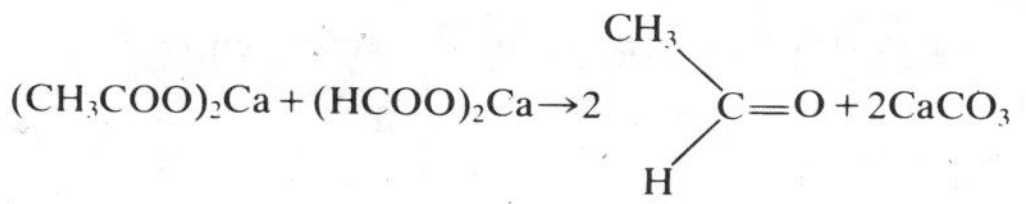

$$(CH_3COO)_2Ca + (HCOO)_2Ca \rightarrow 2 \quad \underset{\overset{|}{H}}{\overset{CH_3}{C}} = O + 2CaCO_3$$

ethanal

(iv) Heating ammonium ethanoate

Ammonium ethanoate is prepared by mixing solutions of ethanoic acid and ammonia. On heating the solid ethanoate, ethanamide is produced.

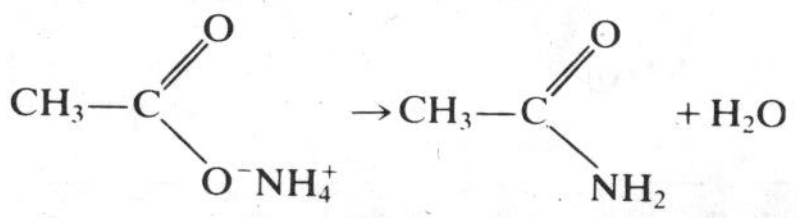

$$CH_3 - \overset{\overset{O}{\parallel}}{C} \underset{O^- NH_4^+}{} \rightarrow CH_3 - \overset{\overset{O}{\parallel}}{C} \underset{NH_2}{} + H_2O$$

ethanamide

33.6   COMMON DIBASIC ACIDS

Ethanedioic acid is a dibasic acid containing two COOH groups.

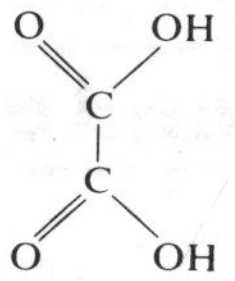

$$\overset{O}{\underset{O}{\overset{\parallel}{\underset{\parallel}{C}}}} \overset{OH}{\underset{OH}{}}$$

Two hydrogen atoms can be lost from each molecule as oxonium ions.

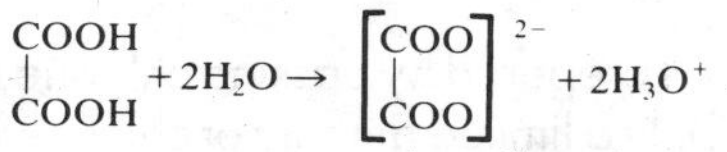

$$\begin{matrix} COOH \\ | \\ COOH \end{matrix} + 2H_2O \rightarrow \begin{bmatrix} COO \\ | \\ COO \end{bmatrix}^{2-} + 2H_3O^+$$

ethanedioate ions

Ethanedioic acid, like methanoic acid, can be readily oxidised with acidified potassium manganate(VII).

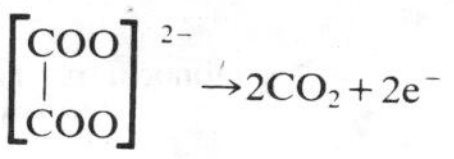

$$\begin{bmatrix} COO \\ | \\ COO \end{bmatrix}^{2-} \rightarrow 2CO_2 + 2e^-$$

Ethanedioic acid is also dehydrated by concentrated sulphuric acid on heating.

$$\begin{matrix} COOH \\ | \\ COOH \end{matrix} \xrightarrow{\quad -H_2O \quad} CO_2 + CO$$

Hexane-1,6–dioic acid (adipic acid) is used in the manufacture of nylon.

$$HOOCCH_2CH_2CH_2CH_2COOH$$

It is manufactured by oxidation of cyclohexene.

$$\bigcirc \xrightarrow{\quad [O] \quad} HOOC(CH_2)_4COOH$$

There are three isomeric benzenedicarboxylic acids (phthalic acids).

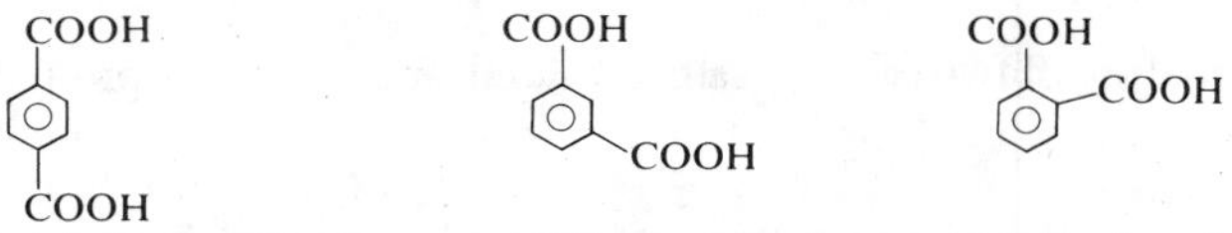

benzene-1,4-dicarboxylic   benzene-1,3-dicarboxylic   benzene-1,2-dicarboxylic
acid   acid   acid
(terephthalic acid)   (phthalic acid)

Benzene-1,4-dicarboxylic acid is used in the manufacture of 'Terylene'. It is made by the oxidation of 1,4-dimethylbenzene with nitric acid.

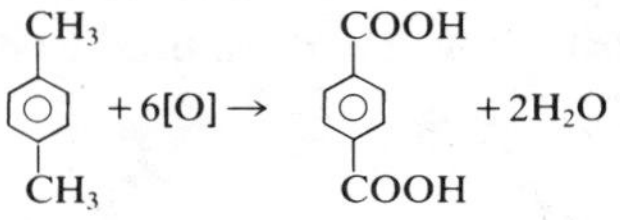

Chapter roundup

Carboxylic acids have the usual properties we would associate with acids, e.g. pH less than 7, carbon dioxide produced with a carbonate, hydrogen produced with magnesium, etc. The strength of a carboxylic acid can be altered according to the structure of the molecule (Chapter 39).

Worked questions and answers

1 Describe how aminoethanoic acid could be prepared from ethanoic acid.

Tutorial note

Monochloroethanoic acid is prepared by passing chlorine into warm ethanoic acid in strong ultraviolet light. Only a limited amount of chlorine is used to prevent further substitution.

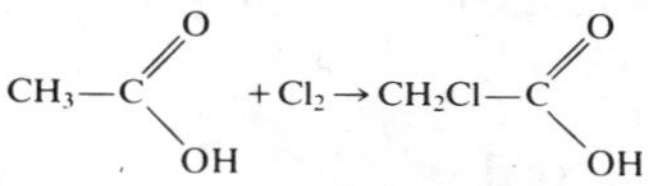

monochloroethanoic acid

Monochloroethanoic acid reacts with concentrated ammonia solution at room temperature to form aminoethanoic acid.

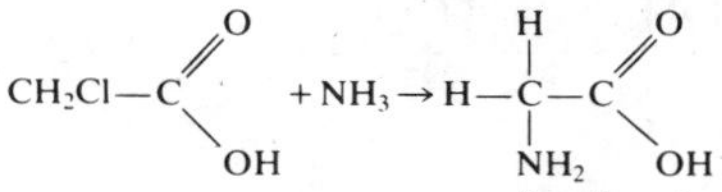

aminoethanoic acid

ACID DERIVATIVES

Units in this chapter

Chapter objectives

In this chapter we will consider a range of different compounds which are closely related to acids and are therefore called acid derivatives. Some of these, e.g. acid chlorides and anhydrides, are useful reagents.

34.1 ACID DERIVATIVES

Acid derivatives are all based upon carboxylic acids but with the OH group of the carboxyl group replaced.

In addition, nitriles will be included as they are closely related to carboxylic acids.

34.2 ACID CHLORIDES

Acid chlorides are prepared by warming the corresponding carboxylic acid with sulphur dichloride oxide (thionyl chloride) or phosphorus chloride.

Acid chlorides are colourless liquids which fume in moist air. They can be used to prepare a wide range of compounds.

Reactions of acid chlorides include the following.

(i) Reaction with water

Aliphatic acid chlorides are **hydrolysed** rapidly with cold water, e.g.

Aromatic acid chlorides are hydrolysed more slowly than the aliphatic compounds.

(ii) Reactions with alcohols

Acid chlorides react with alcohols and phenols to produce **esters** (see 34.4). These reactions take place on mixing the acid chloride and the alcohol without heating, e.g.

With aromatic acid chlorides, sodium hydroxide solution is added to speed up the reaction.

(iii) Reaction with ammonia

Acid chlorides react with a concentrated aqueous solution of ammonia to produce **amides**. These reactions take place on mixing the reactants and without heating, e.g.

ethanoyl chloride   ethanamide

(iv) Reactions with amines

Acid chlorides react with primary and secondary amines to produce **substituted amides**, e.g.

ethanoyl   phenylamine N-phenylethanamide
chloride   (acetanilide)

(In the naming, **N-phenyl** means that a phenyl group is attached to the nitrogen atom of the amide.)

NB In all of these reactions, a hydrogen atom attached to an oxygen or a nitrogen atom

is replaced by a $\overset{R}{\underset{}{\diagdown}}$C=O group. This process is called **acylation**.

If ethanoyl chloride is used, CH_3CO is added to the molecule in place of a hydrogen. This process is called **ethanoylation (acetylation)**. With benzenecarbonyl chloride, **benzenecarbonylation (benzoylation)** takes place when a C_6H_5CO group is introduced. In all of these reactions the other product is hydrogen chloride.

(v) Reaction with the sodium salt of an acid

Distillation of an acid chloride with the anhydrous sodium salt of an acid produces an **acid anhydride**.

ethanoyl   sodium   ethanoic
chloride   ethanoate   anhydride

(vi) Reaction with benzene (see 29.9)

Benzene and acid chlorides react on refluxing in the presence of aluminium chloride to produce a **ketone**. This is the **Friedel–Crafts reaction**.

phenylethanone

34.3 ACID ANHYDRIDES

An **acid anhydride** is the product obtained by joining two carboxylic acid molecules together with the elimination of one molecule of water. Methanoic acid does not form an anhydride.

Some anhydrides can be made simply by distilling dibasic acids, e.g.

butane-1,4-dioic acid   butane-1,4-dioic anhydride

Monobasic acids are not converted to anhydrides directly. Instead, the sodium salt of an acid is distilled with an acid chloride to produce the anhydride.

ethanoic anhydride

Acid anhydrides are high boiling point liquids which are not very soluble in water. They react in a similar way to acid chlorides, but they are considerably less reactive. Reactions with acid anhydrides can be slowed down further by the addition of ethanoic acid.

The reactions of acid anhydrides are similar to the reactions of acid chlorides, but are much slower.

34.4 ESTERS

Esters are sweet-smelling liquids. Naturally occurring fats and oils contain organic esters.

propane-1,2,3-triol   propane-1,2,3-triol   sodium
trioctadecanoate   (glycerol)   octadecanoate
(glyceryl tristearate)   (sodium stearate)

Heating an ester with sodium hydroxide solution gives the corresonding alchohol and the sodium salt of the carboxylic acid. This process of hydrolysis is called **saponification** and the sodium salts produced are **soaps**. The most common component of soap is sodium stearate.

Methods of preparing esters include the following.

(i) Reaction of acid and alcohol in the presence of concentrated sulphuric acid

The reactants are refluxed together. This method is suitable for preparing aliphatic esters.

$$CH_3-C\overset{O}{\underset{OH}{\big|}} + CH_3CH_2OH \rightleftharpoons CH_3-C\overset{O}{\underset{OCH_2CH_3}{\big|}} + H_2O$$

ethanoic acid   ethanol   ethyl ethanoate

(ii) Treat an alcohol with an acid chloride or acid anhydride

With an acid chloride, the reaction takes place without heating, e.g.

$$CH_3CH_2CH_2OH + \langle \bigcirc \rangle -C\overset{O}{\underset{Cl}{\big|}} \rightarrow \langle \bigcirc \rangle -C\overset{O}{\underset{OCH_2CH_2CH_3}{\big|}} + HCl$$

propan-1-ol   benzenecarbonyl chloride   propyl benzenecarboxylate

Refluxing an acid anhydride with an alcohol will produce an ester, e.g.

$$CH_3-C\overset{O}{\big|}\underset{CH_3-C\underset{O}{\big|}}{O} + CH_3CH_2OH \rightarrow CH_3-C\overset{O}{\underset{OCH_2CH_3}{\big|}} + CH_3-C\overset{O}{\underset{OH}{\big|}}$$

ethanoic anhydride   ethanol   ethyl ethanoate   ethanoic acid

(iii) Heating the silver salt of a carboxylic acid with a haloalkane

$$CH_3-C\overset{O}{\underset{O^-Ag^+}{\big|}} + CH_3CH_2Br \rightarrow CH_3-C\overset{O}{\underset{OCH_2CH_3}{\big|}} + AgBr$$

silver ethanoate   bromoethane   ethyl ethanoate

There are only two important reactions of esters.

(i) Hydrolysis of esters

Refluxing an ester with a dilute acid or a dilute alkali solution hydrolyses the ester. If acid is used, the products are the alcohol and the carboxylic acid. With sodium hydroxide solution, the products are the alcohol and the sodium salt of the carboxylic acid. The alkaline hydrolysis is called **saponification**.

Acid hydrolysis

$$CH_3-C\overset{O}{\underset{OCH_2CH_3}{\big|}} + H_2O \rightleftharpoons CH_3-C\overset{O}{\underset{OH}{\big|}} + CH_3CH_2OH$$

ethyl ethanoate   ethanoic acid   ethanol

Alkaline hydrolysis

$$\langle \bigcirc \rangle -C\overset{O}{\underset{OCH_3}{\big|}} + NaOH \rightarrow \langle \bigcirc \rangle -C\overset{O}{\underset{O^-Na^+}{\big|}} + CH_3OH.$$

methyl   sodium   methanol
benzenecarboxylate   benzenecarboxylate

A **hydrolysis** reaction is the splitting up of a molecule with water. The rate of hydrolysis is increased by addition of acid or alkali.

(ii) Reduction of esters

Esters are reduced by lithium tetrahydridoaluminate(III) (lithium aluminium hydride) in dry ethoxyethane to produce a mixture of the corresponding alcohols, e.g.

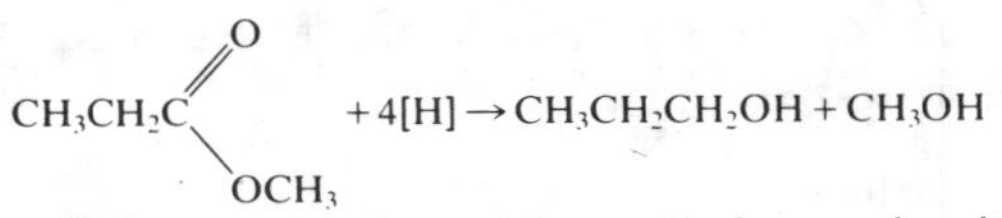

$$CH_3CH_2C \overset{O}{\underset{OCH_3}{\big|}} + 4[H] \rightarrow CH_3CH_2CH_2OH + CH_3OH$$

methyl propanoate   propan-1-ol   methanol

34.5 AMIDES

Amides are white, crystalline solids. They are the least reactive of the organic derivatives of carboxylic acids.

As the name might suggest, amides are made from ammonia. There are two methods of producing amides.

(i) From a carboxylic acid

Ammonia solution is added to the carboxylic acid to form the ammonium salt of the acid. This ammonium salt is heated with a small amount of free acid. The amide distils over. The acid prevents the dissociation of the ammonium salt, e.g.

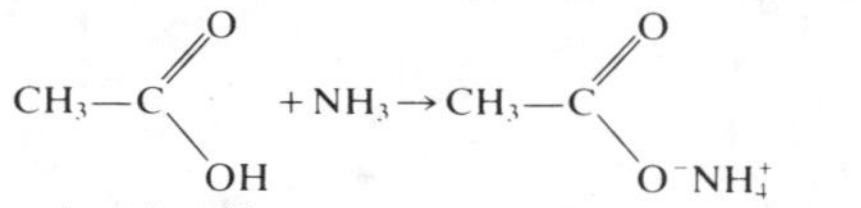

ethanoic acid   ammonium ethanoate 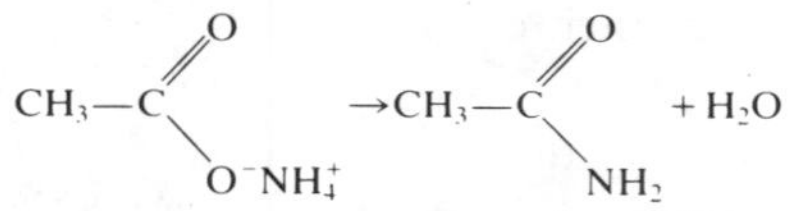   ethanamide

(ii) Reacting an acid chloride or acid anhydride with ammonia (see 34.2)

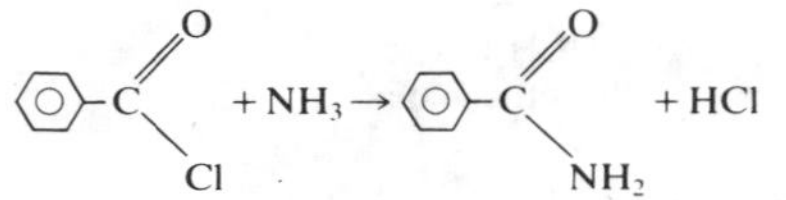

benzenecarbonyl chloride   benzenecarboxamide 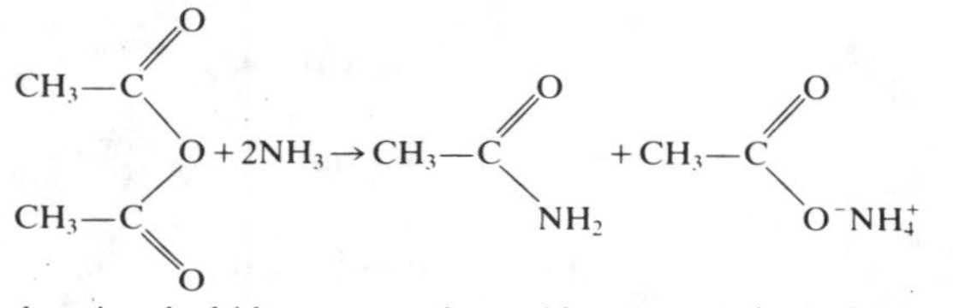   ethanoic anhydride   ethanamide   ammonium ethanoate

Amides show slight basic properties. They form unstable salts with strong acids, e.g.

$$CH_3CONH_2 + H_3O^+ \rightarrow CH_3CONH_3^+ + H_2O$$

Other reactions of amides include the following.

(i) Dehydration

When an amide is heated with phosphorus(V) oxide dehydration takes place to form the corresponding **nitrile**, e.g.

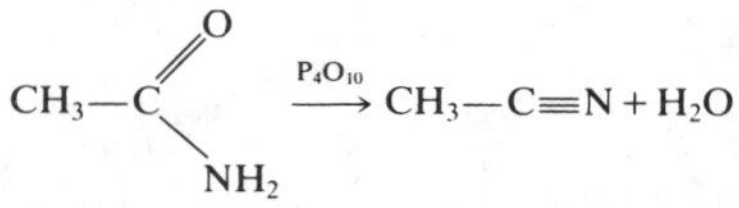

$$CH_3-C\overset{O}{\underset{NH_2}{\big|}} \xrightarrow{P_4O_{10}} CH_3-C\equiv N + H_2O$$

ethanamide   ethanenitrile

(ii) Reaction with sodium hydroxide solution

Sodium hydroxide solution can be used to distinguish an amide from an ammonium salt. Evolution of ammonia occurs when a mixture of an amide and sodium hydroxide solution is heated, e.g.

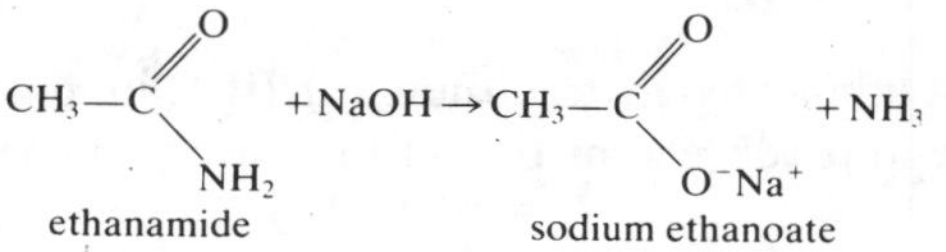

$$CH_3-C\overset{O}{\underset{NH_2}{\big|}} + NaOH \rightarrow CH_3-C\overset{O}{\underset{O^-Na^+}{\big|}} + NH_3$$

ethanamide   sodium ethanoate

Ammonium salts liberate ammonia on addition of sodium hydroxide without heating, e.g.

$$CH_3-C\overset{O}{\underset{O^-NH_4^+}{}} + NaOH \rightarrow CH_3-C\overset{O}{\underset{O^-Na^+}{}} + NH_3 + H_2O$$

(iii) Reaction with nitrous acid (nitric(III) acid)

Nitrous acid (nitric(III) acid) is prepared by adding sodium nitrite (sodium nitrate(III)) to dilute hydrochloric acid.

$$NaNO_2 + HCl \rightarrow NaCl + HONO$$

Nitrous acid (nitric(III) acid) reacts with amides without heating with the evolution of nitrogen gas to form the corresponding carboxylic acid.

$$CH_3-C\overset{O}{\underset{NH_2}{}} + HONO \rightarrow CH_3-C\overset{O}{\underset{OH}{}} + N_2 + H_2O$$
ethanamide   ethanoic acid

(iv) Hofmann degradation

This reaction is important when descending an homologous series (see 37.2). The amide is treated with bromine and sodium hydroxide solution. The solution is heated and an amine is produced.

$$CH_3-C\overset{O}{\underset{NH_2}{}} + Br_2 \rightarrow CH_3-C\overset{O}{\underset{NHBr}{}} + HBr$$
ethanamide

$$CH_3-C\overset{O}{\underset{NHBr}{}} + 3NaOH \rightarrow CH_3NH_2 + Na_2CO_3 + NaBr + H_2O$$
methylamine

34.6 NITRILES

Nitriles are frequently called cyanides since they contain the $C\equiv N$ group. The simplest nitriles are

$$H-\underset{\underset{H}{|}}{\overset{\overset{H}{|}}{C}}-C\equiv N \qquad H-\underset{\underset{H}{|}}{\overset{\overset{H}{|}}{C}}-\underset{\underset{H}{|}}{\overset{\overset{H}{|}}{C}}-C\equiv N$$
ethanenitrile   propanenitrile

Methods of preparing nitriles include the following.

(i) Dehydration of an amide with phosphorus(V) oxide

$$CH_3-C\overset{O}{\underset{NH_2}{}} \xrightarrow{P_4O_{10}} CH_3-C\equiv N + H_2O$$
ethanamide   ethanenitrile

(ii) Action of cyanide on a haloalkane (see 30.3)

A haloalkane is refluxed with a solution of potassium cyanide in ethanol. A substitution reaction takes place to produce a nitrile, e.g.

$$CH_3CH_2Br + KCN \rightarrow CH_3CH_2CN + KBr$$
bromoethane   propanenitrile

This reaction is important in ascending an homologous series (see 37.1). Potassium cyanide is predominantly ionic and a nitrile is produced containing the C≡N group. If this reaction is repeated using silver cyanide, which is predominately covalent, the product is an isonitrile containing the N⇌C group, e.g.

$$CH_3CH_2Br + AgCN \rightarrow CH_3CH_2N{\rightleftharpoons}C + AgBr$$

Isonitriles are isomeric with nitriles. They are evil-smelling liquids and can be prepared by heating a primary amine, trichloromethane and potassium hydroxide dissolved in ethanol, e.g.

$$CH_3NH_2 + CHCl_3 + 3OH^- \rightarrow CH_3N{\rightleftharpoons}C + 3Cl^- + 3H_2O$$
$$\text{isocyanomethane}$$

Reactions of nitriles include the following.

(i) Hydrolysis of nitriles

This can be achieved by boiling with a dilute acid or dilute alkali, e.g.

$$CH_3{-}C{\equiv}N + 2H_2O + HCl \rightarrow CH_3{-}C\!\!\underset{OH}{\overset{O}{\diagdown}} + NH_4Cl$$

ethanenitrile   ethanoic acid

$$CH_3{-}C{\equiv}N + NaOH + H_2O \rightarrow CH_3{-}C\!\!\underset{O^-Na^+}{\overset{O}{\diagdown}} + NH_3$$

sodium ethanoate

(ii) Reduction of nitriles

Nitriles can be reduced to primary amines by sodium and ethanol, e.g.

$$CH_3C{\equiv}N + 4[H] \rightarrow CH_3CH_2NH_2$$
$$\text{ethylamine}$$

Chapter roundup

Acid chlorides and anhydrides are used for acylation, a common process for protecting a reactive group such as NH_2 or OH while other reactions are taking place. The derivatives mentioned in this chapter are all closely related (see Chapter 37).

Worked questions and answers

1 In each of the following cases give the name or structure of *one* compound which fits the information given. Explain your reasoning and write equations for the reactions involved.

(a) R is a liquid which reacts vigorously with concentrated aqueous ammonia to form a solid which is readily dehydrated by warming with phosphorus(V) oxide.

(b) S is a liquid which dissolves in hot, aqueous sodium hydroxide to form a solution which on cooling and acidifying precipitates a white solid. A solution of this solid evolves carbon dioxide with aqueous sodium carbonate.

Tutorial note

(a) R is an acid chloride which reacts with ammonia to form an amide. Amides are dehydrated with phosphorus(V) oxide.

A suitable compound would be ethanoyl chloride:

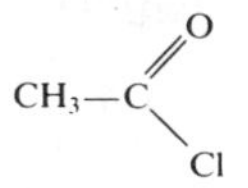

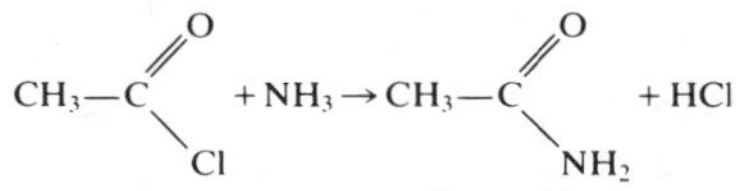

$$CH_3-C\underset{Cl}{\overset{O}{\diagup}} + NH_3 \rightarrow CH_3-C\underset{NH_2}{\overset{O}{\diagup}} + HCl$$
ethanamide

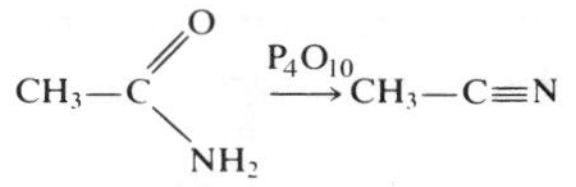

$$CH_3-C\underset{NH_2}{\overset{O}{\diagup}} \xrightarrow{P_4O_{10}} CH_3-C\equiv N$$
ethanenitrile

(b) The white solid which evolves carbon dioxide with aqueous sodium carbonate could be benzenecarboxylic acid (benzolic acid). The liquid S could be an ester such as ethyl benzenecarboxylate:

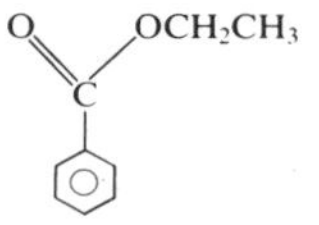

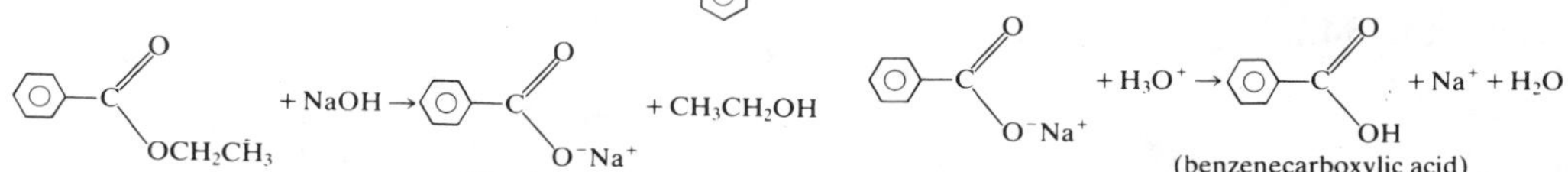

Question bank

1 (a) Explain why butane is a gas at room temperature and pressure but propan-2-ol is a liquid, even though the two have similar values for molar mass.

(b) (i) Give the name and structural formula of the ester formed in the reaction between ethanoic acid and propan-1-ol.

(ii) What catalyst could be used for this reaction?

(c) (i) A naturally occurring ester may be represented as

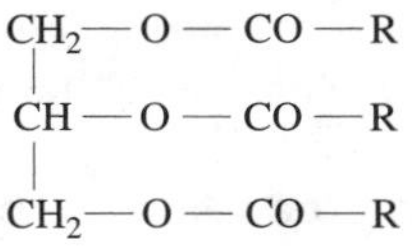

$$\begin{array}{l} CH_2-O-CO-R \\ \;\;|\\ CH-O-CO-R \\ \;\;|\\ CH_2-O-CO-R \end{array}$$

where R represents a long chain alkyl group.

Give the structural formulae of the alcohol and the sodium salt of the acid which are formed when the ester is heated with aqueous sodium hydroxide.

(ii) What is the common use for the sodium salt of this acid?

(d) Naturally occurring esters with a large number of double bonds in their molecules are often liquids and are known as oils. These esters are converted into solids in a commercial process.

(i) Name the reagent and the catalyst used to convert liquid esters into solids.

(ii) What type of reaction is the conversion?

(iii) Give an everyday use for the solid esters produced.

(AEB 1989)

Points

Part (a) of this questions refers back to Chapter 4. In part (d) you should refer to 29.5.

2 (a) What is meant by the term ethanoylation?
(b) Ethanoylation of 4-hydroxybenzoic acid C might give three products D, E and F.

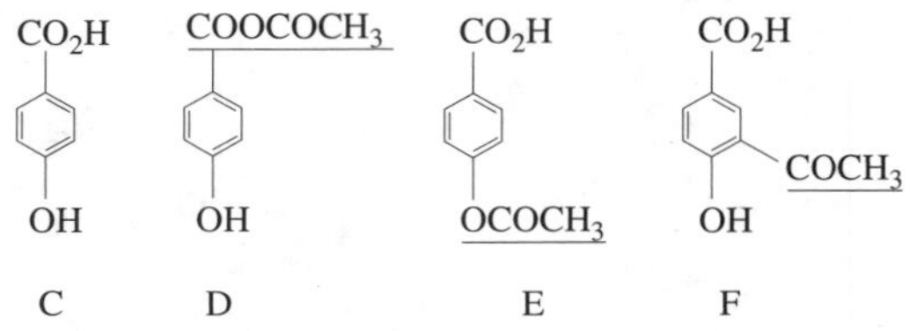

C   D   E   F

Name the types of functional groups underlined and draw the structures for each.
(c) Give two simple chemical tests which would enable you to distinguish E from F.
(d) Reduction of F with LiAlH$_4$ gives a mixture of two isomers, C$_9$H$_{12}$O$_3$. Draw clear diagrams to show the full structures of both of these isomers. Write down the relative proportions of the two isomers you would expect from this reaction, giving your reasoning.

(Oxford 1989)

Points

(a) Refer to 34.2.
(b)

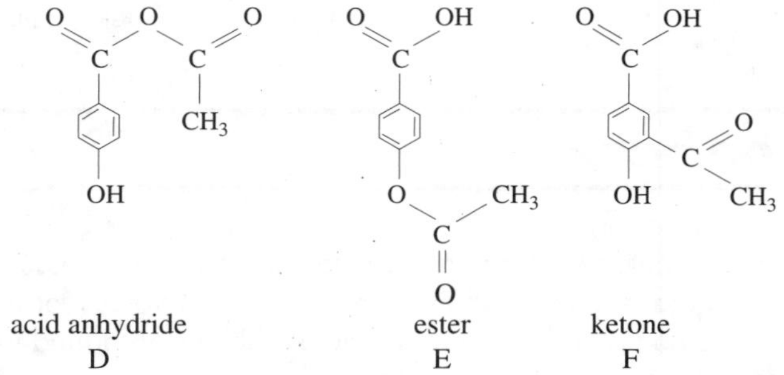

acid anhydride   ester   ketone
D   E   F

(c) F is a ketone and will therefore give a yellow precipitate with 2,4-dinitrophenylhydrazine and will undergo the triiodomethane reaction (31.4).
(d) Reduction will produce

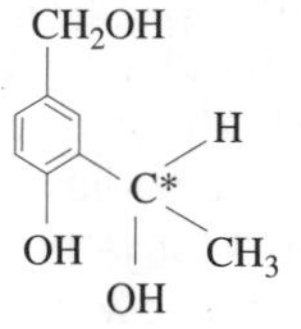

This has a chiral centre and therefore exists as two optical isomers. The mixture should be 50:50 as each product is equally possible.

CHAPTER 35

AMINES

Units in this chapter

Chapter objectives

Amines are compounds formed when hydrogen atoms in ammonia are replaced by alkyl or aryl groups. Just as alcohols can be primary, secondary or tertiary, amines can also be primary, secondary or tertiary. A primary amine is produced when one of the hydrogens in an ammonia molecule is replaced. A secondary amine is produced when two are replaced and a tertiary when three are replaced.

We will see some differences between aliphatic and aromatic amines, especially in their reactions with nitrous acid.

35.1 EXAMPLES OF AMINES

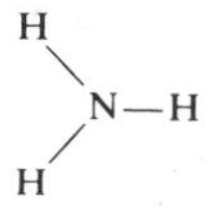

ammonia 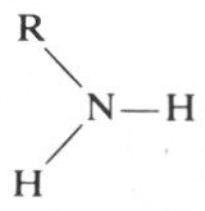   primary amine 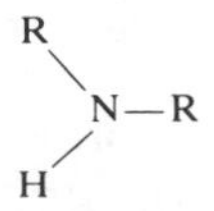   secondary amine 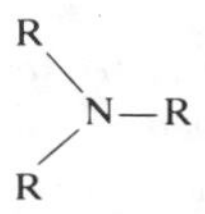   tertiary amine

Common amines include

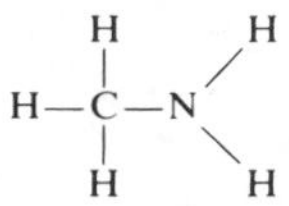

methylamine
(primary)

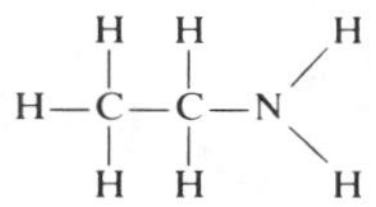

ethylamine
(primary)

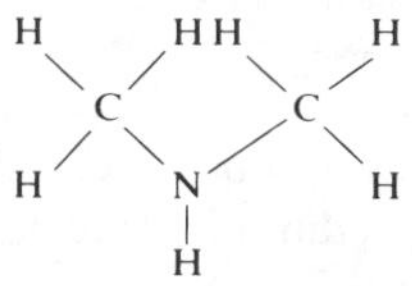

dimethylamine
(secondary)

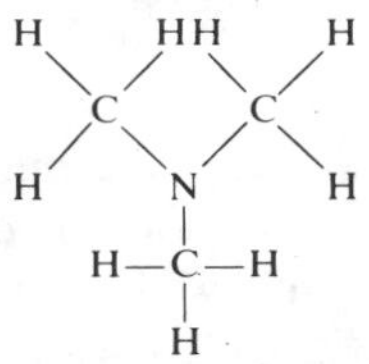

trimethylamine
(tertiary)

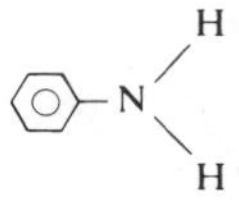

phenylamine
(primary)

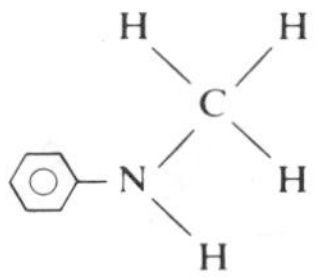

N-methylphenylamine
(secondary)

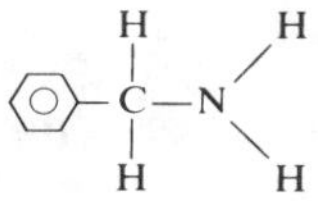

(phenylmethyl)amine (benzylamine)
(primary)

When the amine group is attached to a benzene nucleus the resulting amine is called an **arylamine**. An **alkylamine** is an amine in which only alkyl groups or hydrogen atoms are attached to the nitrogen atom. (Phenylmethyl)amine behaves as an alkylamine because the NH_2 group is not attached directly to the ring.

Quaternary ammonium salts are the organic equivalent of ammonium compounds, e.g.

$$NH_4^+Cl^- \qquad (CH_3)_4N^+Cl^-$$
ammonium chloride $\qquad$ tetramethylammonium chloride

35.2 PREPARATION OF AMINES

(i) Preparation from ammonia

This method of preparation emphasises the close relationships between ammonia and the amines. It is used to produce alkylamines.

When haloalkanes are heated with ammonia under pressure, a series of reactions takes place and a mixture of products is usually obtained, e.g. chloromethane and ammonia

$$CH_3Cl + NH_3 \rightarrow CH_3NH_2 + HCl$$
methylamine
$$CH_3NH_2 + CH_3Cl \rightarrow (CH_3)_2NH + HCl$$
dimethylamine
$$(CH_3)_2NH + CH_3Cl \rightarrow (CH_3)_3N + HCl$$
trimethylamine
$$(CH_3)_3N + CH_3Cl \rightarrow (CH_3)_4N^+Cl^-$$
tetramethylammonium chloride

These amines react with hydrogen chloride and the products isolated initially will be salts, e.g. $CH_3NH_3^+Cl^-$, $(CH_3)_2NH_2^+Cl^-$, $(CH_3)_3NH^+Cl^-$.

(ii) Reduction of nitro compounds

The reduction of nitro compounds to form amines is most important for the production of arylamines. The reduction is usually carried out with tin and concentrated hydrochloric acid, e.g.

$$\langle\bigcirc\rangle-NO_2 + 6[H] \rightarrow \langle\bigcirc\rangle-NH_2 + 2H_2O$$

nitrobenzene $\qquad\qquad$ phenylamine

Following the reduction, the amine reacts to form $(C_6H_5NH_3^+)_2SnCl_6^{2-}$. The phenylamine is obtained by addition of excess sodium hydroxide solution to liberate the free phenylamine, followed by steam distillation.

Reduction can also take place with zinc or iron and hydrochloric acid or with nickel and hydrogen at 300 °C.

(iii) Reduction of a nitrile (see 34.6)

Reduction of a nitrile with sodium and ethanol produces a primary amine, e.g.

$$CH_3C\equiv N + 4[H] \rightarrow CH_3CH_2NH_2$$
ethylamine

35.3 PROPERTIES OF AMINES

The lower members of the homologous series of aliphatic amines are gases or volatile liquids. They are very soluble in water, producing alkaline solutions. They have fishy smells and resemble ammonia in many respects.

Aromatic amines are much less volatile and are virtually insoluble in water.

(i) Basic properties of amines

Primary, secondary and tertiary amines, like ammonia, are all basic. In Chapter 39 the relative strengths of these substances as bases will be discussed.

Amines react with acids to form salts. This process involves the acceptance of a proton

$$CH_3CH_2NH_2 + H_3O^+ \rightarrow CH_3CH_2NH_3^+ + H_2O$$

ethylamine $\qquad\qquad$ ethylammonium ion

The free amine is liberated by the addition of alkali

$$[CH_3NH_3^+]Cl^- + NaOH \rightarrow CH_3NH_2 + NaCl + H_2O$$

methylammonium $\qquad\qquad$ methylamine
chloride

(ii) Ethanoylation (acetylation) of amines (see 34.2)

Ethanoylation of primary and secondary amines involves the replacement of a hydrogen atom attached to a nitrogen atom by the ethanoyl group (CH_3CO). This process takes place with acid chlorides and anhydrides, e.g. in the cold with careful addition of the acid chloride

N-phenylethanamide

or refluxing the amine with the acid anhydride

N,N-diethylethanamide

If a sample of an amine has to be identified, ethanoylation is most useful. The amine is probably a gas or a volatile liquid. Boiling points are difficult to measure accurately and the actual value depends upon the atmospheric pressure.

The amine is ethanoylated by treatment with ethanoyl chloride or ethanoic anhydride. The solid derivative can be purified by recrystallisation and an accurate melting point can be determined. By looking in tables, it is possible to find the ethanoyl derivative with the appropriate melting point.

Ethanoylation can also be used to protect amine groups during reaction. The amine can be restored by hydrolysis.

(iii) Reaction with nitrous acid (nitric(III) acid)

Nitrous acid (nitric(III) acid) is an unstable acid which is prepared from sodium nitrite (sodium nitrate (III)) and dilute hydrochloric acid

$$NaNO_2 + HCl \rightarrow NaCl + HONO$$

Primary arylamines react with nitrous acid (nitric(III) acid) at temperatures below 5 °C to form unstable **diazonium compounds**. These compounds cannot be isolated but, like Grignard reagents, they provide a means of producing a range of other compounds.

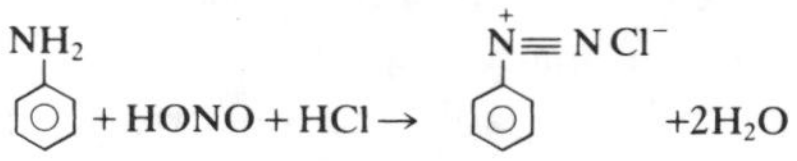

benzenediazonium chloride

An alkylamine reacts with nitrous acid to form a primary alcohol. Diazonium compounds formed from alkylamines are not stable.

$$CH_3CH_2NH_2 + HONO \rightarrow CH_3CH_2OH + N_2 + H_2O$$
ethylamine   ethanol

This difference in the reaction with nitrous acid (nitric(III) acid) is used to differentiate between alkylamines and arylamines.

35.4 DIAZONIUM COMPOUNDS

Primary arylamines form diazonium compounds with nitrous acid (nitric(III) acid) below 5 °C. These compounds are more stable than similar compounds formed by alkylamines because of the presence of the aromatic ring.

The reactions of diazonium compounds can be subdivided into reactions where nitrogen is replaced, and coupling reactions where nitrogen is retained.

(i) Reactions where nitrogen is replaced

1 Replaced by hydroxyl group.
Heating the diazonium compound above 10 °C in aqueous solution produces a phenol, e.g.

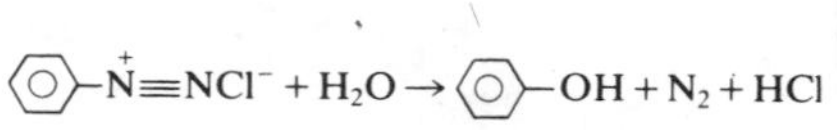

benzenediazonium chloride   phenol

2 Replaced by a chlorine or bromine.
This can be achieved by warming the diazonium compound with hydrogen chloride or hydrogen bromide and the corresponding copper(I) halide, e.g.

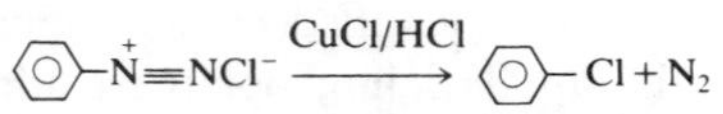

benzenediazonium chloride   chlorobenzene

Alternatively, the diazonium halide can be warmed with powdered copper.

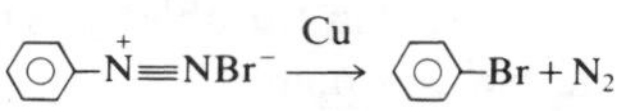

bromobenzene

3 Replaced with iodine.
The diazonium compound is warmed with potassium iodide solution, e.g.

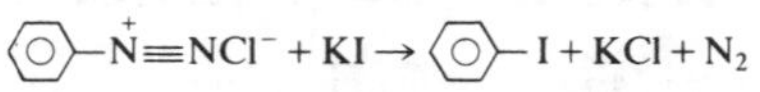

iodobenzene

4 Replaced with nitrile.

The diazonium compound is heated with potassium cyanide solution in the presence of copper(I) cyanide as a catalyst, e.g.

$$\langle O \rangle -\overset{+}{N} \equiv NCl^- + CN^- \rightarrow \langle O \rangle -C \equiv N + N_2 + Cl^-$$

(ii) Reactions where nitrogen is retained – coupling reactions

Diazonium compounds couple with phenols and aromatic amines to give coloured **azo compounds**.

1 With phenols.

The diazonium compound is added to an alkaline solution of phenol. An orange precipitate of (4-hydroxyphenyl)azobenzene is formed.

$$NaOH + \langle O \rangle -OH + \langle O \rangle -\overset{+}{N} \equiv NCl^- \rightarrow HO -\langle O \rangle -N = N -\langle O \rangle + NaCl + H_2O$$

(4-hydroxyphenyl)azobenzene

2 With primary amines.

When a diazonium compound is added to phenylamine an orange precipitate of 4-(phenylazo)phenylamine is formed.

$$\langle O \rangle -NH_2 + \langle O \rangle -\overset{+}{N} \equiv NCl^- \rightarrow NH_2 \langle O \rangle -N = N -\langle O \rangle + HCl$$

4-(phenylazo)phenylamine

Chapter roundup

In many ways, amines resemble ammonia. The simpler members are gases which are basic in their properties. They can form salts like ammonia.

Reactions of amines with nitrous acid are important. The diazonium salts produced by aromatic amines are very useful intermediates (see Chapter 37).

Worked questions and answers

1 For each of the following pairs of compounds, describe one reaction which could be used to distinguish one from another. Describe the effect, if any, of the reagent (or reagents) on both compounds of the pair and explain what has happened.

(a) 1-aminobutane and phenylamine (aniline)

(b) methylamine and ammonia

(AEB)

Tutorial note

(a) Treat both compounds with nitrous acid (nitric(III) acid) below 5 °C. Nitrous acid (nitric(III) acid) is prepared from sodium nitrite (sodium nitrate(III)) and dilute hydrochloric acid.

$$CH_3CH_2CH_2CH_2NH_2 + HONO \rightarrow CH_3CH_2CH_2CH_2OH + N_2 + H_2O$$
$$\text{butan-1-ol}$$

$$\underset{NH_2}{\langle O \rangle} + HONO + HCl \rightarrow \underset{\overset{+}{N} \equiv NCl^-}{\langle O \rangle} + 2H_2O$$

benzenediazonium chloride

The solutions produced by testing with nitrous acid are added separately to samples of an alkaline solution of phenol. Benzenediazonium chloride forms an orange precipitate.

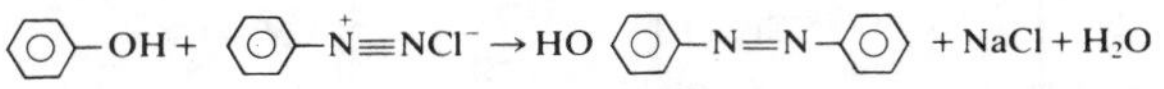

$$\langle O \rangle\text{-OH} + \langle O \rangle\text{-}\overset{+}{N}\equiv NCl^{-} \rightarrow HO\langle O \rangle\text{-}N=N\text{-}\langle O \rangle + NaCl + H_2O$$

(4-hydroxyphenyl)azobenzene

No precipitate is formed with butan-1-ol.

(b) Ammonia does not burn in air but burns in oxygen.

$$4NH_3 + 3O_2 \rightarrow 2N_2 + 6H_2O$$

Methylamine burns in air.

$$4CH_3NH_2 + 9O_2 \rightarrow 4CO_2 + 10H_2O + 2N_2$$

The gas produced turns limewater milky.

Question bank

1 (a) (i) Give two general methods for the synthesis of organic compounds containing NH$_2$ groups.

(ii) How would you prepare **three** of the following:

phenylamine   ethylamine   ethanamide   aminoethanoic acid

(b) (i) Give a balanced equation, using **structural** formulae, for the polymerisation of aminoethanoic acid.

(ii) What method would you use to determine the relative molecular mass of the product?

(iii) Explain whether you expect the strength of a base of aminoethanoic acid to be significantly different from that of ethanamide.

(Oxford 1989)

Points

Refer to 39.3 for the answer to (b)(iii).

LARGE ORGANIC MOLECULES

Units in this chapter

Chapter objectives

Today many of the materials we use are manufactured from raw materials such as petroleum, coal, etc. Most of these materials are made up of long chain molecules called polymers. A polymer is produced by a process of polymerisation, where small repeating units called monomers are linked together to give a long chain. There are different types of polymerisation – addition polymerisation and condensation polymerisation.

Many natural materials, e.g. cellulose, starch and wool, are polymers, and in making synthetic polymers we are actually copying the work of nature.

Finally, the properties of a polymer depend upon the average length of the chains and the extent of any linking between the chains.

36.1 ADDITION (CHAIN) POLYMERISATION

Ethene undergoes a number of addition reactions (see 29.5). A common factor in these reactions is the removal of the double bond. Addition polymerisation involves a series of addition reactions. Examples are shown in Table 36.1.

Poly(ethene) (trade name Polythene) was the first of these addition polymers to be made. At first it was prepared by heating ethene to 250 °C and at a high pressure with a catalyst. Nowadays, polymerisation of ethene can be carried out more easily by bubbling ethene through a hydrocarbon solvent containing complex catalysts discovered by Ziegler and Natta. These catalysts consist of $(C_2H_5)_3Al$ and $TiCl_4$. The polymerisation is usually a free radical process. A peroxide such as dibenzoyl peroxide splits up into free radicals. If the free radical is represented by R·, the following steps in the reaction occur:

$$R· + CH_2{=}CH_2 \rightarrow R{-}CH_2{-}CH_2·$$
$$R{-}CH_2{-}CH_2· + CH_2{=}CH_2 \rightarrow R{-}CH_2{-}CH_2{-}CH_2{-}CH_2·$$
$$R{-}CH_2{-}CH_2{-}CH_2{-}CH_2· + CH_2{=}CH_2 \rightarrow R{-}CH_2{-}CH_2{-}CH_2{-}CH_2{-}CH_2{-}CH_2·$$
etc.

Table 36.1 *Common polymers*

Monomer	Structure of polymer	Name of polymer
ethene		poly(ethene) (Polythene)
chloroethene (vinyl chloride)		poly(chloroethene) (poly(vinyl chloride) or PVC)
phenylethene (styrene)		poly(phenylethene) (polystyrene)
tetrafluoroethene		poly(tetrafluoroethene) (PTFE or Teflon)

Addition polymers of this type have a wide range of uses. Poly(ethene) can be manufactured in two forms.

❶ Low density poly(ethene). This is cheap to produce and is used for wrapping food, plastic gloves for laboratory work, etc. For these uses, great strength is not necessary.

❷ High density poly(ethene). This is more expensive to produce but, in this form, the poly(ethene) is much stronger. The chains are more tightly packed (hence higher density). This form is used for making milk crates, bleach bottles, etc.

Phenylethene (styrene) is very readily polymerised and has a wide range of uses. Poly(phenylethene) can be used in the ordinary form (e.g. flower pots, plastic model kits) or in the expanded form (ceiling tiles).

The importance of these addition polymers often depends upon their lack of chemical reactivity.

Where the alkene monomer is of the form $CH_2=CHX$ (where X is CH_3, C_6H_5, Cl, etc.) when polymerisation occurs, the X groups can be situated:

❶ on the same side of the chain;
❷ on the alternate sides of the chain;
❸ randomly.

These three possibilities are called **isotactic**, **syndiotactic** and **atactic** polymers respectively.

isotactic   syndiotactic   atactic

The type of polymer determines the properties. In isotactic polymers the chains can approach more closely. This increases the crystallinity of the polymer.

Polymers can also be classified as **thermosetting** and **thermoplastic**. All of the addition polymers are thermoplastic. This means that on heating they will soften and melt. As a result they can be moulded or extruded. Thermosetting polymers *(e.g.* phenol–'formaldehyde' resins – condensation polymers) do not melt on heating. When heated they decompose and, therefore, cannot be worked in the same way.

36.2 CONDENSATION (STEP) POLYMERISATION

A condensation reaction is a reaction in which two molecules join together to form a larger molecule with the loss of a small molecule, often water. An example of a condensation reaction, is

$$CH_3-C\overset{O}{\underset{OH}{<}} + CH_3CH_2OH \rightleftharpoons CH_3-C\overset{O}{\underset{OCH_2CH_3}{<}} + H_2O$$

A condensation polymer is formed by a series of condensation reactions using starting materials containing two reactive groups, e.g.

$$HO-\bullet-OH \qquad HOOC-\square-COOH$$
$$\text{diol} \qquad\qquad \text{dicarboxylic acid}$$

The first condensation product

$$HO-\bullet-O-\overset{O}{\overset{\|}{C}}-\square-COOH + H_2O$$

reacts with another molecule of diol to produce

$$HO-\bullet-O-\overset{O}{\overset{\|}{C}}-\square-\overset{O}{\overset{\|}{C}}-O-\bullet-OH$$

which reacts with another molecule of dicarboxylic acid

$$HO-\bullet-O-\overset{O}{\overset{\|}{C}}-\square-\overset{O}{\overset{\|}{C}}-O-\bullet-O-\overset{O}{\overset{\|}{C}}-\square-COOH$$

and so on. This continues until eventually a polymer is formed. In this case, after a series of esterification reactions, the polymer is called a **polyester**.

Terylene is a polyester prepared by heating ethane-1,2–diol with dimethyl benzene-1,4–dicarboxylate (dimethyl terephthalate). The small molecule lost in each step is methanol. The methyl ester is used in preference to the free benzene-1,4–dicarboxylic acid because it is easier to purify.

Terylene:

$$\left[OCH_2CH_2O-\overset{O}{\overset{\|}{C}}-\langle\bigcirc\rangle-\overset{O}{\overset{\|}{C}}\right]_n$$

Nylon is a name given to synthetic polyamides formed by a series of reactions involving diamines and dicarboxylic acids. There are different types of nylon.

Nylon 6, 6

This is prepared by heating hexane-1,6–dioic acid (adipic acid) with hexane-1,6–diamine (hexamethylene diamine).

Nylon 6, 6: $-[CO(CH_2)_4CO.NH(CH_2)_6NH]_n-$

Nylon 6

This is prepared from phenol by a series of reactions.

OH → (hydrogen/nickel, 300°C) → cyclohexanol → (dehydrogenate, pass over copper, 250°C) → cyclohexanone

cyclohexanone → (hydroxylamine) → cyclohexanone oxime → (acidify) → caprolactam → (heat) → $\left[\begin{array}{c} O \\ \parallel \\ C-NH.(CH_2)_5 \end{array}\right]_n$

36.3   AMINO ACIDS AND PROTEINS

Amino acids are obtained by hydrolysis of proteins. The amino acids can be represented by

$$R-\underset{\underset{NH_2}{|}}{\overset{\overset{H}{|}}{C}}-\underset{\overset{}{OH}}{\overset{O}{\overset{\parallel}{C}}}$$

The simplest amino acids are

$$H-\underset{\underset{NH_2}{|}}{\overset{\overset{H}{|}}{C}}-COOH \qquad CH_3-\underset{\underset{NH_2}{|}}{\overset{\overset{H}{|}}{C}}-COOH$$

aminoethanoic acid   2-aminopropanoic acid
(glycine)   (alanine)

2–Aminopropanoic acid and all amino acids except aminoethanoic acid contain an asymmetric carbon atom and exhibit **optical isomerism** (see 7.6).

Since the amino acids contain amino and carboxyl groups, they show the properties of both groups. Amino acids have high melting points and are usually water-soluble.

Amino acids usually exist as **inner salts** or **zwitterions** (i.e. a species containing both positive and negative charges):

$$H-\underset{\underset{COO^-}{|}}{\overset{\overset{H}{|}}{C}}-\overset{+}{N}H_3$$

Amino acids are linked together by peptide linkages.

$$-\underset{}{\overset{O}{\overset{\parallel}{C}}}-\underset{\overset{}{}}{\overset{\overset{H}{|}}{N}}-$$

Amino acid polymers whose relative molecular masses are 10 000 or less are called **polypeptides.** Those with larger relative molecular masses are called **proteins,** e.g. egg albumen, 40 000.

Protein molecules, it is now believed, are constructed from up to 20 different amino acids joined together by peptide linkages. X-ray analysis has shown that protein chains have a zig-zag structure with R groups sticking out alternately in different directions. Different chains are linked by:

❶ disulphide bridges between two reactive R groups,

❷ hydrogen bonding.

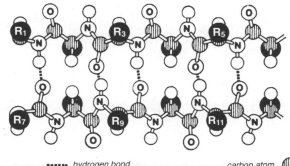

•••••• hydrogen bond   carbon atom ⬛

hydrogen atom ◯

Proteins chains are often arranged in an α-helix.

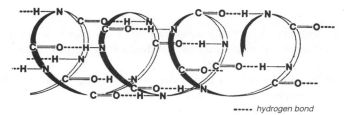

····· hydrogen bond

Proteins can be **denatured** by heating or altering the pH. If egg white (containing the protein ovalbumin) is heated to 60 °C, the protein starts to separate out as a white solid. If the pH of milk is lowered below 4.6, the protein caseinogen starts to precipitate out as a solid. Denaturing involves the permanent breakdown of the crosslinks between the protein molecules and a resulting change in physical, chemical and biological properties.

The presence of protein can be shown by warming the suspected protein with dilute sodium hydroxide solution and copper(II) sulphate solution. A violet colouration confirms the presence of protein.

The particular amino acids present in a protein can be identified by hydrolysis with dilute acid followed by paper chromatography. Ninhydrin produces pink/purple spots on the chromatogram, showing where the amino acids are (see 7.2).

36.4 CROSSLINKING

Crosslinking between polymer chains alters the physical properties of the polymer. It increases the effective relative molecular mass of the polymer and affects its solubility. It also prevents the movement of a chain relative to nearby chains. Crosslinking of some kind is essential if the polymer is to act as a fibre.

Natural rubber is a natural addition polymer. It is unsuitable for use in making rubber tyres unless it is treated with sulphur. Treatment with 30% sulphur hardens the rubber by forming crosslinks between chains. This process is called **vulcanisation**.

Polyamide chains are crosslinked by hydrogen bonding (see 4.5).

$$-N-\overset{O}{\overset{\|}{C}}-(CH_2)_4-\overset{H}{\overset{|}{C}}-N-(CH_2)_6-N-\overset{O}{\overset{\|}{C}}-$$
$$\overset{|}{H} \qquad\qquad \overset{\|}{O} \qquad\qquad \overset{|}{H}$$
$$-\overset{O}{\overset{\|}{C}}-(CH_2)_4-\overset{H}{\overset{|}{C}}-N-(CH_2)_6-N-\overset{O}{\overset{\|}{C}}-(CH_2)_4-$$
$$\overset{\|}{O} \qquad\qquad \overset{|}{H}$$

In Terylene, chains are linked by weaker dipole–dipole attractions. This takes place because carbonyl groups are polarised.

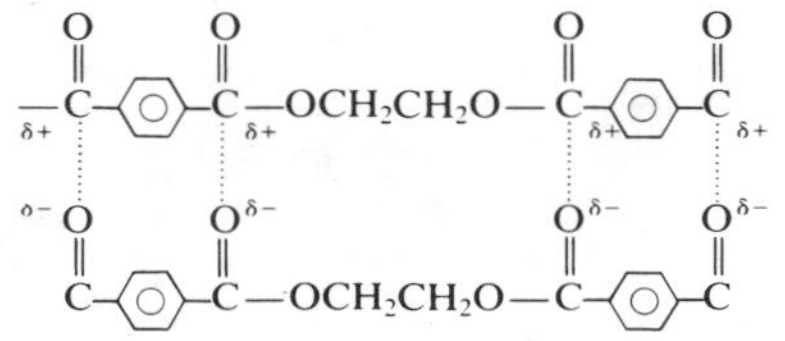

In chains of addition polymers such as Polythene, the only crosslinking is by van der Waals forces (see 4.6).

36.5 CARBOHYDRATES

With proteins and fats, carbohydrates make up the three major classes of nutrients. They are found in plants, where they are produced from carbon dioxide and water by photosynthesis using solar energy.

Carbohydrates contain only carbon, hydrogen and oxygen and fit a formula of $C_x(H_2O)_y$. The simpler carbohydrates are sometimes called sugars. These are crystalline solids which dissolve in water to give a sweet-tasting solution. The simplest of these, including glucose and fructose, are monosaccharides, and contain a six-carbon unit. Disaccharides are made up from two six-carbon units.

Glucose has the formula $C_6H_{12}O_6$ and behaves as an aldehyde. Like an aldehyde, it is a reducing agent (32.6). Glucose is a reducing sugar, forming a red-brown precipitate when heated with Benedict's solution. Glucose was originally given a structure of

4 asymmetric carbon atoms

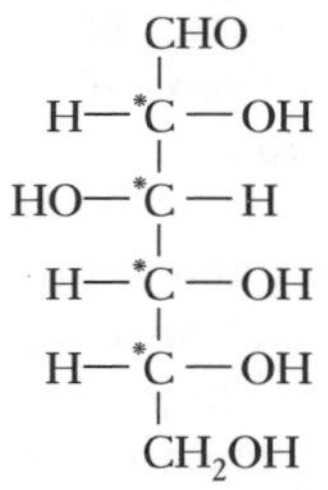

Glucose does not, however, give a pink colour with Schiff's reagent (32.8) and for this reason is not an aldehyde, but is easily converted into one during reactions.

The modern structure of glucose is a hexagonal ring structure.

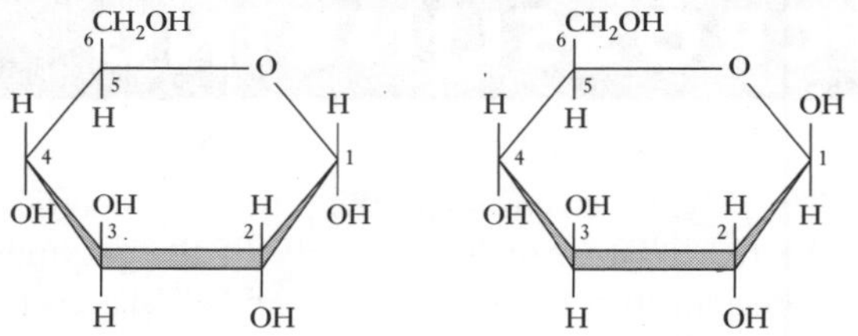

α-D-glucose   β-D-glucose

Glucose solution usually contains an equilibrium mixture of α- and β-forms. The α-form normally crystallises from glucose solutions. The β-form is produced when glucose is crystallised from hot solvents.

Fructose also exists in two cyclic structures.

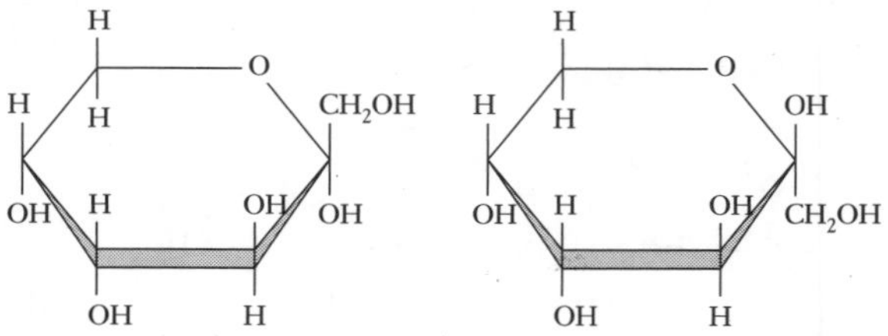

α-D-fructose   β-D-fructose

Disaccharides are formed when two monosaccharides join together, eliminating water. Maltose is a disaccharide.

maltose

Maltose is formed from two connected glucose units and so is a reducing sugar.

Sucrose (ordinary sugar) is a disaccharide made up from one glucose unit and one fructose unit. It is not a reducing sugar.

Polysaccharides are carbohydrates made from long chains of monosaccharide units. They are usually non-crystalline, generally insoluble in water and tasteless. They fit a formula $(C_6H_{10}O_5)_n$. The monosaccharide units can be the same or can differ.

cellulose – a chain of β-D-glucose units

Starch is another polysaccharide. It is a mixture of two polysaccharides, amylose and amylopectin, in a ratio of about 1 to 4. Both are made of glucose units joined together, but in different ways. Amylose is responsible for the blue colour formed when starch reacts with iodine.

Hydrolysis of polysaccharides by boiling with dilute acid splits them up into the component monosaccharides by hydrolysis. The monosaccharides present can be identified by chromatography.

Chapter roundup

Ethene is the commonest example of a monomer for addition polymerisation. It can be polymerised to form poly(ethene). You will remember that in addition polymerisation the monomer always contains a double bond which is lost during polymerisation. Poly(ethene) can be made in various forms depending on the conditions of polymerisation.

Condensation polymers, e.g. nylon, are made up of a series of condensation reactions. The monomer must contain at least two reacting groups if a chain is to be built up. Amino acids form proteins, natural condensation polymers.

Finally, linking between chains, called crosslinking, alters the properties of a polymer. Soft, natural rubber is made suitable for car tyres by adding sulphur which forms links between the chains. This process is called vulcanisation.

Worked questions and answers

1 Describe how you could measure the viscosity of a solution of poly(methyl methacrylate) (Perspex) dissolved in trichloromethane (chloroform).

Tutorial note

The viscosity of a polymer solution is related to the relative molecular mass of the polymer. The longer the chains, the more viscous the solution will be.

A simple method of comparing the viscosities of two polymer solutions is to fill two metre-long tubes with the polymer solutions. Drop a ball bearing into the top of each tube and time until the ball bearing reaches the bottom of the tube. The more viscous the solution the longer it will take for the ball bearing to fall.

The viscosity can be measured accurately using a viscometer. Liquids in a reservoir are allowed to pass through a capillary tube into a lower reservoir. The viscosities can be measured by timing how long this process takes for each liquid. Further details would be found in an A-level Physics text.

2 (a) The first synthetic thread (for surgical stitches) was made from a polyester. A section of the polymer thread is drawn below:

$$-O-CH_2COO-CH_2COO-CH_2CO-$$

(i) Give the structural formula of a monomer (containing two functional groups) that could be used to make this polymer. (2)
(ii) State, giving a reason, whether this polymer would be made by addition or condensation polymerization. (1)
(iii) Suggest how this polymer is broken down in the body. (2)
(iv) Give the names or formulae of two monomers that react to form a polyester that can be used as a fibre, e.g. Terylene (2)
(v) Polyester cotton is frequently used for clothing. Give one advantage of this over pure polyester and one advantage as compared with cotton clothing. (2)

(b) Poly(ethene) itself is not biodegradable, but plastic bags which are biodegradable are made by embedding starch granules into poly(ethene).
(i) Explain what is meant by the term *biodegradable*. (1)
(ii) Suggest why incorporation of starch granules makes the plastic biodegradable. (2)
(iii) Why is it desirable to produce biodegradable plastics, rather than rely on disposal by use of landfill sites? (1)

(Oxford)

Tutorial note

(a) (i) The expanded formula should be written, i.e.

(ii) Condensation polymer, as water is lost each time a linkage is made.
(iii) The ester linkage is hydrolysed.
(iv) e.g. ethane-1,2-diol and benzene-1,4-dicarboxylic acid. You could write structural formulae instead of names.
(v) Pure polyester cannot absorb moisture and polyester cotton dries much more quickly than pure cotton and without creasing.
(b) (i) Broken down by bacteria.
(ii) Microorganisms (or bacteria or enzymes) can break down starch leaving small amounts of poly(ethene) which can degrade more quickly because they have a larger surface area.
(iii) Landfill sites becoming less available or the cost of landfill is increasing.

Question bank

1 Poly(phenylethene), known as polystyrene, is a widely used polymer. The starting material for its manufacture is benzene which is converted into ethylbenzene and then, by catalytic dehydrogenation, into phenylethene.

(a) (i) What reagents and conditions would be used to convert benzene into ethylbenzene (reaction 1)?

(ii) What do you understand by the term *catalytic dehydrogenation*?

(iii) Draw the displayed formula of poly(phenylethene), showing at least two repeat units.

(b) When a small quantity of the compound $CH_2{=}CH{-}\bigcirc{-}CH{=}CH_2$ is added during the polymerisation of phenylethene, crosslinking occurs. This polymer can be sulphonated to give an ion-exchange resin.

(i) What is meant by *crosslinking*?

(ii) Describe one way in which the crosslinked polymer will behave differently from ordinary poly(phenylethene).

(iii) What is the formula of the *sulphuric acid group* which results in the formation of an ion-exchange resin?

(c) The ion-exchange resin formed from poly(phenylethene) can be used to remove metallic cations from an aqueous solution. Draw a clearly labelled diagram of a suitable apparatus for carrying out this procedure.

(d) 10.0 cm³ of a solution containing magnesium ions was passed through a column of the ion-exchange resin and neutralised by 9.0 cm³ of 0.050 mol dm⁻³ sodium hydroxide solution.

(i) Write an equation for the reaction occurring in the column of resin. Represent the resin by the formula RH_2.

(ii) Calculate the concentration of magnesium ions in the original solution.

(ULEAC Nuffield 1990)

Points

This question involves two ideas not included in this book which have come into papers in recent years.

❶ Crosslinking in polymers is covered in 36.4. However, in some syllabuses, e.g. WJEC, the terms thermosetting and thermoplastic are used and they have also appeared in other questions with other boards. Most addition polymers are thermoplastic. This means that on heating they melt and can be remoulded and, as a consequence, recycled. The polymer chains are not linked. Crosslinking will alter the properties and make melting before decomposition unlikely.

❷ Polymers which do not melt before decomposing, e.g. urea–formaldehyde, are called thermosetting polymers. These polymers can be used as ion-exchange resins to soften water. Hard water is passed through a vertical column and calcium and magnesium ions are replaced by sodium or hydrogen ions. This makes the water soft. In this question

$$RH_2 + Mg^{2+} \rightarrow RMg + 2H^+.$$

CHAPTER **37**

CONVERSIONS

Units in this chapter

Chapter objectives

Providing you have studied Chapters 7 and 29–36 you should have built up a good knowledge of organic chemistry. In this chapter you will see the relationships between different organic compounds. Many questions ask you how you would convert one compound to another.

37.1 METHANOL TO ETHANOL

This involves increasing the number of carbon atoms by one (called **ascending the homologous series**). Possible methods are summarised as follows.

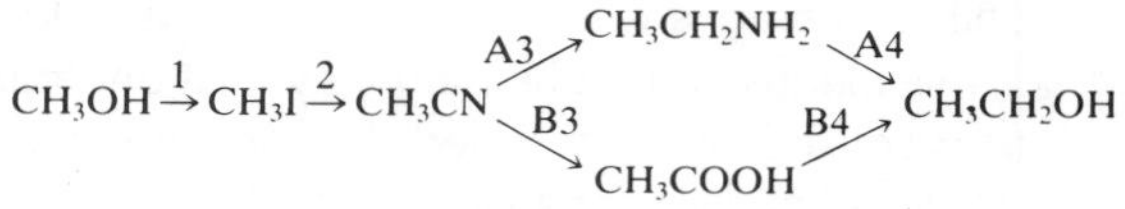

$$CH_3OH \xrightarrow{1} CH_3I \xrightarrow{2} CH_3CN \begin{array}{c} \xrightarrow{A3} CH_3CH_2NH_2 \xrightarrow{A4} \\ \searrow_{B3} \qquad \qquad \nearrow_{B4} \end{array} CH_3CH_2OH$$
$$CH_3COOH$$

Step 1: $CH_3OH \rightarrow CH_3I$

Methanol is refluxed with a mixture of red phosphorus and iodine (which produces phosphorus triiodide PI_3).

$$3CH_3OH + PI_3 \rightarrow 3CH_3I + H_3PO_3$$
$$\text{iodomethane}$$

Step 2: $CH_3I \rightarrow CH_3CN$

Iodomethane is refluxed with a solution of potassium cyanide in ethanol to produce ethanenitrile (acetonitrile).

$$CH_3I + KCN \rightarrow CH_3CN + KI$$

There are two alternative routes from here.

Alternative A

Step 3: $CH_3CN \rightarrow CH_3CH_2NH_2$

Ethanenitrile is reduced to ethylamine using either sodium in ethanol or lithium tetrahydridoaluminate(III) (lithium aluminium hydride) dissolved in dry ethoxyethane as the reducing agent.

$$CH_3CN + 4[H] \rightarrow CH_3CH_2NH_2$$
$$\text{ethylamine}$$

Step 4: $CH_3CH_2NH_2 \rightarrow CH_3CH_2OH$

Ethylamine is dissolved in excess dilute hydrochloric acid and nitrous acid (nitric(III) acid) added.

$$CH_3CH_2NH_2 + HONO \rightarrow CH_3CH_2OH + H_2O + N_2$$

Alternative B

Step 3: $CH_3CN \rightarrow CH_3COOH$

Ethanenitrile is hydrolysed by boiling with dilute hydrochloric acid.

$$CH_3CN + 2H_2O + HCl \rightarrow CH_3COOH + NH_4Cl$$
$$\text{ethanoic acid} \quad \text{ammonium chloride}$$

Step 4: $CH_3COOH \rightarrow CH_3CH_2OH$

Ethanoic acid is reduced to ethanol by lithium tetrahyridoaluminate(III) (lithium aluminium hydride).

$$CH_3COOH + 4[H] \rightarrow CH_3CH_2OH + H_2O$$

It is possible also to bring about this, and many other conversions, by means of Grignard reagents (see 30.3).

A Grignard reagent is prepared by adding dry magnesium turnings to a haloalkane dissolved in dry ethoxyethane. This produces an unstable compound which, when poured onto solid carbon dioxide and hydrolysed with dilute acid, produces an acid which can be reduced to the alcohol. Alternatively, if the Grignard reagent is added to methanal and hydrolysed the alcohol is formed directly.

A similar sequence can be used to convert $CH_3COOH \rightarrow CH_3CH_2COOH$

37.2 ETHANOL TO METHANOL

This is the reverse of the conversion in 37.1 (**descending the homologous series**).

$$CH_3CH_2OH \xrightarrow{1} CH_3COOH \xrightarrow{2} CH_3CONH_2 \xrightarrow{3} CH_3NH_2 \xrightarrow{4} CH_3OH$$

Step 1: $CH_3CH_2OH \rightarrow CH_3COOH$

Ethanol is oxidised by heating with an excess of acidified potassium dichromate(VI) solution.

$$CH_3CH_2OH + 2[O] \rightarrow CH_3COOH + H_2O$$
$$\text{ethanoic acid}$$

Step 2: $CH_3COOH \rightarrow CH_3CONH_2$

Ethanoic acid is neutralised with excess ammonia solution and the ammonium ethanoate formed is heated to produce ethanamide (acetamide).

$$CH_3COOH + NH_3 \rightarrow CH_3COONH_4$$
$$CH_3COONH_4 \rightarrow CH_3CONH_2 + H_2O$$
ethanamide

Step 3: $CH_3CONH_2 \rightarrow CH_3NH_2$

This step removes a carbon atom. The reaction is called the **Hofmann degradation.** Ethanamide is treated with bromine and aqueous sodium hydroxide solution and the mixture is heated.

$$CH_3CONH_2 + Br_2 \rightarrow CH_3CONHBr + HBr$$
$$CH_3CONHBr + 3NaOH \rightarrow CH_3NH_2 + Na_2CO_3 + H_2O + NaBr$$
methylamine

Step 4: $CH_3NH_2 \rightarrow CH_3OH$

Methylamine is treated with nitrous acid (nitric(III) acid).

$$CH_3NH_2 + HONO \rightarrow CH_3OH + H_2O + N_2$$

(NB In practice an ether is the main product, however.)

37.3 ETHANAL TO PROPANONE

Two methods are possible.

Alternative A

Step 1: $CH_3CHO \rightarrow CH_3COOH$

Ethanal is oxidised by heating with potassium dichromate(VI) solution.

$$CH_3CHO + [O] \rightarrow CH_3COOH$$
ethanoic acid

Step 2: $CH_3COOH \rightarrow (CH_3COO)_2Ca$

Ethanoic acid is neutralised by adding solid calcium carbonate.

$$2CH_3COOH + CaCO_3 \rightarrow (CH_3COO)_2Ca + H_2O + CO_2$$
calcium ethanoate

Step 3: $(CH_3COO)_2Ca \rightarrow CH_3COCH_3$

Solid calcium ethanoate is heated (or dry distilled) and decomposes.

$$(CH_3COO)_2Ca \rightarrow CH_3COCH_3 + CaCO_3$$

Alternative B

This again uses a Grignard reagent.

Step 1: $CH_3CHO \rightarrow CH_3CH(OH)CH_3$

A Grignard reagent (e.g. CH_3MgBr) is prepared (see 30.3). Ethanal is added and an intermediate is formed which, on hydrolysis with a dilute acid, produces propan-2-ol (a secondary alcohol).

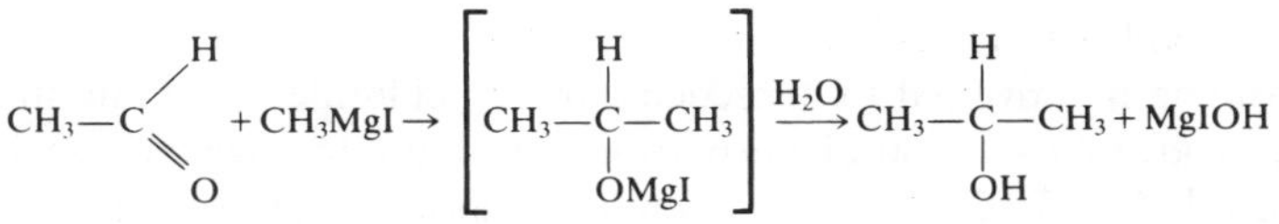

$$CH_3-C\overset{H}{\underset{O}{\diagup}} + CH_3MgI \rightarrow \left[CH_3-\overset{H}{\underset{OMgI}{\overset{|}{C}}}-CH_3 \right] \xrightarrow{H_2O} CH_3-\overset{H}{\underset{OH}{\overset{|}{C}}}-CH_3 + MgIOH$$

Step 2: $CH_3CH(OH)CH_3 \rightarrow CH_3COCH_3$

Propan-2-ol is oxidised to propanone by refluxing with acidified potassium dichromate(VI) solution.

$$CH_3CH(OH)CH_3 + [O] \rightarrow CH_3COCH_3 + H_2O$$
$$\text{propanone}$$

37.4 ETHANAL TO 2-HYDROXYPROPANOIC ACID

This conversion to 2-hydroxypropanoic acid (lactic acid) can be completed in two steps.

Step 1: $CH_3CHO \rightarrow CH_3CH(OH)CN$

This step involves the addition of hydrogen cyanide to ethanal.

$$HCN + CH_3CHO \rightarrow CH_3CH(OH)CN$$
$$\text{2-hydroxypropanenitrile}$$

Step 2: $CH_3CH(OH)CN \rightarrow CH_3CH(OH)COOH$

Hydrolysis of 2-hydroxypropanenitrile by refluxing with dilute hydrochloric acid produces the required product.

$$CH_3CH(OH)CN + 2H_2O + HCl \rightarrow CH_3CH(OH)COOH + NH_4Cl$$

37.5 BENZENE TO PHENOL

The first stage in any conversion starting with benzene is invariably one of the electrophilic substitution reactions (see 29.9). There are two possible routes.

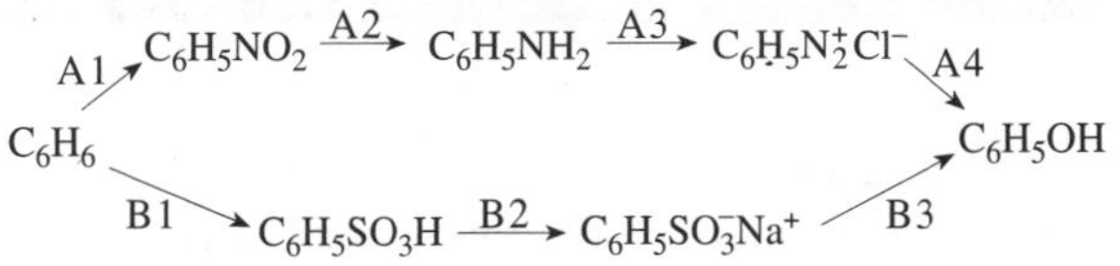

$$C_6H_6 \xrightarrow{A1} C_6H_5NO_2 \xrightarrow{A2} C_6H_5NH_2 \xrightarrow{A3} C_6H_5N_2^+Cl^- \xrightarrow{A4} C_6H_5OH$$
$$C_6H_6 \xrightarrow{B1} C_6H_5SO_3H \xrightarrow{B2} C_6H_5SO_3^-Na^+ \xrightarrow{B3} C_6H_5OH$$

Alternative A

Step 1: $C_6H_6 \rightarrow C_6H_5NO_2$

Nitration of benzene with a mixture of concentrated nitric and sulphuric acids at a temperature below 55 °C to prevent further substitution.

$$C_6H_6 + HNO_3 \rightarrow C_6H_5NO_2 + H_2O$$
$$\text{nitrobenzene}$$

Step 2: $C_6H_5NO_2 \rightarrow C_6H_5NH_2$

Reduction of nitrobenzene with tin and concentrated hydrochloric acid produces phenylamine.

$$C_6H_5NO_2 + 6[H] \rightarrow C_6H_5NH_2 + 2H_2O$$

Step 3: $C_6H_5NH_2 \rightarrow C_6H_5N_2^+Cl^-$

Phenylamine is converted to benzenediazonium chloride by adding nitrous acid (nitric(III) acid) to a solution of phenylamine in dilute hydrochloric acid with the temperature below 5 °C. Benzenediazonium chloride is most useful in aromatic conversions as it is readily converted into a range of other compounds.

Step 4: $C_6H_5N_2^+Cl^- \rightarrow C_6H_5OH$

Phenol is produced when the solution of benzenediazonium chloride is warmed after the addition of more water.

$$C_6H_5N_2^+Cl^- + H_2O \rightarrow C_6H_5OH + N_2 + HCl$$

Alternative B

Step 1: $C_6H_6 \rightarrow C_6H_5SO_3H$

Benzene is sulphonated by heating with fuming sulphuric acid.

$$C_6H_6 + H_2SO_4 \rightarrow C_6H_5SO_3H + H_2O$$

Step 2: $C_6H_5SO_3H \rightarrow C_6H_5SO_3^-Na^+$

Benzenesulphonic acid is neutralised with sodium hydroxide to form sodium benzenesulphonate.

$$C_6H_5SO_3H + NaOH \rightarrow C_6H_5SO_3^-Na^+ + H_2O$$

Step 3: $C_6H_5SO_3^-Na^+ \rightarrow C_6H_5OH$

The solid sodium benzenesulphonate is then fused with solid sodium hydroxide.

$$C_6H_5SO_3^-Na^+ + NaOH \rightarrow C_6H_5OH + Na_2SO_3$$

A common mistake with this conversion is to chlorinate benzene to form chlorobenzene and then hydrolyse with sodium hydroxide solution.

$$C_6H_6 + Cl_2 \rightarrow C_6H_5Cl + HCl$$
$$C_6H_5Cl + NaOH \rightarrow C_6H_5OH + NaCl$$

The second step, however, does not take place under ordinary laboratory conditions.

37.6 METHYLBENZENE TO BENZENECARBALDEHYDE

Step 1: $C_6H_5CH_3 \rightarrow C_6H_5CHCl_2$

Methylbenzene is mixed with chlorine. The mixture is heated in ultraviolet light and a free radical substitution reaction in the CH_3 group takes place. No halogen carrier should be present.

$$C_6H_5CH_3 + Cl_2 \rightarrow C_6H_5CH_2Cl + HCl$$
$$\text{(chloromethyl)benzene}$$
$$\text{(benzyl chloride)}$$
$$C_6H_5CH_2Cl + Cl_2 \rightarrow C_6H_5CHCl_2 + HCl$$
$$\text{(dichloromethyl)benzene}$$
$$\text{(benzal chloride)}$$

Step 2: $C_6H_5CHCl_2 \rightarrow C_6H_5CHO$

Hydrolysis of (dichloromethyl)benzene by refluxing with sodium hydroxide solution produces benzenecarbaldehyde (benzaldehyde).

$$C_6H_5CHCl_2 + 2NaOH \rightarrow C_6H_5CHO + 2NaCl + H_2O$$

37.7 PROPAN-1-OL TO PROPAN-2-OL

Step 1: $CH_3CH_2CH_2OH \rightarrow CH_3CH{=}CH_2$

Propan-l-ol is dehydrated by heating with excess concentrated sulphuric acid at 170 °C to form propene.

$$CH_3CH_2CH_2OH \rightarrow CH_3CH{=}CH_2 + H_2O$$

Step 2: $CH_3CH{=}CH_2 \rightarrow CH_3CH(OH)CH_3$

Propene is passed into concentrated sulphuric acid and the product is then hydrolysed with water.

$$CH_3CH{=}CH_2 + H_2SO_4 \rightarrow CH_3CH(HSO_4)CH_3$$
$$CH_3CH(HSO_4)CH_3 + H_2O \rightarrow CH_3CH(OH)CH_3 + H_2SO_4$$

Chapter roundup

In this chapter we have looked at some of the common conversions. When answering this type of question you should remember the following points.

1 For each step you should give an equation, reaction conditions and names and structures of the major products.

2 The conversion should be completed in the smallest number of stages – usually three or four is sufficient. If you produce longer conversions you will be penalised by the examiner and you will waste time.

3 If you cannot immediately see a solution adopt the following plan:
(i) list all the substances which can be made from the starting material in one step; and
(ii) list all the substances which undergo reaction to give the final product in one step.
Then try to find reactions which convert a substance in list (i) to a substance in list (ii).

4 Only steps which give a good yield should be used. For example, chlorination of ethane to produce 1,2-dichloroethane is not a good reaction as it is impossible to control the formation of other products.

You should spend as much time as you can on worked question 1 as this is a great help in getting relationships cemented.

Worked questions and answers

1 Complete the flow diagrams in Figs. 37.1 and 37.2 by inserting the correct structural formulae and names.

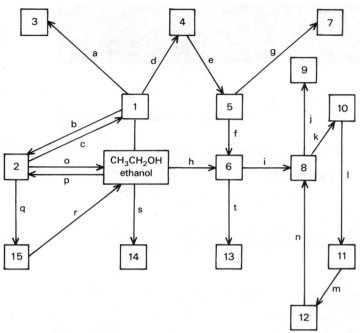

Label this diagram as follows:
a   react with trioxygen (ozone) and hydrolyse
b   react with HBr
c   Reflux with soln of KOH in ethanol
d   reaction with bromine
e   heat with soln of KOH in ethanol
f   pass into warm dil. H_2SO_4 in presence of $HgSO_4$
g   pass through heated copper tube
h   warm with acidified potassium dichromate(VI)
i   further oxidation
j   heat with ethanol in the presence of conc. H_2SO_4
k   react with ammonia solution
l   heat
m   heat with P_2O_5
n   boil with dil. HCl
o   reflux with solution of KOH in water
p   reflux with mixture of red P and bromine
q   heat with ammonia
r   react with nitrous acid (nitric(III) acid)
s   excess ethanol heated with conc. H_2SO_4 at 140 °C
t   react with PBr_5

Fig. 37.1 Aliphatic conversions

Tutorial note

1.   ethene

2.   bromoethane

3.   methanal

4.   1,2-dibromoethane

5.   ethyne

6.   ethanal

7.   benzene

8.   ethanoic acid

9.   ethyl ethanoate

10. ammonium ethanoate

11. ethanamide

12. ethanenitrile CH_3CN

13. 1,1-dibromoethane

14. ethoxyethane $CH_3CH_2OCH_2CH_3$

15. ethylamine $CH_3CH_2NH_2$

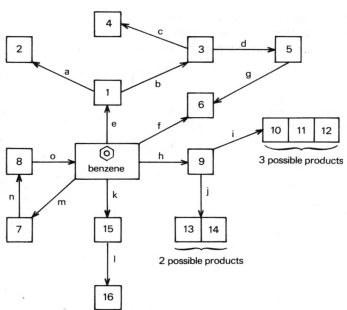

a react with chlorine in presence of halogen carrier
b react with tin and conc. HCl
c react with ethanoyl chloride in the cold
d react with nitrous acid (nitric(III) acid) below 5 °C
e react with conc. HNO$_3$ conc. H$_2$SO$_4$ below 55 °C
f react with chlorine in the presence of halogen carrier
g heat with copper and conc. HCl
h react with chloromethane and aluminium chloride
i react with chlorine in the presence of ultraviolet light
j react with chlorine in presence of halogen carrier
k react with ethanoyl chloride in presence of
   aluminium chloride
l react with zinc and conc. HCl
m react with fuming H$_2$SO$_4$
n react with fused NaOH
o heat with zinc powder

Fig. 37.2 Aromatic conversions

Tutorial note

1. nitrobenzene

2. 1-chloro-3-nitrobenzene

3. phenylamine

4. *N*-phenylethanamide

5. benzenediazonium chloride

6. chlorobenzene

7. benzenesulphonic acid

8. phenol

9. methylbenzene

10, 11, 12.   (chloromethyl)benzene

            (dichloromethyl)benzene

            (trichloromethyl)benzene

13, 14.   1-chloro-2-methylbenzene

          1-chloro-4-methylbenzene

15. phenylethanone

16. phenylethane

Having completed this exercise it is worthwhile spending some time looking at these two frameworks. Draw out the frameworks again, missing out the reaction conditions but putting in the names and formulae. Then list the conditions for each step and write a balanced equation.

2 Describe how the following conversions could be carried out. In each case you should give reagents, conditions of the reactions and the structures of the products.

(a) $CH_2{=}CH_2$ to $\underset{\displaystyle CH_2CO_2H}{\overset{\displaystyle CH_2CO_2H}{|}}$

(b) $CH_3CHBrCH_3$ to $CH_3CHBrCH_2Br$
(c) C_2H_5CN to C_2H_5OH
(d) C_6H_6 to $C_6H_5NHCOCH_3$

Tutorial note

(a) This involves the addition of two carbon atoms (see 37.1).
   Addition of bromine to ethene forms 1,2-dibromoethane.

$$\underset{H}{\overset{H}{}}\!C{=}C\!\underset{H}{\overset{H}{}} + Br_2 \rightarrow H-\underset{Br}{\overset{H}{C}}-\underset{Br}{\overset{H}{C}}-H$$

Pass ethene into liquid bromine until the colour of the bromine is removed. Cool the liquid bromine and cover with a small volume of water to prevent evaporation.
   React with potassium cyanide dissolved in ethanol with gentle refluxing.

$$H-\underset{Br}{\overset{H}{C}}-\underset{Br}{\overset{H}{C}}-H + 2KCN \rightarrow H-\underset{CN}{\overset{H}{C}}-\underset{CN}{\overset{H}{C}}-H + 2KBr$$

Hydrolyse by boiling with dilute hydrochloric acid.

$$H-\underset{CN}{\overset{H}{C}}-\underset{CN}{\overset{H}{C}}-H + 4H_2O + 2HCl \rightarrow HOOC.CH_2CH_2.COOH + 2NH_4Cl$$

(b) Elimination of hydrogen bromide.
   Reflux 2-bromopropane with a solution of potassium hydroxide in ethanol.

$$CH_3CHBrCH_3 + KOH \rightarrow \underset{\text{propene}}{CH_3CH{=}CH_2} + KBr + H_2O$$

Addition of bromine to propene.
Pass propene into liquid bromine until the colour is removed.

$$CH_3CH{=}CH_2 + Br_2 \rightarrow CH_3CHBrCH_2Br$$

(c) This conversion involves descending the homologous series (see 37.2). The nitrile is hydrolysed to the corresponding acid by refluxing with dilute hydrochloric acid.

$$C_2H_5CN + 2H_2O + HCl \rightarrow \underset{\text{propanoic acid}}{C_2H_5COOH} + NH_4Cl$$

The propanoic acid is treated with ammonia solution to form ammonium propanoate and this is heated to dryness to produce propanamide.

$$C_2H_5COOH + NH_3 \rightarrow C_2H_5COONH_4$$
$$C_2H_5COONH_4 \rightarrow C_2H_5CONH_2 + H_2O$$

Hofmann degradation of propanamide by heating the mixture of propanamide, bromine and potassium hydroxide solution produces ethylamine.

$$C_2H_5CONH_2 + Br \rightarrow C_2H_5CONHBr + HBr$$
$$C_2H_5CONHBr + 3NaOH \rightarrow C_2H_5NH_2 + Na_2CO_3 + H_2O + NaBr$$

Finally the ethylamine is treated with nitrous acid (nitric(III) acid) formed from sodium nitrite (sodium nitrate(III)) and dilute hydrochloric acid.

$$C_2H_5NH_2 + HONO \rightarrow C_2H_5OH + H_2O + N_2$$

(d) This involves the first two steps of the conversion of benzene to phenol (37.5). The product phenylamine is finally treated with either
(i) ethanoyl chloride in the cold with careful mixing, or
(ii) ethanoic anhydride dissolved in ethanoic acid. In this case the reaction is slower and refluxing is necessary.

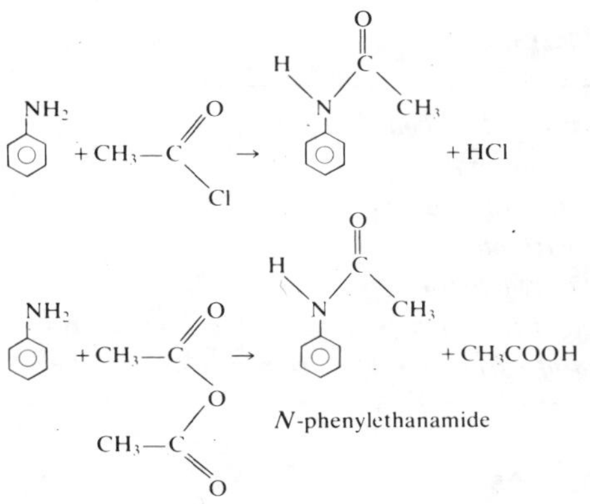

N-phenylethanamide

CHAPTER 38

ORGANIC REACTION MECHANISMS

Units in this chapter

Chapter objectives

At one time organic chemistry syllabuses were just a series of reactions which you had to learn. There was no attempt to explain why and how reactions take place. Now you will be expected to have some understanding of how reactions take place through the various **reaction mechanisms**. This is perhaps conceptually more difficult than the other organic chemistry chapters. There are, however, only a limited number of possible mechanisms for you to understand at A level. Before attempting this chapter, make sure you understand Chapters 4, 5, 7 and 29–37.

38.1 BREAKING A COVALENT BOND

Consider the breaking of the covalent bond between the two carbon atoms in an ethane molecule – it can be broken in two ways.

(i) Homolytic fission

The bond is broken so that, of the two electrons in the bond, one electron goes to each carbon atom.

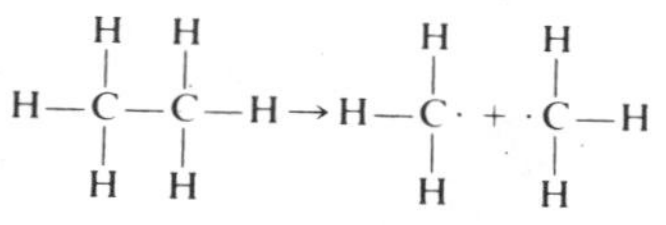

$$
\underset{\substack{|\\H}}{\overset{\substack{H\\|}}{H-C}}-\underset{\substack{|\\H}}{\overset{\substack{H\\|}}{C}}-H \rightarrow \underset{\substack{|\\H}}{\overset{\substack{H\\|}}{H-C}}\cdot + \cdot\underset{\substack{|\\H}}{\overset{\substack{H\\|}}{C}}-H
$$

The resulting species are methyl **free radicals** and they each contain a single unpaired electron. Free radicals are extremely short-lived and readily undergo further reaction. This type of bond breaking usually occurs in the gas phase and in nonpolar solvents, especially in strong light.

(ii) Heterolytic fission

The bond is broken so that one carbon atom receives both electrons while the other receives none.

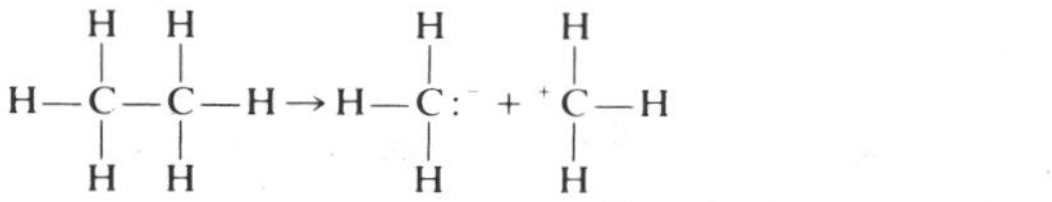

carbanion   carbocation (carbonium ion)

The positively charged ion is called a carbocation (**carbonium ion**) and the positively charged carbon atom is liable to attack by negatively charged species called **nucleophiles**. (Remember nucleophile and negative both begin with the letter n.)

The negatively charged ion is called a **carbanion** and this is liable to attack by positively charged species called **electrophiles**. This kind of species is likely to exist in solutions in polar solvents.

Although free radicals, carbonium ions and carbanions may only exist for the shortest possible period of time, they have a particular importance in controlling how a reaction takes place.

38.2 STABILITY OF CARBONIUM IONS

There are four possible carbonium ions with a formula $C_4H_9^+$. They are:

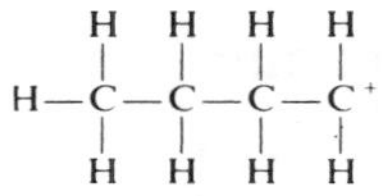

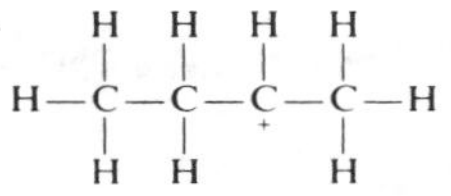

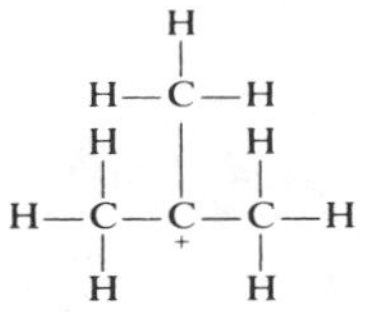

If you have understood the distinction between primary, secondary and tertiary alcohols (see 31.2), you will appreciate that A and D are derived from primary alcohols (by removing OH^-) , B from a secondary alcohol and C from a tertiary alcohol.

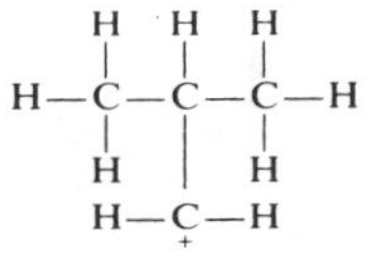

A and D are called primary carbonium ions, B is a secondary carbonium ion and C is a tertiary carbonium ion.

In general, tertiary carbonium ions are more stable than secondary carbonium ions which are, in turn, more stable than primary carbonium ions. It is possible for a rearrangement of carbonium ions to take place. Carbonium ions can eliminate an H^+ ion and produce an alkene, e.g.

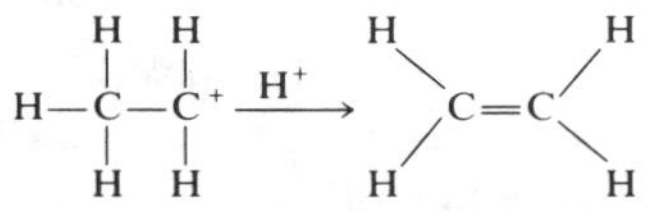

38.3 FREE RADICAL CHAIN REACTIONS

A most commonly quoted free radical chain reaction is the reaction between methane and chlorine (see 29.2). This reaction takes place when a mixture of the gases is subjected to ultraviolet light.

The light energy breaks a few chlorine–chlorine bonds to produce chlorine free radicals (chlorine atoms)

$$Cl_2 \rightarrow Cl\cdot + Cl\cdot \qquad \textit{initiation}$$

The following steps then take place.

$$\left.\begin{array}{l} Cl\cdot + CH_4 \rightarrow CH_3\cdot + HCl \\ CH_3\cdot + Cl_2 \rightarrow CH_3Cl + Cl\cdot \end{array}\right\} \textit{propagation}$$

The following reactions also take place but they do not promote further reaction.

$$\left.\begin{array}{l} CH_3\cdot + Cl\cdot \rightarrow CH_3Cl \\ Cl\cdot + Cl\cdot \rightarrow Cl_2 \\ CH_3\cdot + CH_3\cdot \rightarrow CH_3CH_3 \end{array}\right\} \textit{termination}$$

The mechanism explains why, in practice, small amounts of ethane are detected in the products.

The reactions between hydrogen and chlorine and methylbenzene and chlorine have similar mechanisms.

38.4 ADDITION REACTIONS

In this section a comparison will be made between addition to carbon–carbon double bonds in alkenes (see 29.5) and carbon–oxygen double bonds in aldehydes and ketones (see 32.4).

(i) Addition to alkenes (see 29.5) – electrophilic addition

The carbon–carbon double bond, as in ethene, can be represented by

The double bond between the two carbon atoms consists of a sigma (σ) bond and a pi (π) bond formed by the overlap of p orbitals on the two carbon atoms. There is a concentration of negative charge between the two carbon atoms making it susceptible to attack by electrophiles (positive species).

Consider the addition of hydrogen bromide to ethene:

$$\begin{array}{c} \underset{H}{\overset{H}{\diagdown}}C=C\underset{H}{\overset{H}{\diagup}} + HBr \rightarrow H-\underset{\underset{H}{|}}{\overset{\overset{H}{|}}{C}}-\underset{\underset{H}{|}}{\overset{\overset{H}{|}}{C}}-Br \\ \text{bromoethane} \end{array}$$

There is a dipole within the hydrogen bromide molecule which gives the hydrogen a slight positive charge (shown as $\delta +$) and the bromine a slight negative charge ($\delta -$).

The first step involves the formation of a weak complex between the positive end of the HBr molecule and the electrons of the carbon–carbon double bond.

$$\begin{array}{c} Br^{\delta-} \\ H \quad | \quad H \\ \diagdown \quad H^{\delta+} \quad \diagup \\ C = C \\ \diagup \qquad \diagdown \\ H \qquad\qquad H \end{array}$$

This weak complex may then convert into a more stable carbonium ion.

$$\begin{array}{ccc} & H & H \\ & | & | \\ H - & C - & C^+ \\ & | & | \\ & H & H \end{array}$$

This then reacts rapidly with a bromide ion to form the product.

$$\begin{array}{cccc} H & H & & H & H \\ | & | & & | & | \\ H-C-C^+ + Br^- \rightarrow & H-C-C-Br \\ | & | & & | & | \\ H & H & & H & H \end{array}$$

The reaction between ethene and bromine has a similar mechanism. The bromine molecule Br—Br does not contain a permanent dipole. An induced dipole is formed when it approaches an ethene molecule. This is due to repulsion between electrons in the carbon–carbon double bond and the electrons in the covalent bond between the bromine atoms.

$$\begin{array}{c} H \diagup \qquad \diagdown H \\ C = C \qquad + Br-Br \rightarrow \\ H \diagup \qquad \diagdown H \end{array} \qquad \begin{array}{c} Br^{\delta-} \\ H \quad | \quad H \\ \diagdown \quad Br^{\delta+} \quad \diagup \\ C = C \\ \diagup \quad \diagdown \\ H \qquad H \end{array} \qquad \begin{array}{c} H \quad Br^+ \quad H \\ \diagdown \quad / \diagdown \quad \diagup \\ C \qquad C \\ \diagup \quad \diagdown \quad \diagdown \\ H \quad Br^- \; H \end{array} \rightarrow \begin{array}{c} Br \; H \\ | \; | \\ H-C-C-H \\ | \; | \\ H \; Br \end{array}$$

The reaction between propene and hydrogen bromide can, in theory, lead to two products.

$$\begin{array}{c} CH_3 \diagup \qquad \diagdown H \\ C=C \qquad + HBr \rightarrow \\ H \diagup \qquad \diagdown H \end{array} \quad \begin{array}{c} CH_3 \quad H \\ | \quad | \\ H-C-C-Br \\ | \quad | \\ H \quad H \end{array} \quad or \quad \begin{array}{c} CH_3 \quad H \\ | \quad | \\ Br-C-C-H \\ | \quad | \\ H \quad H \end{array}$$

$$\qquad\qquad\qquad\qquad\qquad 1\text{-bromopropane} \qquad\qquad 2\text{-bromopropane}$$

This can occur because the groups attached to the two carbon atoms, joined by the double bond, are different. The alkene is not symmetrical. In practice, addition produces 2-bromopropane only, according to **Markownikoff's rule**. Markownikoff's rule was based upon observations of a large number of addition reactions. The rule states that during addition the more negative part of the molecule adding to the alkene (Br in this case) adds to the carbon atom attached to the lesser number of hydrogen atoms.

We can now explain Markownikoff's rule in terms of the stability of carbonium ions. Depending upon which carbon atom the H^+ of the hydrogen bromide attaches to, there are two possible carbonium ions which can be formed.

$$\begin{array}{c} H \;\; H \;\; H \\ | \;\;\; | \;\;\; | \\ H-C-C-C-H \\ | \;\;\; + \;\; | \\ H \qquad\; H \end{array} \qquad\qquad \begin{array}{c} H \;\; H \;\; H \\ | \;\;\; | \;\;\; | \\ H-C-C-C^+ \\ | \;\;\; | \;\;\; | \\ H \;\; H \;\; H \end{array}$$

$$\qquad\qquad secondary \qquad\qquad\qquad primary$$

The secondary carbonium ion is more stable than the primary carbonium ion. It is, therefore, formed in preference to the primary carbonium ion and leads to the formation of 2-bromopropane.

Addition of hydrogen bromide to propene to produce 1-bromopropane is called **anti-Markownikoff addition**. It can be achieved by carrying out the reaction in the presence of peroxides. Free radicals are produced rather than carbonium ions.

(ii) Addition to aldehydes and ketones – nucleophilic addition

The carbon–oxygen double bond has a permanent shift of electrons because oxygen is more electronegative than carbon. As a result there is a slight positive charge on the carbon and a slight negative charge on the oxygen.

$$\overset{\delta+}{C}=\overset{\delta-}{O}$$

The carbon atom is then prone to attack by a nucleophile, e.g. CN^- or SO_3Na^-.

$$CN^- + C=O \rightarrow O^- - C - CN$$

$$SO_3Na^- + C=O \rightarrow O^- - C - SO_3Na$$

The ion produced then reacts with a hydrogen ion present in the solution to form the product.

$$H^+ + O^- - C - CN \rightarrow HO - C - CN$$

$$O^- - C - SO_3Na + H^+ \rightarrow HO - C - SO_3Na$$

The slow reaction or lack of reaction of certain ketones with sodium hydrogensulphite can be explained by steric hindrance. If big alkyl groups are attached to the carbonyl group there is insufficient space available for the large SO_3Na^- nucleophile to penetrate and attack the carbon atom.

Condensation reactions involve attack by a molecule containing a nitrogen atom, e.g. hydrazine and phenylhydrazine. This nitrogen has a lone pair of electrons.

$$-H_2N: + \overset{\delta+}{C}=O^{\delta-} \longrightarrow -H_2\overset{+}{N} - C - O^- \rightarrow -HN - C - OH$$

Finally, there is loss of water. $\quad -HN - C - OH \rightarrow -N = C$

38.5 SUBSTITUTION REACTIONS

A substitution reaction is a reaction where an atom or group of atoms replaces an atom or group of atoms already in the molecule.

$$AB + C \rightarrow AC + B$$

The reaction between methane and chlorine (38.3) is a free radical substitution reaction. There are examples of nucleophilic and electrophilic substitution reactions.

(i) Nucleophilic substitution reactions

The hydrolysis of haloalkanes by refluxing with aqueous alkali (see 30.3) is a nucleophilic substitution reaction.

$$RX + KOH \rightarrow ROH + KX$$
$$CH_3CH_2Br + OH^- \rightarrow CH_3CH_2OH + Br^-$$

The carbon atom attached to the halogen is attacked by the nucleophile OH^-.

The rate of hydrolysis of iodoalkanes is greater than the rate of hydrolysis of bromoalkanes which is, in turn, greater than the rate of hydrolysis of chloroalkanes. The rate of hydrolysis is related to the strength of the C—X bond. The stronger the bond between the carbon atom and the halogen, the slower will be the reaction.

Nucleophilic substitution reactions occur more readily with tertiary haloalkanes than secondary, and more readily with secondary than with primary. This can be explained when it is realised that in many cases there is an intermediate carbonium ion formed.

The reaction of a haloalkane with aqueous hydroxide ions can occur in two ways.

(a) *S_N1 mechanism.*

This is a two-stage process that first involves the loss of an X^- ion and the formation of a carbonium ion. The carbonium ion reacts rapidly with an OH^- ion.

$$CH_3-\underset{\underset{CH_3}{|}}{\overset{\overset{CH_3}{|}}{C}}-X \quad \xrightarrow[-X^-]{slow} \quad CH_3-\underset{\underset{CH_3}{|}}{\overset{\overset{CH_3}{|}}{C^+}}+OH^- \quad \xrightarrow{fast} \quad CH_3-\underset{\underset{CH_3}{|}}{\overset{\overset{CH_3}{|}}{C}}-OH$$

The first stage is the rate-determining step and is independent of the concentration of OH^- ions.

$$Rate \propto [haloalkane]$$

The total order of the reaction is one.

(b) *S_N2 mechanism.*

This is a one-stage process involving a simultaneous loss of X^- and a gain of OH^- ion. The rate of reaction is not independent of the concentration of OH^- ions.

$$Rate \propto [haloalkane] [OH^-]$$

The total order of the reaction is two.

Elimination reactions are also possible when haloalkanes are refluxed with sodium hydroxide dissolved in ethanol (see 30.3). There is always competition between substitution and elimination reactions. When a haloalkane is heated with *aqueous* alkali, both substitution and elimination are possible but the substitution is so much more favourable that elimination does not, in practice, occur. In the reaction of a haloalkane with a solution of alkali *in ethanol*, the substitution does not occur, for the reason given shortly, and so elimination takes place.

When the alkali is dissolved in ethanol, the hydroxide ions are solvated with ethanol molecules. The resulting species is too large to approach the positive centre in the carbonium ion and, as a result, substitution is impossible. Instead, the hydroxide ion acts as a base and abstracts a proton.

$$CH_3-\underset{\underset{CH_3}{|}}{\overset{\overset{CH_3}{|}}{C^+}} \xrightarrow{-H^+} CH_2=\underset{\underset{CH_3}{|}}{\overset{\overset{CH_3}{|}}{C}}$$

(ii) Electrophilic substitution reactions (see 29.9)

Common examples of electrophilic substitution are found with benzene and similar aromatic compounds. The common examples are nitration, sulphonation, halogenation and Friedel–Crafts reactions.

Benzene has a ring of negative charge above and below the ring (see 29.8). The following sequence takes place, using X^+ to represent an electrophile.

In the first stage a weak complex is formed between the negative ring on the benzene and the electrophile. A more stable complex is then formed. This complex breaks down with the loss of H^+ to form the product. By doing this the stability of the benzene nucleus is restored.

There are four common electrophilic substitution reactions of benzene.

A *Nitration*

The nitrating mixture is a mixture of concentrated nitric and sulphuric acids. They react to produce the nitryl ion (nitronium ion) NO_2^+.

$$HNO_3 + 2H_2SO_4 \rightleftharpoons NO_2^+ + H_3O^+ + 2HSO_4^-$$

It is possible to isolate salts such as $NO_2^+ClO_4^-$ nitryl chlorate(VII) containing the nitryl ion.

The steps in this reaction are:

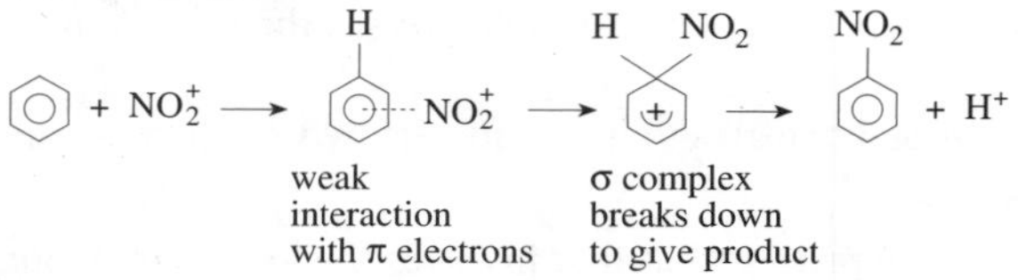

weak
interaction
with π electrons

σ complex
breaks down
to give product

B Sulphonation

The effective electrophile in concentrated sulphuric acid is sulphur(VI) oxide (sulphur trioxide).

$$2H_2SO_4 \rightleftharpoons SO_3 + H_3O^+ + HSO_4^-$$

There is a partial positive charge on the sulphur atom and this bonds to the ring.

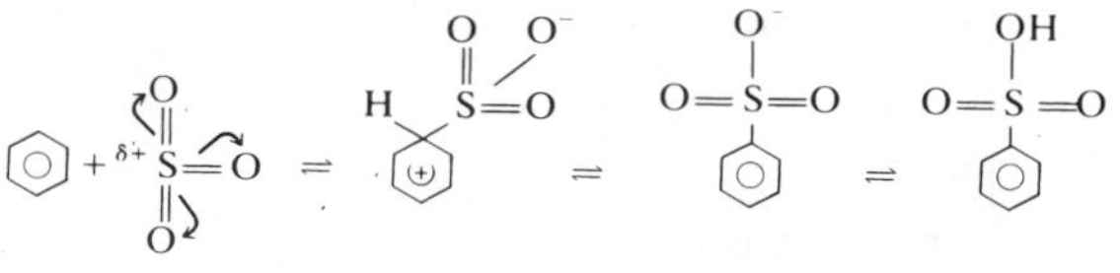

C Halogenation

Substitution of chlorine or bromine into a benzene ring requires a halogen carrier. The halogen carrier is a catalyst and is usually a Lewis acid (see 16.1). Suitable substances include aluminium bromide, $AlBr_3$, and iron(III) bromide, $FeBr_3$.

The halogen carrier causes a polarisation in the halogen molecule, i.e.

$$\overset{\delta+}{Br}\cdots\cdots\cdots Br \cdots\cdots\cdots \overset{\delta-}{AlBr_3}$$

The positive end of this complex attacks the benzene ring and forms a complex with the electrons of the benzene ring.

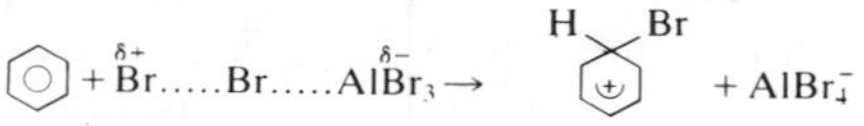

This complex then breaks down to give the product.

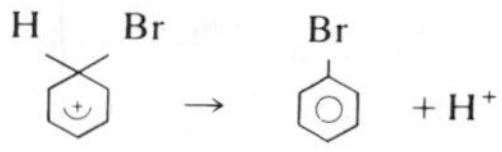

D Friedel–Crafts reaction

These reactions resemble halogenation because they require a halogen carrier, e.g.

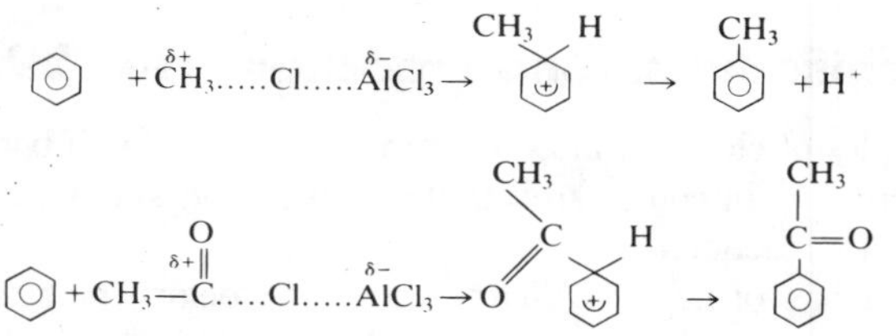

38.6 INTRODUCING A SECOND SUBSTITUENT INTO A BENZENE RING

The rate at which a second substituent can be introduced into a benzene ring and the position of the second substituent, relative to the first, is determined by the substituent already present in the ring.

(i) Rate of substitution

Since the substitution reactions in benzene are electrophilic, if the substituent already present donates electrons to the ring, the rate of reaction will be increased.

Table 38.1 lists the common substituents in order of power of electron donating to or withdrawing from a benzene ring.

Table 38.1 *Common substituents in order of electron donating or withdrawing power*

X

	X	
Electron donating	OH	Decreasing rate of reaction ↓
decreasing power ↓	NH_2	
	OCH_3	
Electron withdrawing	CH_3	
	Cl	
	CHO	
increasing power ↓	SO_3H	
	NO_2	

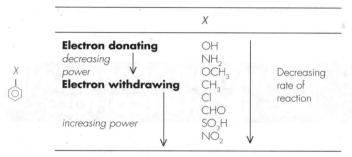

Phenol undergoes electrophilic substitution reactions far more easily than benzene. When bromine water is added to a solution of phenol, a white precipitate of 2,4,6-tribromophenol is formed immediately on mixing in the cold.

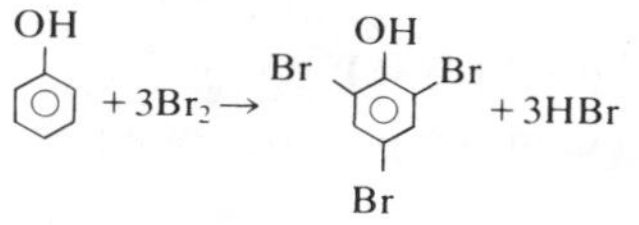

OH
+ 3Br₂ →
OH
Br
Br
Br
+ 3HBr

(ii) Position of substitution

The position of the second substituent is determined by the nature of the substituent already present. There are three possible isomers

X
Y
X
Y
X
Y

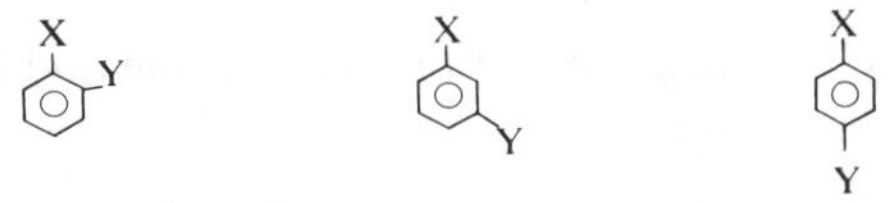

1,2- (or *ortho*) 1,3- (or *meta*) 1,4- (or *para*)

In practice, when carrying out electrophilic substitution with a monosubstituted benzene, either the *meta* (1,3-) product is obtained or some mixture of the *ortho* (1,2-) and *para* (1,4-) is formed. Table 38.2 lists substituents which are *meta* directing and those that are *ortho–para* directing.

Table 38.2 *Directive effects of some common substituents*

Meta directing	*Ortho–para* directing
NO_2	CH_3
COOH	OCH_3
CHO	Cl
CN	NH_2
SO_3H	OH

NB The *meta*-directing substituents all contain at least one double or triple bond, e.g. nitration of nitrobenzene produces 1,3-dinitrobenzene because the nitro group is *meta* directing.

NO₂
+ HNO₃ →
NO₂
NO₂
+ H₂O

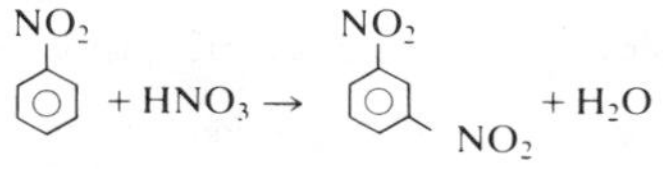

Nitration of phenol produces a mixture of 2-nitrophenol and 4-nitrophenol because the OH group is *ortho–para* directing.

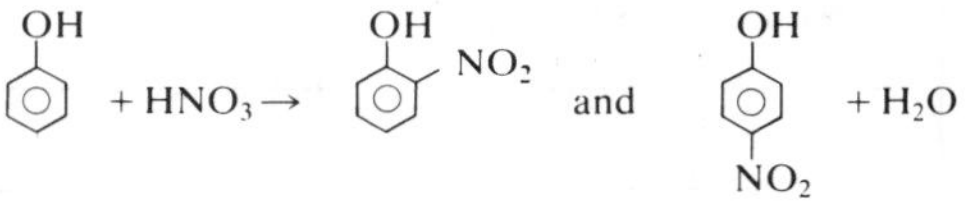

38.7 FORMATION OF CARBONIUM IONS FROM ALCOHOLS

When ethanol is treated with concentrated sulphuric acid, a carbonium ion is produced.

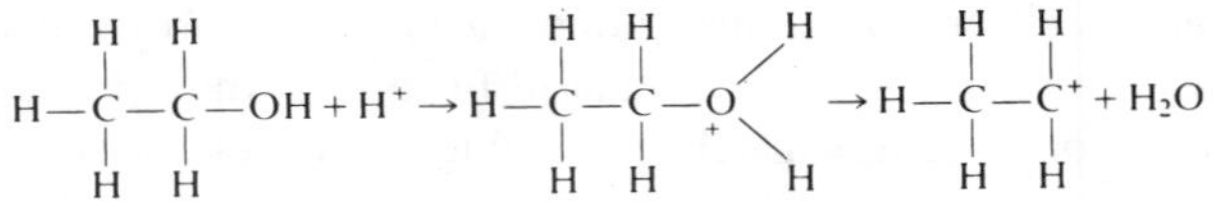

This carbonium ion can behave in two ways.

1 At a temperature of 140 °C in the presence of excess ethanol, ethoxyethane is produced.

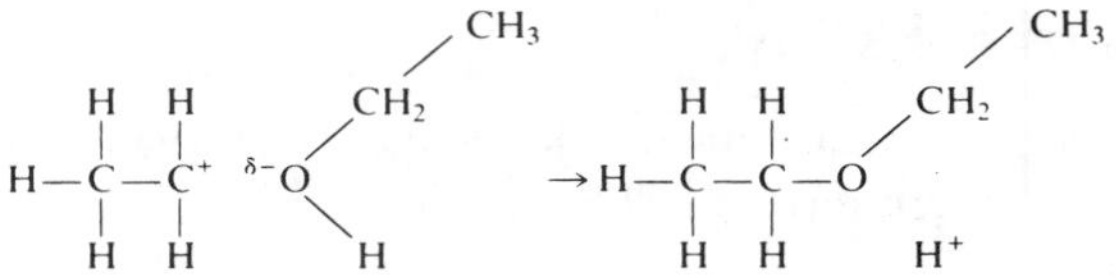

2 At a temperature of 170 °C, the bond between carbon and hydrogen is broken, forming ethene.

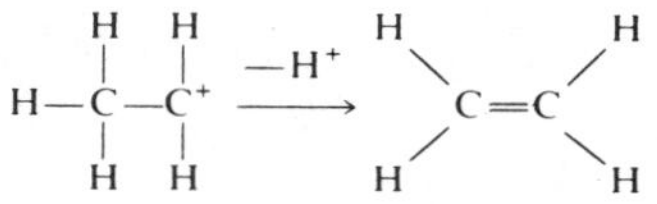

Chapter roundup

The following table summarises the common reaction mechanisms and some examples.

Type of reaction		Examples
substitution	– free radical	methane and chlorine in the presence of ultraviolet light
	– nucleophilic	haloalkanes and aqueous sodium hydroxide, reflux
	– electrophilic	benzene with (i) conc. nitric and sulphuric acids, below 50 °C – nitration (ii) fuming sulphuric acid, reflux 24 hrs – sulphonation (iii) halogen (e.g. chlorine) and halogen carrier – chlorination/halogenation
elimination	– nucleophilic	haloalkane with solution of sodium hydroxide in ethanol
addition	– electrophilic	ethene and bromine or hydrogen bromide
	– nucleophilic	aldehydes and ketones with hydrogen cyanide or sodium hydrogensulphite

Worked questions and answers

1 Methylbenzene, $\bigcirc$—CH_3, can be nitrated using a mixture of nitric acid and sulphuric acid. In an attempt to find out what nitration products result, an experiment was conducted as follows:

"10 drops of concentrated sulphuric acid were carefully added to 10 drops of concentrated nitric acid in a test-tube, while shaking the mixture and cooling the test-tube under a stream of cold water. The mixture of acids was then added to 5 drops of methylbenzene in another test-tube again shaking this mixture under a stream of cold water. The mixture was poured into a beaker containing 10 cm^3 of cold water. The contents of the beaker were transferred to a separating funnel and the organic layer separated off."

(a) When methylbenzene is nitrated:
  (i) what *type of reaction* (addition, elimination, etc.) is said to take place?
  (ii) what *class of reagent* (electrophile, nucleophile, etc.) attacks methylbenzene?
  (iii) what nitrogen-containing ion is believed to be involved in the actual nitration stage of the reaction?
  (iv) why is the reaction mixture cooled?

(b) Suggest briefly how the organic layer resulting from the nitration might be:
  (i) treated to remove residual acids.
  (ii) dried.

(c) The methyl group in methylbenzene is said to direct incoming nitro groups to the 2- and 4- positions of the benzene ring. Using this information, draw structural formulae to show *three* of the possible products of nitration of methylbenzene.

(Nuffield)

Tutorial note

(a) (i) Substitution
  (ii) Electrophile
  (iii) NO_2^+
  (iv) Reaction is very exothermic. Therefore cooled to prevent reactants/products from vaporising, or to prevent acid spitting out.

(b) (i) Shake with aqueous sodium carbonate solution.
  (ii) Add anhydrous sodium sulphate.

(c) Any three of

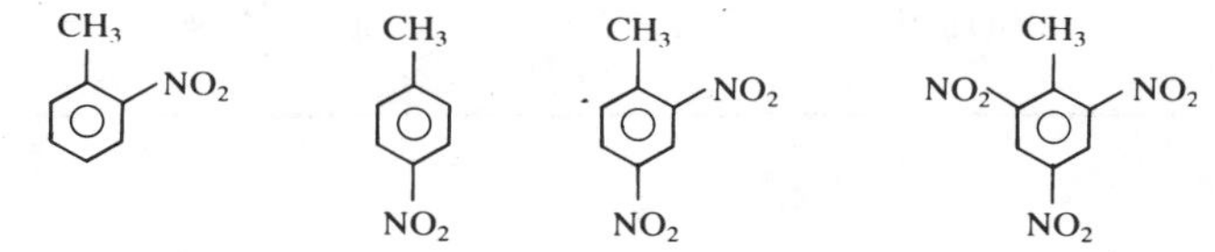

Question bank

1 State what is meant by each of the following terms; give one example for each term.
  (a) A nucleophile
  (b) A (free) radical
  (c) Heterolytic bond fission
  (d) An enantiomer
  (e) A tertiary alcohol

(WJEC 1990)

Points

Enantiomers are optical isomers.

CHAPTER 39

THE STRENGTHS OF ORGANIC ACIDS AND BASES

Units in this chapter

Chapter objectives

In this chapter we will consider the relative strengths of organic acids and bases. We will use pK$_a$ and pK$_b$ values to do this. Before attempting this chapter go back and look at Chapters 15 and 16. You will find in Chapter 16 exactly what is meant by pK$_a$ and pK$_b$. Remember that pK$_a$ is a measure of the strength (i.e. degree of ionisation) of an acid. The smaller the numerical value of pK$_a$ the more ionised (i.e. stronger) is the acid.

Similarly, pK$_b$ is a measure of the strength of a base. The smaller the numerical value of pK$_b$ the stronger is the base.

39.1 ORIGIN OF ACIDITY IN ORGANIC COMPOUNDS

When a compound H—X acts as an acid, the H—X bond breaks heterolytically to form H$^+$ ions. The extent of the acidity depends upon the number of H—X bonds broken in a sample.

The acidity of an organic compound H—X depends upon three factors:

❶ the strength of the H—X bond;

❷ the electronegativity of X; and

❸ any stabilisation of the X$^-$ ion compared with HX – this will be shown by the existence of a number of possible resonance structures.

Comparison of methanol and phenol

Phenol is very slightly acidic, methanol is not. The difference is due to the stabilisation of the $C_6H_5O^-$ ion produced by the loss of the H^+ ion.

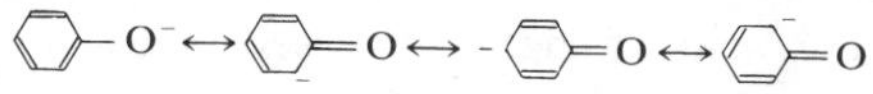

The CH_3O ion is not stabilised. The pK_a values of methanol and phenol are 16 and 9.95 respectively.

Comparison of methanol and ethanoic acid

The carbonyl group in ethanoic acid has an electron withdrawing effect on the O—H bond. This weakens the bond. Also the ethanoate ion is stabilised by the existence of two resonance structures.

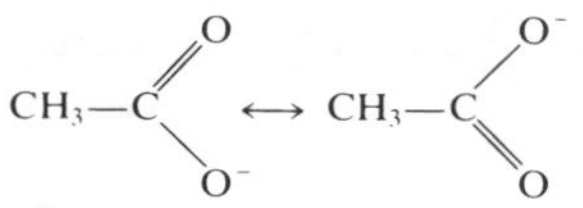

The pK_a values of methanol and ethanoic acid are 16 and 4.76 respectively.

39.2 RELATIVE STRENGTHS OF CARBOXYLIC ACIDS

The pK_a values of some carboxylic acids are given in Table 39.1.

Table 39.1 The pK_a values of some carboxylic acids

Acid		pK_a	Acid		pK_a
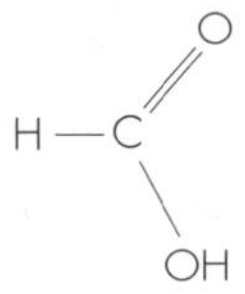	methanoic acid	3.77	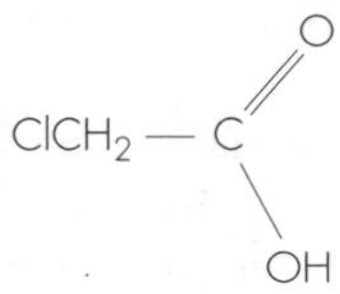	chloroethanoic acid	2.86
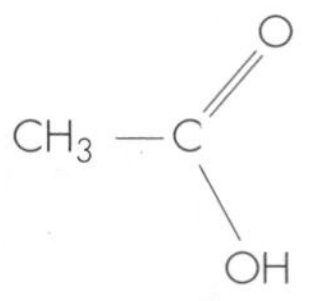	ethanoic acid	4.76	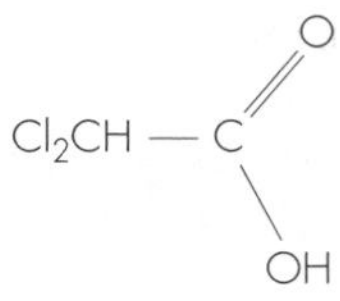	dichloroethanoic acid	1.29
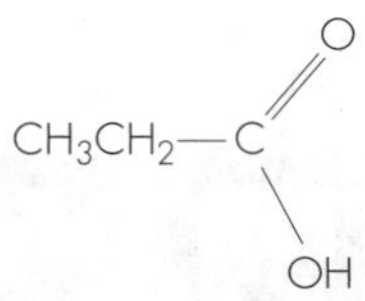	propanoic acid	4.88	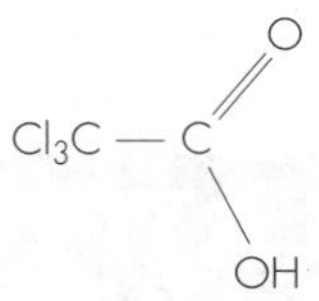	trichloroethanoic acid	0.65

Replacing the nonhydroxylic hydrogen atom of methanoic acid by an alkyl group decreases the strength of the acid. There is a shift of electrons from the alkyl group towards the carboxyl group which reduces the tendency for the O—H bond to break heterolytically, i.e.

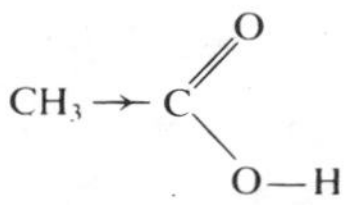

When a hydrogen atom in ethanoic acid is replaced by a chlorine atom to produce chloroethanoic acid, the acid strength increases. This is due to the electron withdrawing effect on the carboxyl group caused by the greater electronegativity of chlorine compared to hydrogen. This assists in the ionisation of the OH group.

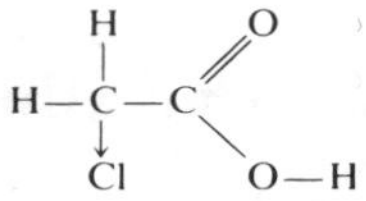

Further substitution of chlorine atoms to produce dichloroethanoic and trichloroethanoic acids produces stronger acids.

Benzenecarboxylic acid is a weaker acid than methanoic acid. This is explained by the overall electron donating effect of the phenyl group compared to hydrogen.

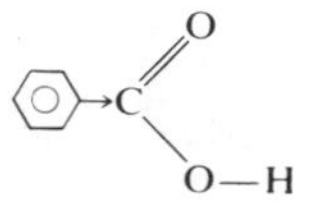

39.3 COMPARISON OF THE pK_b VALUES OF AMINES AND AMIDES

The strength of a nitrogenous base is related to the readiness of the compound to accept protons, i.e. the availability of the unshared pair of electrons on the nitrogen atom.

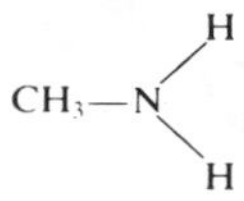

methylamine
pK_b 3.36

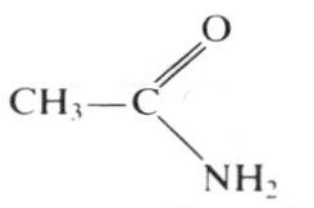

ethanamide
pK_b 14.5

The carbonyl group adjacent to the nitrogen atom in ethanamide has a tendency to withdraw electrons and reduce the availability of the pair of electrons.

As a result, ethanamide is only very weakly basic in water. Methylamine is much more strongly basic than ethanamide.

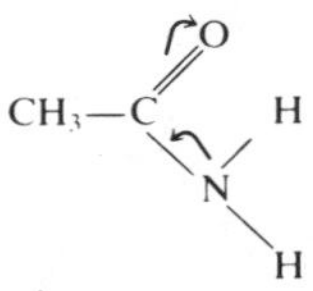

39.4 RELATIVE STRENGTHS OF ORGANIC BASES

The pK_b values of some common bases are given in Table 39.2.

Table 39.2 *The pK_b values of some common bases*

Base		pK_b	Base		pK_b
NH_3	ammonia	4.75	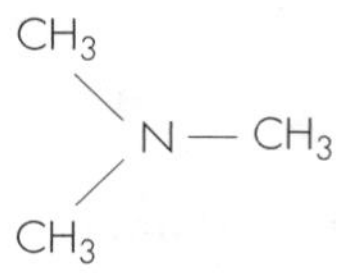		
CH_3NH_2	methylamine	3.36	trimethylamine		4.20
$CH_3CH_2NH_2$	ethylamine	3.33			
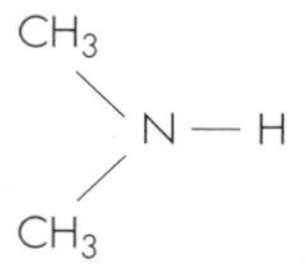	dimethylamine	3.23	phenylamine		9.38

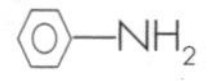

(Do not attempt to remember these values.)

Methylamine is a stronger base than ammonia. This is explained by the electron donating effect of the methyl group increasing the availability of the spare pair of electrons on the nitrogen atom.

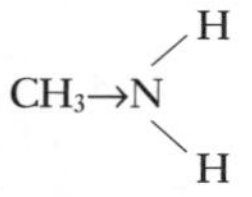

$CH_3 \rightarrow N$ with H and H

The strength of the base is further increased by the substitution of a second methyl group. However, the trisubstituted amine, trimethylamine, is not a stronger base than methylamine and dimethylamine. This is due to a **solvation effect**. The ions produced by methylamine and dimethylamine are stabilised by hydrogen bonding with water molecules. This solvation is not possible with trimethylamine.

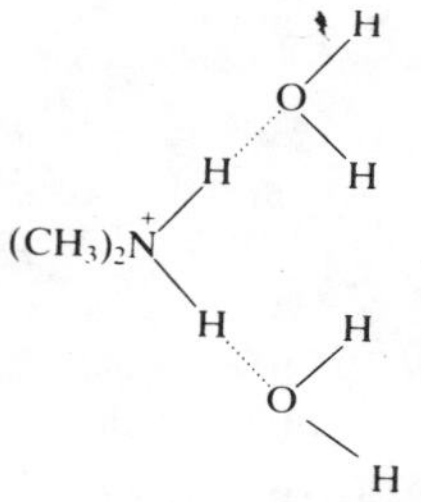

Phenylamine is a much weaker base than ammonia because of the electron withdrawing effect of the phenyl group. The lone pair can be stabilised by delocalisation in the ring.

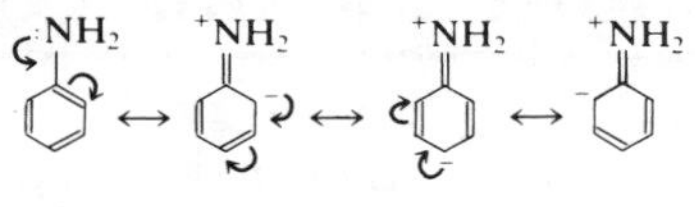

39.5 ASPIRIN AND PARACETAMOL

Aspirin and paracetamol are both analgesics (medicines which remove pain). Aspirin is produced industrially by the following series of reactions.

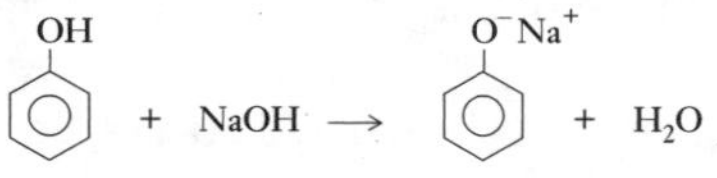

OH (ring) + NaOH → O⁻Na⁺ (ring) + H_2O

sodium phenate

This reaction shows the acidic properties of phenol.

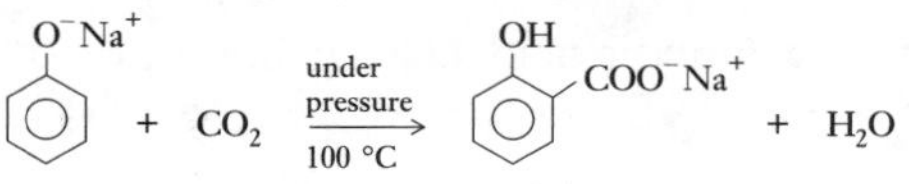

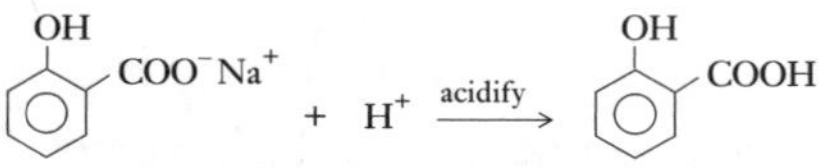

O⁻Na⁺ (ring) + CO_2 $\xrightarrow[100\ °C]{\text{under pressure}}$ OH, COO⁻Na⁺ (ring) + H_2O

OH, COO⁻Na⁺ (ring) + H^+ $\xrightarrow{\text{acidify}}$ OH, COOH (ring)

2-hydroxybenzenecarboxylic acid

Ethanoylation of this acid with ethanoyl anhydride produces 2-ethanoyloxybenzenecarboxylic acid (previously called acetyl salicylate or aspirin).

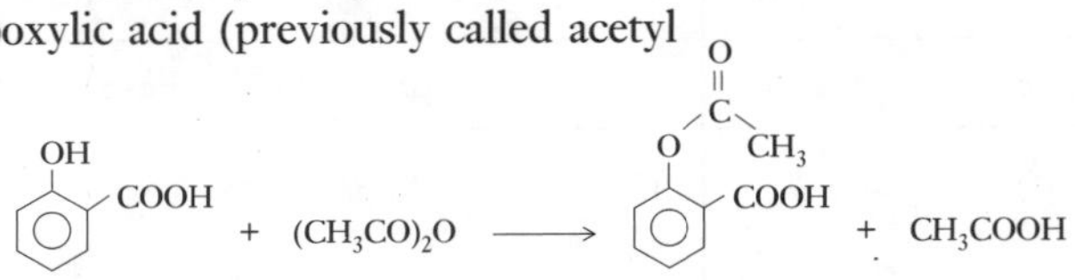

Aspirin is often used in the form of 'soluble aspirin', which is the sodium salt of the acid.

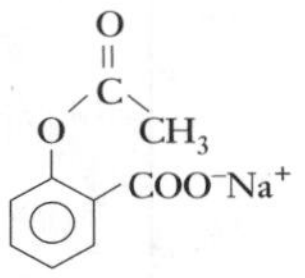

Paracetamol is N-(4-hydroxyphenyl)ethanamide. In the final stage 4-hydroxyphenylamine is reacted with ethanoic acid.

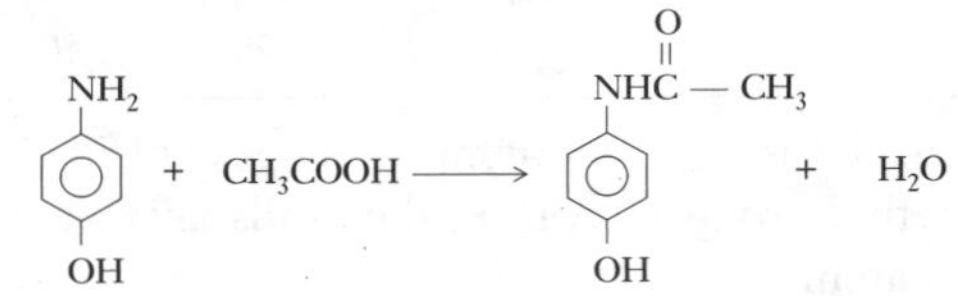

N-(4-hydroxyphenyl)ethanamide

Chapter roundup

You will have noticed that slight molecular changes alter the pK_a or pK_b values. For example

	pK_a
ethanoic acid	4.76
chloroethanoic acid	2.86
fluoroethanoic acid	2.66
dichloroethanoic acid	1.29

Compared against ethanoic acid, these values reflect the different electron withdrawing powers of the halogens.

Worked questions and answers

1 Use the data in the chapter roundup to predict the pK_a values for
   (a) bromoethanoic acid, and
   (b) trichloroethanoic acid.

Tutorial note

(a) The pK_a value for bromoethanoic acid should be greater than 2.86, perhaps in the order of 3. This is because bromine is not as electronegative as fluorine or chlorine.
(b) The pK_a value for trichloroethanoic acid should be less than 1, reflecting the fact that there are three chlorine atoms withdrawing electrons and weakening the O—H bond.

   Incidentally, the values (which you would not be expected to know) are (a) 2.90 and (b) 0.65.

2 The pK_a values for fluoroethanoic acid, chloroethanoic acid and bromoethanoic acid are 2.66, 2.86 and 2.90, respectively. Explain the results.

Tutorial note

Fluoroethanoic acid is the strongest acid (lowest pK_a value). Fluorine is the most electronegative element and withdraws electrons more than chlorine and bromine, weakening the O—H bond to a greater extent.

THE CHEMICAL INDUSTRY

Units in this chapter

Chapter objectives

In Great Britain and throughout the world the chemical industry is extremely important. In this chapter we will look only at some examples of the large scale production of chemicals. You could perhaps look for other examples, such as titanium dioxide and paints, polymers, etc.

At GCSE level you may have studied some of these industrial processes, for example you may have studied the extraction of iron in the blast furnace or aluminium in the smelter. Different extraction methods are used depending upon the position of the metal in the reactivity series.

40.1 METAL EXTRACTION

The standard electrode potential of a metal is a good indication of the ease of extracting a metal from its compounds. However, it is even better to use the free energy change occurring during the process

$$\text{metal oxide} \rightarrow \text{metal}$$

A reaction only occurs, strictly speaking, in a closed system, if there is a decrease in free energy. The equation we met in Chapter 13 was

$$\Delta G = \Delta H - T\Delta S$$

Changes in enthalpy (ΔH) and entropy (ΔS) can be calculated over a wide range of temperature. It is therefore possible to calculate free energy changes over a similar range of temperature. These free energy changes can be shown in graphs. For example, Fig. 40.1 shows the free energy changes (in kJ mol^{-1}) for the formation of aluminium oxide and chromium(III) oxide.

The free energy formation of aluminium is more negative than that of chromium. Aluminium should therefore reduce chromium(III) oxide at all temperatures. Using

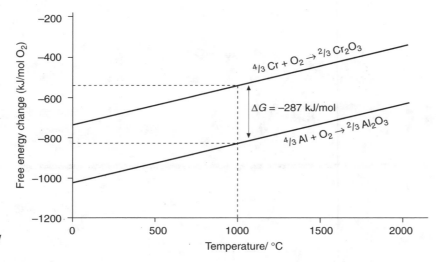

Fig. 40.1

the graph in Fig. 40.1, we can find the ΔG values of -827 kJ mol^{-1} and -540 kJ mol^{-1}. Adding these together we can get an overall value for ΔG of -287 kJ mol^{-1}. Since there is a decrease in free energy the reaction between aluminium and chromium(III) oxide is feasible at all temperatures. It does not, however, take place at low temperatures because reactions between solids generally have high activation energies.

Fig. 40.2 shows the free energy changes at different temperatures for a range of systems. Metals such as aluminium and calcium (with low free energy changes at all

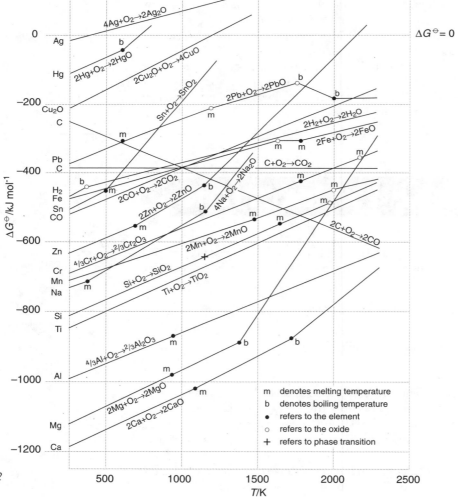

Fig. 40.2

temperatures) are good reducing agents at all temperatures. Magnesium is a good reducing agent up to about 1300 K, then, with a steep rise in ΔG, it becomes less good. These graphs are called Ellingham diagrams and can be used to predict the outcomes of metal reductions.

40.2 AMMONIA

You may be familiar from GCSE with the Haber process for producing ammonia. In Great Britain each year we produce approximately 2 million tonnes of ammonia. Most of this is turned into fertilisers but it is also used for synthetic fibres, dyestuffs, polymers (e.g. polyurethanes) and explosives.

Hydrogen is produced for this process by passing methane or naphtha mixed with steam over a heated nickel catalyst at pressures up to 30 atm. The products are carbon oxides and hydrogen. The gases produced are mixed with steam and passed over a heated catalyst to produce carbon dioxide and hydrogen. The carbon dioxide is dissolved in water under pressure and then recovered for the production of urea.

Nitrogen for the Haber process is produced by the fractional distillation of liquid air.

The equation for the Haber process is

$$N_2(g) + 3H_2(g) \rightleftharpoons 2NH_3(g) \qquad \Delta H = -92 \text{ kJ mol}^{-1}$$

In the Haber process, 2 moles of ammonia are formed from 4 moles of gas (a mixture of 1 mole of nitrogen and 3 moles of hydrogen). According to Le Chatelier's principle, if the pressure is increased, the equilibrium will move to the right to give a smaller volume and hence produce more ammonia (Chapter 15). Again, more ammonia should be produced if the temperature is decreased, that is, according to Le Chatelier's principle, the equilibrium should move in the exothermic direction to compensate for the decrease in temperature. Theoretically, high pressures and low temperatures should give the best yield of ammonia, but other factors have to be considered.

❶ Since unreacted gases can be recycled, does the equilibrium have to be reached?

❷ High pressure equipment becomes increasingly expensive as pressure increases.

❸ At low temperatures reactions are very slow. Even using a catalyst to speed up the reaction may not make the process fast enough to be economical.

❹ At low temperatures catalyst life and activity are prolonged.

In practice, the reaction conditions reflect a compromise and the usual conditions are:

(i) a pressure of 200 atm;

(ii) a temperature around 380–450 °C; and

(iii) a catalyst of finely divided iron containing promoters to stop the catalyst being poisoned.

The conversion under these conditions is about 15% and the equilibrium position is never reached in the converter.

Large ammonia plants are more economical than smaller plants provided that the plant is built with well-tried technology. When siting a new plant it should be close to sources of:

❶ energy, whether coal, oil or natural gas;

❷ water, required in large quantities for the process; and

❸ transport, by road, river, sea or rail.

In Great Britain, ammonia plants are sited at Billingham (close to supplies of North Sea oil and gas), Ince Marsh in Cheshire (close to oil refineries), Avonmouth and Immingham. Ammonia is a profitable use of natural gas and refinery gases and so oil producers often build ammonia plants to increase the value of their products.

40.3 FERTILISERS

World artificial fertiliser demand has increased in the past 50 years in response to growing world population. Between 1945 and 1985 the quantities of nitrogen, phosphorus and potassium (the three elements required in largest quantities by fertiliser plants) have grown as follows.

		Millions of tonnes	
	Nitrogen	Phosphorus	Potassium
1945	2	3	1.5
1985	70	34	26

The chemical industry has expanded to meet these demands.

Fertilisers are often compound fertilisers, providing nitrogen, phosphorus and potassium, e.g. 15% N, 7% P, 17% K, to enable plants to grow, flower and fruit. You will see the meaning of the NPK values for fertilisers printed on the bags. Fertilisers may be solids, usually in a granular form for easy distribution on the land, or liquids, for cases where nutrients are required in a less concentrated form.

The basic raw materials used in the manufacture of fertilisers are air (as a source of nitrogen), phosphate rock (as a source of phosphorus) and sylvinite (as a source of potassium). Various processes have to be carried out before these raw materials can be converted into a fertiliser. Although the sylvinite (a mixture of potassium chloride, sodium chloride and clay) can be used unchanged, nitrogen has to be converted into ammonia and nitric acid.

Ammonia is produced by the Haber process (see 40.2). Ammonia is converted to nitric acid by catalytic oxidation in a three-stage process.

1 $4NH_3(g) + 5O_2(g) \rightarrow 4NO(g) + 6H_2O(g)$

2 $2NO(g) + O_2(g) \rightarrow 2NO_2(g)$

3 $3NO_2(g) + H_2O(l) \rightarrow 2HNO_3(aq) + NO(g)$

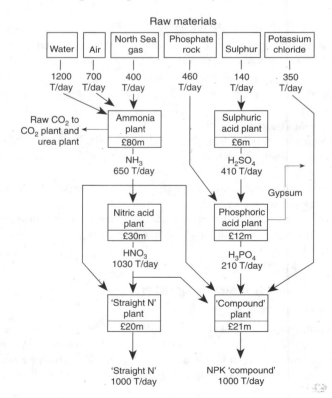

Fig. 40.3 Flow diagram for typical 2000 tonnes per day (T/day) fertiliser factory

The first stage is catalysed by a platinum/rhodium alloy and is very fast, exothermic and up to 98% of the reactants are converted. Stage 2 occurs on cooling and stage 3 on absorption in water.

Phosphate rock is largely in the form of the tricalcium salt and is insoluble in water. Before converting it into a fertiliser it has to be treated with sulphuric acid to make the dihydrogenphosphate, which is water soluble and can be absorbed by the plant.

Fertiliser production involves an integrated series of processes. These processes are summarised in Fig. 40.3.

40.4 CHLORINE AND SODIUM HYDROXIDE

The production of chlorine and sodium hydroxide from natural deposits of sodium chloride (salt) is the basis of the chloralkali industry. Chlorine is widely used to make a range of organic and inorganic chemicals including PVC, chlorine bleaches and so on. Sodium hydroxide (caustic soda) is a widely used alkali, involved in the manufacture of paper, aluminium and soap. Electrolysis of brine (salt solution) produces 1 tonne of chlorine at the same time as 1.13 tonnes of sodium hydroxide and 0.028 tonnes of hydrogen.

There are many different processes used in the electrolysis of brine. An aqueous solution contains the following ions.

$$Na^+, Cl^-, H^+, OH^-$$

We will concentrate on just two processes – the mercury cell and the diaphragm cell.

The mercury cell

This involves the electrolysis of brine using a moving mercury cathode and titanium anodes. It is shown in Fig. 40.4.

The processes taking place at the electrodes are:

Cathode	$Na^+ + e^- \rightarrow Na$
Anode	$2Cl^- \rightarrow Cl_2 + 2e^-$

The sodium produced at the cathode reacts with the mercury and forms mercury amalgam, Na/Hg. The mercury amalgam is then run into water and reacts to produce sodium hydroxide and hydrogen.

$$2Na/Hg + 2H_2O \rightarrow 2NaOH + H_2 + 2Hg$$

The mercury can be recycled.

The diaphragm cell

This process again involves the electrolysis of brine but this time with titanium anodes and steel cathodes. The anodes and the cathodes are separated by a porous asbestos diaphragm. The process is summarised in Fig. 40.5.

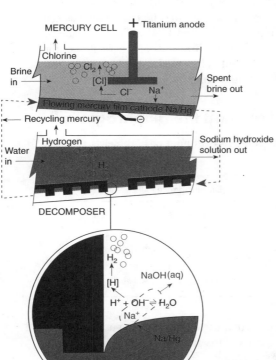

Fig. 40.4 Moving mercury cell

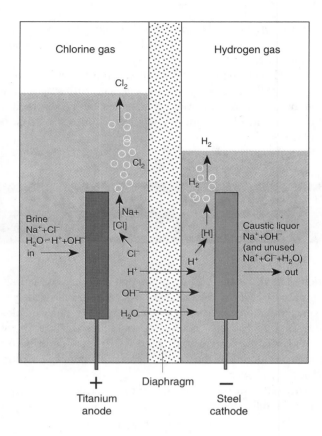

Fig. 40.5 Diaphragm cell

The processes taking place at the electrodes are:

$$\text{Cathode} \qquad 2H^+ + 2e^- \rightarrow H_2$$
$$\text{Anode} \qquad 2Cl^- \rightarrow Cl_2 + 2e^-$$

Saturated brine is pumped into the anode compartment. The brine level in the anode compartment is kept higher than the level in the cathode compartment so that brine seeps through the membrane. The resulting solution leaving the cell, known as cell liquor, contains approximately 12% sodium hydroxide and 15% sodium chloride by mass. When this solution is evaporated to about one-fifth of its original volume, the relatively insoluble sodium chloride crystallises out. The remaining solution contains 50% sodium hydroxide and less than 1% sodium chloride.

Comparison of the mercury cell and the diaphragm cell

The following table compares the construction and running of both cells.

	Mercury cell	Diaphragm cell
Construction	Expensive to set up and supply mercury	Relatively simple and inexpensive
Operation of cell	Mercury potentially hazardous – must be reclaimed	Frequent replacement of diaphragm
Product	High purity product	Must be evaporated to crystallise out salt

Fig. 40.6 summarises the costs of production of the two processes. Let us distinguish between **fixed costs** and **variable costs**. Fixed costs are costs which would exist in setting up the factory and running it irrespective of whether any products were made, e.g. initial building costs, and so on. Variable costs are costs which will vary according to how much of the products are made, e.g. energy costs, raw material costs and so on.

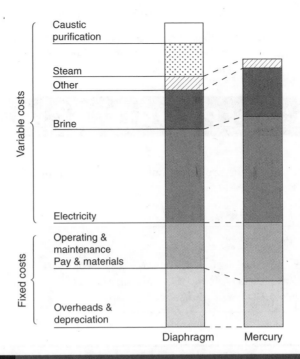

Fig. 40.6

40.5 SODIUM CARBONATE

Sodium carbonate fulfils a world demand for a cheap alkali, with about 29 million tonnes being manufactured annually. Much of this is used for the manufacture of glass. Today sodium carbonate is manufactured from salt by the ammonia–soda (or Solvay) process.

The overall production of sodium carbonate from salt and limestone can be summarised by the equation

$$2NaCl + CaCO_3 \rightarrow CaCl_2 + Na_2CO_3$$

However, the reverse process is competing and more thermodynamically favourable. So favourable is this process that sodium chloride and calcium carbonate are immediately formed if aqueous solutions of calcium chloride and sodium carbonate are mixed. In order to achieve the overall reaction, therefore, a series of reactions is required.

Limestone is decomposed to produced carbon dioxide and the calcium oxide produced is reacted with water to produce calcium hydroxide.

$$CaCO_3 \rightarrow CaO + CO_2$$
$$CaO + H_2O \rightarrow Ca(OH)_2$$

The calcium hydroxide is then heated with ammonium chloride to produce ammonia.

$$2NH_4Cl + Ca(OH)_2 \rightarrow 2NH_3 + 2H_2O + CaCl_2$$

Brine is then saturated with ammonia and this solution is passed into the Solvay towers. As it falls through the towers it comes into contact with carbon dioxide pumped into the bottom of the towers at a pressure of 3 atm. Sodium hydrogencarbonate is precipitated and can be removed by filtration.

$$Na^+ + HCO_3^- \rightarrow NaHCO_3$$

This process produces considerable amounts of heat and any rises in temperature must be carefully controlled because the solubility of sodium hydrogencarbonate increases with temperature and precipitation will not occur if the solution is too warm.

Finally, heating sodium hydrogencarbonate produces sodium carbonate and carbon dioxide.

$$2NaHCO_3 \rightarrow Na_2CO_3 + H_2O + CO_2$$

The only waste material in the entire process is calcium chloride, and even this can be used for refrigeration, concrete curing and ground consolidation.

40.6 SULPHURIC ACID

The industrial process for producing sulphuric acid is summarised in illustrative question 2, Chapter 26.

Chapter roundup

This chapter may have given you some insight into common industrial processes in the chemical industry. Some of the information has been obtained from the ICI magazine for teachers called 'Steam'.

Worked questions and answers

1 The graph shows the variation of free energy for four systems at different temperatures.

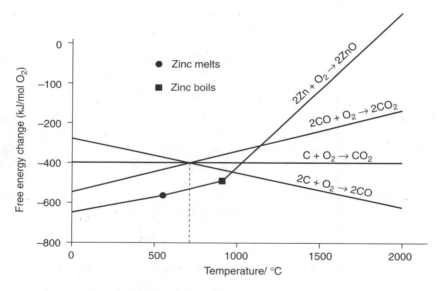

From the graph, calculate the value of ΔG at 710 °C for the reduction of carbon dioxide to carbon monoxide. What can you conclude from this value?

Tutorial note

From the graph

$$2CO(g) + O_2(g) \rightarrow 2CO_2(g) \qquad \Delta G = -400 \text{ kJ mol}^{-1}$$
$$C(s) + O_2(g) \rightarrow CO_2(g) \qquad \Delta G = -400 \text{ kJ mol}^{-1}$$

Reverse the second equation and add the two together.

$$CO_2(g) + C(s) \rightleftharpoons 2CO(g) \qquad \Delta G = 0$$

The system is therefore in equilibrium.

2 (a) The initial stage in the manufacture of nitric acid is the catalytic oxidation of ammonia by air at 850 °C using a platinum–rhodium alloy gauze as catalyst. The reaction is

$$4NH_3(g) + 5O_2(g) \rightleftharpoons 4NO(g) + 6H_2O(g) \qquad \Delta H = -905 \text{ kJ mol}^{-1}$$

State why:
(i) the gauze is heated to start the reaction;
(ii) the gauze remains hot during the reaction; and
(iii) platinum and rhodium are used although they are expensive metals.

(b) In the second stage of the manufacture of nitric acid, the gases from the catalyst unit are cooled to 150 °C when nitrogen dioxide is formed

$$2NO(g) + O_2(g) \rightleftharpoons 2NO_2(g) \qquad \Delta H = -113 \text{ kJ mol}^{-1}$$

Explain why the gases are cooled.

(c) The nitrogen dioxide in (b) is then absorbed in water. The initial reaction is

$$2NO_2(g) + H_2O(l) \rightarrow HNO_3(aq) + HNO_2(aq)$$

Name this type of reaction and give reasons for your answer.

(d) Give two uses of nitric acid.

(e) State one fixed cost and one variable cost incurred in nitric acid production.
(AEB 1990)

Tutorial note

(a) The question asks you to state and provide no explanation.
(i) The gauze is heated to provide the initial activation energy to start the process.
(ii) Once the initial energy is provided, the reaction continues because the reaction is exothermic.
(iii) The platinum–rhodium gauze is a catalyst and is therefore not used up. This is not entirely true in practice. The heat eventually breaks down the fine gauze which has to be sent about every fortnight for reprocessing.

(b) This part requires a different level of answer. The forward reaction is exothermic. Lowering the temperature, according to Le Chatelier's principle (Chapter 15), should move the equilibrium to the right and produce more nitrogen dioxide.

(c) The reaction is a redox reaction (Chapter 6). Nitrogen is in oxidation state +4 in NO_2, +5 in HNO_3 and +3 in HNO_2. This type of self-oxidation and reduction is called **disproportionation**.

(d) Fertilisers and explosives.

(e) Fixed cost – building the plant. Variable cost – raw materials, e.g. ammonia.

3 (a) The diagrams show two items of industrial equipment, A and B.

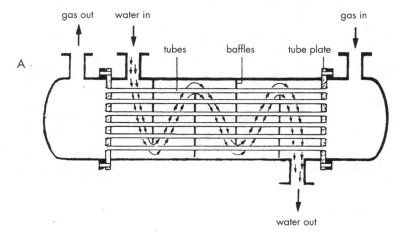

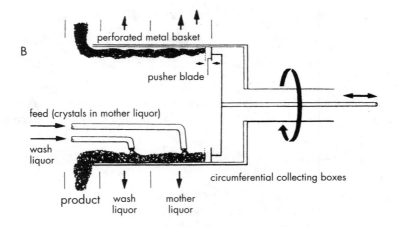

B
perforated metal basket
pusher blade
feed (crystals in mother liquor)
wash liquor
circumferential collecting boxes
product   wash liquor   mother liquor

For each item:
(i) state its name;
(ii) state under which unit operation it is classified;
(iii) describe the purpose for which it is used.
(b) In the laboratory you have determined the liquid–vapour, temperature–composition diagram for a system such as ethanoic acid/water or ethanol/propanone. Describe, giving details, how your diagram was determined. Your description should include comments on:
(i) the apparatus used;
(ii) experimental procedure;
(iii) range of mixtures investigated;
(iv) individual and group work;
(v) standardisation of thermometers used;
(vi) analytical aspects and chemical calculations;
(vii) construction of the diagram.
(c) The diagram below displays the liquid–vapour curve for the ethanol–propanone system.

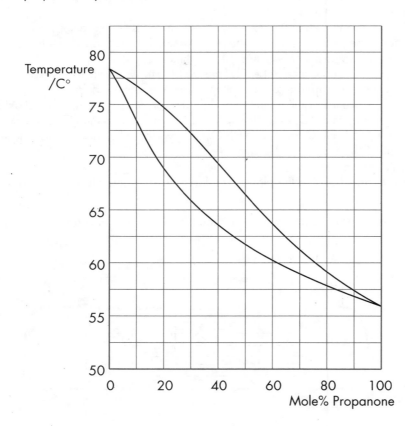

(i) At what temperature does a mixture containing 50 mole% of ethanol boil?

(ii) What is the composition of the vapour when a 50 mole% ethanol mixture boils?

(iii) Starting with a liquid of 50 mole% ethanol, how many consecutive simple distillations would be required to give a mixture containing 90 mole% propanone?

(iv) State and explain whether it would be possible to produce pure propanone by a number of consecutive distillations.

(d) The chemical reactor lies at the heart of any chemical engineering process. Compare and contrast the use in industry of:

(i) homogeneous and heterogeneous reactors;

(ii) isothermal and adiabatic reactors.

Explain, giving ONE example, what is meant by a fluidised bed reactor.

(ULEAC)

Tutorial notes

(a) A (i) Shell and tube heat exchanger.   (ii) Heat transfer.

(iii) First fluid through the tubes, second fluid across the tubes. Can be used to condense and heat medium.

B (i) Centrifuge.   (ii) Separation.

(iii) Vessel rotates, solids to wall, liquid escapes (note washing facilities).

(b) (i) Require flask (pear shaped), side arm adaptor, side Liebig condenser, thermometer (bulb) fully immersed in boiling liquid.

(ii) Record temperature as last bubble emerges from capillary. Reboil and collect 15 cm^3 of distillate.

(iii) Approximately 5 mixtures.

(iv) Each pair to complete one mixture and share results.

(v) Thermometers suspended in beaker of distilled water until water boils – appropriate correction factor.

(vi) 1 g of distillate, 20 cm^3 of distilled water, 3 drops of phenolphthalein. Titrate with 0.05 M NaOH. Calculate number of moles of ethanoic acid in the distillate.

(vii) Any constructive comment, e.g. errors.

(c) (i) 62 °C; move up vertically on 50 mole% line until bottom liquid curve is reached.

(ii) 68 mole% propanone.

(iii) 4.

(iv) No. An infinite number of distillations would be required.

(d) (i) Homogeneous reactor – all reactants are in the same physical state.

Heterogeneous reactor – reactants are in two or more different phases: particularly significant for gas- and/or liquid-phase reactions which take place at the surface of a solid catalyst.

(ii) Most chemical reactions involve significant energy (temperature) changes, either exothermic or endothermic. If no attempt is made to compensate for this by heating or cooling the reaction mixture, then the reactor is said to be operating adiabatically.

With highly exothermic reactions a significant rise in temperature will occur unless heat is removed. When an optimum temperature range is maintained constantly throughout, the reaction is said to be operating isothermally.

Fluidised bed reactor. Reactants (or catalysts) suspended as small granules in a stream of reactant or inert substance. Example – catalytic cracking: catalyst (silica-alumina) suspended as small granules in a stream of hydrocarbon vapour. Provides a large surface area.

Question bank

1 The standard free energies of formation of magnesium oxide and carbon monoxide at temperatures of 1000 °C and 2000 °C for one mole of oxygen at one atmosphere are given below.

	$\Delta G^{\ominus}$ in kJ	
	at 1000 °C	at 2000 °C
$2Mg + O_2 \rightarrow 2MgO$	−941	−314
$2C + O_2 \rightarrow 2CO$	−439	−628

Calculate the free energy change for the reaction

$$2MgO + 2C \rightarrow 2Mg + 2CO$$

at each temperature and comment on your answers.

2 Using the information in 40.4 compare the costs of mercury cell and diaphragm cell processes for the production of sodium hydroxide and chlorine. Are there any circumstances where you would recommend the mercury cell method?

Points

You probably will realise that the purity of the sodium hydroxide produced by the mercury cell method may be the reason for using this process.

TEST RUN

In this section:

Test Your Knowledge Quiz

Test Your Knowledge Quiz Answers

Progress Analysis

Mock Exam

Mock Exam Suggested Answers

■ This section should be tackled towards the end of your revision programme, when you have covered all your syllabus topics, and attempted the practice questions at the end of the relevant chapters.

■ The Test Your Knowledge Quiz contains short-answer questions on a wide range of syllabus topics. You should attempt it without reference to the text.

■ Check your answers against the Test Your Knowledge Quiz Answers. If you are not sure why you got an answer wrong, go back to the relevant unit in the text: you will find the reference next to our answer.

■ Enter your marks in the Progress Analysis chart. The notes below will suggest a further revision strategy, based on your performance in the quiz. Only when you have done the extra work suggested should you go on to the final test.

■ The Mock Exam is set out like real exam papers. It contains a wide spread of topics and question styles, as used by all the examination boards. You should attempt these papers under examination conditions, in the time allowed, and without reference to the text.

■ Compare your answers to our Mock Exam Suggested Answers. We have provided tutorial notes to each, showing why we answered the question as we did and indicating where your answer may have differed from ours.

TEST YOUR KNOWLEDGE QUIZ

1 Write the electron arrangement of sulphur (atomic number 16).

2 Write the equation for the first ionisation energy of sodium.

3 Why is the second ionisation energy of sodium much higher than the first?

4 Write the ionic equation for the reaction of acidified manganate(VII) and iodide ions.

5 Name the reducing agent in 4.

6 sodium   sodium fluoride   tetrachloromethane
   Name the substance from the list above which contains
   (i) ionic bonding,
   (ii) metallic bonding,
   (iii) covalent bonding.

7 C_2H_4 H_2O XeF_4 NH_3
   In which of the compounds above are the atoms not all in the same plane?

8 What is the oxidation state of vanadium in VO_2Cl?

9 Write down the structure of an isomer of 1,2–dibromoethane.

10 ammonium chloride   iron(III) chloride   sodium carbonate
    sodium chloride   sodium hydrogensulphate

    Which of the salts above dissolves to form a neutral solution?

11 What is the pH of a solution of sodium hydroxide (NaOH) of concentration 0.1 mol dm^{-3}?

Questions 12–13 refer to the reaction between 1-bromobutane and OH$^-$ ions

$$C_4H_9Br + OH^- \rightarrow C_4H_9OH + Br^-$$

12 Name the mechanism of this reaction.

13 The results of three experiments (A, B and C) with these chemicals are shown below.

| Experiment | Initial concentration / mol dm^{-3} | | Initial rate of decrease of [OH$^-$]/mol dm^{-3} sec^{-2} |
	C_4H_9Br	OH$^-$	
A	0.1	0.1	1×10^{-5}
B	0.2	0.2	4×10^{-5}
C	0.2	0.05	1×10^{-5}

Calculate the order of reaction with respect to
(i) 1-bromobutane and (ii) the hydroxide ion.

14 Three colligative properties which can be used to calculate the molar mass of an unionised solute are:
    (i) lowering of vapour pressure
    (ii) elevation of boiling point
    (iii) depression of freezing point.
    What is the fourth one?

15 Use the following data to calculate the molar bond dissociation energy of Cl—F.

	$\Delta H_f^{\ominus}(298)$/ kJ mol^{-1}
ClF(g)	−63.4
Cl(g)	121.7
F(g)	79.0

Questions 16–17

Methylbenzene, $C_6H_5CH_3$, can react with chlorine to produce different products depending upon conditions.

A In sunlight or ultraviolet light, a mixture of three compounds may be formed.

B In the presence of aluminium chloride and warming, two other products are formed.

16 In which case, A or B, could one of the products be

(i)    (ii)

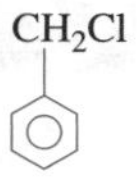

17 What mechanisms can be used to explain A and B?

18 At 60 °C and a total pressure of 1 atmosphere, dinitrogen tetroxide is 50% dissociated

$$N_2O_4(g) \rightleftharpoons 2NO_2(g)$$

Calculate the equilibrium constant K_p at this temperature.

19 Name a suitable indicator for titrating weak acid and strong alkali.

20 Choose one pair of liquids from the list below which form approximately ideal mixtures over the whole composition range.

A Ethanol and methanol

B Methanol and water

C Benzene and methylbenzene

D Water and hydrochloric acid

TEST YOUR KNOWLEDGE QUIZ ANSWERS

In each case the chapter you should refer back to if you made a mistake is given in brackets.

1 $1s^2 2s^2 2p^6 3s^2 3p^4$ (Chapter 1)

2 $Na(g) \rightarrow Na^+(g) + e^-$ (Chapter 2)
   Note: State symbols are essential here.

3 Losing second electron requires losing an electron from $2p$ orbital (Chapter 2)

4 $2MnO_4^- + 10I^- + 16H^+ \rightarrow 2Mn^{2+} + 8H_2O + 5I_2$ (Chapter 6)

5 Iodide ions (Chapter 6)

6 (i) sodium fluoride; (ii) sodium; (iii) tetrachloromethane (Chapter 4)

7 NH_3 (Chapter 5)

8 +5 (Chapter 6)

9

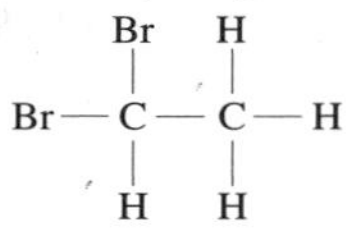

```
        Br  H
        |   |
Br — C — C — H
        |   |
        H   H
```

This is named 1,1-dibromoethane. It could be called 2,2-dibromoethane but we aim to keep numbers as small as possible. (Chapter 7)

10 Only sodium chloride (Chapter 17)

11 13 (Chapter 16)

12 Nucleophilic substitution (Chapter 38)

13 (i) 1 (ii) 1 (Chapter 14)

14 Osmotic pressure   (Chapter 12)
15 +264.1 kJ mol^{-1} (Chapter 13)
16 (i) B   (ii) A   (Chapter 29)
17 (A) Free radical substitution   (B) Electrophilic substitution   (Chapter 38)
18 1.33 atm. Don't forget the units.   (Chapter 15)
19 Phenolphthalein   (Chapter 16)
20 C   (Chapter 11)

PROGRESS ANALYSIS

Place a tick next to those questions you got right.

Question	Answer	Question	Answer	Question	Answer	Question	Answer
1		6		11		16	
2		7		12		17	
3		8		13		18	
4		9		14		19	
5		10		15		20	

My total mark is: _____   out of 20

If you scored 1–5
You need to do some more work. The Mock Exam is intended as a test of exam technique; it will be wasted if your basic syllabus coverage is insufficient. Make a realistic assessment of your understanding of each chapter. This will give you a further revision plan to work from. You will need to attempt the Test Your Knowledge Quiz one more time before you are ready to go on to the Mock Exam.

If you scored 6–10
You need to do a little more work. The Mock Exam is intended as a test of exam technique; it will not be really useful until you have filled in the gaps in your knowledge. If you have time, go through the unit list at the beginning of each chapter and revise all those that look unfamiliar. If you don't think you have time to do this, look through the questions at the end of each chapter, and the notes on points to include. You should then attempt the Test your Knowledge Quiz again.

If you scored 11–15
You are just about ready to attempt the Mock Exam. First, however, you should look through the questions at the end of each chapter, and the notes on points to include; this will be a good guide to which syllabus areas are still unfamiliar. If you do not think you have time to do this, go over those chapters whose reference is given in the Quiz answers for the questions you got wrong. You should then be ready to go on to the Mock Exam.

If you scored 16–20
Congratulations. You have sufficient grasp of the syllabus topics to get real value out of attempting the Mock Exam under exam conditions. First, however, you should go back to the specific chapter referred to in the Test Your Knowledge Quiz answers for each question you got wrong; reassure yourself that there is no real gap in your knowledge.

MOCK EXAM

Paper 1   **Time: 45 minutes**

Multiple choice questions

1   The atomic number of calcium is 20. If Ar represents the electronic structure of an argon atom, the calcium atom may be represented by:
    A Ar   D Ar $3d^1$
    B Ar $4s^1$ E Ar $3d^2$
    C Ar $4s^2$

2   In which one of the following compounds is the bonding most ionic?
    A lithium chloride   D sodium chloride
    B lithium bromide   E sodium iodide
    C lithium iodide

3   Which of the following has the greater polarising power?
    A Li^+ D Sr^{2+}
    B Be^{2+} E Ba^{2+}
    C Ca^{2+}

4   The value of K_a for a weak monobasic acid at 298 K is 4×10^{-5}. Which of the following is the concentration of H^+ ions in a solution of the acid (0.1 mol dm^{-3})?
    A 2×10^{-2} mol dm^{-3} D 2×10^{-4} mol dm^{-3}
    B 2×10^{-3} mol dm^{-3} E 4×10^{-5} mol dm^{-3}
    C 4×10^{-4} mol dm^{-3}

5   When a Group I metal atom X reacts to become an ion X^+:
    A the diameter of the particle increases
    B the positive charge on the nucleus increases
    C the atomic number of X decreases
    D the number of occupied electron shells decreases by 1
    E the number of protons increases

6   The usual method of extracting alkali metals and alkaline earth metals from their ores is:
    A reduction of the oxide with carbon
    B electrolysis of an aqueous solution of the chloride
    C electrolysis of the molten chloride
    D strongly heating the oxide in air
    E reduction of the oxide with aluminium

7   1,2-Dibromo-3-chloropropane (DBCP) has been used in the control of earthworms. Which of the following would be the best method of making it?
    A $CH_3CH_2CH_2Cl + 2Br_2 \rightarrow DBCP + 2HBr$
    B $CH_3CHBrCH_2Br + Cl_2 \rightarrow DBCP + HCl$
    C $CH_2{=}CHCHBr_2 + HCl \rightarrow DBCP$
    D $CH_2{=}CHCH_2Cl + Br_2 \rightarrow DBCP$
    E $ClCH_2CH{=}CH_2 + PBr_5 \rightarrow DBCP + PBr_3$

8   0.20 g of a monobasic acid required 8.0 cm^3 of 0.40 mol dm^{-3} sodium hydroxide for complete reaction. What is the relative molecular mass of the acid?
    A 62.5   D 640
    B 250   E 2500
    C 625

9   Aspirin was prepared in an industrial laboratory. Before it can be made into tablets it has to be purified by recrystallisation using hot water. Which one of the following is the most important factor for choosing hot water as the solvent for recrystallisation?
A readily available
B non-flammable
C inexpensive
D large change in solubility of aspirin with temperature
E aspirin dissolves readily in hot water

10 What is the oxidation state of chromium in the complex ion $[Cr(H_2O)_4Cl_2]^+$?
A 0
B +1
C +2
D +3
E +6

11 In which of the following is the enthalpy change called lattice energy of sodium chloride?
A $Na(s) + \frac{1}{2}Cl_2(g) \rightarrow NaCl(s)$
B $Na(g) + Cl(g) \rightarrow NaCl(s)$
C $Na(l) + \frac{1}{2}Cl_2(g) \rightarrow NaCl(s)$
D $Na(s) + \frac{1}{2}Cl_2(l) \rightarrow NaCl(s)$
E $Na^+(g) + Cl^-(g) \rightarrow NaCl(s)$

12 1,2-Dibromoethane reacts with potassium iodide dissolved in methanol according to the equation:

$$C_2H_4Br_2 + 2KI \rightarrow C_2H_4 + 2KBr + I_2$$

The rate expression for this reaction is
A rate = $k[KI]^2[C_2H_4Br_2]$
B rate = $k[KI][C_2H_4Br_2]$
C rate = $k[KI]^2$
D rate = $k[C_2H_4Br_2]$
E not possible to say

13 The pH value of an aqueous solution of two compounds remains at 5 even when contaminated with small quantities of acid or alkali. Which one of the following pairs of compounds would produce such a solution?
A Ammonia and ammonium chloride
B Ethanoic acid and sodium ethanoate
C Hydrochloric acid and sodium chloride
D Potassium hydroxide and potassium bromide
E Sodium hydroxide and sodium ethanoate

14 In aqueous acid, iodate(VII) ions $IO_4^-(aq)$ react with iodide ions to give iodine and water. The number of moles of aqueous hydrogen ions required for the complete reaction of one mole of aqueous iodate(VII) ions is
A 2
B 3
C 6
D 7
E 8

15 The relative atomic mass of boron, which consists of the isotopes $^{10}_5B$ and $^{11}_5B$ is 10.8. What is the percentage of $^{11}_5B$ atoms in the isotopic mixture?
A 0.8%   B 8.0%   C 20%   D 80%   E 92%

16 Which of the following is a redox reaction?
A $AlH_3(g) + H^-(g) \rightarrow AlH_4^-(g)$
B $Al^{3+}(aq) + 3OH^-(aq) \rightarrow Al(OH)_3(s)$
C $2Al(s) + 3Cl_2(g) \rightarrow 2AlCl_3(s)$
D $AlO_2^-(aq) + H^+(aq) + H_2O(l) \rightarrow Al(OH)_3(s)$
E $Al_2Cl_6(g) \rightarrow 2AlCl_3(g)$

17 X, Y and Z are elements in the same short period of the Periodic Table. The oxide of X is amphoteric, the oxide of Y is basic and the oxide of Z is acidic. What is the order of increasing atomic (proton) number for these elements?
A XYZ   B XZY   C YXZ   D YZX   E ZXY

18 In which of the following changes at constant temperature does the entropy of the SYSTEM decrease?
A Evaporation of one mole of pentane:
$C_5H_{12}(l) \rightarrow C_5H_{12}(g)$
B Decomposition of one mole of hydrogen peroxide:
$H_2O_2(l) \rightarrow H_2O(l) + \frac{1}{2}O_2(g)$
C Decomposition of two moles of ammonia:
$2NH_3(g) \rightarrow N_2(g) + 3H_2(g)$
D Formation of one mole of water from its elements:
$H_2(g) + \frac{1}{2}O_2(g) \rightarrow H_2O(l)$
E Reaction of one mole of zinc with hydrochloric acid:
$Zn(s) + 2HCl(aq) \rightarrow ZnCl_2(aq) + H_2(g)$

19 $N_2(g) + 2O_2(g) \rightarrow 2NO_2(g) \quad \Delta H = +88$ kJ
$N_2(g) + 2O_2(g) \rightarrow N_2O_4(g) \quad \Delta H = +10$ kJ
The enthalpy change for the reaction $2NO_2(g) \rightarrow N_2O_4(g)$ will be
A +98 kJ
B +78 kJ
C –78 kJ
D –98 kJ

20 The mean bond dissociation enthalpy of the C—H bond is equal to $\frac{1}{4}$ of the value of ΔH for one of the following reactions.
Identify the reaction.
A $CH_4(g) \rightarrow C(g) + 4H(g)$
B $CH_4(g) \rightarrow C(s) + 4H(g)$
C $C(s) + 2H_2(g) \rightarrow CH_4(g)$
D $CH_4(g) + 2O_2(g) \rightarrow CO_2(g) + 2H_2O(g)$

21 Butadiene has the following structure
$$CH_2{=}CH{-}CH{=}CH_2$$
Which of the following pairs of hydrocarbons are isomers?
A Butane and cyclobutane
B Butadiene and cyclobutene
C Butadiene and 1-methylprop-1-ene
D But-1-ene and butadiene
E Cyclobutane and cyclobutene

22 The formula for the amino acid alanine may be displayed as

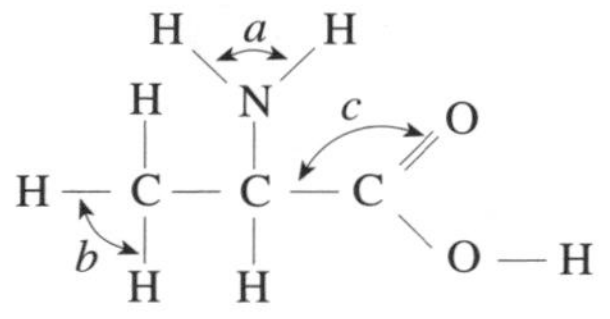

What are the approximate values of the bond angles a, b and c in the compound?

	a	b	c
A	106°	109°	110°
B	106°	109°	120°
C	120°	109°	110°
D	120°	90°	110°
E	120°	90°	120°

23 The conversion of linoleic acid, $C_{18}H_{32}O_2$, into stearic acid, $C_{18}H_{36}O_2$, is likely to be achieved by
A hydrogenation
B hydrolysis
C hydration
D dehydrogenation

24 On complete hydrolysis a peptide produced 5 amino acids, represented by the letters P, Q, R, S and T. The following fragments were produced on partial hydrolysis:

$$\text{Peptide} \xrightarrow[\text{hydrolysis}]{\text{partial}} \text{TS + QP + RT + SQ}$$

Which of the sequences below could be the correct one for the arrangement of amino acids in the peptide?
A P–T–S–Q–R
B R–T–S–P–Q
C Q–P–T–S–R
D R–T–S–Q–P

25 'Superglue' contains the compound

It is rapidly polymerised by traces of bases on the surface of the objects to be stuck together.
Which of the following represents the repeat unit of the polymerised form?

A   B   C

D   E

26 Which one of the following ions in aqueous solution *cannot* be estimated by iodine/thiosulphate titrimetry?
A Cu^{2+}
B MnO_4^-
C Ag^+
D IO_3^-

27 A mixture of gases contains 64 g of methane, 64 g of oxygen and 64 g of sulphur dioxide. The pressure of the mixture is 210 kPa.
What is the partial pressure (in kPa) of the methane expected to be?
A 30 $M_r(CH_4) = 16$
B 60 $M_r(O_2) = 32$
C 70 $M_r(SO_2) = 64$
D 120

28 An equilibrium is represented by the following equation.

$$N_2(g) + 3H_2(g) \rightleftharpoons 2NH_3(g); \; \Delta H^\ominus = -x \text{ kJ mol}^{-1}$$

Which of the following changes would affect *both* the value of the equilibrium constant K_p and the proportion of ammonia present at equilibrium?

A adding a catalyst of finely divided iron
B reducing.the temperature
C increasing the mass of nitrogen
D removing ammonia from the system
E increasing the mass of hydrogen

29 What is the effect of a catalyst on the rate constants k_1, for the forward reaction, and k_{-1}, for the reverse reaction, and on the equilibrium constant K for a reversible reaction?

	k_1	k_{-1}	K
A	increases	decreases	no effect
B	increases	decreases	increases
C	increases	increases	no effect
D	increases	increases	increases
E	no effect	no effect	increases

30 Which one of the following functional groups will usually be attacked only by electrophiles?

A $\diagdown C = C \diagup$ B $\diagdown C = O$

C $-\overset{|}{\underset{|}{C}} - Br$ D $-\overset{|}{\underset{|}{C}} - NO_2$

E $-\overset{|}{\underset{|}{C}} - OH$

31 A metal M forms a compound with hydrogen that proves, on analysis, to have the composition MH_2. The metal is most likely to be
A aluminium
B lead
C magnesium
D sodium
E iron

32 Which one of the following formulae could represent a compound capable of forming an addition polymer?
A C_2H_6
B C_3H_6
C C_2H_5Cl
D CH_3CH_2OH
E $HOCH_2CH_2OH$

33

	ΔH/kJ mol^{-1}
$H_2S(g) \rightarrow H(g) + HS(g)$	+326
$HS(g) \rightarrow H(g) + S(g)$	+366

From the table it follows that the mean bond energy, in kJ mol^{-1}, for the covalent bond between hydrogen and sulphur is
A +40   B +163   C +173   D +183   E +346

34 Which one of the following aqueous reagents could be used to identify the sulphate ion in an aqueous solution?
A barium chloride
B ammonia
C iron(II) sulphate
D hydrochloric acid
E sodium hydroxide

Multiple completion questions

A	B	C	D
1, 2, 3	2, 3	1	3
correct	only correct	only correct	only correct

35 For one mole of gas in the van der Waals equation
$$(P + a/V^2)(V - b) = RT$$
  1   R is a correction for the temperature
  2   a/V^2 is a correction for the forces between the molecules
  3   b is a correction for the volume occupied by the molecules

36 Correct statements about the compound with the formula $(NH_4)_2Cr_2O_7$ include
  1   its solution in sulphuric acid is orange
  2   its solution in sodium carbonate is yellow
  3   it produces an alkaline gas when heated with aqueous sodium hydroxide

37 Using the following information
  $Zn^{2+}(aq) + 2e^- \rightarrow Zn(s)$ $E^\ominus = -0.76$ V
  $Ni^{2+}(aq) + 2e^- \rightarrow Ni(s)$ $E^\ominus = 0.25$ V
  Which of the following statements about the cell is (are) true?
  $Zn(s) \mid Zn^{2+}(aq):Ni^{2+}(aq) \mid Ni(s)$
  1   the concentration of nickel ions increases during the operation of the cell
  2   the electrons travel through the external circuit from the zinc to the nickel
  3   the e.m.f. of the cell is 0.51 V

38 Which of the following systems contain delocalised electrons?
  1 cyclohexene   2 benzene   3 graphite

39 The bond angles are less than 109.5° (tetrahedral) in
  1 NH_3 2 BF_3 3 CH_4

40 A compound represented by the formula H_2NCH_2COOH would
  1   react with an acid and alkali
  2   evolve nitrogen when mixed with nitrous acid
  3   form an ester with ethanol

Paper 2   Time: 2 hours

1   Calcium hydride is melted and electrolysed.
    (a) Write the ion–electron equation for the half reaction occurring at the **positive** electrode.   (1)
    (b) What are the products when calcium hydride is added to water?   (1)
                                        (*SEB 1990*)

2   Excess zinc was added to 2M sulphuric acid at room temperature, and the volume of hydrogen produced was plotted against time as shown.
    (a) Why does the gradient of the curve decrease as the reaction proceeds?   (1)
    (b) Copy the graph (no graph paper required) and add the corresponding curves obtained when the reaction is repeated
    (i) at a higher temperature;
    (ii) using an equal volume of 1M sulphuric acid instead of 2M.
    (Label each curve carefully)   (2)
                                        (*SEB 1990*)

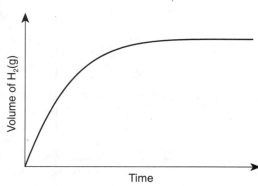

3 There are three isotopes of hydrogen:

isotope	symbol	stability
hydrogen	$_1^1H$	stable
deuterium	$_1^2D$	stable
tritium	$_1^3T$	radioactive

Tritium emits low energy β-radiation

(a) (i) Sketch the structure of a tritium atom showing subatomic particles.
    (ii) Explain what is meant by β-radiation. (4)

(b) The half-life of tritium is 12.35 years. How long will it take for 16 µg (microgram) of tritium to decay to 1 µg? (2)

(c) Tritium is used to place a radioactive label in molecules. For instance, Cornforth has investigated the action of the enzyme *ethanol dehydrogenase* on ethanol labelled with tritium, i.e. CH_3CHTOH.
    (i) Explain why CH_3CHTOH is considered to be chiral.
    (ii) Draw the two stereoisomers of CH_3CHTOH showing their three-dimensional nature. (4)

(d) Tritium gas (T_2), or tritium oxide (T_2O), is used to introduce tritium into compounds.
    Write balanced equations to show how you could prepare the following compounds using T_2 or T_2O.
    (i) TCl
    (ii) NT_3
    (iii) $Ca(OT)_2$ (6)

(*NICCEA 1991*)

4 The tables below show some of the elements arranged as in the Periodic Table. Table 1 gives covalent (atomic) radii in nm; Table 2 gives ionic radii.

Table 1 *Covalent (atomic) radii*

				N	O	F
				0.074	0.074	0.072
Na	Mg	Al	Si	P	S	Cl
0.157	0.136	0.125	0.117	0.110	0.104	0.099

Table 2 *Ionic radii*

				N^{3-}	O^{2-}	F^-
				0.171	0.132	0.133
Na^+	Mg^{2+}	Al^{3+}	Si^{4+}	P^{3-}	S^{2-}	Cl^-
0.097	0.066	0.051	0.042	0.212	0.184	0.181

(a) (i) Explain why the ions of sodium, magnesium, aluminium and silicon are much smaller than the corresponding atoms. (1)
    (ii) Explain why there is a large increase in ionic radius from silicon to phosphorus. (1)
    (iii) What do all the **ions** from nitrogen to silicon have in common? (1)
    (iv) Explain why the ionic radii tend to decrease along the sequence from nitrogen to silicon. (1)

(b) (i) Which two elements given above will form the compound with most ionic character? (1)
    (ii) Give a reason for your choice. (1)

(c) (i) Name the oxide of a metal given in the tables which reacts with acids and also with alkalis. (1)
    (ii) What name is given to an oxide of this type? (1)
    (iii) Name *or* give the formula of the compound formed in solution when this oxide reacts with sodium hydroxide. (1)

(iv) Write a balanced chemical equation for the reaction between the oxide and hydrochloric acid. (1)

(d) The following are different types of structure considered to exist among the elements.

A Molecular gas
B Closely packed molecules
C Atomic gas
D Covalent network
E Ionic lattice with delocalised electrons

Answer the following by giving the appropriate letter in each case.

Which structure best describes the normal state of
(i) fluorine;
(ii) sodium;
(iii) phosphorus;
(iv) silicon? (2)

(SEB 1989)

5 (a) Describe, with the aid of dot and cross diagrams when appropriate, the bonding in
(i) calcium chloride
(ii) methane
(iii) metallic sodium (6)

(b) (i) Show the arrangement of ions in a sodium chloride crystal.
(ii) What is the name of this type of structure?
(iii) Give the coordination numbers (nearest neighbours) of the sodium and chloride ions. (4)

(c) Comment on the statement that 'since sodium chloride has a very high melting point while tetrachloromethane boils below 100 °C, ionic bonds are much stronger than covalent bonds'. (4)

(d) With the aid of an example, indicate what is meant by the term dative covalent bond. (2)

(e) How does the structure of the alkali metals differ from the structure of most other common metals? (2)

(ULEAC 1990)

6 When chlorine is dissolved in water, a green solution smelling of chlorine is produced. This is solution A. If aqueous alkali is added, the smell of chlorine disappears, but the solution, solution B, is still strongly oxidising.

(a) Chlorine reacts with water as follows:

$$Cl_2 + H_2O \rightleftharpoons HCl + HOCl$$

Use this equation to explain why
(i) the solution A smells strongly of chlorine.
(ii) the addition of aqueous alkali removes the smell.
(iii) solution B is a powerful oxidant. (5)

(b) Write an equation for the disproportionation of ClO^- and use it to explain the following:

Solution B has excess silver(I) ions added to it, and the resulting suspension is filtered to give a clear solution. On warming, a white precipitate slowly forms. (Note: silver(I) salts of the chlorate ions are all soluble in water.) (5)

(c) Gaseous chlorine is now banned as a swimming pool disinfectant. One replacement system uses trichloroisocyanuric acid, which reacts with aqueous alkali to produce chlorate(I) ions and the stable compound cyanuric acid in an equilibrium reaction.

Trichloroisocyanuric acid + $OH^- \rightleftharpoons ClO^-$ + cyanuric acid

The chlorate(I) is used up continuously in oxidising bacteria and nitrogenous matter. By reference to this equilibrium reaction, explain why
(i) it is important to control the pH of a pool using this disinfecting system.

(ii) it is necessary to monitor the concentration of cyanuric acid in the pool on a regular basis. (4)

(d) Suggest a method of determining the concentration of chlorate(I) in the pool water. (5)

(ULEAC 1990)

7 (a) What is meant by the terms *activation energy* and *catalyst*?

Substances A and B react together exothermically to give C and D. Draw sketches of the reaction profile for this reaction when it takes place both with and without a catalyst. (7)

(b) Explain what is meant by the term *heterogeneous catalysis*. Write an equation for an industrial process which involves a heterogeneous catalyst and give the name of the catalyst used. (5)

(c) Peroxodisulphate(VI) ions are capable of oxidising iodide ions to iodine according to the equation

$$S_2O_8^{2-}(aq) + 2I^-(aq) \rightarrow 2SO_4^{2-}(aq) + I_2(aq)$$

The reaction can be catalysed by some *d*-block metal ions. Describe in outline an experiment to investigate the catalytic effect of $Fe^{2+}(aq)$ and $Zn^{2+}(aq)$ on the reaction. (7)

(d) $Fe^{2+}(aq)$ ions are found to catalyse the reaction. Given the standard reduction potentials in the table suggest with relevant equations a possible explanation for this.

Electrode reaction	$E^\ominus$ /V
$Fe^{3+}(aq) + e^- \rightarrow Fe^{2+}(aq)$	+0.77
$I_2(aq) + 2e^- \rightarrow 2I^-(aq)$	+0.54
$S_2O_8^{2-}(aq) + 2e^- \rightarrow 2SO_4^{2-}(aq)$	+2.01

Why is it unlikely that the reaction would be catalysed by $Zn^{2+}(aq)$? (6)

(AEB 1991)

8 (a) Compounds Q and R are isomers (M_r = 72.08) and contain 66.6% carbon, 22.2% oxygen and 11.2% hydrogen by mass.

Show that the molecular formula for the compounds is C_4H_8O. (3)

(b) Some reactions of Q and R are summarised in the table.

Reaction	Q	R
Gives an orange precipitate with 2,4-dinitrophenylhydrazine	Yes	Yes
Reacts with sodium tetrahydridoborate(III)	Yes	Yes
Forms a red precipitate on warming with Fehling's solution	Yes	No
Forms yellow crystals when warmed with aqueous iodine and sodium hydroxide	No	Yes

(i) Deduce, giving your reasons, the structural formulae of Q and R.

(ii) Give the equation for the reaction of either Q or R with 2,4-dinitrophenylhydrazine. (6)

(c) Give the names and draw the structures of the organic products formed when R reacts with

(i) aqueous iodine and sodium hydroxide

(ii) sodium tetrahydridoborate(III).

Give the name of the type of reaction which occurs for R in (ii). (6)

(d) Describe what would be observed if Q was shaken with a saturated solution of sodium hydrogensulphite. Write an equation for the reaction and name the type of mechanism which occurs in the reaction. (4)

(e) Q and R can be prepared in the laboratory by the reaction of warm acidified aqueous dichromate(VI) with different isomeric alcohols of molecular formula $C_4H_{10}O$.

(i) Give the name of the type of reaction occurring.

(ii) Write equations for *both* reactions.

(iii) State any essential conditions necessary for the preparation of Q which need not be followed when preparing R. Explain your answer. (6)

(AEB 1991)

Total 120 marks

MOCK EXAM SUGGESTED ANSWERS

Answers to Paper 1

1 C;   2 D;   3 B;   4 B;   5 D;   6 C;   7 D;   8 A;   9 D;
10 D;   11 E;   12 E;   13 B;   14 E;   15 D;   16 C;   17 C;   18 D;
19 C;   20 A;   21 B;   22 B;   23 A;   24 D;   25 C;   26 C;   27 D;
28 B;   29 C;   30 A;   31 C;   32 B;   33 E;   34 A;   35 B;   36 A;
37 B;   38 B;   39 C;   40 A.

Answers to Paper 2

1   This question relies on you recognising that, in calcium hydride, hydrogen exists as an anion, H^-, rather than the more common cation, H^+, i.e. CaH_2 contains Ca^{2+} and H^- ions.

(a) Hydride ions are attracted to the positive electrode and discharged.

$$2H^- \rightarrow H_2 + 2e^-$$

(b) Products are calcium hydroxide and hydrogen.

2   This question is testing your understanding of rates of reaction. It is slightly more searching than a corresponding GCSE question.

(a) During the reaction sulphuric acid is used up and its concentration decreases. The rate of reaction of zinc with sulphuric acid decreases progressively as the acid becomes less concentrated. The rate of reaction is shown by the gradient (steepness) of the graph at any point.

(b)

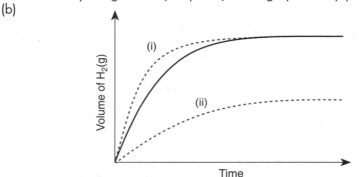

Note: (i) steeper but reaching same final volume; (ii) less steep, reaching half of the previous final volume.

3   This question appears harder to students than it really is. It is about atomic structure, radioactivity, chirality and reactions of tritium. Remember that tritium is an isotope of hydrogen, and therefore has the properties you would associate with hydrogen.

(a)(i) Tritium contains 1 proton and 1 electron (like all hydrogen atoms). It also contains 2 neutrons.

(ii) β-Radiation is high-energy electrons from the nucleus.

(b) $16 \rightarrow 8 \rightarrow 4 \rightarrow 2 \rightarrow 1$

4 half-lives

Time $= 4 \times 12.35 = 49.40$ years

(c) (i) One carbon atom is attached to four different groups.

(ii)

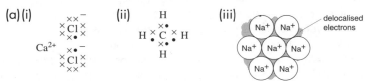

(d) (i) $T_2 + Cl_2 \rightarrow 2TCl$

(ii) $N_2 + 3T_2 \rightarrow 2NT_3$

(iii) $Ca + 2T_2O \rightarrow Ca(OT)_2 + T_2$

4 Many questions rely on you being able to give electronic structures of elements correctly (Chapters 1 and 28). Using the Periodic Table you should be able to work out the electronic structures of the first 36 elements. Do not try to remember them and do not write them in the form Na 2,8,1. This is expected at GCSE level but at A level you must identify s, p, d orbitals.

(a) (i) Sodium atom $\quad\quad\quad 1s^2 2s^2 2p^6 3s^1$

       Sodium ion $\quad\quad\quad\;\, 1s^2 2s^2 2p^6$

       Magnesium atom $\quad\;\; 1s^2 2s^2 2p^6 3s^2$

       Magnesium ion $\quad\quad 1s^2 2s^2 2p^6$ etc.

In each case electrons are lost from $3s$ (and $3p$) orbitals.

No third-shell electrons.

(ii) Si^{4+} $\quad\quad\quad\quad\quad\quad 1s^2 2s^2 2p^6$

    P^{3-} $\quad\quad\quad\quad\quad\quad 1s^2 2s^2 2p^6 3s^2 3p^6$

(iii) Same electron arrangement $1s^2 2s^2 2p^6$

(iv) Although there is the same electron arrangement, there is an additional proton each time. Greater nuclear attraction on electrons.

(b) (i) Sodium fluoride

(ii) Largest difference in electronegativity

(c) (i) Aluminium oxide

(ii) Amphoteric

(iii) Sodium aluminate, $NaAlO_2$

(iv) $Al_2O_3 + 6HCl \rightarrow 2AlCl_3 + 3H_2O$

(d) (i) A   (ii) E   (iii) B   (iv) D

5 This question concerns structure and bonding.

(a) (i)   (ii)   (iii)

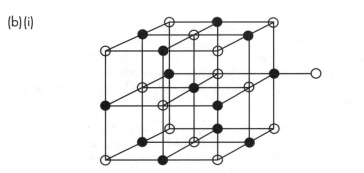

(b) (i)

(ii) Lattice

(iii) Sodium ions: 6   chloride ions: 6

(c) Sodium chloride has a high melting point because of strong electrostatic forces between ions. All forces involved are strong forces.

In tetrachloromethane all bonds between carbon and chlorine within each molecule are strong single covalent bonds. However, the forces holding the molecules together are very weak.

(d) A dative covalent bond is similar to a covalent bond but both electrons in the bond are donated by the same atom.

Both electrons in the N—B bond are donated by the nitrogen atom.

(e) Ions in most metals are close packed. In alkali metals ions are in a body centred cubic structure. Ions in this structure are not close packed. Alkali metals, therefore, have a lower density than other metals.

6 This is a novel question linking different parts of the course. Essentially, it is a question about equilibrium (Chapter 15). In (d) candidates tend not to go into enough detail about experimental method.

(a) (i) Chlorine is a gas and when it escapes from the solution, the equilibrium moves to the left to produce more chlorine.

(ii) Alkali neutralises HCl and HOCl. Equilibrium moves to the right to produce more of these. This reduces the chlorine present.

(iii) HOCl readily loses oxygen,

e.g. in sunlight $2HOCl \rightarrow 2HCl + O_2$

This oxygen can be used for oxidation.

(b) $$3ClO^- \rightarrow 2Cl^- + ClO_3^-$$

When silver(I) nitrate is added to B, silver chloride is precipitated.

$$Ag^+ + Cl^- \rightarrow AgCl(s)$$

Silver(I) chlorate is soluble and passes through the filter paper with excess silver ions. On warming, disproportionation occurs and a fresh sample of silver chloride is produced from the excess silver ions and the chloride ions produced during disproportionation.

(c) (i) As chlorate(I) is used up the equilibrium moves to the right to produce more chlorate(I). OH^- ions are used up. Excess H^+ ions build up increasing the acidity.

(ii) Monitoring the concentration of cyanuric acid gives an indication of the position of the equilibrium.

(d) Add potassium iodide solution to a known volume of pool water. Excess potassium iodide. Acidify the solution with dilute sulphuric acid. This liberates free iodine. Titrate iodine liberated with standard sodium thiosulphate solution.

7 This question is essentially about catalysis (Chapter 14). Again there is a part where your knowledge of practical procedures is required.

(a) Activation energy is the energy which must be provided for a reaction to start. It is usually represented by E_a and is quoted in units of kJ mol^{-1}.

A catalyst is a substance which alters the rate of a chemical reaction without being used up. Using a catalyst lowers the activation energy of the reaction.

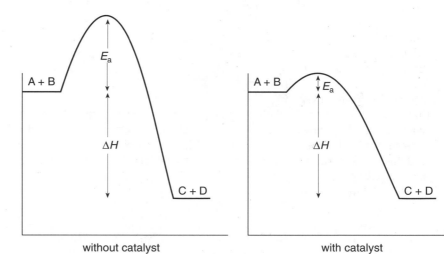

without catalyst   with catalyst

(b) Heterogeneous catalysts are catalysts which act by providing a surface where reactants can be absorbed and from which the products can be desorbed. This compares with homogeneous catalysts where the reaction takes place in a single phase.

There are many examples you could give but be careful, the question wants an industrial example. You could give, for example, the addition reaction of unsaturated fats and oils with hydrogen to produce margarine. The catalyst here is nickel at a temperature of 140 °C. Perhaps better is the Haber process, where a symbolic equation is easy to write.

$$N_2(g) + 3H_2(g) \rightleftharpoons 2NH_3(g)$$

The catalyst here is finely divided iron.

(c) Pipette 25 cm^3 samples of standard sodium peroxodisulphate(VI) solution and standard potassium iodide solution into a conical flask. After two minutes (say) titrate the solution with standard sodium thiosulphate solution using starch solution as an indicator near the end point. From these results, the concentration of iodine produced in the uncatalysed reaction can be calculated.

The procedure is repeated with fresh samples, first with 1 cm^3 of iron(II) sulphate solution and then with 1 cm^3 of zinc sulphate solution.

(d) In the catalysed reaction with Fe^{2+}(aq) ions.

Fe^{3+}(aq) ions act as an intermediate.

Fe^{2+}(aq) $\rightarrow Fe^{3+}$(aq) $+ e^-$ $\qquad E^{\ominus} = -0.77$ V
$S_2O_8^{2-}$(aq) $+ 2e^- \rightarrow 2SO_4^{2-}$(aq) $\qquad E^{\ominus} = +2.01$ V
$\qquad\qquad\qquad\qquad$ Add together $+1.24$ V

Equation
$2Fe^{2+}$(aq) $+ S_2O_8^{2-}$(aq) $\rightarrow 2Fe^{3+}$(aq) $+ 2SO_4^{2-}$(aq)
$E^{\ominus}$ is positive and so the reaction takes place.

$2I^-$(aq) $\rightarrow I_2$(aq) $+ 2e^-$ $\qquad E^{\ominus} = -0.54$ V
Fe^{3+}(aq) $+ e^- \rightarrow Fe^{2+}$(aq) $\qquad E^{\ominus} = +0.77$ V
$\qquad\qquad\qquad\qquad$ Add together $+0.23$ V

Equation
$2I^-$(aq) $+ 2Fe^{3+}$(aq) $\rightarrow I_2$(aq) $+ 2Fe^{2+}$(aq)
$E^{\ominus}$ is positive and so the reaction takes place.
$2Fe^{2+}$(aq) $+ S_2O_8^{2-}$(aq) $\rightarrow 2Fe^{3+}$(aq) $+ 2SO_4^{2-}$(aq)
$2I^-$(aq) $+ 2Fe^{3+}$(aq) $\rightarrow I_2$(aq) $+ 2Fe^{2+}$(aq)
On addition: $2I^-$(aq) $+ S_2O_8^{2-}$(aq) $\rightarrow 2SO_4^{2-}$(aq) $+ I_2$(aq)
It is unlikely that Zn^{2+}(aq) ions will catalyse the reaction as zinc cannot exist in other oxidation states.

8 This is a typical organic question about aldehydes and ketones.

(a)

	C	O	H
Percentage	66.6	22.2	11.2
A_r	12	16	1
Percentage /A_r	5.55	1.38	11.2
Divide by smallest	4	1	8

Empirical formula C_4H_8O

Molecular mass of empirical formula = 48 + 8 + 16 = 72 g

Molecular formula C_4H_8O

(b)(i) Q and R both contain the carbonyl group as form orange precipitate with 2,4-dinitrophenylhydrazine and react with sodium tetrahydridoborate(III). Fehling's solution positive with aldehyde, therefore Q is an aldehyde. R is a ketone. Positive triiodomethane test, therefore R contains the CH_3CO group.

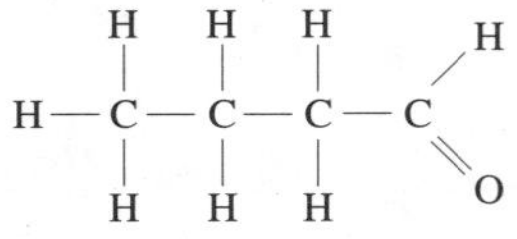

Q 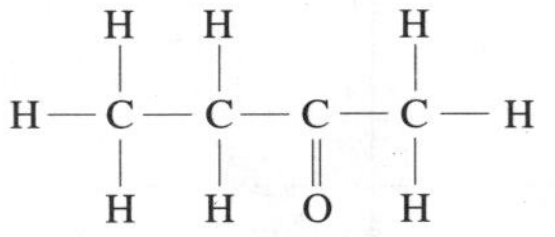   R

(ii)

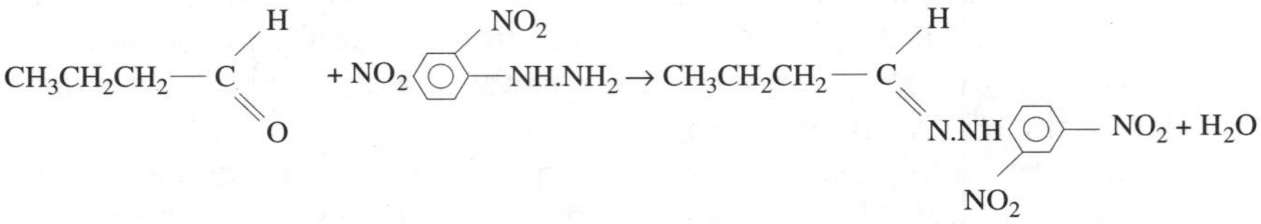

(c) (i)

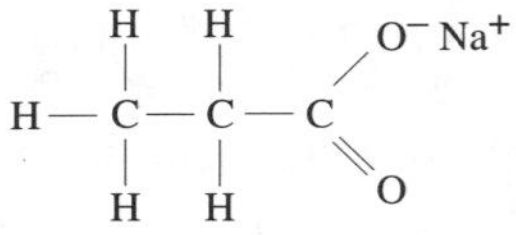

sodium propanoate 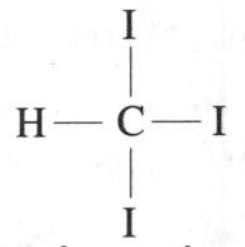   triiodomethane

(ii)

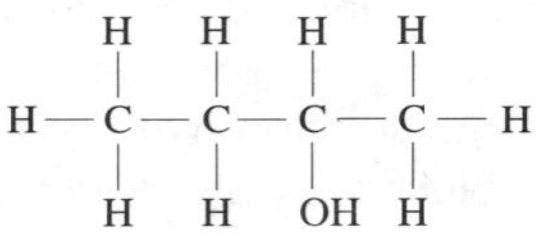

butan-2-ol

This reaction is a reduction.

(d) A white crystalline precipitate is produced.

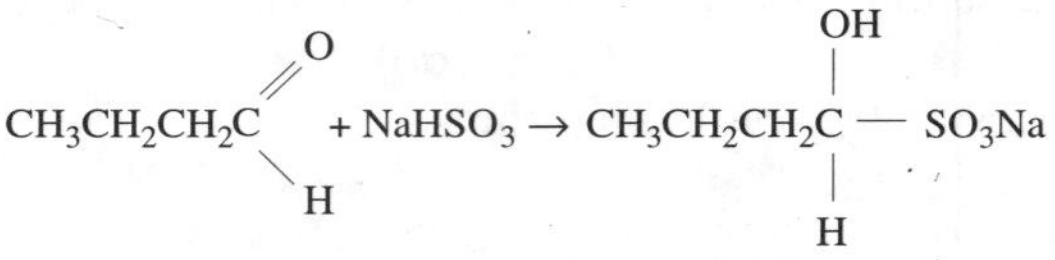

$$CH_3CH_2CH_2C \overset{O}{\underset{H}{\diagdown}} + NaHSO_3 \rightarrow CH_3CH_2CH_2C \overset{OH}{\underset{H}{\mid}} - SO_3Na$$

Nucleophilic addition

(e) (i) Oxidation.

(ii) $CH_3CH_2CH_2CH_2OH + [O] \rightarrow CH_3CH_2CH_2CHO + H_2O$
   butan-1-ol   Q

$CH_3CH_2CH(OH)CH_3 + [O] \rightarrow CH_3CH_2CCH_3 + H_2O$
                                              $\overset{\|}{O}$

   butan-2-ol   R

(iii) Butan-1-ol is warmed and acidified dichromate(VI) added so that the alcohol is always in excess. Q distils off. Q can be further oxidised to a carboxylic acid by excess acidified dichromate(VI). R cannot. This further reaction is minimised by keeping the alcohol in excess. Aldehyde distils off on formation because it has a lower boiling point than the corresponding alcohol.

INDEX

absorption coefficient 110
acetylation 299
acid–base titrations 174
acids 150, 290
activation energy 145
acylation 299
addition polymerisation 313
addition reactions 252, 283, 334
alcohols 269
aldehydes 281
aldol condensation 286
aliphatic compounds 76, 249
alkali metals 189
alkaline earth metals 189
alkanes 249
alkenes 251
alkylamines 308
alkynes 254
allotropy 202, 221
aluminium, extraction of 196
amides 299, 302
amines 307
amino acids 316
amphoteric oxides 218
anisotropy 107
anodising 197
aromatic compounds 76, 259
arylamines 308
aryl halides 266
atactic polymers 314
atomic number 32
atomic volume 46
autocatalysis 138
Avogadro's hypothesis 93
azeotropic mixtures 113

Balmer series 37
bases 150
benzene 256
benzenecarbonylation 299
benzoylation 299
binding energy 145
bond enthalpies 129
bonding
   coordinate 61, 237
   covalent 59
   dipole–dipole attractions 62
   hydrogen 61, 113, 229, 277, 317
   ionic 57
   metallic 62

Born–Haber cycle 130
Boyle's law 91
Bragg equation 104
Brownian motion 100
buffer solutions 160

Cannizzaro reaction 286
carbanion 333
carbonium ion 333
carbon monoxide 204
carbonyl group 283
catalyst 138
catenation 203
chain reactions 334
Charles' law 91
chelates 238
chemical industry 347
chirality 83
chlorides 186
chromatography 79
colligative properties 117
common ion effect 162
complexes 237
condensation 284
condensation polymerisation 315
conjugate acid 151
conjugate base 151
Contact process 222
coordinate bonding 61, 237
coordination compounds 237
coordination number 106
coupling reactions 311
covalent bonding 59
covalent crystals 107
critical point 101
critical pressure 100
critical temperature 100
crystallisation 78

Dalton's law 92
Daniell cell 166, 170
dative covalency 61, 237
dehydration 302
diagonal relationships 47
diamagnetism 236
diaphragm cells 351
diazonium compounds 310, 326
dibasic acids 295
diffraction, X-ray 104
dipole–dipole attractions 62
dipoles 59

disproportionation 231, 245
dissociation constant 151
distillation 77
distribution 146
dynamic equilibrium 142

electrochemical cells 165
electrochemical series 44, 169
electrode potential 44, 166
electromotive force 166
electron affinity 44
electron arrangement 34
electronegativity 45
electrophiles 333
electrovalent bonding 57
elimination 264
Ellingham diagrams 348, 349
empirical formulae 81
enantiomers 84
enantiomorphs 84
energetics 125
enthalpy changes 127
entropy 132
equations 53
equilibrium 142
esters 276, 298, 300
ethanoylation (acetylation) 299
ethers 277
evaporation 100

fermentation 270
fertilisers 350
fission 181
formulae 50
fractional distillation 78
free energy 133, 170
free radicals 139, 334
Friedel–Crafts reactions 338
functional groups 81
fusion 181

Gay Lussac's law 93
germanes 206
Grignard reagents 265, 323–325
groups 40

Haber process 349
half cells 165
half equations 70
half-life 179
halides 230

377